DRAMA

for Reading & Performance

Collection Two

Nineteen Full-length
Plays
for Students

including information, lessons, and assignments
for understanding and performance

DRAMA
for Reading & Performance
Collection Two

Perfection Learning
Logan, Iowa 51546-0500

Editorial Director   Julie A. Schumacher
Senior Editor   Gay Russell-Dempsey
Design   Mary Ann Lea
Electronic Technology   Pegi Bevins, Stella Zee, Digital Talkies, Kiecker Design
Permissions   Laura Pieper, Meghan Schumacher, Oliver Oertel

Cover Image   A masked character from Carlo Gozzi's 18th-century *commedia dell'arte* play *The King Stag*, produced at the American Repertory Theater, Cambridge, Massachusetts, by Julie Taymor, 1984.

Warning
The editors have made every effort to trace the ownership of all copyrighted materials found in this book and to make full acknowledgment for their use.

Acknowledgments

A Waitress in Yellowstone by David Mamet. Copyright © 1984 by David Mamet. Reprinted by permission of Rosenstone/Wender. CAUTION: All inquiries concerning rights to the play should be addressed to the author's agent: Howard Rosenstone, ROSENSTONE/WENDER, 3 East 48th Street, New York, NY 10017.
A Young Lady of Property by Horton Foote. Copyright © 1954, 1955, 1983 by Horton Foote. Reprinted by arrangement of Horton Foote and the Barbara Hogenson Agency. CAUTION: Inquiries on all rights (except as indicated below) should be addressed to the Barbara Hogenson Agency, 165 West End Avenue, Suite 19C, New York, NY 10023. Stock and ama-teur production rights to *A Young Lady of Property* are controlled exclusively by the Dramatists Play Service, Inc., 440 Park Avenue South, New York, NY 10016. No stock or amateur performance of this play may be given without obtaining in advance the written permission of the Dramatists Play Service, Inc., and paying the requisite fee.
The Night Thoreau Spent in Jail by Jerome Lawrence and Robert E. Lee. Copyright © 1970 by Lawrence and Lee, Inc. Reprinted by permission of Hill and Wang, a division of Farrar, Straus and Giroux, LLC. CAUTION: All performance inquiries should be directed to Farrar, Straus & Giroux, LLC 19 Union Square West, New York, NY 10003.

(Continued on page 439.)

Contents

How to Read a Play

vii

A Waitress in Yellowstone *by David Mamet*
The Fable in Literature/Blocking in Theatre   2

A Young Lady of Property *by Horton Foote*
Characterization in Literature/The Stage in Theatre   18

The Night Thoreau Spent in Jail *by Jerome Lawrence and Robert E. Lee*
Biographical Fiction in Literature/The Set in Theatre   44

The Love Doctor *by Molière adapted by Marvin Kaye*
Stereotype in Literature/Physical Comedy in Theatre   96

Haiku *by Katherine Snodgrass*
Flashback in Literature/Lighting in Theatre   110

Sorry, Right Number *by Stephen King*
Suspense in Literature/The Screenplay in Theatre   126

Death Knocks *by Woody Allen*
Dialogue in Literature/Comic Timing in Theatre   144

The Actor's Nightmare *by Christopher Durang*
Style in Literature/Costumes in Theatre   154

The Post Office *by Rabindranath Tagore*

Theme in Literature/Ensemble Acting in Theatre   170

The Migrant Farmworker's Son *by Silvia Gonzalez S.*

Magical Realism in Literature/Sound in Theatre   192

The Janitor *by August Wilson*

Allusion in Literature/ Character Analysis in Theatre   224

Shirley Jackson's **The Lottery** *dramatized by*
Brainerd Duffield

Symbolism in Literature/Movement in Theatre   230

Survival *by Alfred Brenner*

Plot in Literature/Camera Shots in Theatre   246

Madman on the Roof *by Kikuchi Kan*

Motivation in Literature/Voice in Theatre   268

Lost in Yonkers *by Neil Simon*

Tone in Literature/Listening and Reacting in Theatre   278

My Children! My Africa! *by Athol Fugard*

Protagonist and Antagonist in Literature/Dramatic Monologue in Theatre   330

Phaeton and the Sun Chariot *by Wim Coleman*

Myth in Literature/Roles in Theatre   380

Sure Thing *by David Ives*

Satire in Literature/Improvisation in Theatre   404

Back There *by Rod Serling*

Foreshadowing in Literature/The Teleplay in Theatre   414

Glossary   430

How to Read a Play

Reading a play is different from reading other kinds of literature because a play is different from other kinds of literature. Short stories, poems, novels, and so on are all complete on the printed page. But a printed play—also called a *script*—is not complete. It becomes complete when it is performed by actors for an audience. The play is what happens on the stage or screen.

Because of this, you—as reader—must bring a little more of yourself to reading a play. Of course you will bring your imagination, as you do to reading short stories and novels. And you will also make an effort to visualize the characters and actions, and to imagine their thoughts and emotions. What else can you do to help make your reading more complete and satisfying? Here are some tips.

Reading Tips

- Read the **stage directions.** *(They are often in parentheses and printed in italic type, like this.)* Stage directions are not meant for an audience; they are messages from the playwright to the people who stage the play. They may tell the actors when and where to move, what emotions to express, what props (hand-held objects, such as a newspaper or a coffee cup) to pick up and what to do with them. They may tell the director where to position the actors or what the overall mood of a scene should be. They may tell the designers what the set looks like, what costumes the actors should wear, what music or sounds are heard, or what time of day the lighting should suggest. Stage directions are usually not read aloud, even when the actors rehearse a show.

UR Upstage Right	**UC** Upstage Center	**UL** Upstage Left
R Right	**C** Center	**L** Left
DR Downstage Right	**DC** Downstage Center	**DL** Downstage Left

- Understand the **stage areas.** Stage directions often include abbreviations like *R* for *right* or *L* for *left.* (These mean the actors' right or left sides as they face the audience.) Other abbreviations are *U* for *upstage* or *D* for *downstage* or *C* for *center.* (*Downstage* means toward the audience; *up* and *down* are terms left over from the days when stages actually slanted.)

- Pay attention to the characters' names. They tell who says what speeches.

- Read the speeches aloud. They are, after all, meant to be heard. Read with as much feeling as you can, to get the most out of the speeches. Even if you're reading the play by yourself, you can play all the parts, changing your voice for the different characters. This will give you a better understanding of the characters, who they are and what they are doing.

- Look for a **subtext.** This is, simply, what the characters are thinking or feeling, and it is not always the same as what they are saying. For example, a character may say, "Of course I'll take my little sister to the movie, Dad," but actually be thinking, "How can you *do* this to me? What will my friends think?"

Theatre Conventions

A **convention** is an accepted way of doing things. The more plays you see on stage, the better you will understand the conventions, the things that make a play a play. Here are some common conventions.

Narrator Sometimes an actor will speak directly to the audience, to explain who the characters are or what is happening. Sometimes a character will speak directly to the audience and then go back to speaking to the other characters. When they do, they serve the function that a narrator serves in short stories or novels.

The "Fourth Wall" In realistic plays, the actors may behave as if the audience simply isn't there. It's as if the audience is eavesdropping on the action through an invisible "fourth wall" of a room, whether the set is actually an enclosed room or not.

Dramatic Time The time an action is supposed to take onstage isn't necessarily the time that same action would take in real life. For example, actors may take seven minutes to eat a meal that they would spend twenty-five minutes on in reality. Just accept what the play tells you about how much time has elapsed.

Lapses of Time If you go to the movies, you're probably familiar with the convention that several minutes or days or even years elapse from one scene to another. It's the same with plays—a curtain or change of lighting may suggest that any amount of time has passed. When you read a play, the stage directions will usually specify what is happening.

The World Offstage Actors are trained to keep in mind, when they enter or exit, just where it is they're supposed to be coming from or going to. This helps them create their characters more realistically. When you're reading a play, try to imagine the lives the characters are leading when they're not onstage. This will help you understand the characters and their subtexts better, and will give you a better understanding of the play as a whole.

Sharing the Experience

Seeing a play performed live onstage can be a truly thrilling experience. As a reader, you can share some of that thrill if you read attentively, with imagination, and if you try actively to enter into the world of the characters and of the play. In this book are many different kinds of plays in different styles from playwrights all over the world. Enjoy them.

The Play as Literature: The Fable

You've probably read plenty of fables in your life, from Aesop's stories of animals scurrying to outwit one another (or themselves) to Native American trickster tales featuring Rabbit and Coyote. While it is true that fables often have animals as their central characters, there are many that do not. Fables can even assume play form, as you will soon see.

The primary distinguishing feature of a fable is this: It has a moral, or life lesson. The moral may be subtly stated or broadcast in large letters, but it is unmistakable. The moral of *A Waitress in Yellowstone* is right there in the subtitle—*Always Tell the Truth.* As you read the play, decide whether this moral holds true in the play.

The Play as Theatre: Blocking

How, when, and where an actor moves or stands on stage must be planned out long before the curtain goes up. The actor's every movement, as well as the location of the sets and the props in any given scene, is called *blocking.* Even before the sets are designed or rehearsals begin, the director helps the actors understand what the sets will look like, where they will be, and how the cast will maneuver around them.

The actors must work with the director as the stage action is being blocked—incorporating the movement into their characters' on-stage presence. Patience and cooperation between cast and director is essential while the preparation of blocking occurs.

WARM UP!

In pairs, play "freeze tag" while working on a two-character scene (*Romeo and Juliet* is a possibility, but you might want to try a scene from the play you are about to read). Begin to block the scene. When either one of you says, "Freeze," you must stop in place for a moment. Discuss your positions and how they reflect the characters' personalities and emotions.

A WAITRESS IN YELLOWSTONE

or Always Tell the Truth

by David Mamet

SETTING

The Southwest

CHARACTERS

RANGER
WAITRESS
OLD MAN (old couple)
WINNIE MAGEE
CONGRESSMAN JOHN LARUE
BOSS
COP
DOUG MAGEE, WINNIE's son (age 10)
RADIO ANNOUNCER (voice over only)
POLICEMAN
SECOND POLICEMAN
JUDGE
BAILIFF
LAWYER FOR CONGRESSMAN
CONVICT (female)
GUARD
BUS DRIVER
STATE TROOPER
SECOND STATE TROOPER

TIME

The present

Narrator takes stage. Dressed as park ranger.

RANGER. Winnie was a waitress. She worked for tips. Here is a tip: a bad situation generally grows worse. Things which cannot get worse improve. There are exceptions: here is not one. Winnie caught a guy lifting a tip off of her table. Told him, "Who do you think you are?" and she read him out to the on-looking crowd, what sort of you-fill-in-the-blank that he *was* . . . which he was.

It turns out this man was a congressman. In an election year. He had to keep a shining image in the public eye, which is exactly where he kept it.

Would have been better off to be what he wished to seem, but barring that he took the secondary course, lived like a thief and made the Public pay.

Winnie and her son Doug. Had planned a trip to Yellowstone. To celebrate his Tenth Birthday. He'd, as you might imagine, looked forward to that trip all year. And it was the object of much of their talk and much of their joint happiness.

At the restaurant.

WAITRESS. Hey, Winnie, quit dreaming, table number three wants the check!

(Old Couple)

OLD MAN. Could I have the check, please.

WINNIE. Here you are.

OLD MAN. Thank you. See you tomorrow, Winnie . . .

WINNIE. No you won't, sir. Tomorrow my boy and I leave for our vacation. I'll see you in two weeks.

OLD MAN. Where are you going?

WINNIE. Yellowstone Park.

OLD MAN. That's right, you told me. Here's a little extra, you have a fine trip.

(The Old Couple starts up to leave.)

WINNIE. That's very generous of you, sir . . .thank you . . .*(Before she can gather the money, etc., she is called to another table.)*

CONGRESSMAN. Miss!

WINNIE *(to* OLD MAN*).* Thank you very much.

CONGRESSMAN. Miss!

WINNIE. I'm coming. *(To* CONGRESSMAN*)* Yes, sir?

CONGRESSMAN *(of check).* What is the meaning of this?

WINNIE *(checking bill).* Ninety-five cents, for a substitution. You had beans instead of the creamed spinach.

CONGRESSMAN. You never told me that.

WINNIE. Yes, sir, I did.

CONGRESSMAN. You certainly did *not.* You did *not* tell me that.

WINNIE. Yes, sir, I am certain, you said "I'll have the Special." Look: It's not important. If you take the check to the boss, I'm sure that he'll . . .

CONGRESSMAN. Well, that's not the point, is it? The point is that you never *told* me . . .

WINNIE. Well, if that's true, I'm sorry, sir.

CONGRESSMAN. No: *say* you never told me . . .

WINNIE. Excuse me . . .

CONGRESSMAN. You owe me an apology.

WINNIE. I think that I apologized, excuse me . . . *(She walks away. To another* WAITRESS.*)* Some people have too much salt in their diet . . . *(To* CONGRESSMAN*)* WAIT A SECOND WAIT A SECOND WAIT A SECOND: *WAIT* A SECOND THERE!

(She walks back to his table, which he has gotten up from. He is standing near the table vacated by the OLD COUPLE. *To* CONGRESSMAN.*)*

You wanna put something back? *(Pause)* You wanna put something back, or you want me to call the police?

CONGRESSMAN. I don't know what you're talking about.

WINNIE. I'm talking about you just lifted my tip off of that table. Now: you put it back or I call the cops.

CONGRESSMAN. You're saying . . . *(Pause)* You're saying I did whhh . . . ? Get out of my way. *(Tries to push past her)*

WINNIE. In a pig's *eye* I will. Somebody call the cops! Somebody call the cops, this guy took my tip off the . . . *(To* CONGRESSMAN*)* You aren't going anywhere!

BOSS. What's the trouble?

WINNIE. This guy took my tip off the table.

CONGRESSMAN. Lady, you're in a world of trouble here.

WINNIE. Well, we're just going to see . . .

COP. What seems to be the trouble?

WINNIE. This guy lifted my tip off the table.

CONGRESSMAN. Not only is it not true, but I want to tell you you've just caused yourself a lot of pain. What's your name, Officer? I'm John Larue, I am the congressman for this district, and this deranged and sick individual has just slandered me. Pick her *tip* off the table? You know WHO I *AM* ???

(The CONGRESSMAN *sings about the exalted position he enjoys. He finishes singing.)*

CONGRESSMAN. Now: I'll give you one last chance to retract what you said and take back your vicious lie, or you're going to wish you never were born.

WINNIE. Well, to wish you never were born you have to be born. Which gives you the option, and I think I'll stick with the truth. You should be ashamed of yourself. Good-bye.

(The cop takes the CONGRESSMAN *away.)*

WINNIE. What kind of a world is it? That guy should be setting an example . . .

*(*WINNIE *and the assembled customers sing "What Kind of a World Is It?" peppering the song with examples from their own lives. The second verse is: "On the Other Hand," where* WINNIE *sings about some of the good things* which may be had simply in life, in her case, the trip with her son to Yellowstone Park.

As the clock strikes twelve she sings "My Day Is Done, and I'm Going on Vacation," and leaves the restaurant. She walks home.)*

WINNIE. Look at the stars, what a beautiful night it is. Always various. *(She walks into her house.)* Look at my son, isn't he gorgeous. And now we have all this vacation time to be alone together. All the rest is basically illusion.

RANGER. And so she fell asleep, and she and her son dreamed the same dream. In which they were in Yellowstone Park, high upon a ridge, upon a summit, looking down, and they saw mountain sheep, and they saw deer, and when the rain came unexpectedly they made a shelter from a fallen tree. And as in the wild of sleep and as in the wild of the forest their cares fell away. And when Winnie awoke, she saw her son, already dressed, sitting at the breakfast table, and he had made her a cup of tea.

(They are both dressed in full camping regalia.)

WINNIE. Good morning. What are you doing up so early?

DOUG. Oh, I couldn't sleep.

WINNIE. Why? You worried about school, shouldn't you be off to school?

DOUG. Well, I thought I wouldn't go to school today?

WINNIE. Wouldn't go to school? Why, of course, you have to go to school today, why wouldn't you?

DOUG. 'CAUSE WE'RE GOING TO YELLOWSTONE PARK!!!!!

(They jump up and down and sing a song about how they must make sure they've taken the right things. They sing about the contents of a rucksack, and emergency gear, which they inspect on each other's person. This gear includes: waxed matches in a waterproof container [several containers secreted in various parts of the clothing and generally high up to keep them dry should one fall into waist-high water], a compass, a spare compass, a topographic map of the area to be camped in. A candle for helping to light fires, needle and thread, steel wool which, though it is not generally known, is, in its superfine variety, great tinder and can just be wrung out when wet, extra clothing, rain gear, pencil and paper, fishing line and hook, bandages, whistle, etc. They finish the song, and, having checked each other out, decide that they are ready to proceed to the bus, which they have ten minutes to catch. In deciding which coat to wear, they turn on the radio to catch a weather report.)

DOUG. I can't believe we're really going.

WINNIE. Have I ever lied to you?

DOUG. No!

WINNIE. Well, then, there you are.

RADIO ANNOUNCER *(voice over).* In other news, Congressman John Larue, up for reelection, yesterday was accosted for the misdemeanor of Attempting to Defraud of Services, or, to put it simply, a waitress at a restaurant he frequents, accused the congressman of lifting her tip off her table.

WINNIE. . . . Come on, let's get out of here . . .

CONGRESSMAN *(voice over).* You know, it's easy to accuse, and, I think by far the simplest thing would be to let this sick accusation pass, and go my way, but there comes a time . . .

WINNIE. Turn that creep off; let's go to the country . . .

DOUG *(turns off radio).* What'd he do?

WINNIE. The creep. Lifted a tip off of a waitress's table. Can you believe that?

DOUG *(opening door).* What a life.

WINNIE. On to the Wilds!

(In the door are two burly plainclothes POLICEMEN.*)*

POLICEMAN. Winnie Magee?

WINNIE. I . . . uh, what is it?

POLICEMAN. Are you Ms. Winnie Magee?

WINNIE. I can't talk to you now, we have to catch a bus.

POLICEMAN. ARE YOU WIN . . . ?

WINNIE. Yes, but I can't talk . . .

POLICEMAN *(simultaneously with "talk").* You're under arrest. Would you come with us, please?

WINNIE. I . . .

DOUG. Wait, you can't, what's this all . . . ?

POLICEMAN. Slander, Malicious Mischief, Defamation of Character, would you please . . . ?

WINNIE. Who, what . . . ?

DOUG. What are you doing to my mother?

SECOND POLICEMAN. She insulted a congressman, kid.

WINNIE. But we . . . we just have ten minutes to catch the bus . . .

They are in a court of law.

And we're going to Yellowstone P . . . what is this, what's going on here . . . ?

JUDGE. You are accused of wantonly, maliciously, and with malice afore-thought having verbally assaulted, insulted, and impugned[1] the charac-ter of one John Larue, congressman for the Seventh District of . . .

WINNIE. HOLD ON A SECOND. I insulted wh . . . ?

JUDGE. You have no voice in this court, would you please, who is your counsel?

WINNIE. Say that again?

BAILIFF. Who's your lawyer?

WINNIE. I don't have a lawyer, why should . . . What's going on here? *(Pause)* Come on, I have to catch a *bus. (Pause)*

JUDGE. You are accused by the con-gressman here (CONGRESSMAN *stands)* of, in simple terms, of lying about him in such a way as to damage his reputation.

WINNIE. Ah.

JUDGE. When you said that he stole your tip.

WINNIE. He *did* steal my tip.

JUDGE. The court will now appoint you a lawyer.

WINNIE. I don't need a lawyer, I don't *want* one. Let's settle this here and now, 'cause I'm on my vacation time, alright? You tell me how you want to do this, and let's get this done.

JUDGE. You wish to act as your own lawyer?

WINNIE. That's . . . okay. *(Pause)* Okay.

JUDGE. You're making a mistake.

WINNIE. I've made them before. Nothing to be scared of, now: what is the thing?

DOUG. Mom, what's going on . . .?

(WINNIE *and* DOUG *hold a whispered consul-tation while the* BAILIFF *and the* JUDGE *sing about the charge and the procedure in this case. They are joined by the lawyer for the* CONGRESSMAN *and the* CONGRESSMAN, *who sing about her heinous behavior and the grave damage that has been done. They stop. Pause.)*

WINNIE. Now what?

JUDGE. You may present your case.

WINNIE. It's my turn to speak?

JUDGE. Yes.

WINNIE *(sings).*

Let me preface my remarks by saying
that I have to catch a bus
Because I am enroute to
Yellowstone Park
Where, my son and I are taking
a long-planned vacation
In the wilds of this great land.
I am a simple kind of gal which
is to say
I'm just as complex as the rest of
us here but
there are some basic things that I
believe in
one of which is
that we are entitled to a just pay
for the work that we do

———————
1. impugn, attack as false or lacking honesty

in my case a waitress
which is to say that I work for tips.
Okay?
My salary is directly tied to this
one thing:
my ability to *please*, which is to say, to
make comfortable
the *patrons* of my restaurant, who
have come out to eat.
The first rule of which is:
THE CUSTOMER IS ALWAYS
RIGHT.
Which rule I do adhere to.
IN THIS CASE HOWEVER. ONE:
The man performed a criminal
act . . .

CONGRESSMAN. . . . I DID NOT.

WINNIE. AND I asked him . . .

LAWYER. What was that act?

WINNIE. He stole my tip.

LAWYER. I rest my case.

WINNIE. I asked him to replace it. He
did not, and TWO: I called upon the
customers to help me out. That's the
beginning and the end, and that is
what occurred. Now; are we free to
leave?

DOUG. Can we go now?

(End of song)

JUDGE. Can you prove that he took
your tip?

WINNIE. No.

JUDGE. You cannot?

WINNIE. No. The only proof is that I
saw him.

JUDGE. We will now consider this case.

DOUG. Mom, do we have time to make
the bus . . . ?

WINNIE *(simultaneously with "bus")*. Just
barely. If he does this quick.

JUDGE. Here are my feelings: this has
gotten out of hand. I think it can be
settled quickly. *(Pause)* As we all have
better things to do. *(Pause)* I think
that a simple apology will suffice.

WINNIE. I'll accept that. Your Honor. I
notice that you didn't say that he had
to give back my tip. There is a principle involved, but I am willing to forget that, in the interest of getting out
of town . . . *(To DOUG, as she checks her
watch)* Okay, let's go, we can just
make it . . . *(They walk toward the
courtroom doors carrying their rucksacks.)*
And I will waive that principle and
accept the congressman's sincere
apology. Also, he has to say he'll
never do it again.

JUDGE. You misunderstand me. *You'll*
have to apologize to him.

(Pause)

WINNIE. I . . . *what?*

JUDGE. *You* will have to . . .

WINNIE. *I* . . .

JUDGE. Apologize to the congressman.

(Pause)

WINNIE. For *what?*

JUDGE. For maligning his reputation.

WINNIE. HE STOLE MY *TIP*.

JUDGE. We have no way of knowing
what he might have done, except
your word. His reputation, which is a
weighty thing, is at stake, and rather
than *prolong* this, and to allow you to
catch your bus, if you will just
state that you . . . *could* have made
a mistake . . .

LAWYER. I OBJECT.

JUDGE. Excuse me: if you will just say that you could have made a mistake, this case will be closed and you can go to Yellowstone.

(Pause)

WINNIE. You want me to say he didn't steal my tip. *(Pause)* I do that and we can go.

JUDGE. Yes.

WINNIE. What if I don't say that?

JUDGE. You will go to jail.

WINNIE. Hmm.

(Pause)

JUDGE. The choice is yours. What do you choose to do? And I would remind you that you have but five minutes to catch your bus.

WINNIE. Well. This would seem to be the crux of the whole matter here.

RANGER. I would say so.

WINNIE *(to* DOUG*).* Whaddya think, kid? This guy stole my tip, and if I lie about it we can go free, if not . . . it's, it's your *trip*, you tell mmm . . . naa, that's *ridiculous*. What am I going to do? Teach my kid his mom's a liar for the sake of *expediency*?[2]

LAWYER. He wants to go camping.

WINNIE. So he won't go camping. That's not under my control, and I never promised him that I was *superhuman*, all that I told him was I'd tell the truth.

JUDGE. And so?

WINNIE. Take me to jail and be damned with you. He stole my tip. *(She is led from the courtroom, amidst catcalls.)*

CONGRESSMAN. What kind of a mother are you?

LAWYER. You're going to be a convict . . .

WINNIE. Hey, I'd rather be me than you.

BAILIFF. You promised the child you'd take him camping.

DOUG. Mama!

WINNIE. Well, there's nothing we can do about it . . .

RANGER. And so Winnie was taken to the jail, and they took her picture and her fingerprints, and they gave her a uniform and put her in a cell.

(In the cell. With another CONVICT*.)*

CONVICT. You want to play gin?

WINNIE. Don't bother me.

RANGER. And she was full of longing for her son, whom she missed. And she worried about him. And she thought about him.

*(*WINNIE *sings a song about how incredibly difficult it is to bring up children. And how hard it is to live your life according to first principles. The song ends.)*

CONVICT. The first night is the hardest.

WINNIE. I'm sure that's true.

CONVICT. It *is* true. *(Pause)* How long are you in for?

WINNIE. I don't know. 'Til I apologize. *(Sighs)* And we were supposed to be camped out beneath the stars. *(Pause)* How long are *you* in for?

CONVICT. Can you keep a secret?

---

2. expediency, achieving self-interest rather than principle.

WINNIE. No. *(Pause)*

CONVICT. What's *that* supposed to mean?

WINNIE. Nobody can keep a secret. If you don't want me to know your business don't tell it to me.

CONVICT. We're breaking out.

WINNIE. What does that mean?

CONVICT. We're breaking out of jail tonight.

WINNIE. Swell.

There is a huge explosion, and the prison wall collapses. All the CONVICTS run. She finds herself among them.

GUARD. Stop! Stop!

WINNIE. Look, I just, I was just sitting in my *cell* . . .

(The GUARD *fires at her.)*

WINNIE. Oh gosh . . . ! *(She runs.)*

RANGER. And so Winnie ran from the prison, along with the other convicts. And she wandered in the dark corners of the streets. And she found herself at home.

(Outside her apartment. Her son, listening to the radio.)

ANNOUNCER *(voice over).* And now a medley of Songs That You Love To Dream Along With. From the Fantasy Ballroom.

(Old-time music begins to play. WINNIE *goes inside.)*

DOUG. Mama! *(They embrace.)* Mama! I knew that you'd come home. I knew that you'd come home!!!

WINNIE. How are you, Sweetie?

DOUG. I knew that you'd come back. I knew they'd let you out. So we could go *camping.*

WINNIE. Doug, look: I, uh . . . I don't think we can . . .

ANNOUNCER *(voice over).* We interrupt this program to bring you a special report. Inmates from the Women's Correctional Institute escaped tonight in a mass breakout, wounding five guards in the attempt. Considered armed and dangerous, be on the lookout for . . .

(She turns off the radio.)

WINNIE *(pause).* Um . . .

DOUG. I'll just get my pack. *(He checks bus schedule.)* And we can catch a bus at . . .

WINNIE. . . . Doug . . .

DOUG. We can catch the one forty-five A.M. bus. And tomorrow! . . . Tomorrow . . . that's right: Yellowstone P . . .

WINNIE. Doug . . . *(Pause)* Hm. Get your pack.

RANGER. They disguised themselves, and got on the bus bound for Yellowstone.

(On the bus. In wigs, and so on.)

DOUG. Will everything be alright?

WINNIE. Everything is never alright; but the thing of it is you never have to worry about "everything." And, for the moment, what we're going to do is just go camping. Now you go to sleep.

(He goes to sleep, as she sings him a song about Yellowstone, a lullaby, featuring the admonition not to feed the bears, and to look out not to miss Old Faithful.)

RANGER. The bus sped West, and they fell asleep rocked to the rhythm of the bus.

(WINNIE is suddenly awake. To BUS DRIVER.)

WINNIE. Why are we slowing down?

DRIVER. There's something up ahead. It's a roadblock.

(The lights come on in the bus. STATE TROOPERS enter.)

TROOPER. Would everyone please keep their seats.

(They start down the aisle, looking at a picture and at the passengers.)

DRIVER. What's the trouble?

TROOPER. We're looking for some escaped convicts . . .

DOUG. What are we going to do?

WINNIE. Be calm.

DOUG. How can I, how can I be calm? They're going to Take you Away.

WINNIE. Just, Sweetie, just be . . . just, whatever I say, you pretend you're asleep.

TROOPER *(to WINNIE)*. What is your name?

DOUG. She's You Don't Want Her. She isn't anybody. Don't . . . don't take her. Mama. Come on. Let's Run!

WINNIE. Officer, I . . .

DOUG. She's not the one you want . . . Come ON!

RANGER. He and his mother escaped through a back window of the bus. And they ran into the woods.

DOUG. Keep running . . .

WINNIE *(sighs)*. Oh, my god . . .

DOUG. No, all we have to do is just keep running. They won't . . . they won't find us . . .

WINNIE. Alright.

DOUG. Don't go back. You can't go back. They'll put you back in Prison.

WINNIE. Alright.

RANGER. In the deep dark they became lost. In the woods.

WINNIE. Are you alright?

DOUG. I'm cold.

WINNIE *(of compass)*. We'll just keep walking North. We're going to find a road.

DOUG. How do you know?

WINNIE. Because I have the compass and I have a map.

DOUG. How do you know that there *is* a road?

WINNIE. Because I see it on the map.

DOUG. What will we do when we find it?

WINNIE. Give ourselves up, because you're cold, and you should be warm, and sleep. And we can't run forever. And that's what we're going to do.

DOUG. We're going the wrong way. We *passed* this way before.

WINNIE. No. We didn't.

DOUG. How do you know?

WINNIE. Because I have my compass.

DOUG. I don't think it's working. Yes it is. We'll trust it now. And everything will be alright.

WINNIE. Now; for a moment. What's the first thing that you do if you get scared and you're lost in the woods?

DOUG. I don't know.

WINNIE. Yes. You do. You Sit Down and Think. *(Pause)* Now we'll sit down a moment.

(They sit. WINNIE *sings: "Just Because You're Lost Don't Think Your Compass Is Broken." She sings: "We Must Abide, in Moments of Stress, by Those Things We Have, in Moments of Peace, Decided Are Correct." She finishes singing.)*

Now, let's go on, and soon we'll find the road, and then you'll be warm.

DOUG. Look!

WINNIE. What is it?

DOUG. A light!

RANGER. They walked in the forest to a little hut made out of wood. A sign over the door said "Ralph Blum."

WINNIE. Ralph Blum.

DOUG. Who is that?

WINNIE. I don't know, but I hope that he'll help.

She knocks on the door. Pause. She knocks again. Pause.

DOUG. Let's go in.

*(*WINNIE *tries the door.)*

WINNIE. It's locked. Well, we're going to get you warm. We'll break a window.

(They start around the side of the cabin, the door opens.)

RALPH. Who are you?

WINNIE. May we come in? My son is . . .

RALPH. Why didn't you come to the door?

WINNIE. We *did* come to the door. We knocked and knocked and . . .

RALPH. I didn't hear you. Come in.

(They go into the cabin.)

RALPH. The boy's cold? Let's get him something to eat. Here. Put on those warm clothes and I'll put the bed by the fire.

WINNIE. Thank you.

RALPH. What?

WINNIE. Thank you.

RALPH. Not at all.

RANGER. So they sat around the fire and the man gave them soup.

RALPH. Now, you two should go to bed, because you look like you could use the rest. You go to sleep, now.

WINNIE. I don't think that I can sleep.

RALPH. You sleep, and everything will look brighter in the morning, whatever it is.

WINNIE. I don't think so.

(Pause)

RALPH. Is there anything that I can help you with?

WINNIE. Thank you, you're very kind, I don't see how you can.

RALPH. You never know. Did you know that? That's one of the true things. You never know.

WINNIE. I'm sure you're right.

RALPH. What?

WINNIE. I said I'm sure you're right.

RALPH. I am right. Lived in the forest all my life. You think that's crazy?

WINNIE. Not at all. Quite the contrary.

RALPH. Eh?

WINNIE. I think that's the best place one could live.

RALPH. You *do?*

WINNIE. Yes.

RALPH. Huh. Huh. Huh. *(Pause)* Well, I'm going to tell you what: Us Outdoorsmen have got to help each other. Don't you think? *(Pause)* Don't you think?

WINNIE. Mm. Yes.

RALPH. Well, we *do*. And I'm going to help *you*. I don't know what your *problems* are, 'n' it's none of my business . . .

WINNIE. My problems are I have to go to jail and be separated from my son tomorrow.

RALPH. Then I'm going to help you.

WINNIE. How?

(Pause)

RALPH. Can you keep a secret?

WINNIE. If it will help me and my son.

RALPH. It will.

WINNIE. Then I'll keep a secret.

RALPH. You give me your solemn oath?

WINNIE. I do.

RALPH. Alright. *(Pause)* I am the Magic Woodsman. *(Pause)* I have the Power to grant Wishes of the Heart.

(He sings the "Song of the Magic Woodsman." He finishes. Pause.)

And now you have two wishes. Anything your Heart Desires.

(Pause)

WINNIE. I can wish for anything?

RALPH. Yup. And it will be granted.

(Pause)

WINNIE. Is that true?

RALPH. Yes. It is.

(Pause)

WINNIE. Thank you.

RALPH. What?

WINNIE. Thank you.

RALPH. That is alright. Now, you take your time, and whatever you . . .

WINNIE. I don't have to take time. I am going to wish . . .

RALPH. Oh, oh, oh. I forgot: *(Pause)* First you have to guess my name. Nothing to it. *(Pause)* You have to guess my name and then I grant your wishes. Understand?

WINNIE. Yes.

RALPH. Think you can do it?

WINNIE. Yes.

RALPH. Alright, then. Now: what are your wishes?

WINNIE *(pause)*. I wish that everything was just the way it was before the congressman came in the restaurant . . .

RALPH. . . . alright . . .

WINNIE. And I wish my son and I were in Yellowstone Park. *(Pause)*

RALPH. Good. You tell me my name your wishes shall be granted.

WINNIE. Your name is Ralph Blum. *(Pause)*

RALPH. I'm very sorry, Miss.

WINNIE. That's not your name?

RALPH. I'm very sorry. *(Pause)* I'm very sorry.

WINNIE. Do I get another chance?

RALPH. No. It is not within my power. *(Pause)* I'm very sorry. *(Pause)* I . . . you and the boy. Feel free to stay here tonight. I, I'm sure everything will, will look brighter in the morning. *(Pause)* I hope that everything works out. I'm very sorry.

(The MAGIC WOODSMAN leaves the cabin. WINNIE waits. Sits down at the table, smokes a cigarette.)

RANGER. The false dawn came, that time before the dawn, and, after it, the dawn, and Winnie sat at the table smoking her cigarette while her son slept.

(WINNIE *sings a song of remorse, how, standing on principle, she has sacrificed the well-being of her child. She finishes.* DOUG *wakes up.*)

DOUG. Where are we . . . ?

WINNIE. Come on. Get up, Sweetheart, we . . .

DOUG. What's that . . . ?

RANGER. They heard the baying of dogs. Drawing closer.

WINNIE. They're coming to get us.

(*Through a megaphone we hear a* TROOPER.)

TROOPER. We know you're in there . . .

SECOND TROOPER. Be careful, she's dangerous.

TROOPER. You have one minute to come out, you and the boy . . .

DOUG. What are we going to do?

WINNIE. I have to give myself up . . .

DOUG. No! What will they do to . . .

WINNIE. I'm sure everything will be al . . .

TROOPER. Alright, we're coming in . . .

WINNIE (*She embraces* DOUG.) Sweetheart, I'm sure that everything will be al . . . (*The door opens. She shields* DOUG. *It is* RALPH BLUM.)

RALPH. Wait a second. Did you say "Ralph *Blum*"?

WINNIE. What?

RALPH. Did you say "Ralph *Blum*"? My *name*?

WINNIE. Yes.

RALPH. You *did*.

WINNIE. Yes.

RALPH. 'Cause, that *is* my name. It's on, you know, it's on a sign right outside the *door.*

WINNIE. I, I, I *know*.

RALPH. What?

WINNIE. I said that I *know*.

RALPH. I thought you said "Brown." But you said "Ralph *Blum*."

WINNIE. Yes.

RALPH. Word of honor?

WINNIE. Yes.

RALPH. Well, then you get your *wish!* I'm sorry . . . such a silly . . . I don't hear so . . .

(*They are transported.* WINNIE *is back in the restaurant with the* CONGRESSMAN.)

RANGER. And they were magically transported back in time. To the time before she saw the congressman take the tip from the table.

At the restaurant

CONGRESSMAN. Miss.

WINNIE. Yes, sir, I'm coming.

CONGRESSMAN (*of check*). What is this? Ninety-five cents for a substitution?

WINNIE. You had beans instead of the creamed spinach.

CONGRESSMAN. I'm not going to pay it.

WINNIE. Then I will pay it for you. 'Cause I bet you've had a hard day.

CONGRESSMAN. Uh. You will?

WINNIE. Yes.

CONGRESSMAN. That's, uh, you know, it's not the money, it's the principle of the thing.

WINNIE. I know that it is.

CONGRESSMAN. That's very kind of you.

WINNIE. Just Pass it On.

(Another WAITRESS *and she talk.)*

WAITRESS. That fellow giving you a hard time?

WINNIE. Well, you know, it takes all kinds.

WAITRESS. Hey, your vacation starts tomorrow.

WINNIE. You bet. Me and my Son are going to Yellowstone.

WAITRESS. I bet that you wish you were there right now.

WINNIE. I surely do.

RANGER. And they were all instantly transported to Yellowstone Park, the congressman, the judge, the bailiff, the guards and the prisoners, and Winnie and her son. For two weeks of life in the Great Outdoors.

They all sing a chorale. To wit:

Always tell the truth.
Never insult a congressman.
Don't go to court without a lawyer.
Be calm at roadblocks.
Do not feed the bears.

A WAITRESS IN YELLOWSTONE

Responding to the Play

1. Do you think Mamet really intends that "Always Tell the Truth" be the moral of this play? Why or why not?
2. Fables often contain elements of magic. How does magic help move this play along?
3. In what way is *A Waitress in Yellowstone* a realistic play? In what way is it unrealistic?
4. Make a drawing or drawings showing the stage blocking of the scene in which Winnie and Doug run into the woods (p. 12).
5. Create a television ad promoting the upcoming worldwide premier of *A Waitress in Yellowstone*.

About Acting Terminology

The theatre has its own terminology, and knowing the words below will help you better understand what is required of the actor.

Aside   When an actor approaches the audience and speaks directly to it. Other characters cannot hear an aside.

Build   To pick up one's volume or the pace of one's speech in order to create a dramatic moment in a play.

Cue   The last line spoken by a character; the line to which another character must respond.

Drop   To decrease the volume of speech at the end of the sentence.

Top   Say a line more forcefully or loudly than the lines before.

CREATING AND PERFORMING

1. Ralph the Magic Woodsman is obviously a bit deaf. What other characteristics would you incorporate into a portrayal of him?
2. The stage directions call for a number of songs to be sung in this play. Write the lyrics to either "Just Because You're Lost Don't Think Your Compass Is Broken" or "Song of the Magic Woodsman." Be prepared to share your lyrics with the class.
3. With a partner, block out the scene in which Ralph realizes he may have misheard Winnie when she said his name (p. 15).

A Waitress in Yellowstone by David Mamet   **17**

A YOUNG LADY OF PROPERTY

The Play as Literature: Characterization

One of the most important things an author thinks about is *charac-terization*—creating characters that come alive. In the hands of Horton Foote, characterization produces memorable characters. (For more about Horton Foote see p. 43.)

In works of fiction, the author often uses direct exposition to char-acterize—telling the reader how a character looks, acts, and thinks. When reading a play, however, one must interpret much of this for oneself. When viewing a play, the audience understands the author's intent through the actors' interpretation of the dialogue.

In addition, a character may be static or dynamic. A *dynamic character* is one who changes as the result of actions and experi-ences. A *static character* changes very little. Things happen *to* but not *within* the static character. In *A Young Lady of Property* you will find both static and dynamic characters. Try to identify them.

The Play as Theatre: The Stage

There are three basic types of stages: The *thrust* stage, the *arena* stage (also called theatre-in-the-round), and the *proscenium* stage.

The oldest type of stage is the *thrust*, dating back to the Greek the-atre. This stage extends well into the audience, who sit in a half circle around it. Scenery cannot be used in the front of the stage because it would obstruct the view. It is positioned in the back.

The *arena* stage offers seating that goes completely around the stage. Scenery must be three dimensional because the audience sits on all sides.

The latest and most common stage is the *proscenium.* The name comes from the frame (the proscenium arch) around one side of the stage. Walls of scenery can be positioned on three sides of the stage. Scene changes are made in the backstage area, hidden from view.

WARM UP!

Draw a map of your school's stage or performance area. Identify whether it is a thrust, arena, or proscenium space. Be prepared to add sets and props to your map.

A Young Lady of PROPERTY

by Horton Foote

SETTING	CHARACTERS	TIME
Harrison, Texas	**MISS MARTHA DAVENPORT** **MR. RUSSELL WALTER GRAHAM** **WILMA THOMPSON** **ARABELLA COOKENBOO** **LESTER THOMPSON** **MRS. LEIGHTON** **MINNA BOYD** **MISS GERT** **MAN**	Late spring, 1925

The stage is divided into four areas. Area one, directly across the front of the stage, is a sidewalk. Area two, just above the sidewalk left of center, is part of a kitchen. A table, with a portable phonograph on it, and four chairs are placed here. Area three is above the sidewalk right of center. It has a yard swing in it. Area four is directly upstage center. In it is a post office window.

The lights are brought up on the post office window. It is attended by two people, MISS MARTHA DAVENPORT, who is inside the window, and MR. RUSSELL WALTER GRAHAM, who is leaning on the outside ledge of the window. It is about three-thirty of a late spring day. MISS MARTHA and MR. RUSSELL WALTER look very sleepy. Two girls around fifteen come in with schoolbooks in their arms. They are WILMA THOMPSON and ARABELLA COOKENBOO. WILMA is a handsome girl with style and spirit about her. ARABELLA is gentle looking, so shy about growing into womanhood that one can't really tell yet what she is to look like or become. She is WILMA's shadow and obviously her adoring slave. They go up to the window. MR. RUSSELL WALTER sees them and punches MISS MARTHA.

RUSSELL. Look who's here, Miss Martha. The Bobbsey twins.

(MISS MARTHA gives a peal of laughter that sounds as if she thinks MR. RUSSELL WALTER the funniest man in five counties.)

MISS MARTHA (again giggling). Now, Mr. Russell Walter, don't start teasing the young ladies. How are you, girls?

WILMA and ARABELLA. Fine.

RUSSELL. Can I sell you any stamps? We have some lovely special deliveries today. Our ones and twos are very nice too.

MARTHA (giggling). Isn't he a tease, girls?

WILMA. Mr. Russell Walter, when's the next train in from Houston?

RUSSELL. Why? Going on a trip?

MARTHA (rolling at his wit). Now, Mr. Russell Walter, stop teasing the young ladies. The next mail doesn't come in on the train, dear ones; it comes in on the bus. And that will be at six. Although the Houston mail is usually very light at that time, there are a few special deliveries. Do you think your letter might come by special delivery, Wilma?

WILMA. No ma'am. Regular.

MARTHA. Oh. Well, in that case I don't hold out much hope for it on that delivery. It's usually mostly second-class mail. You know, seed catalogs and such. The next Houston mail heavy with first-class is delivered at five tomorrow morning.

RUSSELL. Which she knows better than you.

MARTHA (giggling). Now, Mr. Russell Walter, stop teasing the young ladies.

WILMA. Arabella and I were discussing coming here from school, Mr. Russell Walter, that the mail sometimes gets in the wrong box.

RUSSELL. Rarely, Miss Wilma. Rarely.

WILMA. Arabella says that once a Christmas card meant for her got put by mistake in Box 270, instead of her box, which is 370, and she didn't get it back until the third of January.

RUSSELL. Well, if that happens, nothing we can do about it until the person whose box it got into by mistake returns it.

WILMA. Yes sir. (A pause). I don't suppose any mail has been put in my box since my Aunt Gert was here last.

RUSSELL. Well, seeing as she was here just a half hour ago, I don't think so.

MARTHA. Who are you expecting a letter from, young lady?

WILMA. Somebody very important. Come on, Arabella. (They start out. They pause. She goes back to the window.) Mr. Russell Walter, once I had a movie star picture, Ben Lyons I think, that was addressed to Wilma Thomas instead of Thompson, and if you remember, Mr. Peter was new at the time and put it into General Delivery, and it wasn't until two weeks later that you discovered it there and figured it belonged to me.

RUSSELL. Well, Mr. Peter isn't new here now.

WILMA. But I thought maybe accidentally someone put my letter in General Delivery.

RUSSELL. Nope.

MARTHA. Oh, Mr. Walter. Go ahead and look. It won't hurt you.

RUSSELL Now, Miss Martha . . .

MARTHA. Now just go ahead . . . (She hands him a stack of letters.)

RUSSELL. All right . . . Anything to please the ladies. (He goes over to the letters and starts looking into them.)

MARTHA. Wilma, I saw your daddy and Mrs. Leighton at the picture show together again last night. Maybe you'll be having a new mother soon.

WILMA. Well, I wouldn't hold my breath waiting if I were you.

MARTHA. I was saying to Mr. Russell Walter, I see the tenants have left the Thompson house. Maybe they were asked to leave so Mr. Thompson might move in with a bride.

WILMA. They were asked to leave because they were tearing it to pieces. They had weeds growing in the yard and had torn off wallpaper. My Aunt Gert asked them to leave . . . .

MARTHA. Oh, of course. They didn't take any pride in it at all. Not like when your mother was living. Why, I remember your mother always had the yard filled with flowers, and . . . *(The phone rings.)* Excuse me. (MISS MARTHA *answers it.)* Post office. Yes. Yes. She's here. Yes, I will. *(She puts the phone down.)* That was your Aunt Gertrude, Wilma. She said you were to come right home.

WILMA. All right.

MARTHA. Found any mail for Wilma, Mr. Russell Walter?

RUSSELL. Nope, Miss Wilma. No mail and no female either.

MARTHA *(giggling).* Isn't he a sight? You come back at six, Wilma. Maybe we'll have something then.

WILMA. Yes ma'am. Come on, Arabella. *(They go outside the area and walk directly down the center of the stage and pause at the apron, looking up and down. They are now on the sidewalk area.)*

WILMA. I'd like to scratch that old cat's eyes out. The idea of her saying old lady Leighton is going to be my mother. She's so nosy. I wonder how she'd like it if I asked her if Mr. Russell Walter was going to ask her to marry him after she's been chasing him for fifteen years.

ARABELLA. Well, just ignore her.

WILMA. I intend to.

ARABELLA. What are you going to do now, Wilma?

WILMA. Fool around until the six o'clock mail.

ARABELLA. Don't you think you ought to go home like your aunt said?

WILMA. No.

ARABELLA. Have you told your Aunt Gert about the letter you're expecting yet?

WILMA. No.

ARABELLA. When are you going to tell her?

WILMA. Not until it comes. I think I'll go over and see my house. Look at how those tenants left it. I may have to sell it yet to get me to Hollywood.

ARABELLA. Wilma, is that house really yours?

WILMA. Sure it's mine. My mother left it to me.

ARABELLA. Well, do you get the rent for it and tell them who to rent to like Papa does his rent houses?

WILMA. No. But it's understood it's mine. My mother told Aunt Gert it was mine just before she died. Daddy had put it in her name because he was gambling terrible then, and Aunt Gert says Mama was afraid they'd lose it. I let Daddy rent it and keep the money now. Aunt Gert says I should, as he is having a very hard time. His job at the cotton gin doesn't pay hardly anything. Of course, I feel very lucky having my own house.

ARABELLA. Well, I have a house.

WILMA. Do you own it yourself?

ARABELLA. No. But I live in it.

WILMA. Well, that's hardly the same thing. I own a house, which is very unusual, Aunt Gert says, for a girl of fifteen. I'm a young lady of property, Aunt Gert says. Many's the time I thought I'll just go and live in it all by myself. Wouldn't Harrison sit up and take notice then? Once when I was thirteen and I was very fond of my Cousin Neeley I thought I'd offer it to him to get through law school. But I'm glad I didn't, since he turned out so hateful. *(A pause)* Do you remember when I used to live in my house?

ARABELLA. No.

WILMA. Well, it's a long time ago now, but I still remember it. My mama and I used to play croquet in the yard under the pecan trees. We'd play croquet every afternoon just before sundown, and every once in a while she'd stop the game and ask me to run to the corner without letting the neighbors know what I was doing, to see if my father was coming home. She always worried about his getting home by six, because if he wasn't there by then she knew it meant trouble. My mother always kept me in white starched dresses. Do you remember my mother?

ARABELLA No. But my mother does. She says she was beautiful, with the disposition of a saint.

WILMA. I know. Her name was Alice. Isn't that a pretty name?

ARABELLA. Yes. It is.

WILMA. There's a song named "Sweet Alice Ben Bolt." Aunt Gert used to sing it all the time. When Mama died, she stopped. My mama died of a broken heart.

ARABELLA. She did?

WILMA. Oh, yes. Even Aunt Gert admits that. Daddy's gambling broke her heart. Oh, well. What are you gonna do about it? Boy, I used to hate my daddy. I used to dream about what I'd do to him when I grew up. But he's sorry now and reformed, so I've forgiven him.

ARABELLA. Oh, sure. You shouldn't hate your father.

WILMA. Well, I don't know. Do you know something I've never told another living soul?

ARABELLA. What?

WILMA. Swear you won't tell?

ARABELLA. I swear.

WILMA. I love him now. Sometimes I think I'd give up this whole movie-star business if I could go back to our house and live with Daddy and keep house for him. But Aunt Gert says under the circumstances that's not practical. I guess you and every-body else know what the circum-stances are. Mrs. Leighton. She's got my daddy hogtied. Aunt Gert says she isn't good enough to shine my mother's shoes, and I think she's right. *(MISS* MARTHA *comes out of the post office area upstage center. She walks halfway down the center of the stage.)*

MARTHA. Are you girls still here?

WILMA. Yes ma'am.

MARTHA. Minna called this time,

Wilma. She said you were to come home immediately. (MISS MARTHA *goes back inside the post office area and into her window upstage center.*)

ARABELLA. Now come on, Wilma. You'll just get in trouble.

WILMA. All right. (*They start off right.* WILMA *stops. She looks panicky.*) Wait a minute, Arabella. Yonder comes my daddy walking with that fool Mrs. Leighton. I'd just as soon I didn't have to see them. Let's go the other way. (*They turn around and start left. A man's voice calls in the distance: "Wilma, Wilma."* WILMA *and* ARABELLA *stop.* WILMA *whispering.*) That's the kind of luck I have. He saw me. Now I'll have to speak to old lady Leighton.

ARABELLA. Don't you like her?

WILMA. Do you like snakes?

ARABELLA. No.

WILMA. Well, neither do I like Mrs. Leighton and for the same reason. (LESTER THOMPSON *and* MRS. LEIGHTON *enter from downstage right.* LESTER *is a handsome, weak man in his forties.* MRS. LEIGHTON *is thirty-five or so, blond, pretty, and completely unlike* WILMA's *description. There is a warmth about her that we should wish that* WILMA *might notice.* LESTER *goes over to* WILMA.)

LESTER (*as he leaves* MRS. LEIGHTON). Excuse me, Sibyl. Wilma . . .

WILMA. Yes sir.

LESTER. Say hello to Mrs. Leighton.

WILMA (*most ungraciously*). Hello, Mrs. Leighton.

MRS. LEIGHTON (*most graciously*). Hello, Wilma.

LESTER. What are you doing hanging around the streets, Wilma?

WILMA. Waiting to see if I have a letter.

LESTER. What kind of letter, Wilma?

WILMA. About getting into the movies. Arabella and I saw an ad in the *Houston Chronicle* about a Mr. Delafonte who is a famous Hollywood director.

LESTER. Who is Mr. Delafonte?

WILMA. The Hollywood director I'm trying to tell you about. He's giving screen tests in Houston to people of beauty and talent, and if they pass they'll go to Hollywood and be in the picture shows.

LESTER. Well, that's all a lot of foolishness, Wilma. You're not going to Houston to take anything.

WILMA. But, Daddy . . . I . . .

LESTER. You're fifteen years old and you're gonna stay home like a fifteen-year-old girl should. There'll be plenty of time to go to Houston.

WILMA. But, Daddy, Mr. Delafonte won't be there forever.

LESTER. Go on home, Wilma.

WILMA. But, Daddy . . .

LESTER. Don't argue with me. I want you to march home just as quick as you can, young lady. I'm going to stand right here until you turn that corner, and if I ever catch you hanging around the streets again, it will be between you and me.

WILMA. Yes sir. Come on, Arabella. (*She and* ARABELLA *walk out left.* LESTER *stands watching.* SIBYL LEIGHTON *comes up to him.*)

MRS. LEIGHTON. Have you told her we're getting married, Lester?

LESTER. No, I'm telling Gert tonight.

MRS. LEIGHTON. Aren't you going to tell Wilma?

LESTER. No. Gert's the one to tell her. Wilma and I have very little to say to each other. Gert has her won over completely.

MRS. LEIGHTON. They must be expecting it. Why would they think you're selling your house and quitting your job?

LESTER. I don't think they know that either. I'll explain the whole thing to Gert tonight. Come on. She's turned the corner. I think she'll go home now.

They walk on and off. The lights are brought up downstage left in area 2. It is part of the kitchen in GERTRUDE MILLER's house. MINNA BOYD, a thin, strong Negro woman in her middle forties, is seated at the table. She has a portable, hand-winding Victrola on the table. She is listening to a jazz recording. WILMA and ARABELLA come in upstage center of the kitchen area.

MINNA. Well, here's the duchess. Arrived at last. Where have you been, Wilma? What on earth do you mean aggravating us this way? Your Aunt Gert was almost late for her card party worrying over you.

WILMA. You knew where I was. You called often enough. I was at the post office waiting for the mail.

MINNA. How many times has Miss Gert told you not to hang around there? Where's your pride? You know Mr. Russell Walter called and told her you were about to drive them crazy down at the post office. He said when you get your letter, he's gonna be so relieved he'll deliver it in person. Your aunt says you're to get right to your room and study.

WILMA. We're just going. Come on, Arabella.

MINNA. And without Arabella. I know how much studying you and Arabella will do. You'll spend your whole time talking about Hollywood and picture shows. Clara Bow this and Alice White[1] that. You go in there and learn something. The principal called your auntie this morning and told her you were failing in your typing and shorthand.

WILMA (very bored). Well, I don't care. I hate them. I never wanted to take them anyway.

MINNA. Never mind about that. You just get in there and get to it. (WILMA pays no attention. She goes deliberately and sits in a chair, scowling.) Wilma . . .

WILMA. What?

MINNA. Now why do you want to act like this?

WILMA. Like what?

MINNA. So ugly. Your face is gonna freeze like that one day and then you're gonna be in a nice how-do-you-do.

ARABELLA. I'd better go, Wilma.

WILMA. All right, Arabella. Someday soon I'll be established in my own house, and then you won't be treated so rudely.

---

1. Clara Bow and Alice White, stars of silent films in the 1920's

MINNA. You come back some other time.

ARABELLA. Thank you, I will.

WILMA. I'll never get out of the house again today, Arabella, so will you check on the six o'clock mail?

ARABELLA. All right.

WILMA. Come right over if I have a letter.

ARABELLA. All right. Good-bye.

(ARABELLA *goes out upstage center of the kitchen area and goes offstage.* WILMA *plucks an imaginary guitar and sings, in an exaggerated hillbilly style*)

"Write me a letter. Send it by mail. Send it in care of Birmingham jail."

MINNA. Wilma, what is that letter about you're expectin'? Have you got a beau for yourself?

WILMA. Don't be crazy.

MINNA. Look at me.

WILMA. I said no, and stop acting crazy. I'm expecting a letter from Mr. Delafonte.

MINNA. Mr. who?

WILMA. Mr. Delafonte, the famous movie director.

MINNA. Never heard of him.

WILMA. Well, I wouldn't let anyone know if I was that ignorant. The whole world has heard of Mr. Delafonte. He has only directed Pola Negri and Betty Compson and Lila Lee[2] and I don't know who all.

MINNA. What are you hearing from Mr. Delafonte about?

WILMA. A Hollywood career.

MINNA. What are you going to do with a Hollywood career?

WILMA. Be a movie star. You goose. First, he's going to screen-test me, and then I'll go to Hollywood and be a Wampus baby star.

MINNA. A what?

WILMA. A Wampus baby star. You know. That's what you are before you are a movie star. You get chosen to be a Wampus baby star and parade around in a bathing suit and get all your pictures in the papers and the movie magazines.

MINNA. I want to see Miss Gert's face when you start parading around in a bathing suit for magazines. And what's all this got to do with a letter?

WILMA. Well, I read in a Houston paper where Mr. Delafonte was in Houston interviewing people at his studio for Hollywood screen tests. So Arabella and I wrote him for an appointment.

MINNA. And that's what your letter is all about? No gold mine. No oil well. Just Mr. Delafonte and a movie test.

WILMA. Yes. And if you be nice to me, after I win the screen test and sell my house I might take you out with me.

MINNA. Sell your what?

WILMA. My house.

MINNA. Wilma . . . why don't you stop talking like that?

WILMA. Well, it's my house. I can sell it if I want to.

MINNA. You can't.

WILMA. I can.

MINNA. That house wasn't give to you to sell. A fifteen-year-old child. Who do you think is gonna let you sell it?

---

2. Pola Negri and Betty Compson and Lila Lee, stars of silent films in the 1920's

WILMA. Haven't you told me the house was mine? Hasn't Aunt Gert?

MINNA. Yes, but not to sell and throw the money away. And besides, it looks like to me the house is gonna be having permanent visitors soon.

WILMA. Who?

MINNA. What you don't know won't hurt you.

WILMA. If you mean my daddy and old lady Leighton, I'd burn it down first.

MINNA. Wilma.

WILMA. I will, I'll burn it down right to the ground. *(MISS GERT comes in downstage left of the kitchen area. She is in her forties, handsome and tall.)*

MINNA. Hello, Miss Gert . . .

GERT. Hello, Minna. Hello, Wilma.

MINNA. How was the party?

GERT. All right. Minna, Nealey is going to be away tonight so don't fix any supper for him, and we had refreshments at the party so I'm not hungry. *(She suddenly bursts out crying and has to leave the room. She goes running out downstage left of the kitchen area.)*

WILMA. Now what's the matter with her?

MINNA. Sick headache likely. You stay here, I'll go see.

WILMA. All right. If she wants any ice, I'll crack it. *(MINNA goes out downstage left of the kitchen area. WILMA turns on the phonograph and plays a popular song of the 1920's.)*

MINNA *(comes back in).* We better turn that off. She's got a bad one. First sick headache she's had in three years. I remember the last one.

WILMA. Does she want any cracked ice?

MINNA. No.

WILMA. Did she hear any bad news?

MINNA. I don't know.

WILMA. Can I go in to see her?

MINNA. Nope. You can please her, though, by getting into your studying.

WILMA. If you won't let me sell my house and go to Hollywood, I'll just quit school and move over there and rent out rooms. Support myself that way.

MINNA. You won't do nothin' of the kind. You go in there now and study.

WILMA. Why do I have to study? I have a house . . . and . . .

MINNA. Wilma, will you stop talking crazy?

WILMA. I'm not talking crazy. I could think of worse things to do. I'll rent out rooms and sit on the front porch and rock and be a lady of mystery, like a lady I read about once that locked herself in her house. Let the vines grow all around. Higher and higher until all light was shut out. She was eighteen when the vines started growing, and when she died and they cut the vines down and found her she was seventy-three, and in all that time she had never put her foot outside once. All her family and friends were dead . . .

MINNA. I know you're crazy now.

WILMA. Minna . . . Minna . . . *(She runs to her.)* I'm scared. I'm scared.

MINNA. What in the name of goodness are you scared of?

WILMA. I'm scared my daddy is going to marry Mrs. Leighton.

MINNA. Now . . . now . . . *(Holds her)*

WILMA. Minna, let me run over to my house for just a little bit. I can't ever go over there when there's tenants living in it. I feel the need of seeing it. I'll come right back.

MINNA. Will you promise me to come right back?

WILMA. I will.

MINNA. And you'll get right to your studying and no more arguments?

WILMA. No more.

MINNA. All right, then run on.

WILMA. Oh, Minna. I love you. And you know what I'm going to do? I'm going to be a great movie star and send my chauffeur and my limousine to Harrison and put you in it and drive you all the way to Hollywood.

MINNA. Thank you.

WILMA. H.O.B.

MINNA. H.O.B.? What's H.O.B.?

WILMA. Hollywood or Bust! . . . *(She goes running out upstage center of the kitchen area.* MINNA *calls after her:)*

MINNA. Don't forget to get right back. *(We hear* WILMA*'s voice answering in the distance, "All right." The lights are brought immediately up in the kitchen, a half hour later.* AUNT GERT *comes in downstage left of the area. She has on a dressing gown. Twilight is beginning. She switches on a light. She looks around the room. She calls.)*

GERT. Minna, Minna. *(A pause. She calls again.)* Minna. Minna. *(In comes* ARABELLA *upstage center of the area. She is carrying two letters.)*

ARABELLA. Hello, Miss Gertrude.

GERT. Hello, Arabella.

ARABELLA. Where's Wilma?

GERT. I don't know. The door to her room was closed when I went by. I guess she's in there studying.

ARABELLA. Yes'm. *(She starts out of the room downstage left of the area.)*

GERT. Arabella. *(*ARABELLA *pauses.)*

ARABELLA. Yes'm.

GERT. Wilma's gotten behind in her schoolwork, so please don't ask her to go out anyplace tonight, because I'll have to say no, and . . .

ARABELLA. Oh, no ma'am. I just brought her letter over to her. She asked me to get it if it came in on the six o'clock mail, and it did.

GERT. Is that the letter she's been driving us all crazy about?

ARABELLA. Yes ma'am. I got one too. *(She holds two letters up. Puts one on the table.)*

GERT. Oh. Well . . . *(*ARABELLA *starts out again downstage left of the area.)* Arabella, what is in that letter?

ARABELLA. Hasn't Wilma told you yet?

GERT. No.

ARABELLA. Then you'd better find out from her. She might be mad if I told you.

GERT. All right. *(*ARABELLA *starts out of the room.)* You didn't see Minna out in the backyard as you were coming in, did you?

ARABELLA. No.

GERT. I wonder where she can be. It's six-fifteen and she hasn't started a thing for supper yet.

(ARABELLA *goes out downstage left of the area and looks out an imaginary window right center. She comes back in the room.*)

ARABELLA. Wilma isn't in the bedroom.

GERT. She isn't?

ARABELLA. No ma'am. Not in the front room either. I went in there.

GERT. That's strange. Isn't that strange? (MINNA *comes in upstage center of the area. She has a package in her hand.*) Oh, there you are, Minna.

MINNA. I had to run to the store for some baking soda. How do you feel? (MINNA *puts the package on the table.*)

GERT. Better. Where's Wilma?

MINNA. You don't mean she's not back yet?

GERT. Back? Where did she go?

MINNA. She swore to me if I let her go over to her house for a few minutes she'd be back here and study with no arguments.

GERT. Well, she's not here.

MINNA. That's the trouble with her. Give her an inch and she'll take a mile.

GERT. Arabella, would you run over to Wilma's house and tell her to get right home?

ARABELLA Yes ma'am. (*She picks the letter up off the table and takes it with her as she goes out downstage left of the area. A knock is heard offstage.*)

GERT (*calling*). Come in. (MISS MARTHA *comes in upstage center of the area.*) Oh, hello, Miss Martha.

MARTHA. Hello, Gert. Hello, Minna.

MINNA. Hello, Miss Martha . . .

MARTHA. I thought you'd be back here. I knocked and knocked at your front door, and no one answered, but I knew somebody must be here this time of day, so I just decided to come on back.

GERT. I'm glad you did. We can't hear a knock at the front door back here. Sit down, won't you?

MARTHA. I can't stay a second. I just wanted to tell Wilma that her letter arrived on the six o'clock bus.

GERT. She knows, thank you, Miss Martha. Arabella brought it over to her.

MARTHA. Oh, the address on the back said the Delafonte Studio. I wonder what that could be?

GERT. I don't know.

MINNA. I knows. It's the moving pictures. She wrote about getting into them.

GERT. I do declare. She's always up to something.

MARTHA. Well, I never heard of moving pictures in Houston. I just heard the news about Lester. Was I surprised! Were you?

GERT. Yes, I was.

MARTHA. When's the wedding taking place?

GERT. I don't know.

MARTHA. Oh, I see. Well, I have to run on now.

GERT. All right, thank you, Miss Martha, for coming by. I know Wilma will appreciate it.

MARTHA. I'll just go out the back way if you don't mind. It'll save me a few steps.

GERT. Of course not.

MARTHA. Good night.

GERT. Good night, Miss Martha. (*She goes out upstage center of the area.*)

MINNA. What news is this?

GERT. Oh, you must know, Minna. Lester and Mrs. Leighton are getting married at last. That's why I came home from the party all upset. I had to hear about my own brother's marriage at a bridge party. And I know it's true. It came straight from the county clerk's office. They got their license this morning.

MINNA. Well, poor Wilma. She'll take this hard.

GERT. She's going to take it very hard. But what can you do? What can you do?

(*They both sit dejectedly at the table. The lights fade in the area downstage left as they come up on the area downstage right.* WILMA *comes in from upstage center of the downstage right area. It is the yard of her house. She sits in the swing rocking back and forth, singing "Birmingham Jail" in her hillbilly style.* ARABELLA *comes running in right center of the yard area.*)

WILMA. Hey, Arabella. Come sit and swing.

ARABELLA. All right. Your letter came.

WILMA. Whoopee. Where is it?

ARABELLA. Here. (*She gives it to her.* WILMA *tears it open. She reads:*)

WILMA. "Dear Miss Thompson: Mr. Delafonte will be glad to see you any time next week about your contemplated screen test. We suggest you call the office when you arrive in the city, and we will set an exact time. Yours truly, Adele Murray." Well . . . Did you get yours?

ARABELLA. Yes.

WILMA. What did it say?

ARABELLA. The same.

WILMA. Exactly the same?

ARABELLA. Yes.

WILMA. Well, let's pack our bags. Hollywood, here we come.

ARABELLA. Wilma . . .

WILMA. Yes?

ARABELLA. I have to tell you something . . . Well . . . I . . .

WILMA. What is it?

ARABELLA. Well . . . promise me you won't hate me, or stop being my friend. I never had a friend, Wilma, until you began being nice to me, and I couldn't stand it if you weren't my friend any longer . . .

WILMA. Oh, my cow. Stop talking like that. I'll never stop being your friend. What do you want to tell me?

ARABELLA. Well . . . I don't want to go to see Mr. Delafonte, Wilma. . . .

WILMA. You don't?

ARABELLA. No. I don't want to be a movie star. I don't want to leave Harrison or my mother or father . . . I just want to stay here the rest of my life and get married and settle down and have children.

WILMA. Arabella . . .

ARABELLA. I just pretended like I wanted to go to Hollywood because I knew you wanted me to, and I wanted you to like me . . .

WILMA. Oh, Arabella . . .

ARABELLA. Don't hate me, Wilma. You see, I'd be afraid . . . I'd die if I had to go to see Mr. Delafonte. Why, I even get faint when I have to recite before the class. I'm not like you. You're not scared of anything.

WILMA. Why do you say that?

ARABELLA. Because you're not. I know.

WILMA. Oh, yes, I am. I'm scared of lots of things.

ARABELLA. What?

WILMA. Getting lost in a city. Being bitten by dogs. Old lady Leighton taking my daddy away . . . *(A pause)*

ARABELLA. Will you still be my friend?

WILMA. Sure. I'll always be your friend.

ARABELLA. I'm glad. Oh, I almost forgot. Your Aunt Gert said for you to come on home.

WILMA. I'll go in a little. I love to swing in my front yard. Aunt Gert has a swing in her front yard, but it's not the same. Mama and I used to come out here and swing together. Some nights when Daddy was out all night gambling, I used to wake up and hear her out here swinging away. Sometimes she'd let me come and sit beside her. We'd swing until three or four in the morning. *(A pause. She looks out into the yard.)* The pear tree looks sickly, doesn't it? The fig trees are doing nicely though. I was out in back and the weeds are near knee high, but fig trees just seem to thrive in the weeds. The freeze must have killed off the banana trees . . . *(A pause.* WILMA *stops swinging—she walks around the yard.)* Maybe I won't leave either. Maybe I won't go to Hollywood after all.

ARABELLA. You won't?

WILMA. No. Maybe I shouldn't. That just comes to me now. You know sometimes my old house looks so lonesome it tears at my heart. I used to think it looked lonesome just whenever it had no tenants, but now it comes to me it has looked lonesome ever since Mama died and we moved away, and it will look lonesome until some of us move back here. Of course, Mama can't, and Daddy won't. So it's up to me.

ARABELLA. Are you gonna live here all by yourself?

WILMA. No. I talk big about living here by myself, but I'm too much of a coward to do that. But maybe I'll finish school and live with Aunt Gert and keep on renting the house until I meet some nice boy with good habits and steady ways, and marry him. Then we'll move here and have children, and I bet this old house won't be lonely anymore. I'll get Mama's old croquet set and put it out under the pecan trees and play croquet with my children, or sit in this yard and swing and wave to people as they pass by.

ARABELLA. Oh, I wish you would. Mama says that's a normal life for a girl, marrying and having children. She says being an actress is all right, but the other's better.

WILMA. Maybe I've come to agree with your mama. Maybe I was going to

Hollywood out of pure lonesomeness. I felt so alone with Mrs. Leighton getting my daddy and my mama having left the world. Daddy could have taken away my lonesomeness, but he didn't want to or couldn't. Aunt Gert says nobody is lonesome with a house full of children, so maybe that's what I just ought to stay here and have . . .

ARABELLA. Have you decided on a husband yet?

WILMA. No.

ARABELLA. Mama says that's the bad feature of being a girl; you have to wait for the boy to ask you and just pray that the one you want wants you. Tommy Murray is nice, isn't he?

WILMA. I think so.

ARABELLA. Jay Godfrey told me once he wanted to ask you for a date, but he didn't dare because he was afraid you'd turn him down.

WILMA. Why did he think that?

ARABELLA. He said the way you talked he didn't think you would go out with anything less than a movie star.

WILMA. Maybe you'd tell him different . . .

ARABELLA. All right. I think Jay Godfrey is very nice. Don't you?

WILMA. Yes, I think he's very nice and Tommy is nice . . .

ARABELLA. Maybe we could double-date sometimes.

WILMA. That might be fun.

ARABELLA. Oh, Wilma. Don't go to Hollywood. Stay here in Harrison and let's be friends forever . . .

WILMA. All right. I will.

ARABELLA. You will?

WILMA. Sure, why not? I'll stay here. I'll stay and marry and live in my house.

ARABELLA. Oh, Wilma. I'm so glad. I'm so very glad.

(WILMA *gets back in the swing. They swing vigorously back and forth. A* MAN *comes in right center of the yard area.*)

MAN. I beg your pardon. Is this the Thompson house? *(They stop swinging.)*

WILMA. Yes sir.

MAN. I understand it's for sale. I'd like to look around.

WILMA. No sir. It's not for sale. It's for rent. I'm Wilma Thompson. I own the house. My daddy rents it for me . . .

MAN. Oh, well, we were told by Mr. Mavis . . .

WILMA. I'm sure. Mr. Mavis tries to sell everything around here. He's pulled that once before about our house, but this house is not for sale. It's for rent.

MAN. You're sure?

WILMA. I'm positive. We rent it for twenty-seven fifty a month. You pay lights, water, and keep the yard clean. We are very particular over how the yard is kept. I'd be glad to show it to you . . .

MAN. I'm sorry. I was interested in buying. There must have been a mistake.

WILMA. There must have been.

MAN. Where could I find your father, young lady?

WILMA. Why do you want to see him?

MAN. Well, I'd just like to get this straight. I understood from Mr. Mavis . . .

WILMA. Mr. Mavis has nothing to do with my house. My house is for rent, not for sale.

MAN. All right. *(The* MAN *leaves. He goes out right center of the yard area.)*

WILMA. The nerve of old man Mavis putting out around town that my house is for sale. Isn't that nervy, Arabella? *(*ARABELLA *gets out of the swing.)*

ARABELLA. We'd better go. It'll be dark soon. The tree frogs are starting.

WILMA. It just makes me furious. Wouldn't it make you furious?

ARABELLA. Come on. Let's go.

WILMA. Wouldn't it make you furious?

ARABELLA. Yes.

WILMA. You don't sound like you mean it.

ARABELLA. Well . . .

WILMA. Well . . . what?

ARABELLA. Nothing . . . Let's go.

WILMA. Arabella, you know something you're not telling me.

ARABELLA. No, I don't. Honest, Wilma . . .

WILMA. You do. Look at me, Arabella . . .

ARABELLA. I don't know anything. I swear . . . .

WILMA. You do. I thought you were my friend.

ARABELLA. I am. I am.

WILMA. Well, then why don't you tell me?

ARABELLA. Because I promised not to.

WILMA. Why?

ARABELLA. Well . . . I . . .

WILMA. What is it? Arabella, please tell me.

ARABELLA. Well . . . Will you never say I told you?

WILMA. I swear.

ARABELLA. Well, I didn't tell you before because in all the excitement in telling you I wasn't going to Hollywood and your saying you weren't going, I forgot about it . . . until that man came . . .

WILMA. What is it, Arabella? What is it?

ARABELLA. Well, I heard my daddy tell my mother that Mr. Lester had taken out a license to marry Mrs. Leighton.

WILMA. Oh, well. That doesn't surprise me too much. I've been looking for that to happen.

ARABELLA. But that isn't all, Wilma . . .

WILMA. What else?

ARABELLA. Well . . .

WILMA. What else?

ARABELLA. Well . . .

WILMA. What else, Arabella? What else?

ARABELLA. Well . . . My daddy heard that your daddy had put this house up for sale . . . .

WILMA. I don't believe you . . . .

ARABELLA. That's what he said, Wilma. . . . I . . . He said Mr. Lester came to him and wanted to know if he wanted to buy it.

WILMA. Well. He won't do it. Not my house. He won't do it! *(*WILMA *has jumped out of the swing and runs out of the yard upstage center.)*

ARABELLA. Wilma . . . Wilma . . . Please . . . don't say I said it . . . Wilma . . . .

She is standing alone and frightened as the lights fade. The lights are brought up in the area left of center. MINNA *is mixing some dough on the table.* MISS GERT *comes in.*

GERT. She's not back yet?

MINNA. No. I knew when Arabella took that letter over there she wouldn't be here until good dark.

GERT. I just put in a call for Lester . . . He is going to have to tell her about the marriage. It's his place. Don't you think so?

MINNA. I certainly do. I most certainly do. (WILMA *comes running in upstage center of the kitchen area.*)

WILMA. Aunt Gert, do you know where I can find my daddy?

GERT. No, Wilma . . . I . . .

WILMA. Well, I've got to find him. I went over to the cotton gin, but he'd left. I called out to his boarding-house and he wasn't there . . .

GERT. Well, I don't know, Wilma . . .

WILMA. Is he gonna sell my house?

GERT. Wilma . . .

WILMA. Is he or isn't he?

GERT. I don't know anything about it . . .

WILMA. Well, something's going on. Let me tell you that. I was sitting in the swing with Arabella when a man came up and said he wanted to buy it, and I said to rent, and he said to buy, that Mr. Mavis had sent him over, and I told him he was mistaken, and he left. Well, I was plenty mad at Mr. Mavis and told Arabella so, but she looked funny, and I got suspicious, and I finally got it out of her that Daddy was going to marry old lady Leighton and was putting my house up for sale . . . (GERT *is crying.*) Aunt Gert. Isn't that my house?

GERT. Yes. I'd always thought so . . .

WILMA. Then he can't do it. Don't let him do it. It's my house. It's all in this world that belongs to me. Let Mrs. Leighton take him if she wants to, but not my house. Please, please, please. (*She is crying.* MINNA *goes to her.*)

MINNA. Now, come on, honey. Come on, baby . . . .

WILMA. I wouldn't sell it, not even to get me to Hollywood. I thought this afternoon, before the letter from Mr. Delafonte came, I'd ask Aunt Gert to let me sell it, and go on off, but when I went over there and sat in my yard and rocked in my swing and thought of my mama and how lonesome the house looked since we moved away . . . I knew I couldn't . . . I knew I never would . . . I'd never go to Hollywood before I'd sell that house, and he can't . . . I won't let him. I won't let him.

MINNA. Now, honey . . . honey . . . Miss Gert, do you know anything about this?

GERT (*wiping her eyes*). Minna, I don't. I heard at the card party that he was marrying Mrs. Leighton . . . but I heard nothing about Lester's selling the house . . .

MINNA. Well, can he? . . .

GERT. I don't know. I just never thought my brother, my own brother . . . Oh, I just can't stand things like this. You see, it's all so mixed up. I don't think there was anything said in writing about Wilma's having the house, but it was clearly Alice's intention. She called me in the room before Lester and made him promise just before she died that he would always have the house for Wilma . . .

MINNA. Well, why don't we find out?

GERT. Well . . . I don't know how . . . I left a message for Lester. I can't reach him.

MINNA. I'd call Mr. Bill if I were you. He's a lawyer.

GERT. But, Minna, my brother.

MINNA. I'd call me a lawyer, brother or no brother. If you don't, I will. I'm not gonna have what belongs to this child stolen from her by Mr. Lester or anybody else . . .

GERT. All right. I will. I'll go talk to Bill. I'll find out what we can do legally. *(She starts out downstage left of the area.* LESTER *comes in upstage center of the area.* MINNA *sees him coming.)*

MINNA. Miss Gert. (GERT *turns and sees him just as he gets inside the area.)*

LESTER. Hello, Gert.

GERT. Hello, Lester.

LESTER. Hello, Wilma.

WILMA. Hello.

GERT. Wilma, I think you'd better leave. . . .

WILMA. Yes'm. *(She starts out.)*

LESTER. Wait a minute, Gert. I've something to tell you all. I want Wilma to hear.

GERT. I think we know already. Go on, Wilma.

WILMA. Yes'm.

*(*WILMA *leaves downstage left of the area.* MINNA *follows after her. A pause.)*

GERT. We've heard about the marriage, Lester.

LESTER. Oh, well. I'm sorry I couldn't be the one to tell you. We only decided this morning. There was a lot to do, a license and some business to attend to. I haven't told anyone. I don't know how the news got out.

GERT. You didn't really expect them to keep quiet about it at the courthouse?

LESTER. Oh. Well, of course I didn't think about that. *(A pause)* Well, the other thing is . . . You see . . . I've decided to sell the house.

GERT. I know. Wilma just found out about that, too.

LESTER. Oh. Well, I'll explain the whole thing to you. You see, I felt . . . (GERT *starts to cry.)* Now what's the matter with you, Gert?

GERT. To think that my brother, my own brother, would do something like this.

LESTER. Like what? After all it's my house, Gert.

GERT. There's some dispute about that. The least I think you could have done, the very least, was come to tell your own child.

LESTER. Well, I'm here now to do that. I only put it up for sale at noon today. I've nothing to hide or be ashamed of. The house is in my name. Sibyl, Mrs. Leighton, doesn't like Harrison. You can't blame her. People have been rotten to her. We're moving to Houston. I'm selling this house to pay down on one in Houston. That'll belong to Wilma just the same, someday. Sibyl's agreed to that, and Wilma will really get a better house in time. And we always want her to feel like it's her home, come and visit us summers . . . and like I say, when something happens to me or Sibyl, the house will be hers. . . .

GERT. That's not the point, Lester.

LESTER. What do you mean?

GERT. You know very well.

LESTER. I can't make a home for her over there, can I? She'll be grown soon and marrying and having her own house. I held on to this place as long as I could. Well, I'm not going to feel guilty about it.

GERT. I'm going to try to stop you, Lester. . . .

LESTER. Now look, Gert. For once try and be sensible. . . .

GERT. Legally I'm going to try and stop you. I'm going . . .

LESTER. Please, Gert . . .

GERT. . . . to call Bill and tell him the whole situation and see what we can do. If we have any rights I'll take it to every court I can. Brother or no brother. . . .

LESTER. Now look, don't carry on like this. Maybe I've handled it clumsily, and if I have I'm sorry. I just didn't think. . . . I should have, I know . . . but I . . .

GERT. That's right. You didn't think. You never do. Well, this time you're going to have to. . . .

LESTER. Can't you look at it this way? Wilma is getting a better house and . . .

GERT. Maybe she doesn't want a better house. Maybe she just wants this one. But that isn't the point either. The sickening part is that you really didn't care what Wilma thought or even stopped for a moment to consider if she had a thought. You've never cared about anyone or anything but yourself. Well, this time I won't let you without a fight. I'm going to a lawyer.

LESTER. Gert . . .

GERT. Now get out of my house. Because brother or no, I'm through with you.

LESTER. All right. If you feel that way.

(*He leaves upstage center of the area.* GERT *stands for a moment, thinking what to do next.* MINNA *comes in downstage left of the area.*)

MINNA. I was behind the door and I heard the whole thing.

GERT. Did Wilma hear?

MINNA. No, I sent her back to her room. Now you get right to a lawyer.

GERT. I intend to. He's gotten me mad now. I won't let him get by with it if I can help it. I think I'll walk over to Bill's. I don't like to talk about it over the telephone.

MINNA. Yes'm.

GERT. You tell Wilma to wait here for me.

MINNA. Yes'm. Want me to tell her where you've gone?

GERT. I don't see why not. I'll be back as soon as I finish.

MINNA. Yes'm.

(GERT *leaves upstage center of the area.*)

MINNA *(goes to the door and calls).* Wilma. Wilma. You can come here now. *(She fills a plate with food and puts it on the table.* WILMA *comes in downstage left of the area.)* You better sit down and try to eat something.

WILMA. I can't eat a thing.

MINNA. Well, you can try.

WILMA. No. It would choke me. What happened?

MINNA. Your aunt told him not to sell the house, and he said he would, and so she's gone to see a lawyer.

WILMA. Does she think she can stop him?

MINNA. She's gonna try. I know she's got him scared. . . .

WILMA. But it's my house. You know that. He knows that. . . . Didn't she tell him?

MINNA. Sure she told him. But you know your daddy. Telling won't do any good. We have to prove it.

WILMA. What proof have we got?

MINNA. Miss Gert's word. I hope that's enough. . . .

WILMA. And if it isn't?

MINNA. Then you'll lose it. That's all. You'll lose it.

WILMA. I bet I lose it. I've got no luck.

MINNA. Why do you say that?

WILMA. What kind of luck is it takes your mama away, and then your daddy, and then tries to take your house? Sitting in that yard swinging I was the happiest girl in the world this afternoon. I'd decided not to go in the movies and to stay in Harrison and get married and have children and live in my house. . . .

MINNA. Well, losing a house won't stop you from staying in Harrison and getting married. . . .

WILMA. Oh, yes. I wouldn't trust it with my luck. With my kind of luck I wouldn't even get me a husband. . . . I'd wind up like Miss Martha working at the post office chasing Mr. Russell Walter until the end of time. No mother and no father and no house and no husband and no children. No, thank you. I'm just tired of worrying over the whole thing. I'll just go on into Houston and see Mr. Delafonte and get on out to Hollywood and make money and get rich and famous. *(She begins to cry.)*

MINNA. Now, honey. Honey . . .

WILMA. Minna, I don't want to be rich and famous. . . . I want to stay here. I want to stay in Harrison. . . .

MINNA. Now, honey. Try to be brave.

WILMA. I know what I'm gonna do. *(She jumps up.)* I'm going to see old lady Leighton. She's the one that can stop this. . . .

MINNA. Now, Wilma. You know your aunt don't want you around that woman.

WILMA. I can't help it. I'm going. . . .

MINNA. Wilma . . . you listen to me . . . (WILMA *runs out upstage center of the area.*)

Wilma . . . Wilma . . . you come back here. . . . (*But* WILMA *has gone.* MINNA *shakes her head in desperation.*)

The lights fade. When the lights are brought up, it is two hours later. MINNA *is at the kitchen table reading the paper.* GERT *comes in upstage center of the area.*

GERT. Well, we've won.

MINNA. What do you mean?

GERT. I mean just what I say. Lester is not going to sell the house.

MINNA. What happened?

GERT. I don't know what happened. I went over to see Bill and we talked it all through, and he said legally we really had no chance, but he'd call up Lester and try to at least bluff him into thinking we had. And when he called Lester, he said Lester wasn't home, and so I suggested his calling you know where.

MINNA. No. Where?

GERT. Mrs. Leighton's. And sure enough he was there, and then Bill told him why he was calling, and Lester said, well, it didn't matter as he'd decided not to sell the house after all.

MINNA. You don't mean it?

GERT. Oh, yes, I do. Where's Wilma?

MINNA. She's over there with them.

GERT. Over where with them?

MINNA. At Mrs. Leighton's.

GERT. Why, Minna . . .

MINNA. Now don't holler at me. I told her not to go, but she said she was going, and then she ran out that door so fast I couldn't stop her.

(WILMA *comes running in upstage center of the area.*)

WILMA. Heard the news? House is mine again.

MINNA. Do you know what happened?

WILMA. Sure. Mrs. Leighton isn't so bad. Boy, I went running over there expecting the worst . . .

GERT. Wilma, what do you mean going to that woman's house? Wilma, I declare . . .

WILMA. Oh, she's not so bad. Anyway we've got her to thank for it.

MINNA. Well, what happened? Will somebody please tell me what happened?

WILMA. Well, you know I was sitting here and it came to me. It came to me just like that. See Mrs. Leighton. She's the one to stop it and it's got to be stopped. Well, I was so scared my knees were trembling the whole time going over there, but I made myself do it, walked in on her, and she looked more nervous than I did.

GERT. Was your father there?

WILMA. No ma'am. He came later. Wasn't anybody there but me and Mrs. Leighton. I'm calling her Sibyl now. She asked me to. Did Arabella come yet?

MINNA. Arabella?

WILMA. I called and asked her to come and celebrate. I'm so excited. I just had to have company tonight. I know

I won't be able to sleep anyway. I hope you don't mind, Aunt Gert . . . .

MINNA. If you don't tell me what happened . . .

WILMA. Well . . . Mrs. Leighton . . . I mean Sibyl . . . (ARABELLA *comes in upstage center of the area.* WILMA *sees her.*) Oh, come on in, Arabella.

ARABELLA. Hi. I almost didn't get to come. I told my mama it was life or death, and so she gave in. But she made me swear we'd be in bed by ten. Did you hear about Mr. Delafonte?

WILMA. No. What?

ARABELLA. He's a crook. It was in the Houston papers tonight. He was operating a business under false pretenses. He had been charging twenty-five dollars for those screen tests and using a camera with no film in it.

WILMA. My goodness.

ARABELLA. It was in all the papers. On the second page. My father said he mustn't have been very much not to even get on the front page. He wasn't a Hollywood director at all. He didn't even know Lila Lee or Betty Compson.

WILMA. He didn't?

ARABELLA. No.

MINNA. Wilma, will you get back to your story before I lose my mind?

WILMA. Oh. Yes . . . I got my house back, Arabella.

ARABELLA. You did?

WILMA. Sure. That's why I called you over to spend the night. A kind of celebration.

ARABELLA. Well, that's wonderful.

MINNA. Wilma . . .

WILMA. All right. Where was I?

GERT. You were at Mrs. Leighton's.

WILMA. Oh, yes. Sibyl's. I'm calling her Sibyl now, Arabella. She asked me to.

MINNA. Well . . . what happened? Wilma, if you don't tell me . . .

WILMA. Well, I just told her the whole thing.

MINNA. What whole thing?

WILMA. Well, I told her about my mother meaning for the house to always be mine, and how I loved the house, and how I was lonely and the house was lonely, and that I had hoped my daddy and I could go there and live someday but knew now we couldn't, and that I had planned to go to Hollywood and be a movie star but that this afternoon my friend Arabella and I decided we didn't really want to do that, and that I knew then that what I wanted to do really was to live in Harrison and get married and live in my house and have children so that I wouldn't be lonely anymore and the house wouldn't. And then she started crying.

GERT. You don't mean it.

WILMA. Yes ma'am. And I felt real sorry for her, and I said I didn't hold anything against her, and then Daddy came in, and she said why didn't he tell her that was my house, and he said because it wasn't. And then she asked him about what Mother told you, and he said that was true but now I was going to have a better house, and she said I didn't want to have a better house, but my own house, and that she wouldn't marry him if he sold this house, and she said they both had jobs in Houston and would manage somehow, but I had nothing, so then he said all right.

GERT. Well. Good for her.

MINNA. Sure enough, good for her.

WILMA. And then Mr. Bill called and Daddy told him the house was mine again, and then she cried again and hugged me and asked me to kiss her and I did, and then Daddy cried and I kissed him, and then I cried. And they asked me to the wedding and I said I'd go and that I'd come visit them this summer in Houston. And then I came home.

MINNA. Well. Well, indeed.

GERT. My goodness. So that's how it happened. And you say Mrs. Leighton cried?

WILMA. Twice. We all did. Daddy and Mrs. Leighton and me. . . .

GERT. Well, I'm glad, Wilma, it's all worked out.

WILMA. And can I go visit them this summer in Houston?

GERT. If you like.

WILMA. And can I go to the wedding?

GERT. Yes, if you want to.

WILMA. I want to.

MINNA. Now you better have some supper.

WILMA. No. I couldn't eat, I'm still too excited.

MINNA. Miss Gert, she hasn't had a bite on her stomach.

GERT. Well, it won't kill her this one time, Minna.

WILMA. Aunt Gert, can Arabella and I go over to my yard for just a few minutes and swing? We'll be home by ten. . . .

GERT. No, Wilma, it's late.

WILMA. Please. Just to celebrate. I have it coming to me. We'll just stay for a few minutes.

GERT. Well . . .

WILMA. Please . . .

GERT. Will you be back here by ten, and not make me have to send Minna over there?

WILMA. Yes ma'am.

GERT. All right.

WILMA. Oh, thank you. *(She goes to her aunt and kisses her.)* You're the best aunt in the whole world. Come on, Arabella.

ARABELLA. All right. *(They start upstage center of the area.* GERT *calls after them.)*

GERT. Now remember. Back by ten. Arabella has promised her mother. And you've promised me.

WILMA *(calling in distance).* Yes ma'am.

*(*GERT *comes back into the room.)*

GERT. Well, I'm glad it's ending this way.

MINNA. Yes ma'am.

GERT. I never thought it would. Well, I said hard things to Lester. I'm sorry I had to, but I felt I had to.

MINNA. Of course you did.

GERT. Well, I'll go to my room. You go on when you're ready.

MINNA. All right. I'm ready now. The excitement has wore me out.

GERT. Me too. Leave the light on for the children. I'll keep awake until they come in.

MINNA. Yes'm.

GERT. Good night.

MINNA. Good night.

*G*ert goes out downstage left of the area. MINNA *goes to get her hat. The lights fade. The lights are brought up in the downstage right area.* WILMA *and* ARABELLA *come in upstage center of the area and get in the swing.*

WILMA. Don't you just love to swing?

ARABELLA. Uh huh.

WILMA. It's a lovely night, isn't it? Listen to that mockingbird. The crazy thing must think it's daytime.

ARABELLA. It's light enough to be day.

WILMA. It certainly is.

ARABELLA. Well, it was lucky we decided to give up Hollywood with Mr. Delafonte turning out to be a crook and all.

WILMA. Wasn't it lucky?

ARABELLA. Do you feel lonely now?

WILMA. No, I don't feel nearly so lonely. Now I've got my house and plan to get married. And my daddy and I are going to see each other, and I think Mrs. Leighton is going to make a nice friend. She's crazy about moving pictures.

ARABELLA. Funny how things work out.

WILMA. Very funny.

ARABELLA. Guess who called me on the telephone.

WILMA. Who?

ARABELLA. Tommy . . . Murray.

WILMA. You don't say.

ARABELLA. He asked me for a date next week. Picture show. He said Jay was going to call you.

WILMA. Did he?

ARABELLA. I asked him to tell Jay that you weren't only interested in going out with movie actors.

WILMA. What did he say?

ARABELLA. He said he thought Jay knew that. *(A pause.* WILMA *jumps out of the swing.)* Wilma. What's the matter with you? Wilma . . . *(She runs to her.)*

WILMA. I don't know. I felt funny there for a minute. A cloud passed over the moon and I felt lonely . . . and funny . . . and scared. . . .

ARABELLA. But you have your house now.

WILMA. I know . . . I . . . *(A pause. She points offstage right.)* I used to sleep in there. I had a white iron bed. I remember one night Aunt Gert woke me up. It was just turning light out, and she was crying. "I'm taking you home to live with me," she said. "Why?" I said. "Because your mama's gone to heaven," she said. *(A pause)* I can't remember my mama's face anymore. I can hear her voice sometimes calling me far off, "Wilma, Wilma, come home." Far off. But I can't remember her face. I try and I try, but finally I have to go to my bureau drawer and take out her picture and look to remember. . . . Oh, Arabella. It isn't only the house I wanted. It's the life in the house. My mama and me and even my daddy coming in at four in the morning. . . .

ARABELLA. But there'll be life again in this house.

WILMA. How?

ARABELLA. You're gonna fill it with life again, Wilma. Like you said this afternoon.

WILMA. But I get afraid.

ARABELLA. Don't be. You will. I know you will.

WILMA. You think I can do anything. Be a movie star . . . . Go to Hollywood. *(A pause)* The moon's from behind the cloud. *(A pause. In the distance we can hear the courthouse clock strike ten.)* Don't tell me it's ten o'clock already.

I'll fill this house with life again. I'll meet a young man with steady ways and nice habits . . . *(Far off* AUNT GERT *calls: "Wilma. Wilma."* WILMA *calls back)* We're coming. You see that pecan tree out there?

ARABELLA. Uh huh.

WILMA. It was planted the year my mother was born. It's so big now I can hardly reach around it. *(*AUNT GERT *calls again: "Wilma. Wilma."* WILMA *calls back:)* We're coming.

(She and ARABELLA *sit swinging.* WILMA *looks happy and is happy as the lights fade.)*

A YOUNG LADY OF PROPERTY

Responding to the Play

1. Did the play end as you thought it would. Why or why not?
2. Why do you think the house is so important to Wilma?
3. Do you agree with Gert that Lester doesn't care about anyone but himself? Explain.
4. Is Wilma a static or dynamic character? What about her father and aunt? Support your opinions with examples from the play.
5. Would this play be different if it were set in the present in a northern city? Explain.

About Horton Foote

Like young Wilma, Horton Foote had dreams of acting. He left his home in Wharton, Texas, at 16 to study acting in California. From there he went to New York City to become an actor and a writer. Since then he has written plays for radio, television, stage, and film.

Foote identified strongly with great novelists. He successfully adapted John Steinbeck's *Of Mice and Men*, William Faulkner's *Tomorrow*, and Harper Lee's *To Kill a Mockingbird* into screenplays. And like them, Foote let his plots unfold slowly but surely, never broadcasting his message. Foote's cycle of plays about the town of Harrison, Texas, exemplifies this. He applied Sherwood Anderson's advice to William Faulkner to "find a small piece of land and write about it."

Foote won the 1995 Pulitzer Prize for Drama for his play *The Young Man from Atlanta.* His screenplays for *To Kill a Mockingbird* and *Tender Mercies* both won Academy Awards.

CREATING AND PERFORMING

1. Indicate the stage area and sets for this play by adding them to the map you drew for the Warm Up on page 18.
2. Improvise a scene between Wilma, Lester, and her new stepmother after the couple's wedding.
3. Work with other classmates to develop a Texas accent, then read a scene from the play.

The Night Thoreau Spent in Jail

The Play as Literature: Biographical Fiction

Biographies tell the story of a person's life with the help of documentation such as newspapers, legal papers, letters, memoirs, diaries, and journals. Biographers often draw conclusions about their subject, but they do not attribute to their subject undocumented actions or words. Writers of biographical fiction and plays take up that challenge. Based on research, they imagine what their subject might have done and said under particular circumstances. Then they shape it into a story or play.

"If a man does not keep pace with his companions, perhaps it is because he hears a different drummer. Let him step to the music which he hears, however measured, or far away."

—Thoreau

As you read *The Night Thoreau Spent in Jail,* note how the authors used biographical details to develop the character of Thoreau and frame the story they wanted to tell. (For more about Henry David Thoreau see p. 95.)

The Play as Theatre: The Set

In most plays, the set performs two different, but related, functions. The set helps define the location and circumstances in which the action of a play takes place. It also communicates a mood or message that is central to the meaning of the play. With realistic sets, the first function is the most prominent. With abstract or symbolic sets, the mood or message takes precedence.

The set of *The Night Thoreau Spent in Jail* is symbolic. Actors work on a bare stage with multi-functional set pieces meant to suggest scenery and furniture. As you read the play, think about the message conveyed by the set.

Warm Up!

Pair up with one classmate and use exactly two minutes to tell the story of your life. Then let your partner use two minutes to tell the story of his or her life. Take turns telling each other's stories to the class. How accurately did you recall the details of your partner's life?

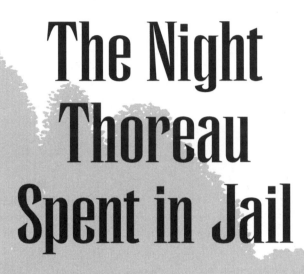

The Night Thoreau Spent in Jail

by Jerome Lawrence
and
Robert E. Lee

Setting	Characters	Time
Concord, Massachusetts	WALDO LYDIAN MOTHER HENRY JOHN BAILEY BALL ELLEN SAM EDWARD WILLIAMS PASSER-BY DRUNK FARMER WOMAN TOWNSPEOPLE	1846

ACT ONE

Center is the skeletal suggestion of a prison cell: two crude cots, a chair, a wooden box which serves as a clothes locker. An imaginary window downstage looks out on Concord Square.

A thrust extends forward, not part of the cell—nor are the playing areas at either side. The cell itself is raked. The cell door, imaginary, is upstage center.

Surrounding the cell is the sky over Concord. There are night bird sounds, distant. Two men lie on the cots, motionless. Striped moonlight through the prison bars falls across HENRY, but the man on the other cot is in shadow.

Time and space are awash here.

Into a weak winter light, unrelated to the cell, an old man enters on the arm of his wife. He walks with studied erectness, using an umbrella as a cane. The wife is handsomely patrician. The old man has a shawl over his shoulders, a muffler around his neck. He stops.

WALDO (suddenly, as if somebody had stolen his wallet). What was his name?

LYDIAN. Whose name?

WALDO. I've forgotten the name of my best friend!

LYDIAN. Did you ever have a best friend?

WALDO. The boy. Who put the gloves on the chickens.

LYDIAN. Henry?

WALDO (vaguely). I keep thinking his name was David.

(Light strikes HENRY's MOTHER as she comes

into another area, also apart from the cell. She is distressed, piling disheveled hair onto the top of her head.)

MOTHER. David Henry! What have you gone and done?

(HENRY rises on the cot. He is 29, clean-shaven, with liquid eyes. His clothes are simple, the colors of the forest. This is a young man—with a knife-like humor, fierce conviction, and devastating individuality.)

HENRY. I have not gone and done anything, Mother. I have gone and *not* done something. Which very much needed the *not* doing.

MOTHER. Oh, good heavens! *(Calling off stage)* Louisa! David Henry's gone and not done something again.

HENRY *(correcting her).* Henry David.

MOTHER. David Henry, you're being strange again.

WALDO *(distantly).* He was strange. I almost understood him.

LYDIAN. Sometimes.

MOTHER. Sometimes I don't know who you are.

HENRY. I'm myself, Mother. *(He lifts himself and sits on the edge of the cot.)* If I'm not, who will be?

MOTHER. When you're baptized, they tell you who you are.

HENRY. I wasn't listening.

MOTHER. At the christening you didn't cry once, not once. Reverend Ripley said how remarkable it was for a baby not to cry at a christening.

HENRY. You think I knew what they were doing to me?

MOTHER. I suppose not.

HENRY. That's why I didn't cry.

WALDO. He was the saddest happy man I ever knew.

LYDIAN. The happiest sad man, I think.

WALDO. He worked on Sundays, and took the rest of the week off. *(Staring at his umbrella, puzzled)* Who's this?

LYDIAN. It's your umbrella.

WALDO. Oh, yes. *(He studies the umbrella affectionately, as if it were a lost old friend.)* Yes, my . . . uh . . . my . . . *(But again he's lost the name.)* Yes.

(LYDIAN helps the vague WALDO off, as the lights fall away on them.)

MOTHER. I wouldn't mind your being peculiar. But do you have to work at it so hard, David Henry?

HENRY. Henry David.

MOTHER. Getting everything backward. How did you learn your letters?

HENRY. Must the alphabet begin with *A? (He stands.)* Why not with *Z? Z* is a very sociable letter. Like the path of a man wandering in the woods. *A* is braced and solid. *A* is a house. I prefer *Z. Z-Y-X-W-V-U-T-S—(He makes a zig-zag course out of the cell into the thrust area.)*

MOTHER. Oh, dear—!

HENRY. Or mix them up. Start with *H.* Start with *Q.*

(WALDO, younger and straighter, has moved to a lectern where the light makes his face glow with an inner radiance. He is at the climax of an address.)

WALDO *(projecting).* Cast Conformity behind you.

(HENRY sees WALDO, and sinks to the floor, sitting squat-legged as a youthful admirer at the feet of an idol.)

HENRY (*as if memorizing a Commandment*). "Cast . . . Conformity . . . Behind You . . . !"

(JOHN *enters, stands beside his disturbed mother. Both look at* HENRY, *as he sits in a Yoga-esque fixation, staring up into empty air.* JOHN *is taller than his brother—affable, more extroverted.* JOHN *moves smoothly, easily, in contrast to the explosively erratic movements of his younger brother.*)

MOTHER. You know what David Henry's trouble is, John?

JOHN. What?

MOTHER. He keeps casting conformity behind him!

JOHN (*shrugging*). What the hell, he's been to Harvard.

MOTHER (*offended*). *Never* say—

JOHN. Harvard? I'm sorry, Mother, I'll never say it again. (MOTHER *goes off, and* JOHN *saunters toward his brother, who still sits transfixed. He looks at* HENRY *with some amusement.*) Now here's a rare specimen—

WALDO (*the vital glow still upon his face*). There is an infinitude in the private man! If a single man plants himself indomitably[1] on his instincts, and there abide, the huge world will come round to him . . .

(*The light falls away on* WALDO *as he goes off. The light intensifies on* HENRY *and* JOHN—*the amber of sunny fields.*)

HENRY (*still squatting; to himself*). . . . and there abide!

(JOHN *circles* HENRY *playfully, as if examining a specimen.*)

JOHN. Hm! Is this one wild or tame? Wild, I think. Known to haunt the woods and ponds. Dull plumage. But a wise bird. Americanus something-or-other. I have it! It is the species— BROTHER!!!

(*This joshing has broken* HENRY's *near-trance. He leaps up.*)

HENRY (*embracing him*). John!

JOHN. Welcome home. How's your overstuffed brain?

HENRY. I've forgotten everything already.

JOHN. At least you've got a diploma!

HENRY. No, I don't.

JOHN. Why not?

HENRY. They charge you a dollar. And I wouldn't pay it.

JOHN. But think how Mama would love it—your diploma from Harvard, framed on the wall!

HENRY. Let every sheep keep his own skin. (JOHN *gives him a disparaging shove on the shoulder, and they tussle like boys. Breathless, they sit side by side.*) John, I got more from one man— not even a professor—than I learned in four years of academic droning and snorting at Cambridge. And the strangest thing—he wasn't a stranger. I knew him, I'd seen him. You know him. You walk by him on the street, you say hello; he's just a man, just a neighbor. But this man speaks and a hush falls over all of Harvard. And there's a light about him—that comes out of his face. But it's not the light of one man. I swear to you, John, it's the light of all Mankind!

---

1. indomitable, unstoppable; not able to be subdued

JOHN (askance). Idolator!

(HENRY *slaps the ground with the palm of his hand.*)

HENRY. Is this the Earth?

JOHN. I hope so.

HENRY (*coming slowly to his feet*). No. It's you. And I. And God. And Mr. Emerson. And the Universal Mind!

JOHN. And Aunt Louisa?

HENRY. Yes, Aunt Louisa, too—false teeth and all. (*Scratching his head*) It isn't easy to think of Aunt Louisa, swimming in the Milky Way. But that's the way of things, I'm sure of it.

JOHN. And if she can't keep afloat, you can dive in and save her! (*They laugh.* JOHN *gets up, speaks more seriously.*) Now that you've turned your backside on Harvard, what do you plan to do?

HENRY (*pacing about*). Well, I think I'll think for a while. That'll be a change from college!

JOHN. But what do you want to be? Do you have any idea?

HENRY. Yes, I know exactly. I want to be as much as possible like Ralph Waldo Emerson.

(*The two brothers look at each other gravely. Light falls away from them. The light rises on* WALDO *and* LYDIAN. *He has the stature of a younger man, but he seems confused as he leafs through a manuscript.*)

LYDIAN. Your lecture was splendid, dear.

WALDO. I think I read one paragraph twice. I lost my place.

LYDIAN. Nobody noticed, dear.

WALDO. If nobody noticed, then nobody was listening!

LYDIAN. They thought you did it for emphasis.

(WALDO *looks at his wife uncertainly. There is snoring from the other cell-cot.* HENRY, *during the* WALDO-LYDIAN *action, has returned to his own cot in the cell.*)

WALDO (*starts off, then turns to his wife again*). Did you see that one fellow? In the third row? With his eyes closed. You don't think he was sleeping, do you?

LYDIAN. Concentrating, dear.

(*Almost reassured,* WALDO *moves off with his wife. The snoring grows to a crescendo as the key of moonlight rises in the prison cell.* HENRY *rises to a sitting position on his cot, looks at his sleeping cell-partner.*)

HENRY (*gently*). My friend—

(*His fellow prison snorts, comes groggily awake.*)

OTHER COT. Huh? Why—?

HENRY. Every human being has an inalienable right to snore. *Provided* it does not interfere with the inalienable right of *other* men to snore. (*The man on the other cot stares at him.*) I couldn't hear what's going on.

OTHER COT. Nothin' goes on in here. Night half the time. Then day. Then night again. Don't make much difference.

HENRY. Sshh! (HENRY *hears with every pore. There is the distant sound of a nightbird.*) Did you hear that? (*He comes to the imaginary downstage window.*)

OTHER COT (BAILEY). I didn't hear nothin'. Just a bird.

HENRY (indignantly). "Just a bird"! Can *you* make a cry like that? Or feed on flowers? Or carry the sky on your wings? Friend, you and I can't even fly.

(There is a pause. BAILEY rubs his eyes.)

BAILEY (foggily). I missed part of that. Guess I'm not full awake.

HENRY (studying him). Nobody is. If I ever met a man who was completely awake, how could I look him in the face?

BAILEY. What you do to get yourself locked up?

HENRY. What do you think?

BAILEY. Well-l-l—a man who talks educated like you—he can't 'a' done something small. Must be murder or worse.

HENRY. That's what I've done, by their lights, out there in the dark: murder or worse. (Change) No. I refuse to commit murder. That's why I'm here.

BAILEY. Who they want you to kill?

HENRY. Mexico.

BAILEY. Who's that?

HENRY. That's where the war is.

BAILEY. What war?

HENRY (amazed, pacing). Friend, this cell may be the only place in the United States that's at peace.

BAILEY. Who's fighting who?

HENRY. I'm not fighting anybody.

BAILEY. Neither'm I.

HENRY. But we've got a President who went out and boomed up a war all by himself—with no help from Congress and less help from me.

BAILEY. First I heered of it. (Warily) Which side you on? (Pointing emphatically downstage, toward Concord) Are you agin' them?

HENRY. "Them" . . . ?

BAILEY. Or are you *one* of them?

HENRY (thinks). I'm one of Me.

BAILEY. That don't make no sense.

(Far off, there is another bird-cry, forlornly wise. Again HENRY comes to the downstage imagined window.)

HENRY. Hear that? Old friend of mine. He's a night flyer. Doesn't have to see where he's going—or maybe he can see what we can't. Or hear . . . (The bird cries again. BAILEY looks at HENRY as if he were a bit daft.) He's headed for the pond. Did you ever make friends with a loon?

(There is a pause.)

BAILEY. Not till tonight.

HENRY. Anytime you hear a man called "loony," just remember that's a great compliment to the man and a great disrespect to the loon. A loon doesn't wage war, his government is perfect, being nonexistent. He is the world's best fisherman and completely in control of his senses, thank you. (BAILEY still is not sure about his new cellmate.) What are you here for, friend?

BAILEY. I'm waitin' trial.

HENRY. What did you do?

BAILEY. Nothin'.

HENRY. What do they *say* you did?

BAILEY (grudgingly). Burned down a barn. (Defiantly) But I didn't do it. All I did was snuck in to get some sleep and I guess the sparks from my pipe fell in the hay and—

HENRY. Tell 'em that!

BAILEY. The tellin' time is the trial. That's what I've been waitin' here for for three months.

HENRY *(rising in a fury).* You've been locked up here for three entire months, waiting for a chance to say you're innocent?

BAILEY. That's about it.

HENRY. It's outrageous! *(Calling)* Staples! Sam Staples!

(BAILEY stops him.)

BAILEY. Now don't make a ruckus. I'm not a troublemaker. I just want to earn my keep, make a little tobakky money, and get along.

HENRY. "Get along!" Those words turn my stomach. Mister—what's your name?

BAILEY. Bailey.

(A figure crosses the Village Square pompously. HENRY hears with animal keenness.)

HENRY. Mr. Bailey, listen! What do you hear?

BAILEY. Nothing—'cept footsteps.

HENRY. Footsteps of what?

BAILEY. A man, I guess.

HENRY. Where's he walking?

BAILEY. How would I know?

HENRY. I know where he's going. He's going where he's *supposed* to go. So he can *be* where he's supposed to be, at the time he's supposed to be there. Why? So he'll be *liked.* My God, a whole country of us who only want to be liked. *(Jutting his face squarely at* BAILEY*)* But to be *liked,* you must never disagree. And if you never disagree, it's like only breathing in and never breathing out! A man can suffocate on courtesy. *(He paces.)* What if God wanted to be *liked* instead of loved? What if the Almighty delayed every decision until He was sure it would please the majority? Great whales might have offended some legislature, which God knew would rise up some day to speak endlessly of the Common Good! *(Vehemently)* Common Good be damned! Give me something magnificently uncommon!

BAILEY. I don't understand what you're sayin', but it's a marvel to hear the way the words roll out!

HENRY. I'll put it in plain Anglo-Saxon, Mr. Bailey: you're an uncommon man. You were protesting against the barnbuilder who shut you in with clapboard and daily working hours.

BAILEY. Don't say that to no judge! If I burned down a barn, they'd throw me in jail.

HENRY. Friend, where do you think you are? You might as well have done the deed you didn't do!

BAILEY. But I'm not a man who goes around burning things down!

HENRY *(thoughtfully).* Good for you. Fire inside burns hotter than fire outside. A man's conviction is stronger than a flame or a bullet or a rock. *(Sinking onto the cot, thoughtfully)* I wonder if they'll keep *me* here three months, waiting trial! Who'll weed my bean patch? *(A little laugh)* Of course, I might get some brain work done.

BAILEY. It feels good to talk to a smart fella. I bet you can even write.

HENRY. Sometimes.

BAILEY. I wish I was a writer. If I could write my name, I'd die happy.

HENRY. Then you'd do better than most writers. *Bailey's* not a hard name.

BAILEY. I know the start of it. It's the start of the alphabet backward.

HENRY (*stooping to the floor*). I'll teach you the rest!

(*A light comes up briefly on* HENRY'*s* MOTHER.)

MOTHER. Oh, David Henry's an expert at getting things backward!

(*The light on her falls away.* HENRY *writes with his fingers on the dust of the floor.* BAILEY *eagerly kneels beside him.*)

HENRY. *B . . . A . . .*

BAILEY. That's as far as I know.

HENRY. Who's Bailey?

BAILEY. *I* am.

HENRY. That's your next letter. *I!* I am I.

BAILEY. How do you write it?

HENRY (*making a stroke in the dust*). Simple as a beanpole. Straight up and down. *B-A-I*—there, you're halfway through your name already. So you turn the corner—like this: (*He draws an* L.) That's an *L—B-A-I*-"turn the corner." Now. Here's a rough one. (*He squints up at the goggle-eyed* BAILEY.) How much hair have you got?

BAILEY. Enough to comb.

HENRY. That's it. Bailey needs a comb to comb his hair! (*Drawing in the dust*) There it is: *E!* And when you're all through, you want a nice tree to sit under. So you make a beanpole with branches on the top: that's *Y!* (*He draws it.*) And there's your name.

BAILEY. Jehosophat! You make it simple! (*As he traces the letters on the floor, turning to* HENRY *for approval*) B-A-Beanpole-Turn the Corner-Comb-Tree.

HENRY. You've got it! Now you can write your name! *Bailey!*

BAILEY. I'll leave this jail an educated man! (*Abruptly*) You must be a teacher!

HENRY. Being a teacher is like being in jail: once it's on your record, you can never get rid of it.

H ENRY *takes the chair from the cell and places it at the foremost edge of the thrust.* BAILEY *sinks into shadows on his cot, rehearsing his name from the letters on the floor.*

HENRY *becomes the young schoolmaster, addressing the audience as if they were a classroom full of unseen children.*

HENRY. Students, hold your hand up in front of you, like this.

(*He looks about to see that they are all doing just as he is: holding the open palm of the hand eighteen inches in front of the face.*)

Is there anything between my nose and my fingers? Nothing? My young friends, there are millions of tiny, dancing particles, whizzing back and forth, running into each other, and bouncing off! Stars, worlds, planets, universes. Right here!

(He blows a puff of breath into the empty space, then claps his hands together. BALL, *a pompous townsman with a silver-topped cane, stalks in, listening to the end of* HENRY's *remarks to the schoolroom.)*

And now—I give you a mystery! How do we know that these particles are there?

*(*HENRY *flicks his other hand through the seeming emptiness in front of him.)*

BALL. How indeed?

*(*HENRY *is startled, turns, sees the pompous visitor—then addresses the class.)*

HENRY. Ah, we have a surprise guest in the classroom today. The Chairman of the Concord School Committee, Deacon Nehemiah Ball.

BALL. I am not here to interrupt your scheduled curriculum. *(He pronounces it English-style: "sheduled.")*

HENRY. Thank you, sir. These particles—

BALL. Just an observer, that's all I am.

*(*HENRY *is getting irritated.* BALL *folds his arms behind his back, his cane dangles tail-like behind him;* HENRY *starts to speak again, but* BALL *interrupts.)*

HENRY. Scientists have—

BALL. Try to forget I'm in the room.

HENRY *(clearing his throat).* We'll try, sir. *(To his class)* Now. In recent years, scientists have discovered that—

BALL. How is it that I see no school books open here?

HENRY. We're . . . huckleberrying, sir.

BALL. You're what?

HENRY. We're scrambling for ideas the way we hunt for huckleberries in the woods.

BALL. That's no way to learn anything. All they need to know is clearly spelled out in the approved school texts.

HENRY. All, Deacon Ball? Young Potter, here—*(Pointing to a student in the first row)*—just asked me if I really think there is a God.

BALL. Young heathen!

HENRY. He simply asked why, since we never *see* God, should we believe He exists?

BALL *(addressing Potter).* Matters of Theology, boy, are discussable with your spiritual leader.

HENRY. Potter has already asked his "spiritual leader"—but the Reverend Whoever-It-Is called him an atheist! For committing the primary sin of *doubt. (To the student)* Mr. Potter, I'll try to answer you just as I once replied to the same question put to me by an annoying, inquisitive young man—myself.

BALL *(narrowly).* Will this be a *theological* opinion?

HENRY *(slowly).* It will be a *human* opinion. *(Again to the student, reasonably)* If I go into a shop and see all the nicely finished wheels, gears, pinions, springs of a watch lying spread out on a bench, then later find them put together exactly and working in unison to move the hands across a dial and show the passage of time, do I believe that these pieces have been flung together by blind chance? Certainly not. I believe that somebody with thought and plan and power has been there. An INTELLIGENCE!

(WALDO, *in academic robes, has come to a pulpit in his area.*)

WALDO. An Intelligence governs the universe. And in this worship service we shall celebrate our gratitude to that Intelligence. Let us pray. *(He lowers his head, praying silently.)*

HENRY. Nor do I think that the sun is rising above Concord this morning was an accident. I hope you saw it, Mr. Potter. And you, too, Deacon Ball. It was a brilliant sunrise. *(Emphatically)* We are all related, Mr. Potter—and interrelated to a *Universal Mind.*

BALL. That's atheism!

(It is not easy for HENRY to restrain himself.)

HENRY. I've often wondered, Deacon Ball, if atheism might even be popular with God himself.

BALL *(shocked).* Transcendental blasphemy![2]

WALDO. The Universal Mind is the divine part of all of us; and we partake, knowingly or not, in the wonder of that Universal Mind.

(The light falls away on WALDO, but he remains at the pulpit in meditation.)

HENRY *(softly).* Does all this make any sense to you, Potter?

BALL. It makes no sense to me. You will teach the textbooks, sir!

HENRY. I find your texts somewhat behind the century.

BALL. *You* find them so!

HENRY. Yes, sir, I do!

BALL. And you choose to ignore the books which have been *pro*scribed by the School Committee?

HENRY. My students have the ache of curiosity, which I'm afraid your *pro*scriptions will not cure!

(There are a couple of young laughs—quickly stifled. They seem to come from the class. BALL turns stern eyes toward the imagined pupils.)

BALL *(imperiously).* Silence! You will show respect for your elders! And you, Schoolmaster, will teach strictly according to text! No *huckleberrying!*

HENRY *(after a pause).* Class. You've heard the Deacon. We shall stick to the approved books. Your eyes must not wander from the page—to look at a leaf, or an unauthorized butterfly. You must not listen to a cricket or smell a flower that has not been approved by the School Committee. You'd better close both ears and hold your nose—though you may have to grow an extra hand to do it.

(He pantomimes the difficulty of covering successively two ears, then his nose and one ear, then the other ear and his nose. At this there is uninhibited laughter from the unseen classroom—through a loudspeaker at the foot of the thrust.)

BALL *(waddling to the forestage).* Silence! Is this the gratitude you show to the municipality which feeds your minds? *(The veins bulge in his forehead,*

---

2. Transcendental blasphemy, Transcendentalists believed in a reality beyond the known world. Because their beliefs did not totally subscribe to the Christianity of the day, they were thought by some to be showing disrespect for God.

he pounds with his silver-topped cane.)
You will show decent respect! (*The laughter continues.* BALL *turns to* HENRY.) Make them be silent, sir! (HENRY *simply lifts his hand; the laughter stops.*) The lack of order in this classroom will most certainly be reported to the full School Committee, which I intend to call into extraordinary session tonight.

(JOHN *appears, speaks as if to* HENRY's *mind.*)

JOHN. Henry, give the man a penny apology. Two-cents-worth of humility!

HENRY. Why should I?

JOHN. So they won't cut you off from the class. If you're stubborn, what will happen when Potter asks questions?

(*A pause—then* HENRY *makes the supreme effort at contrition. He takes a deep breath, turns to face* BALL.)

HENRY (*with much difficulty*). Deacon Ball. I'm sorry that you've had a rather ragged time in my classroom today. I have intended no offense to you or the School Committee.

BALL. Well, we've come to expect a certain degree of unruliness from Harvard men. Your apology shows that you recognize this flaw in your character. But your students don't have Harvard as an excuse. They must be punished.

HENRY. I shall lecture them.

BALL. You will *flog* them!

HENRY (*stunned*). What?

BALL. You will flog them—for showing irreverence to authority!

HENRY (*defiantly*). No, sir!

BALL. I beg your pardon.

HENRY. I said "No." I do not believe in corporal punishment.

BALL. What you believe is irrelevant. Your opinion, as a teacher, has not been asked for. I direct you to FLOG!

(HENRY *hesitates.*)

HENRY. Why?

BALL. It is policy. Offending students are whipped.

HENRY. And what would that teach them?

BALL. Obedience. An essential quality in subordinates, whether they are pupils in a classroom or soldiers on a battlefield.

HENRY. They are not training to be soldiers. Not *my* students.

BALL. These young people are not *yours*. They have been sent to you by the tax-paying citizens of Concord, who expect you to abide by the rules laid down by the school administrators. (*Silence.* HENRY *does not move.*) Perform your duty, Schoolmaster Thoreau, if you expect to retain your post in this community.

(HENRY *slowly unbuckles his belt, then whips it off, taking a short step toward* BALL, *who pulls back, thinking perhaps* HENRY *is about to flog him. Then* HENRY *turns front, to the class.*)

HENRY (*bitterly, to his class*). *Six* of you. *Any* six. Come forward. It doesn't matter who. You are all—all of you—accused of the damning crimes of laughter, curiosity, and candid self-expression! Bigelow! (HENRY *grabs the chair, spins it over as if he were putting a boy across his knee. Eyes closed,* HENRY *lashes the chair fiercely and painfully with his belt.*) Coleman! (*Again he lashes the chair.*) Loring! (*Another lash*) McClain! (*He whips the chair again, blindly, loathing what he is doing.*) Henderson. (*Another lash. Then a hesitation.*) Potter!

(*This whipping is the most painful of all. He turns his head away. Now finished, breathless,* HENRY *opens his eyes, stares at the belt as if it were something filthy and revolting. He flings it away from him, far offstage.*)

BALL. I congratulate you. I am happy to be able to report to the School Committee that Schoolmaster Thoreau—

HENRY. —has administered the Sacrament of the Schoolroom; and he resigns as a "teacher" in the Public Schools of Concord!

(BALL *icily falls back into the shadows and disappears. The light on the pulpit comes up in full brilliance on* WALDO.)

WALDO (*in the midst of an inner struggle*). —but I cannot comply with custom! I cannot perform the rites required of me by this congregation. For I have searched the Scriptures and can find nothing which calls on us to repeat endlessly the ceremony of the Last Supper. Intellectually, emotionally, spiritually, I cannot administer this Sacrament. So I resign my position as pastor of the Second Unitarian Church of Boston.

(HENRY *has put the chair—his "student"— back in the jail cell. Sadly he comes down into the light.*)

HENRY. I shall never teach again.

WALDO. I shall never preach again.

(*Light rises on* MOTHER *and* JOHN.)

MOTHER. Have you ever noticed, John, how much Mr. Emerson talks like our David Henry?

(JOHN *notices the disconsolate* HENRY *and goes to him.*)

JOHN (*quietly*). A school doesn't need a School Committee. Or Trustees. Or Governors. Or Lumber. Or approved textbooks. All a school needs is a mind that sends, and minds that receive.

HENRY. Nobody can teach anybody anything.

JOHN (*blithely*). Of course not. Teach them how to teach themselves.

HENRY (*fired with an idea*). Our own school, John. No buildings. Break out of the classroom prison. All we need is sky! (*The cyclorama [3] becomes ablaze with blue, and sunlit clouds. There is the screech and wheeling of birds, and a great sense of freedom.*) The universe can be our schoolroom, John—the great, vast world of the Concord countryside.

(HENRY *claps a broad straw hat on his head, sticks a notebook under his arm. There is a flood of light on the forestage.* HENRY *seems to be marching across the open sunlit fields.* JOHN *follows with a telescope.*) Students!

---

3. cyclorama, a curved wall or drop at the back of a stage, used to create an illusion of wide space or for lighting effects

(The students, though imaginary, are presumably all around him.) Watch! Notice! Observe! *(He takes the telescope from* JOHN *and uses it as a pointer.)* See what is happening around you. Did you ever have any idea so much was going on in Heywood's Meadow? I'll wager even Heywood doesn't know. *(A discovery)* The cypripedium is already in flower! *(He leafs back through his notebook.)* Last year it didn't bloom until tomorrow! *(He makes an entry in his notebook.)* Do you know how few people know what we've just discovered? Stumbling on the first morning of a new flower! Most of Concord is too busy eating meals and going to the post office!

(A strikingly beautiful girl—twenty perhaps—stands at the edge of the light, watching and listening, fascinated.) Oh, I would be sad and sorry to remember that I once was in the world and noticed nothing remarkable. Not so much as a prince in disguise. *(Looking sideways at his brother)* John, are you a prince in disguise?

JOHN. Of course.

*(*HENRY *paces about the meadow.)*

HENRY. Wouldn't it be dreadful if I had lived in the Golden Age as a *hired man?* Or visited Olympus, and fell asleep after dinner—and completely missed the conversation of the gods. Or imagine living in Judea eighteen hundred years ago—and never knowing that Jesus was my contemporary! What are you doing?

(He has, in his peripatetic [4] *outpouring, come face-to-face with the girl, who has taken out a notebook; she is absorbed in writing, jarred by his question.)*

ELLEN. I'm writing.

HENRY. What?

ELLEN. What you've been saying. So I'll remember.

HENRY. Don't just remember what I said. Remember what I'm talking about. *(Obediently, she closes her notebook.* HENRY *crosses to* JOHN, *lowering his voice.)* Who's that?

JOHN. It's a girl.

(Both stare at her, impressed.)

HENRY. One of ours? I mean, does she belong to us? Is she one of our students?

JOHN *(taking a good look at her).* I wouldn't mind. Would you?

HENRY *(crossing back to her).* Excuse me, Miss. But I think you're a little old to be a member of this class.

JOHN. Henry, a young lady is never too old for anything.

HENRY. It's just that—well—most of our students are twelve—or thereabouts. And you're—well, not exactly thereabouts.

(The girl laughs.)

ELLEN. Does it make so much difference really? I just want to come along and listen and watch. I won't be any bother or ask any questions.

HENRY. Why not?

ELLEN. My little brother is the only one who has the right to ask questions: he's paying tuition.

---

4. peripatetic, moving or traveling from place to place

The Night Thoreau Spent in Jail by Jerome Lawrence & Robert E. Lee

HENRY (*points a finger at her*). You're Sewell.

ELLEN. How'd you know?

HENRY. If I can spot a cypripedium, I can spot a Sewell.

JOHN. There's only one rule in this class: no rules. So, of course, you're welcome to come along—any time you'd like.

ELLEN. What about tuition?

JOHN. You've already paid it. If you were ugly, we'd charge you. Or twelve. Or thereabouts.

(ELLEN *and* JOHN *laugh.* HENRY *does not; he merely looks at her.*)

ELLEN. You're John Thoreau. (*Turning*) And you're the thundercloud. Henry.

(HENRY *frowns.*)

HENRY. What previous educational experience have you had?

ELLEN. Finishing school.

HENRY. Dear God.

ELLEN. I survived.

HENRY. I warn you, Miss Sewell, that John and I are not finishers. Nobody leaves us with a smooth surface. We rough up the consciousness, scrape the moss off young minds.

ELLEN. Please, Mr. Thoreau. Go back to your students. I've interrupted.

HENRY. Of course you have. Every creative event that ever happened in the world was an interruption. Unexpected. Unplanned for. The only people who ever get anyplace interesting are the people who get lost. That's why the planets are so much better company than the stars—they keep wandering back and forth across the sky and you never know where you're going to find them. (*To the unseen class*) Students. We have another Sewell. Edmund's sister. (*To the girl*) You have a first name?

ELLEN. Ellen.

HENRY. Ellen Sewell. Our textbook, Miss Sewell, is Heywood's Meadow. Approved by the Almighty, if not by the School Committee. (*To the class*) In this single pasture, there are *three hundred* distinct and separate varieties of grass. I know; I have catalogued them myself. You look down and say: "That's grass. Grass is grass." Ridiculous. You have missed the splendid variety of the show. There's camel grass, candy grass, cloud grass, cow-quake, mouse-barley, fox-tail, Londonlace, devil's knitting needle, feather-top buffalo grass, timothy and barnyard grass and clovers enough to sweeten the bellies of all the lambs since creation. (ELLEN *has taken down her notebook and is writing. Suddenly* HENRY *leans down, seeing something, and plucks an imaginary blade of grass.*) John, look at this. What would you say it is?

JOHN. I've never seen it before.

HENRY. It's *Coix Lacryma-jobi,* which means Job's Tears. I've never seen a specimen here. Students, I beg your pardon. We are in the midst of three hundred and *one* varieties of God-made grasses. (*He jots this information in his notebook. Out of the corner of his eye, he sees* ELLEN *writing.*) You're writing again.

ELLEN. Just "Job's Tears."

HENRY. Why?

ELLEN. When you go to school, you're supposed to write things down, so you remember what you've been taught.

HENRY. Then it's the notebook that does the remembering, not you.

ELLEN. You keep a notebook.

HENRY. I also wear a ridiculous straw hat. That doesn't mean that you should wear a ridiculous hat. You'd look ridiculous in it. Nature didn't stuff this meadow full of identical blades of grass, each an imitation of another. They're all different! Follow-the-leader is not the game we're playing here! Young lady, BE YOUR OWN MAN!

JOHN (low). Henry, don't shout at her.

ELLEN. I won't take notes. I promise you. Not one.

HENRY. Why not? If you want to take notes, go ahead. But not because I'm doing it, or because I told you to. (Gently) Miss Sewell, I want you to be yourself—not your idea of what you think is somebody else's idea of your-self. (Turning to students) Perhaps, students, Miss Sewell's interruption has given us the essence of the text-book we call Heywood's Meadow. The multiple grasses beneath our feet. The infinity of the sky above us. (Riffling through his notebook) And if I have jotted down a note about a cloud-flame, or about sunlight on bird-wings, don't you write, just because I am writing. Don't ape me, or copy me. (Intensely, but quietly) If you wish merely to listen to the sky, or smell the sky, or feel the sky with your finger-tips, do that, too! (With great conviction) Because I think there should be as many different persons in the world as possible. So—each of you—be very careful to find out and pursue your own way!

(As the lights dim on the sunlit field, HENRY goes back to the dimly lit cell.)

BAILEY (rapturously). Bailey, Bailey, Bailey! I kin write! Watch! Watch me do it all by myself—!

(BAILEY starts again to trace his name in the dust on the cell floor. HENRY bitterly erases the pattern of letters in the dust with his foot. BAILEY looks up, puzzled.)

HENRY. Don't learn to write your name.

BAILEY. I already learned.

HENRY (splenetic[5]). Unlearn it. Writing your name can lead to writing sentences. And the next thing you'll be doing is writing paragraphs, and then books. And then you'll be in as much trouble as I am!

BAILEY (wonderingly). You write books?

(HENRY sits on the cot.)

HENRY (wryly). Yes.

BAILEY. If my mother'd lived to see me sittin' in the same jail cell with a man who writ a book, ohhhh-ee, she'd be proud of me. Tell me somethin'. Do you make up all the words yourself?

HENRY. Oh, now and then I stick in a word or two that's been used before. The base trick is to pick the right words and put 'em in the right order.

----

5. splenetic, marked by bad temper or spite

BAILEY. Must be a fortune in it. I hear tell some books cost more'n a dollar!

HENRY. But they haven't been perfected yet. They've gotta put legs on them. As it is now, a book just sits in a shop and has to wait for somebody with legs on to come in and find it.

BAILEY (*blankly*). Oh?

(BAILEY *has taken tobacco from his rough coat in the locker, thus freeing the box for the next scene.*)

HENRY. My first book—also my last book—was a very stationary model. The publisher brought out a thousand copies!—and gave me the privilege of paying for the printing. So all the copies that didn't sell belonged to the author. And they came running home to me, legs or not. (*Gravely*) Right now, Mr. Bailey, I have a library of nearly nine hundred volumes!—seven hundred of which I wrote myself. (*Pointing to the scuffed-up letters in the dust of the floor*) My friend, give up your literary career.

Suddenly, HENRY *takes the locker-box from the cell, flips it over, open-side up, and drags it down onto the thrust.* JOHN *comes on, helping him with the "boat."*

HENRY. John, today I thought we'd make a complete circuit of the pond. If this boat isn't large enough for the whole class, I'll take the first trip, you take the second.

JOHN. It'll be large enough.

HENRY. We lost another pupil?

JOHN. No. We lost two.

HENRY (*defensively*). Good. Education should not be a mass process!

JOHN. With us, it isn't.

HENRY. The whole idea of our school is that the size of the classroom grows larger and larger—

JOHN. —while the size of the class grows smaller and smaller.

HENRY. How many do we actually have left?

JOHN (*avoiding his eyes*). Mother's got the name of a new family, just moved to Concord.

HENRY. How many children?

JOHN. Be patient, Henry. The wife is pregnant.

(JOHN *starts to leave.*)

HENRY. Where are you going?

JOHN. Back to the pencil factory.

HENRY. Why?

JOHN. It might be a little overpowering—to have twice as many teachers as pupils.

HENRY. Only one left?

(JOHN *goes off.* HENRY, *alone, scowls, kicks at the box-boat.* ELLEN *appears.*)

ELLEN. Mr. Thoreau—?

(HENRY *turns.*)

HENRY. Good morning—

ELLEN. I—I came to tell you that you shouldn't wait for Edmund. Just go ahead and start the class without him. He—uh—won't be coming today.

HENRY. I hope he's not ill?

ELLEN. No. (*Pause*) It's my Father—

HENRY. He's ill?

ELLEN. Not exactly. Father's worried—because he thinks Edmund's learning too much.

HENRY. That's good news. I thought Edmund was a bit sluggish myself. Compared with the other students. That is, when we had other students to compare him with. *(Briskly)* Well, tell your Father not to worry. I'll slow down with Edmund.

ELLEN. I'm afraid Father doesn't want him to come to your school at all any more.

HENRY *(bridling).* Oh. Your Father's opposed to knowledge.

ELLEN. No. He's opposed to Transcendentalists. That's what he says you are. And your brother, too. "A whole family afflicted with Transcendentalism."

HENRY. What the devil does your Father think Transcendentalism is?

ELLEN. I asked him and he tried to explain it to me. And the more he explained, the less I understood it. Father has a gift that way.

HENRY. A born *non*-teacher. *(Suddenly)* Miss Sewell. Get into the boat.

ELLEN. Oh?

HENRY. Since I find myself unexpectedly unemployed, I shall take you on a voyage of exploration. No tuition charge. *(HENRY helps her into the boat.)* Keep your eye on the line between the water and the sky. I'll row. *(He pantomimes pushing the boat off; the light narrows, the background trembles with the wavering pattern of sunlight reflected from water. With no visible oars, he rows. Suddenly, he points.)* There

used to be a row of cedars on that far shore. *(Sighing)* But we have lost that link with Lebanon.

ELLEN. Where have they gone?

HENRY. Into firewood—and up in smoke. Into houses. Do you know what we're doing, Miss Sewell? We're poisoning paradise. Shearing off the woods, making the poor earth bald before her time.

ELLEN. But we have to have houses, Mr. Thoreau. Or should we all live in caves?

HENRY. What's the use of a house if you haven't got a tolerable planet to put it on? Did you know that trees cry out in pain when they're cut? I've heard them. But what bells in town toll for them? We prosecute men for abusing children; we ought to prosecute them for maltreating nature.

ELLEN. My father says God put everything here for men to *use.*

HENRY. Oh? Did the Good Father put us here to root and snort and glut ourselves like pigs? No, the pigs are better; pigs may be the most respectable part of the population: at least they consume the rubble instead of contributing to it. *(In the distance, the whistle of a railroad train)* Hear that? There goes a carload of two-legged pigs, off to market . . . emasculating the landscape with their tracks . . .

ELLEN. I rather like the railroad. Far better than a horse and carriage.

HENRY. Why?

ELLEN. It's smoother, and much faster.

HENRY. And dirtier. And uglier. Thank God men haven't learned to fly: they'd lay waste the sky as well as the earth . . . chop down the clouds!

ELLEN *(somewhat puzzled).* Is that in Transcendentalism, Mr. Thoreau?

HENRY *(laughs).* No. Yes, it is—in a way. Take your father. Do you love the man?

ELLEN. Of course.

HENRY. Why?

ELLEN. He's my father.

HENRY. Is he beautiful?

ELLEN. Dear me, no!

HENRY. Does he create beauty? Paint? Play a musical instrument?

ELLEN. No.

HENRY *(pointing up, then down).* Can he fly like that bird? Or swim, like that fellow down there?

ELLEN. He can swim a little. He used to. But not like that fish.

HENRY. Nevertheless you *love* him.

ELLEN. Of course.

HENRY. Your love *transcends* what your father is—and he is not. Every consciousness is capable of going beyond itself. Every—(ELLEN *frowns a bit.)* Dammit, I've lost you. Put your hand in the water. *(She does.)* Can you touch bottom?

ELLEN *(reaching down).* It's too deep.

HENRY. For the length of your arm. Not for the length of your mind. *(He has stopped rowing.)* Miss Sewell. Why should your reach stop with your skin? When you transcend the limits of yourself, you can cease merely living—and begin to BE!

ELLEN. I don't mind *living*—

HENRY. But *being* is so much more interesting.

ELLEN *(taking her hand out of the "water").* I'm a little bit afraid—just—to "be"!

HENRY. Think how free it is. If you're never afraid.

ELLEN. Aren't you ever afraid?

(He thinks, stares at her.)

HENRY. Yes. I'm afraid that I might "live" right through this moment— and only live—*(He leans forward on his oars, looking into her face.)*—look at you and only see you. Oh, it doesn't hurt at all to look at you, believe me. But what if there's more—and I miss it?

ELLEN. Miss what?

HENRY. What if all that is beautiful, in women, in the world—or worlds— what if all of it is totaled up in this face here, in front of me—and I am empty enough to think I am merely seeing *one* face?

(ELLEN doesn't follow him precisely, but she's pleased.)

ELLEN. That's Transcendentalism?

(HENRY has lost interest in Transcendentalism and is more interested in ELLEN.)

HENRY *(resumes rowing).* If you like.

ELLEN. I don't think that's wicked. I think it's rather nice.

HENRY. Who says it's wicked?

ELLEN. Father. Last night at the dinner table, Edmund gave Father a sermon on the Over-Soul.

HENRY. Good for Edmund! Most dining rooms are tabernacles where only the father gets the pulpit.

ELLEN. Oh, Father got it right back. He was still shouting at breakfast. He broke off with an incomplete sentence last night, and picked it right up this morning at porridge.

HENRY. Well, I'm a little older than Edmund. But I have yet to hear the first syllable of valuable advice from my seniors. *(His eyes going to the horizon)* We are born as innocents. We are polluted by advice. Here is life in front of us, like the surface of this pond, inviting us to sail on it. A voyage, an experiment. Waiting to be performed. Has your father tried it before? That's no help to me. Or to you. Keep your innocence, Edmund!

ELLEN. Ellen.

HENRY. Ellen, yes. You look very much alike, you know. The eyes. You both listen with your eyes.

ELLEN. I have to go back.

HENRY. Why?

ELLEN. Father expects me.

HENRY. Surprise him.

ELLEN. Edmund did. He's braver than I am.

HENRY. Stand up to your father! *(He stands. The boat rocks.)*

ELLEN. Please, Mr. Thoreau—not in the boat!

HENRY. Oh—*(He sits.)*

ELLEN. Will you row me back to shore, please?

HENRY. No. Listen to me. If I were to say, "I Love You, Sewell—Miss Sewell. Ellen"—you wouldn't think much of it as a statement of fact if you knew it was just an echo, a mouthing, of something somebody *told* me to say.

(Disparagingly) Some father! *(Quietly)* But if I say "I love you" out of myself, out of my own experience—or lack of it—out of my innocence, then you and God had better believe me.

(The light comes up on JOHN *and* MOTHER, *as* ELLEN *turns away from* HENRY, *staring at the water.)*

JOHN *(running in).* Mother, Henry's in love.

MOTHER *(worried).* Who's he in love with?

JOHN. A girl.

MOTHER. Thank God.

(Light falls away on JOHN *and* MOTHER.*)*

ELLEN *(icily).* I'm not one of your fish, nor one of your birds, Mr. Thoreau. So I can neither swim nor fly back to dry land. I must simply sit here and hope that you are gentleman enough to row me ashore.

*(*HENRY *doesn't move. He looks at her. She's beautiful, but he knows he's missed his chance, and it frustrates him.)*

HENRY *(with a sigh).* Miss Sewell. I apologize. And I'll row you to shore on one condition.

ELLEN. I have to accept it.

HENRY. Come to church on Sunday.

ELLEN. You don't go to church.

HENRY. Of course not. I can't stand sitting in a pew, having the Sabbath despoiled by a sermon.

ELLEN. But still you invite me to church?

HENRY. With John. *We* have a strong family resemblance, too. And if you find a single syllable in me worth writing in a notebook, you'll find *paragraphs* of it in John! Where I am cantankerous, he is amiable. Where I am thorns and brambles, he is a garden. Where I am a bare hill in winter, he is spring.

(He begins to row, slowly.)

ELLEN. How do you know that your brother would want to take me to church?

HENRY. Didn't you notice that day in Heywood's Meadow—when he proposed to you?

ELLEN. He barely spoke to me.

HENRY. That's why you didn't hear him. You missed the eloquence of his silence.

(The boat presumably comes to shore. HENRY jumps out, pantomimes pulling it onto the bank, then helps ELLEN as she steps out. ELLEN, having won her point, wonders . . . . have I really lost?)

ELLEN *(with mixed pride and regret).* Good day, Mr. Thoreau. Thank you for making Transcendentalism so clear.

HENRY. Did I? If there's anything I missed, just ask Edmund.

ELLEN. What will happen to your school?

HENRY *(turning away).* I'm going back to it. As a pupil. Maybe I can learn from Nature—and from John: a pasture can be raucous with flowers, and not make a single sound. But a man—presumably wiser than a daffodil—can beat so loudly on the eardrums that nobody hears what he's trying to say.

(ELLEN is bewildered. Then, in his silence, HENRY seems almost fierce to her, and she

runs off, frightened. He looks wistfully toward the air where ELLEN was. Then he stares down into the empty boat, kicks it. That emptiness is something of the vacancy he feels within himself.

Slowly, HENRY moves up into the area of the jail cell. The wavering pattern of light-on-water falls away. Only the long nocturnal shadows of the cell remain. BAILEY is asleep on his cot, snoring lightly. HENRY looks down at him.)

HENRY. Mr. Bailey, what do you think of marriage? *(BAILEY gives out a derisive snore, which suggests that subconsciously he may have heard the question. HENRY nods.)* That seems to be the majority opinion. *(He settles back on his own cot. The clock strikes eleven. The sound dilates, louder and louder, pulsing with standing waves.)* Bailey, did you hear that? I don't think I've ever felt those waves of sound from the clock tower. *(A laugh)* That's ridiculous—that a man has to be put in a stone box before he can hear the music of his own village! *(HENRY calls through the barred window.)* Thank you, Concord! Thank you for locking me up so I'm free to hear what I've never heard before. You put me behind iron bars and walls four feet thick! How do you know that I'm not the free one? The freest man in the world! And you, out there, are chained to what you have to do tomorrow morning! *(Now he whispers through the cell grating.)* Speak softly, Concord—I can hear you breathing. *(BAILEY lets out a snore.)* Quiet, Bailey. We free men should listen to the cry of prisoners.

(The light falls away on the cell. There is the projection of a stained glass window.)

Facing upstage is a standing row of worshipers: DEACON BALL, SAM STAPLES, WALDO, LYDIAN, MRS. THOREAU, JOHN *and* ELLEN *beside him, and townspeople. All are dressed Sunday-best and singing the last stanza of a hymn: "Blest Be the Tie that Binds," Pilgrim Hymnal 272.)*

CHURCHGOERS *(singing in unison).*

Blest be the tie that binds
Our hearts in Christian love;
The Fellowship of kindred minds
Is like to that Above.
A-men.

(Halfway through the hymn, EDWARD *scratches his bottom.* LYDIAN *pulls his hand away.)*

After the "Amen" there is the swell of organ music, as the worshipers begin to file out into the tree-dappled light of a Sunday noon. ELLEN *comes out, on* JOHN's *arm. There is a cluster of conversation around the* EMERSONS.*)*

DEACON BALL. Tell me, Doctor Emerson. What is the feeling of a clergyman when he hears another pastor in the pulpit?

WALDO. Relief.

DEACON. That you don't have to give the sermon?

WALDO *(dryly).* That it's over.

(The MOTHER *is beaming at* JOHN *and* ELLEN. *Suddenly she sees something which turns her soul to ice. The others look, with varying degrees of shock, as* HENRY, *his shirt unbuttoned, pushes a wheelbarrow full of earth. Blithely he crosses directly in front of the washed and starched churchgoers.* ELLEN *looks down,* JOHN *suppresses a grin,* WALDO *and* LYDIAN *turn gracefully away, and* DEACON BALL *tries to look as much as possible like Moses on the mountain.)*

MOTHER. Oh, David Henry! *Not* on Sunday!

HENRY *(pleasantly).* This *is* Sunday, isn't it. Have all of you been shut up inside? On this beautiful morning? What a pity!

DEACON. We've been feeding our souls!

HENRY. How selfish of you. *(He reaches into the wheelbarrow and sprinkles some of the unseen contents at the feet of the churchgoers.)* I've been feeding the flora of Concord. *(They wince at the aroma.)* Bringing loaves and fishes to the lilacs. *(Waving cheerfully,* HENRY *trundles the wheelbarrow off. All eyes follow him.)*

DEACON. Labor on the Sabbath, and the Devil's in Massachusetts.

JOHN. Henry worships in the woods.

DEACON BALL. Then what do we have churches for?

WALDO. I sometimes wonder.

LYDIAN *(quickly).* Dr. Emerson means that the Good Lord is everywhere.

DEACON BALL. The Lord I know rested on the Seventh Day.

WALDO. Why, Deacon Ball, you're older than I thought! *(Before* BALL *can really take offense, the warm-hearted* EMERSON *pats his shoulder.)* For you and me, Deacon, the Declaration of Independence has already been written. Young Thoreau has to declare it every day—Sundays included. *(Starting off, with* LYDIAN*)* So what's the harm if he sweats his psalms

---

The Night Thoreau Spent in Jail by Jerome Lawrence & Robert E. Lee **65**

instead of singing them? *(The worshipers disperse.* JOHN *and* ELLEN *go off together.* MRS. THOREAU *is left alone. She looks off toward the vanished* HENRY.)

MOTHER. Oh, David Henry—why did God and I have to make you so peculiar? *(Eyes to heaven)* And please, dear Lord, don't let John get too strange. Perhaps, if it isn't too much trouble, you could slip the word "yes" into that young lady's mouth. Amen.

(She goes off. The stained glass window fades. The cyclorama becomes sunlit clouds. Amplified and echoing, JOHN's *laughter spills across the open field.* HENRY *comes on, takes a triumphant stance.)*

HENRY. She said "Yes!!!" *(*JOHN *bursts on, almost drunk with his own laughter.)* Congratulations—I'm happy for you, John! Are you going to do it right away? Or do you have to go through those tribal rites—posting the banns, all that primitive nonsense?

*(*JOHN, *in a paroxysm[6] of laughter, embraces his brother.)*

JOHN. She said—she said—*(He breaks off again, laughing.)*

HENRY. She said "Yes," naturally! *(*JOHN, *laughing, can't answer.)* She didn't say "No!"?

JOHN. No, she didn't say "No!"

HENRY. What the devil did she say?

JOHN *(still laughing)*. She quoted her father.

HENRY. Heavenly or here?

JOHN. The one her mother married.

HENRY. Well, what did old Porridge-Face have to say?

JOHN. He said—*(Laughing)* She said he said . . . that marriage to either of the Thoreau brothers was unthinkable!

HENRY. Amen! The Thoreau brothers never had any intention of marrying her father! *(Hopefully)* But she stood up to him?

JOHN. I wasn't there—but evidently she sat down. *(He sits.)*

HENRY. So you wasted six good summer Sundays taking her to church!

JOHN. I swear to you, I didn't pray. I kept looking at that face out of the corner of my eye. Wondering what she was thinking. I finally realized she wasn't thinking at all!

HENRY. She's a girl. Who'd want a wife who went around thinking?

JOHN *(starts laughing again)*. When I asked her to marry me, there was a pregnant pause. Well, not pregnant, but a pause. Then she said: "Oh, dear . . . " At first, I thought she was being affectionate, then I realized she was only saying, "Oh, dear!"

HENRY. Then what?

JOHN. Then she said, "Why doesn't Henry ask me?" And I said, "If he does, will you say yes?" And she said, "No, but why doesn't he ask me anyhow?"

HENRY. It's an outrage! She wants to wear *both* of our scalps on her petticoat strings!

JOHN. She won't marry you, and she won't marry me. But I think she'd marry *us* in a minute.

---

6. paroxysm, a sudden, violent outburst

HENRY. That's carrying Unitarianism too far!

JOHN. If we were Mohammedans—

HENRY. Wouldn't help. Moslems take multiple wives, not multiple husbands.

JOHN. But then, Henry, I destroyed the whole thing. I killed it. I laughed. *(HENRY laughs a little.)* Not like that. Bigger! *(They both begin to laugh.)* Not at her, the dear girl; at *us!* I almost shattered the most sacred tradition of the Thoreau tribe: celibacy!

HENRY *(laughing).* You're a good-hearted man, John! You saved the girl from marrying a monk.

JOHN. Or a pair of them!

(They laugh more heartily.)

HENRY. Who in our brood has ever committed marriage?

JOHN. Mama and Papa.

HENRY. Only legally. Except for a couple of slips that brought about you and me, Papa is pure bachelor and Mama is a living pillar of spinsterhood. Thanks to your courageous inaction, the Thoreaus remain a race of maiden aunts and bachelors. All of us, December Virgins!

JOHN. Henry, I never told you about one April—

(HENRY lifts one hand in mock forgiveness.)

HENRY. Boy, if Father can falter, so can you!

(They laugh together, then grow serious.)

JOHN. It makes for a rather lonely-looking future.

HENRY. Lonely? Never! Why, when I'm ninety and you're a mere infant of eighty-eight, you'll come around and comfort me.

JOHN. When you're ninety, Henry, I'll be a "mere infant" of ninety-two.

(HENRY grasps his brother's hand.)

HENRY. And that's the time we'll both go after the hand of Ellen Sewell!

(HENRY and JOHN leap about, laughing, as if they were a pair of nonagenarians[7] who have been injected with "youth-juice." Then they fall into each other's arms, laughing helplessly.)

The light goes black. In utter darkness, the church-bell tolls mournfully. Dimly the stained glass window of the church appears. Then a cold white spot, directly above, strikes the box which was the boat and has now been turned over to become a coffin.

VOICE OF MINISTER. Unto Almighty God we commend the soul of our brother departed, John Thoreau, and we commit his body to the ground, in the sure and certain hope of the Resurrection unto Eternal Life. Let us pray. *(Four black-coated townspeople carry off the casket. The MOTHER is in black. HENRY comes slowly to her side. She looks into his face.)*

MOTHER. David Henry. *Pray* with me!

(MOTHER kneels, facing front. Almost like a sleep-walker, HENRY sinks to his knees. His face is mask-like. His MOTHER clasps her hands. Automatically HENRY does the same.)

---

7. nonagenarian, someone ninety years old, or between nintey and 100 years of age

MOTHER (*with difficulty*). Our Father, which art in Heaven, hallowed be— (*She breaks off, looks at her silent son, who has lowered his hands.*)

HENRY. I can't, Mother. I can't pray.

MOTHER. It helps.

HENRY. Does it? I prayed before. What good did it do?

MOTHER. We should pray for John's soul.

HENRY. John's soul can take care of itself.

MOTHER. We should pray for under-standing—

(HENRY *suddenly gets up, angrily.*)

HENRY. I understand! God has stopped listening, Mother—if He ever did listen. What kind of God would fail to see the godliness in John? I can't pray to Him. (HENRY *turns away, then comes back, kisses his* MOTHER*'s head. Quietly.*) Mother. Pray for *both* your sons.

(*The* MOTHER *lowers her head, praying as she moves off. The stained-glass projection fades.* ELLEN *hurries on.*)

ELLEN (*sympathetically*). What happened?

HENRY (*shrugs*). He died.

ELLEN. I was in Winthrop. I didn't even hear about it until after the funeral . . .

HENRY. We managed.

ELLEN. How did—didn't anybody know, beforehand—?

HENRY. What do you want, a medical report? To feed a morbid curiosity?

ELLEN. Even though I couldn't marry him—

HENRY. Couldn't you? Well, that's your business.

ELLEN. Henry, don't be so selfish with your sorrow! *I care too!*

HENRY. He had a glamorous death. Like the Knights of the Table Round who slashed at each other with rusty swords until they had all died of blood-poisoning.

ELLEN. I don't understand.

HENRY. John, three mornings ago, happened to think of something very funny while he was shaving. He burst out laughing, and cut himself. The razor was old, and vicious, and it despised the blood in his veins. And so—(*Confronting her fiercely*)—would you like the details? The spasms, the retching, the murderous ineptitude of doctors, the paralysis of the tongue, the choking, the clamping of the jaw, the blood-black face, the eyes pleading for oxygen, the—

(HENRY *suddenly is seized with the symptoms of psychosomatic lockjaw, and seems to be going through his brother's agony.*)

ELLEN (*aghast*). Henry!

(*He overcomes the illusion, breathes heavily, gets control of himself.*)

HENRY (*depleted, but intensely*). If a lightning bolt had struck him, that might have been worthy of the size of the man. But a nick in the finger from a dull razor—what an indignity! What kind of God would drain away such youth and energy and laughter! A sneak attack from the Almighty. (*Turning his face to the sky*) You plagued Job, but you spared him!

Why couldn't you have been as fair with John?

(ELLEN *moves toward him, wants to touch him, to comfort him—but she doesn't.*)

ELLEN. I wonder if—if God lets us be hurt—so we can learn to *transcend* the pain . . . ? (*She speaks very softly and simply.*) In the boat, I didn't understand, really. But is it possible, Henry, that—even though he's stopped *living*, John continues to *be*?

(HENRY *turns and looks at her. She did understand! There is a strong urge in* HENRY *to embrace her; but a stronger reserve, which prevents him.*

The light falls away on them. Another light picks up WALDO, *seated, presumably in his study.* LYDIAN *stands behind him.* HENRY *shifts his weight from one foot to the other as* WALDO *studies him thoughtfully.*)

WALDO. Well, what sort of work would you like to do?

HENRY. Anything. I wish to use my hands.

WALDO. And what about your head?

HENRY. It could be useful. For burrowing, perhaps. (LYDIAN *laughs.*) I could beat it into a ploughshare. It might be a better tool than it's been for thinking.

WALDO. You're giving up *thinking*?

HENRY. For this lifetime, yes.

WALDO (*turning to his wife*). We could certainly use a handyman, Lydian. (*To* HENRY) Mrs. Emerson will assure you that, of all God's creatures, I am the least handy of men. My skill at carpentry stops at cutting cheese.

(*They laugh,* HENRY *a bit uneasily.*)

LYDIAN. There's a great deal that needs doing. The wall by the back meadow needs mending.

HENRY. I am a mason.

WALDO. You are?

HENRY (*quickly*). No, of course I'm not a *Mason*[8]—but I *do* masonry.

WALDO. The weeds are at war with the marigolds. And the last time I looked, the weeds were winning.

HENRY. They're doomed. Being a weed myself, I infiltrate their ranks.

WALDO. What about children, Mr. Thoreau?

HENRY. What about them?

LYDIAN. You've had experience with them?

HENRY. Well, I was a child once myself. Briefly.

LYDIAN (*to* WALDO). It would be so good for Edward—to have someone who could take him boating and hiking . . . (*to* HENRY) Dr. Emerson has so little time to be a father—he's so occupied with his lectures and writing.

HENRY. When I'm with your son, Dr. Emerson, I might turn my brain back on—temporarily.

WALDO. I think this might prove to be a very good arrangement. Of course, there's the matter of compensation.

HENRY. I've been paid. (WALDO *lifts his eyebrows, puzzled.*) With something far more extraordinary than money. And more valuable. The words you

---

8. Mason, a member of the Freemasons, an organization that had certain secret rituals

fling into an audience from the lecture platform—you never know what happens to them, do you? No more than a Roman Emperor knew what happened to the coins he scattered to the crowd as he rode through the streets.

WALDO. The Roman Emperors were trying to buy popularity.

HENRY. And the poor fellows only had gold. No wonder Rome fell! *(Growing more intense)* But I sat on the grass at Harvard Yard and heard you speak for the first time. I was at the very edge of the assembly—but I think I caught more coins than the crowd at the wheels of your chariot.

WALDO *(to LYDIAN)*. This may be interesting, having a Harvard man as a handyman. *(To HENRY)* I'm vain, you know. Of necessity. I'm not as lucky as the Caesars; I have to mint all my own coins. So a man sits at his desk and doubts constantly: is it gold or is it tin?

HENRY. I apologize. It was a faulty metaphor. Money is merely money. You can never spend a thought. It still belongs to you—though it makes other men rich!

WALDO *(accusingly)*. You're thinking, Mr. Thoreau. Incidentally, if we're going to have you around here— you, and your hands, and your head—I can't possibly go on calling you "Mr. Thoreau." Your mother calls you "David," I believe?

HENRY. I call myself "Henry."

WALDO *(dryly)*. My mother called me "Ralph." You may call me "Waldo." *(They laugh and shake hands.)* And

Lydian, of course, is "Lydian." And Edward—where's Edward? *(Calls)* Edward!

LYDIAN. It's important, I think, for you to meet Edward. To be sure that you two are . . . companionable.

WALDO. Why shouldn't they be?

(EDWARD comes on. He is eight, and has the shyness and reserve of the son of a famous father.)

EDWARD *(reporting to his father)*. Yes, sir?

WALDO. A firm handshake, Edward, for Mr. Thoreau. *(EDWARD and HENRY shake hands.)* You're going to be extremely good friends.

HENRY *(easily, but not glibly)*. I don't see why not.

EDWARD *(stiffly)*. How do you do, sir.

(EDWARD is cautious in his friendships.)

LYDIAN. Isn't it nice, Edward—having a new member of the family?

EDWARD *(obediently)*. Yes, ma'am.

LYDIAN *(to her husband)*. But we can't expect Henry to work for the same munificent[9] salary we pay Edward— which is nothing.

WALDO. Not true. Every Saturday morning, wet or fair, Edward gets a shiny new dime.

EDWARD *(surprised)*. I do?

WALDO. Which I promptly put in the bank for him.

LYDIAN *(with a faint smile)*. *Some* weeks he's overpaid.

(The boy laughs—and it is clear that he is more at ease with his mother than with his father.)

---

9. munificent, very generous

WALDO (*dismissing the boy, rather automatically*). That will be all, Edward. Back to your studies.

EDWARD. Yes, Father.

(*The boy scoots off.*)

HENRY (*watching the boy go*). If it will make you feel better, I'll take the same pay as Edward—and try to be worth it.

WALDO. Henry, you're not a very good businessman.

HENRY. I'm not a businessman at all. If you don't pay me a regular salary, then I won't feel obliged to keep regular hours. I love a broad margin to my life . . . (*Quickly*) But I assure you, the work will be done.

WALDO. Then you must have weekly wages . . .

HENRY. But must it be *money*? Could it be—(*He breaks off. There is a soft, leafy-green projection and the distant music of a flute.* HENRY *pauses to hear it.* WALDO *and* LYDIAN *stare at him strangely, as he stares way off, toward* WALDEN, *far in the back of the auditorium or beyond.*) How far does it extend, your back meadow?

WALDO. To the woods.

HENRY. Including the woods?

WALDO. A section of it. To the shore of the pond.

(*The flute music rises, accelerates: the idea is accelerating inside his head.*)

HENRY. Perhaps, some day, if my work has been useful to you, and if we remain friends, I may ask you for a bit of your woods—(*Quickly*) A small square, no bigger than this room.

Not as a gift, I don't want to own it! Simply an understanding between friends—who know that the land really belongs to the woodchucks, anyhow!

LYDIAN. What will you do with it?

HENRY. I'm not quite sure. It's an idea I have . . . an "experiment" . . .

(*The flute melody lingers, then falls away, as does the leafy projection.*)

WALDO. Good thinking, Henry. You're planning 'way up ahead, for your retirement.

HENRY. Retirement? What an absurd idea! Why spend the best part of your life earning money so that you can enjoy a questionable liberty during the least valuable part of it? Why work like a dog so you can pant for a moment or two before you die?

(WALDO *laughs.*)

WALDO. Carlyle told me about an Englishman who went off to India— "Injah," he called it—to make a huge fortune so that he could come back to the Lake Country and live the life of a poet.

HENRY. If there was a poem in him, he should have rushed straight up to his garret.

WALDO. He should have! He died in the Punjab—immensely wealthy, but without a sonnet to his name

LYDIAN. Can Henry have his parcel of woods? For his "experiment"?

WALDO. Well, I don't know what kind of experiment you have in mind. But if the woodchucks don't object, why should I?

HENRY. Thank you, Doctor—uh—*(Corrects himself)*—Waldo.

WALDO *(to his wife).* I don't really have time to make a list of all the things that need doing. Lydian, could you go into the details with Henry—various things that—

HENRY. Don't make a list. *Things* will tell me what needs to be done.

WALDO. Oh, what a relief! The hell of having people help you is that they are constantly completing what you gave them to do—and they come knocking on your door, saying: "What shall I do next?" Always when you are in the midst of doing what you your*self* should be doing next!

HENRY. I respect a man's privacy. I'll never knock at the door of your study.

WALDO. Don't be too much a stranger, Henry. Uh—I might interrupt *your* work now and then—and ask you to help me mend a cracked wall or pull a few weeds in a lecture I'm writing.

HENRY. I'm not a polite man. I'll be as frank with you as I am with the back meadow.

(HENRY leaves. LYDIAN and WALDO stare after him.)

LYDIAN. Not many people will understand that young man. He doesn't want anything.

WALDO. Perhaps he wants too much.

All light falls away, except the moonlight glow on the jail cell. HENRY *walks back into the cell, stands by the barred casement and listens again to the sounds of Concord.* BAILEY *jerks awake, sits up suddenly.*

BAILEY. What time is it?

HENRY. Where were you planning to go?

BAILEY. Back to sleep. But I like to know how much of the night has swum by.

HENRY. In Samarkand, it is not quite noon.

BAILEY. That near Boston?

HENRY. It's as far away from Boston as you can get—before you start coming *back* to Boston again.

BAILEY. I never could figger out how it could be *one* time here and *another* time somewheres else. Isn't it *now* all over?

HENRY. You're wiser than most men who wear watches. I don't know what good it does to hang numbers on the hours. You can't count a river while it moves by you. The best thing to do is take off your clothes and go swimming in it. And when you feel the water all around you, then you're part of the total river—where it's been, where it is, where it's flowing. Plunge in!

BAILEY. I don't swim good.

HENRY. There's no trick to it. Yes, there is. One trick. You can't struggle with the water. If you fling your arms around and thrash and fight the stream, it fights back. And you go under.

(A drunk, laughing incoherently, staggers across the thrust, a mug of ale still in his hand. He drains the mug, thrashes about wildly. BAILEY *rises from his cot, crosses to the window beside* THOREAU. *They both look out.)*

BAILEY. That one's gone pretty far under.

(With the broken melody of a drinking song, the drunk weaves off.)

HENRY. Drowned and drunk with ale and civilization.

BAILEY. Do you drink?

HENRY. Do you?

BAILEY. When I can afford it.

HENRY. It doesn't cost anything to be drunk. It needn't. It shouldn't. A man can be drunk all the time. Where I live, you can get drunk on the air.

BAILEY *(deliciously intrigued).* Where's that? When they let me out, maybe I'll come get drunk with you. When they let *you* out. Where's it at?

HENRY. In the woods. By a pond.

(The flute melody drifts in with a leafy-green projection.)

BAILEY. *Away* from everything?

HENRY. Oh, where I live, I have a great deal of company. But no people.

BAILEY. Don't you get scared? At night—in the dark?

HENRY. Why be afraid? The witches are all hung. Christianity and candles have been invented.

BAILEY. You live there all the time?

HENRY. All the time.

BAILEY *(wistfully).* I wish I had a place to *belong.* It's always been a marvel to me how a man can git the money together to own himself a house that belongs to *him.*

HENRY. Want to hear how much my mansion cost me? Twenty-eight dollars, twelve and a half cents!

BAILEY. Man-a-mighty! I alwuz thought a house cost a fortune. Hundred dollars or more! How do you eat?

HENRY. Very well. I have a bean patch, some Indian corn. Now and then Walden serves me up a fish.

BAILEY. What happens in winter?

HENRY *(starting to take off one shoe).* It snows. So I don't even have to go to the pond for fresh water—just reach out the door for a handful of snow. Melt it, and it's sweet as the sky. *(Flute and woods projections fade.)* Oh, there are a few things you have to get in town. So you walk into town.

(HENRY pulls off his shoe, thrusts his hand into it and pokes his finger through a hole in the sole. Then, one shoe on and one shoe off, he comes into the foreground. The light subsides on the jail cell and BAILEY lies back on his cot in the shadows.

It is late afternoon of a hot July day, and the thrust is the main street of Concord. Several people pass by HENRY. They look questioningly at his curious condition; one shoe on and one shoe off. But HENRY seems oblivious to it. He nods, saluting the passers-by with his shoe. DEACON BALL comes by, looks at HENRY disdainfully.)

BALL. You've condescended to pay a call on civilization, Mr. Thoreau?

HENRY. Briefly. And reluctantly.

BALL. How is life among the savages?

HENRY. If I'm in Concord long enough, Deacon, I may find out.

(Blithely, HENRY salutes him with his shoe and limps on. SAM STAPLES ambles toward HENRY. He has a piece of paper which he holds distastefully.)

SAM *(clearing his throat).* Hullo, Henry.

HENRY. Oh, hello, Sam.

SAM. What's wrong with your foot?

HENRY. Foot's fine. Got a sick shoe. *(He wiggles a finger through the hole in the sole.)* Cobbler'll cure it.

(HENRY starts to walk down the street.)

SAM. Henry. I—uh—got something here for ya.

HENRY. Oh?

SAM *(awkwardly).* I can understand how a man could forget—bein' as busy as you are—out there—uh—writin' about them birds and talkin' to the fish and whatever else it is you do out there by yourself. Naturally it don't occur to you to think much about *taxes.*

HENRY. No, I don't think much of taxes.

SAM. But they gotta be paid.

HENRY. Why?

SAM. It's the law. I ain't blamin' you for bein' forgetful, Henry. May surprise you to learn you ain't paid your tax for two years.

HENRY. Six.

SAM *(firming up).* I got this order. And I got to serve it on ya. Here! *(He thrusts the legal paper on HENRY.)*

HENRY *(with a kind of arrogant calm).* Why, thanks, Sam. *(He takes the document, glances at it, then folds it slowly, creasing it carefully. Then he slides it inside his shoe and pulls the shoe on. He stands on it, tests it with a few steps.)* Fits just fine! Exactly what I needed. I may not have to go to the cobbler after all.

SAM *(irked).* Now, Henry. That there is an official paper. You can't walk over it like that.

HENRY. Why not? Best thing I ever got from the government. Most practical, anyhow.

SAM. Look, it don't pleasure me none, servin' a court order on you. Sometimes this is an unpleasant job!

HENRY. Then quit. If you don't like bein' constable, Sam, resign.

SAM. Somebody's got to do the work of the people.

HENRY. Oh, you work for the people?

SAM. Yes!

HENRY. Well, I'm "people"—and you don't have to work for me. You're *free!* If it'll make you any happier, I'll fire you!

SAM. Lookee here, Henry. You gonna pay up your tax or ain't ya?

HENRY. You pay *your* tax, Sam?

SAM. If I didn't, I'd have to arrest myself.

HENRY. Are you going to arrest *me?*

(There is a long pause. The two men look at each other evenly.)

SAM. I don't *want* to, Henry. But the government gets persnickety about taxes when we got a war goin'. *(Quietly, the blood is beginning to boil within HENRY.)* After all, it ain't a big sum of money. If—if you're hard up, why *I'll* pay it.

HENRY *(erupting).* Don't you dare!

SAM. A loan, just. You can pay me back when—

(Now all the molten outrage within HENRY DAVID THOREAU bursts out like lava from a live volcano.)

HENRY. I will not pay one copper penny to an unjust government! I wouldn't pay the tithe and tariff to the church, so I signed off from the church! Well, I'm ready right now, Sam, to sign off from the government. Where do I sign? Where?

SAM. You can't do that.

HENRY. Why not?

SAM (*lamely*). Well, even the President has to obey the laws!

HENRY. The poor President! What with preserving his popularity and doing his duty, he doesn't know what to do.

SAM. If the majority says—

HENRY. I'm the majority. A majority of one!

BALL (*from the edge of the crowd*). Arrest him!

SAM (*plaintively*). I don't want to arrest him—

HENRY. Go ahead, Constable. An honest man can't come into town to have his shoes fixed. Not even a pair—one shoe—(*He tugs the shoe off his foot, yanks the paper out from inside and brandishes it.*)—without his neighbors coming around to *paw* him with their dirty institutions. (*For the first time,* HENRY *realizes that he is surrounded by a little ring of people, so he addresses them as well as* SAM.) I'll tell you this. If one thousand . . . If one hundred . . . If ten men . . . ten honest men, only . . . If one honest man in this state of Massachusetts had the conviction and the courage to withdraw from this unholy partnership and let himself be locked up in the County Jail, it'd be the start of more true freedom than we've seen since a few farmers had the guts to block the British by the bridge up the road. (*He points off.*)

ANOTHER VOICE. Lawbreaker!

HENRY. What law ever made men free? Men have got to make the law free. And if a law is wrong, by Heaven, it's the duty of a man to stand up and say so. Even if your oddfellow society wants to clap him in a jail.

FARMER. That's revolution!

HENRY. Yes, sir, that's revolution! What do you think happened at Concord Bridge? A prayer meeting? (*Pointing again, emphatically*)

SAM. What are you tryin' to do, Henry? Wipe out all the laws?

HENRY. As many as possible.

FARMER. What's the whole stew about?

SAM. He don't want to pay his tax.

FARMER. Neither do I.

SAM (*pointing to* HENRY). Yeah, but he ain't payin' his.

FARMER. Henry, it would upset your maw if you run amuck ag'in society.

HENRY. Society's "run amuck" against *me.* I'm just going to the cobbler, minding my own business. I ask nothing from the government. Why should it take from me?

BALL. Throw him in jail!

HENRY. What're you waiting for, Sam? Get out the chains. Drag me off to jail.

SAM. There must be somethin' almighty wrong when a man's so willing to go!

HENRY. Sam. It's very simple. What the government of this country is doing *turns my stomach!* And if I keep my mouth shut, I'm a criminal. To my Conscience. To my God. To Society. And to *you*, Sam Staples. You want a dollar from me? If I don't approve the way that dollar's spent, you're not going to get it!

SAM. I swear I can't figger what makes you so ornery, Henry.

HENRY. Have you heard what they're doing down in Washington?

SAM. I—well, I don't have much time for newspapers. And I read slow.

HENRY. Open up your ears, then. Find out what he's up to—your Hired Man in the White House.

SAM. He's not just *my* President; he's yours, too.

HENRY. No, sir. I'm not paying his salary. He's fired!

SAM. You think high of Dr. Emerson, don't you?

HENRY. Usually.

SAM. He's paid his tax.

HENRY. That's his problem. I'm not paying mine.

SAM. All I know is, it ain't fittin' to throw a Harvard Man in jail. 'Specially a Thoreau. A honester man than you, Henry, I never knew.

HENRY. Is that a compliment, Sam?

SAM. Yes, sir.

HENRY. Well, thanks. Now clap me in your Bastille.

(HENRY *puts out his hands to be manacled.* SAM *sighs, looks around at the little cluster of townsmen. He shrugs helplessly, then leads* HENRY *off. There is a shocked pause.)*

FARMER. Somebody better go tell his maw.

WOMAN. But don't let his Aunt Louisa know; she'll have a conniption fit. *(Thinks—then with relish)* I'm gonna go tell her!

(She hurries off. The cluster dissipates in various directions, and the light in the foreground falls away.

HENRY *and* SAM *come into the cell.* BAILEY *is on the cot, covered by a blanket.* HENRY *doesn't realize at first that he has a cellmate.* SAM *carries a ring of keys, which he tosses on the bed, and a well-worn ledger book.* HENRY *looks around.)*

SAM. Ain't much, but it's clean.

*(*BAILEY *emits a loud snore.)*

HENRY. Music, too. Very soothing.

SAM *(as he wets the stub of pencil in his mouth).* Now, Henry, I gotta put down your age.

HENRY. Twenty-nine summers.

SAM *(writing painfully).* Two-nine. Occupation?

HENRY. What do you need that for, Sam?

SAM. If I don't fill this all out correct, the Selectmen don't pay your board.

HENRY *(nodding toward the sleeper).* What's *his* occupation?

SAM. Him? He's a vagrant.

HENRY. So am I.

SAM *(unhappy about the whole thing).* Henry, that's no occupation. That's another charge! Gimme somethin' to put down. What *are* you, exactly?

HENRY. What am I? *(Thinking)* Oh, Ho-er of Beans. Fisherman. Inspector of Snowstorms . . .

SAM *(impatiently).* Them won't do.

HENRY. You want *respectable* trades? Let's see. Pencil-maker—occasionally. Schoolteacher—once. Surveyor. Carpenter. Author—alleged. Huckleberry-hunter—expert …

SAM *(writing).* Carpenter. That'll do.

HENRY. Risky, Sam. You'll shock the clergy if you lock up a carpenter.

SAM *(after a little thought).* It's writ.

(He slaps his ledger book shut and goes off, shaking his head. The lighting in the cell slowly, imperceptibly, turns into night.

There is the urgent jangling of a bell-pull. The lights rise on the EMERSON area. LYDIAN appears in a night-robe. She is reading a note—puzzled and concerned.)

WALDO'S VOICE *(from off).* Who is it? I'll get it.

LYDIAN. I already have, dear.

(WALDO comes on in nightdress, wearing a nightcap.)

WALDO *(sleepily).* I'll get it. I've got it. Oh, Lydian—what are you doing up?

LYDIAN *(to WALDO, indicating the note).* It's about Henry. He's in jail.

WALDO. God help us! Why? What did he do?

LYDIAN. It isn't clear—

WALDO. He murdered Deacon Ball! One of Henry's acts of mercy.

LYDIAN. No—

WALDO. They've found Deacon Ball murdered, and they're accusing Henry!

LYDIAN. Deacon Ball hasn't been murdered.

WALDO. Oh? That's too bad. Let me look at that.

(She hands him the note. Simultaneously, the light rises on MRS. THOREAU, distraught.)

MOTHER. Every night, Louisa. Every night I have this terrible nightmare. I dream that David Henry is in jail. But tonight I didn't even have to go to sleep!

(The light on MRS. THOREAU fades. In the cell, SAM reenters, standing at the cell door.)

SAM. Before I take my boots off for the night, Henry, why don't you pay up an' let me let you outa here?

HENRY *(gently).* Take off your boots, Sam.

(SAM still hesitates. In the EMERSON area, WALDO grows fully awake.)

WALDO. Lydian. I've got to get on my boots. Where's my coat? I've got to go down to Concord Square—! *(He sits, pulling on a pair of high-topped shoes over his naked feet. LYDIAN hands him a black topcoat, which he puts on over his nightshirt.)*

LYDIAN. You're going to go like that?

WALDO. That boy's in trouble!

(He starts out. LYDIAN quickly pulls off his nightcap as WALDO hurries off. The light in the EMERSON area fades.)

SAM *(pleading).* Please pay up, Henry.

(Previously, HENRY has been volcanic. Now the lava has cooled but firmed.)

HENRY. If you call on me to pay for a rifle, Sam, it's the same as asking me to fire it! You're making me as much a killer as the foot-soldier who crash-es across the border into faraway Mexico, charges into his neighbor's house, sets fire to it, and kills his children! *(The two men study each other. Troubled,* SAM *starts to leave.* HENRY *goes to the cot, calls.)* Sam! *(*SAM *races back eagerly, thinking* HENRY *may have changed his mind.)* You forgot your keys. *(He hands* SAM *the ring of keys.)*

SAM *(disappointed).* Oh.

(He takes them, goes out, locks the door. HENRY *stares through the bars, listening to the night silence of the village. From the back of the theatre, as if shouting across Concord Square, a voice breaks the quiet.)*

WALDO. Henry! Henry! What are you doing in jail?

*(*HENRY *turns, faces front, responding to the challenge.)*

HENRY *(defiantly, pointing accusingly across Concord Square).* Waldo! What are you doing *out* of jail?

(The lights fade.)

ACT TWO

The light rises on the jail cell—moon-light casting shadows through the bars at a later angle. No light falls on either cot, but on the space between them. The town clock strikes two. The dim light gradually reveals the forms of the two men, each motion-less, seemingly asleep. HENRY stirs, coughs, gets up restlessly, paces a few times, goes to the barred casement. His hand reaches up in the white clarity of the moonlight. He touches the bars. Then, with a musical fancy, he pretends to pluck each bar as if it were a harp-string.

HENRY *(imitating the sound of a harp-string).* Ting . . . ting . . . ting . . . ting. *(He riffles the bars as if he were doing arpeggios, which he vocalizes idly. Stops suddenly, looks toward his cell-mate.)* In the prison of heaven, that's how the angels make music. *(He paces.)* I am told. *(Paces some more)* Not having been there. *(Paces more)* And not likely to be invited. *(*HENRY *sits on his own cot and talks to the sleep-ing* BAILEY.*)* You know what the gov-ernment said to me, Bailey? "Your money or your life." I won't give it my money. And they think they have my life! *(Laughs a little)* Only my body. I'm a free man. Free to touch my nose if I like. *(He touches his nose.)* Or not. *(He takes his hand down.)* Free to stand. Or free not to stand. They can't lock up my thoughts! What I *believe* goes easily through these walls—as if the stones were air. *(He gestures front—where the wall, in fact, does not exist.)* The state is so afraid of us, Bailey, that it locks us up. The state is timid as a lone woman with her silver spoons! We have fright-ened her out of her wits.

(The light comes up on LYDIAN.*)*

LYDIAN. Henry, you have wits enough to know that, in order to *get* along, you have to *go* along!

*(*HENRY *the volcano erupts again.)*

HENRY *(shouting, contemptuously).* GO ALONG! GO ALONG! GO ALONG!

*(*LYDIAN *has reached for a little straw berry-basket.)*

LYDIAN. Edward? *(The little boy comes*

running to her.) Go along with Mr. Thoreau.

EDWARD. Where are we going?

(HENRY *saunters down from the cell onto the thrust. Rakishly he puts on the wide-brimmed straw hat which he wore before. The thrust becomes a sunny meadow.*)

HENRY. Huckleberry-hunting, my boy! Would you like to study composition with Mozart? Painting with Michelangelo? Study huckleberry-hunting with Thoreau, it's the same thing! (EDWARD *laughs;* LYDIAN *slips off as the huckleberry-hunters parade through the sun-drenched field.*) Now, when I was your age—if I was ever your age—my mother used to bake huckleberry pudding. Best in Concord. But all my mama and my papa and Uncle Charlie and Aunt Louisa and my brother John got—all *they* got—was the pudding. I had the glory of discovering the huckleber-ries! A half-day of wild adventure under the Concord sky.

EDWARD. How do you find huckleber-ries? *I* want to discover some!

HENRY (*imparting a great secret*). Huckleberries are very difficult to find. Because most people think that . . . they're over *there!* (*He makes a dramatic gesture.*)

EDWARD. Should I go over there?

HENRY. No, sir! The *best* huckleberries have a sly way . . . of being . . . exactly . . . where . . . you . . . are . . . standing! Here! (*He bends down quickly, picks an imaginary huckleberry.*) The trick of it is: you have to know where to stand!

EDWARD (*plucking one*). Can I taste one? Right now?

HENRY (*thinking*). Well . . . yes. But for every one you taste, you have to take two home.

EDWARD (*tasting*). Mmmmm . . . They're good! Where's your basket?

HENRY. I use my hat. Since my head is precisely the size of a huckleberry pudding!

(EDWARD *runs about, seeming to gather huckleberries.*)

EDWARD (*shouts*). Here's a whole patch of them!

HENRY. Ahhh, you have talent—no doubt about it.

EDWARD (*running from bush to bush*). Let's race and see who can get the most first.

(*But* HENRY *is no racer. He has paused to savor a particular berry.*)

HENRY (*swallowing, benignly*[10]). *That* was a happy huckleberry!

(*Little* EDWARD *is plunging about, grasping handfuls of huckleberries as fast as he can.*)

EDWARD. Look! I've got more than you have!

HENRY. Everybody does.

(*With deliberate relaxation,* HENRY *is pluck-ing the berries, tossing them in his hat. His ease and calm is in contrast with the boy's bounding energy.* HENRY *seems to be choosing the precise berry at each bush—the one which promises the best flavor.*)

EDWARD. How does a huckleberry get to be a huckleberry instead of a strawberry?

---

10. benign, showing kindness or gentleness

HENRY. Well, there are a number of books on the subject. But *meeting* a huckleberry makes you more of an expert than any botanist who ever wrote a dull book.

(*Now* EDWARD *has completely filled his basket, and comes running joyfully to* HENRY, *to show him.*)

EDWARD. Look! Look, Henry! Mine's all the way to the top. Mama should've given me a bigger basket! (*Suddenly the running boy trips, falls—and the whole basket of berries—imaginary—spills out over the ground.* EDWARD *is aghast at the accident. His bright-eyed ecstasy turns to tears.*) They're all spilled and spoiled!

(HENRY *drops to his knees, puts his arm around the shoulder of the dejected boy, who sobs uncontrollably.*)

HENRY. Don't you know what you've done? You have planted whole patches of huckleberries, for an entire generation of Edward Emersons!

EDWARD. I have . . . ? (*Through his subsiding tears*) How?

HENRY. Because that's the way things are: Nature has provided that little boys gathering huckleberries should, now and then, stumble and scatter the berries. Edward, you have been as helpful as a honeybee!

EDWARD (*now delighted*). Let's pick some more—and *spill* 'em! (*With a grin,* EDWARD *wipes his sleeve across his eyes, reversing his previous misery.* HENRY *pours his hatful of huckleberries into* EDWARD's *basket.* EDWARD *looks up into his face.*) But those are yours . . . !

HENRY (*solemnly*). I surrender title.

EDWARD. What does that mean?

HENRY. Like most of the voodoo of ownership, it means absolutely nothing.

(*The boy takes* HENRY's *hand.*)

EDWARD. Henry, I wish you were my father . . . !

(HENRY *looks at the boy, wishing he were, too, but not saying it. The lighting fades on them and simultaneously rises on* LYDIAN, *who is seated, writing a letter. She looks up as* HENRY *and* EDWARD *walk into the* EMERSON *area.* EDWARD *swings his basket of borrowed huckleberries . . . but carefully!*)

EDWARD (*running to his mother*). These are for you, Mama! (*And he gives the basket to* LYDIAN.)

LYDIAN. My, what a present! Thank you, Edward.

EDWARD (*the honesty forcing it out of him*). I guess—really—you should thank Henry.

LYDIAN (*correcting him*). Mr. Thoreau, dear.

EDWARD. Henry says I should call him "Henry."

HENRY. There's not too much formality in the huckleberry-hunting business.

(*They laugh a little.*)

EDWARD. And, Mama. I've asked Henry to be my father.

(LYDIAN *and* HENRY *look at each other.* HENRY *shrugs, a bit embarrassed.*)

LYDIAN. Oh? What about your real father?

EDWARD. He's never here. He's always 'way on the other side of the ocean, or out somewhere making speeches, or up in his room where I can't disturb him. But Henry—

(A pause)

HENRY. —is here.

(LYDIAN hesitates, then hands the basket back to EDWARD.)

LYDIAN. Take your huckleberries to the kitchen, will you, dear?

(The boy starts off, then turns, at the edge of the light.)

EDWARD *(with a fresh thought)*. If Henry's my father, that means you've got a husband, Mama. Not in England or someplace else all the time, but right here in our house. Wouldn't that be nicer? For you?

(LYDIAN and HENRY exchange glances, and the boy goes off.)

LYDIAN. I—I suppose it isn't wise. For you to keep on working here while Waldo's away.

HENRY. Please don't be afraid of me ...

LYDIAN. Shouldn't I be? *(She gets up, restlessly.)* Oh, you're going to tell me that you have too much respect. For the Sage of Concord.

HENRY. And his wife.

LYDIAN. Respect is based on friendship. And friendship is based on love. And love is so . . . accidental. Isn't it, Henry?

(HENRY moistens his lips.)

HENRY. We love without knowing it. A man—or a woman—can't love on schedule. I don't wake up in the morning and say: "I shall start loving at nine-twenty, and continue until ten-fifteen." Yes, it *is* accidental. And it's everywhere—it's the wind, the tide, the waves, the sunshine.

LYDIAN *(very quietly)*. Henry. If love is all around you, like huckleberries—why do you pick loneliness?

(EDWARD bursts in carrying a protesting live chicken.)

EDWARD. Mama! Henry! Look what happened to the chicken's feet! *(The boy holds up the chicken.)* He's wearing gloves!

LYDIAN. No, Edward, that's not poss—it *is* wearing gloves! *(She turns, puzzled, to HENRY.)*

HENRY *(a little sheepishly)*. The other day you said they were scratching in your garden, uprooting your rose plants. So I gave a little elegance to the ladies of the henhouse. They've scratched their last. Your roses are safe.

LYDIAN *(examining the chicken-gloves)*. You made these for all the chickens?

HENRY. I'm opposed to social distinctions. Once one chicken is gloved, you can't expect the other ladies to go about bareclawed.

(They laugh.)

EDWARD *(eagerly)*. Can I take him out and show him to everybody?

LYDIAN. He's a "she," dear. Yes, I suppose you can.

HENRY. But bring the lady home and latch the gate. If you want an omelette for breakfast.

(EDWARD scurries off with the chicken.)

LYDIAN. My roses thank you.

HENRY. Oh, they're very welcome.

LYDIAN. Get married, Henry. Find a face—and teach yourself to love it.

HENRY. I have. (LYDIAN *looks at him quizzically.*) But I'm a crusty and resolute bachelor. And Nature is my mother-in-law.

LYDIAN. There are so many pretty young girls—

HENRY. I would drive them promptly into old age. I'm not that cruel.

LYDIAN. You need a brain to toss on the pillow next to you. What about Margaret Fuller?

(HENRY *repeats the name, as if he were rinsing it out of his mouth.*)

HENRY. Margaret . . . Fuller . . . ? Oh, I couldn't marry her.

LYDIAN. Why not?

HENRY. Two reasons. First, I'm not stupid enough to ask her. Second, she'd never be stupid enough to accept. (*Turning*) You want to be a matchmaker, Lydian? Find me something innocent and natural and uncomplicated. A shrub-oak. A cloud. A leaf lost in the snow.

LYDIAN. But isn't it lonely, Henry?

HENRY. Lonely! (*He laughs.*) I am no more lonely, Lydian, than the North Star, or the South Wind, or the first spider in a new house. (*Then gently*) What about your loneliness? Is it enough to go to bed each night with nothing but a letter from England? Telling about your husband's overwhelming passion . . . for Carlyle? (*She looks down.* HENRY *reaches out, touching her sleeve.*) Isn't it a pity that you are so "safe" with me?

(*In the cell,* BAILEY *seems in the midst of a conversation.*)

BAILEY. I'm skeered of a trial. I ain't got no lawyer. 'Course the food ain't too bad here. (HENRY *has crossed back into the cell and the lights have faded on* LYDIAN.) Would you be my lawyer?

HENRY (*stops short*). I'm no lawyer!

BAILEY. Couldn't you be one—for me? You talk like a lawyer. And you're smart as most.

HENRY. Bailey, I would give you my coat, or my shoes, or my last peck of beans; I would chop wood for you, or push a wheelbarrow for you. But I would not stoop to being a lawyer for anyone! I think Lucifer was a lawyer: that's why the Devil still gives advice to Presidents.

BAILEY. Who'm I gonna get?

HENRY. If I were God, Bailey—instead of just a speck of Him—I wouldn't let you die away in the dark.

(BAILEY *is panicky. He gets up from the cot.*)

BAILEY. Tell me what to do!

HENRY (*rubbing his chin*). Well, you might try getting yourself born in a more just and generous age. That's not a very practical suggestion. (*Another thought*) I suppose you could try prayer.

BAILEY. I'm not very good at it.

HENRY. Neither am I.

BAILEY. But could you say one for me?

HENRY. Is the Lord so almighty absentminded that He needs a tap on the shoulder—to remind Him that Adam had children?

BAILEY. A prayer couldn't hurt none.

HENRY. All right. Let's send God a telegram. *(He clasps his hands in semi-solemnity.)*

"Blessed are the Young,
For they do not read the President's speeches.
Blessed are they who never read a newspaper,
For they shall see Nature and, through her, God.
And Blessed is Bailey, for he's a good fellow and deserves better treatment than you've been giving him—even though he *is* a man of letters.
Amen."

BAILEY. Amen. Do you think it got through?

HENRY. I wouldn't know. I don't usually pray with words. I prefer a flute.

As BAILEY *sinks back onto his cot, the lights dip in the cell.* HENRY *moves forward into the amber sunlight of the forestage, and the background takes on again the leaf-woven texture of the Walden woods.* HENRY *reaches for a flute and begins to play something strange and peaceful—an unconventional forest idyll. The shadowy figure of a man climbs out of the pit as* HENRY *plays. Crouching, the man creeps through the brush, unseen by* HENRY. *The man is* WILLIAMS, *a black, in dirty, tattered clothes. He is husky but terrified. Still* HENRY *does not notice him, although he thinks he may have been detected—so he darts behind another imaginary bush. With a sigh,* HENRY *puts aside his flute and bends down to reach for something on the ground.* WILLIAMS *thinks he is going for a gun. He leaps into the*

back of the astonished HENRY, *clamping a huge hand over* HENRY*'s mouth.)*

WILLIAMS. You ain't takin' no gun on me!

(Calmly HENRY *rotates the handle of the implement he was reaching for. It is a hoe.* WILLIAMS *relaxes a little, takes his hand off* HENRY*'s mouth.)*

HENRY. You thought this was a rifle? A rifle's no good for hoeing beans. *(He is gentle.)* Mind if I go ahead? *(*WILLIAMS *is afraid, uncertain.)* There isn't a gun within three-quarters of a mile of here. *(*HENRY *is unhanded and begins to hoe. The black man watches.)* What can I do for you?

WILLIAMS. I need vittles. Gimme some vittles!

HENRY. Well, sit down, neighbor. It'll take about three weeks for these beans to come up.

WILLIAMS. By then I'll be sleepin' wi' them beans! I gotta git to Cañada.

HENRY. To where?

WILLIAMS. Cañada. Cañada! North as I kin git! They say the Norther ya git, the *free-er* ya git!

HENRY *(as he hoes).* There's a quarter loaf of bread inside the hut. Help yourself.

*(*WILLIAMS *starts to move in the direction* HENRY *has indicated—then hesitates, turns back.)*

WILLIAMS. You trustin' me to go inside your place? Without you watchin'?

HENRY. Why not? *(*WILLIAMS *pauses—then darts into the shadows while* HENRY *placidly hoes his beans. Then he calls toward the off-stage hut.)* If you want to stay till supper, I'll catch us a fish. What's your name?

(Almost immediately WILLIAMS *reappears with a chunk of bread which he chews on ravenously.)*

WILLIAMS *(his mouth full).* Williams.

HENRY. I'm Henry Thoreau. *(He reaches out his hand.* WILLIAMS *marvels—then reaches out tentatively for* HENRY's *handshake, first wiping his hand on his pantleg.)* Williams your first name or your last name?

WILLIAMS. It's all my name. *(Suddenly)* But I ain't no slave. I ain't goin' back to bein' no slave. No man gonna take me back. *(With fire)* I *borned* myself two weeks ago.

HENRY. Good for you, Mr. Williams.

WILLIAMS. I belonged to Mr. Williams. I was Mr. Williams' Williams. No more. *(*HENRY *studies him.* WILLIAMS *is wary.)* You gonna turn me in?

HENRY. I've got no more stomach for slavery than you do. Here you're as free as I am.

*(*WILLIAMS *begins to breathe more easily. He looks around.)*

WILLIAMS. How come you live like a black man? In a slave shack?

HENRY *(laughs).* Maybe to prove that *less* is *more.* You see, I'm really very wealthy; I just don't have any money, that's all.

WILLIAMS *(still suspicious).* Where's your wife? An' chillun?

HENRY. Well, my bride is this bean patch, Mr. Williams. And I've adopted several woodchucks. And a few rather unappreciative squirrels.

WILLIAMS. Nobody "Mistered" me before—not ever.

HENRY. You better get used to it. If you're going to be a free man. You'll have to have a first name, too—oh, you don't have to. But it's handy.

WILLIAMS *(tentatively).* Henry, maybe . . . ? Could I call myself "Mr. Henry's Williams" . . . ?

HENRY. No!

WILLIAMS *(startled).* Why you shoutin' at me?

HENRY. You don't belong to anybody, sir. Except yourself. Least of all to me. Watch out—or you'll run right into what you're running away from.

WILLIAMS *(tasting it).* Henry . . . Williams . . .

HENRY. If you don't like the fit of that, there's a David in my name; you can have it, I don't use it much.

WILLIAMS. I like Henry Williams! That sound good! That's a *free* man's name! *(He cups his hands and shouts.)* HENRY WILLIAMS!

HENRY. But there's slavery in the North, too. Every man shackled to a ten-hour-a-day job is a work-slave. Every man who has to worry about next month's rent is a money-slave. Don't let that happen to you, Mr. Williams. Keep free!

WILLIAMS. I *do* feel free—here—now! With you. Never before. I hain't scared now.

HENRY. Why should you be?

WILLIAMS *(abruptly).* You let me stay here? I'll work. Take my chances with the law. I'm good at hidin'! Nobody know I'm here!

HENRY. I welcome you here. But ...you've got to find your *own* Walden, Henry Williams! Where they don't have sickening laws which keep black men in suppression. Here in Massachusetts, the color of your face is a flag. You can't hide blackness in blindness. If you want any light in your life, you'll have to find a place to live where men think of themselves as men—not as white men. *(Putting his hand on* WILLIAMS' *shoulder.)* Go to "Canyada"!

(The light fades on the black man and the white man in the foreground. In the EMERSONS' *area, the light picks up* WALDO *in the midst of an argument. His stance is twisted—almost a contortion—as if he were trying to stand simultaneously on opposite sides of a question—which he is.)*

WALDO. I have cast my vote! I've done it. I put it in the ballot box. What more do you expect me to do?

*(*HENRY *moves into the scene.)*

HENRY *(aflame with indignation).* Cast your whole vote. Not just a strip of paper! Your whole influence!

WALDO *(turning).* We have to go along with the majority—!

HENRY *(exasperated).* "Go along!"

WALDO *(reasonably).* Henry, one must consider the economic and sociological ramifications. When white people and black try to live together, it's infinitely complicated.

HENRY *(pounding his fist in the palm of his hand).* Then simplify! Simplify!

WALDO *(shaking his head).* You complicate things all the more by *rushing* them. You're a naturalist, Henry. You understand the slow evolving of the seasons. It's the same with human relationships. You can't rush a sunrise.

HENRY *(with tethered anger).* When a man leaps from a moving freight train—and tries to scramble through the woods to cross the border into Cañada—

WALDO. Where?

HENRY *(impatiently).* Into Canada! A free-er country even though they still have the Crown. But they *don't* have a Fugitive Slave Law. When a man, at the border of freedom, is stopped by the rifle of a Boston policeman, he doesn't have time for Dr. Emerson's leisurely sermon on "the slow evolving of the seasons."

WALDO. Henry, I am just as shocked at the death of this man as you are. What was his name?

HENRY *(quietly).* Henry Williams. A new man. With a new name. Hardly used!

WALDO. I am just as concerned—

HENRY. Are you? To you, Henry Williams is an abstraction. You may be able to use him sometimes as a digression in a Lyceum lecture.

WALDO. How can you be so unpleasant to me when I'm trying to agree with you?

(The fever between the men is rising.)

HENRY. I expect more from you than from anybody else; that's why I'm more disappointed in you.

WALDO. Well, *what* do you expect of me?

HENRY. Speak out!

WALDO. I speak.

HENRY. It's not enough. Shout!

WALDO. I am not a shouter.

HENRY. Not with your voice-box! With your brain! Waldo, *I* can't reach anybody. I can't catch the attention of people. Nobody listens to me. *(Passionately)* But my God, you are EMERSON! *(There are almost tears in* HENRY's *eyes as he experiences a mixture of admiration and contempt for his idol.)* Darling of the Lyceum, Lord of the Lecture Circuit! Every word you say from the platform is treasured, like an heirloom. Stand up, Waldo, and say what you believe!

WALDO *(distantly).* Sometimes I think I invented you, Henry. Or at least prophesied you. Because you *live* what I talk about. I couldn't exist the way you do, Henry; I like my warm toast and tea and soft-boiled egg brought to me on a tray in bed each morning. Whenever I even *think* of Walden, I get a cold. But I admire you, Henry, I really do. You're my walking ethic!

*(*HENRY *stares at* WALDO, *marveling at how he can drift off the point.)*

Those are the exact words I used to describe you to Carlyle. Did you know that I told Carlyle about you?

HENRY *(frustrated, turning away).* I don't care what you told Carlyle.

WALDO. I said to Carlyle: "Of all the men in Concord, Henry Thoreau is the best of the lot!" That's what I told him. *(Enjoying quoting himself)* "A poet as full of buds of promise as a young apple tree." That's what I said.

HENRY. Waldo, don't talk *about* me—talk *to* me. Listen to me.

WALDO *(his thoughts still in England).* Whu?—How was that?

HENRY *(evenly).* Can you lie in bed every morning? Have your breakfast brought to you—your soft-boiled egg, your toast and tea? Can you lift your right hand to your mouth while your left hand—which is also you—your government—is killing men in Mexico? How can you swallow, Waldo? How can you taste? How can you breathe? You cast your ballot with your right hand—but has your left hand killed Henry Williams, running to be free?

WALDO. Because I don't rant like Jeremiah, do you think I'm not outraged? I do what *can* be done!

HENRY. That's not enough. Do the impossible. That's what you tell people in your lectures. But you don't really believe any of it, do you? You trundle up and down New England, stepping to the lectern with that beneficent smile, accepting the handshake of mayors and the polite applause of little old ladies. You go on singing your spineless benedictions.

WALDO. What I say is not spineless!

*(*LYDIAN *enters, drawn by their raised voices.)*

HENRY. Well, occasionally you've sounded a battle-cry. But you—you yourself—refuse to hear it.

WALDO *(squirming).* You are a very difficult man!

HENRY. Good. The world is too full of *easy* men.

WALDO. Do you want me to go out and advocate violence and rebellion?

HENRY. I ask you to *stop* violence. As for rebellion, do you think this country was hatched from a soft-boiled egg? *(Gesturing)* Look around Concord; what do you see? We have *become* everything we protested against!

WALDO. And what are you doing about it, young man? You pull the woods up over your head. You resign from the human race. Could your woodchucks, with all their wisdom, have saved Henry Williams? Are your fish going to build roads, teach school, put out fires?

(For a moment, HENRY is caught without a ready reply.)

Oh, it's very simple for a hermit to sit off at a distance and proclaim exactly how things should be. But what if everybody did that? Where would we be?

HENRY. Where *are* we, Waldo?

WALDO. We are at war. I am aware of it.

HENRY. Are you aware of the reasons—slave-holders grasping for more slave territory? *More* slavery and less freedom, is that what you want?

WALDO. Henry, we must work within the framework of our laws. The end to this war—the condition of the blacks—this is the business of the President. And the Congress.

HENRY. Do you really believe that? Then I guess I'm wrong. I thought you had the same disgust that I have for what the military is doing. But if it doesn't trouble you, then I must've made a mistake. *(With acid sarcasm)* You're right to keep still. I'll go back to the woods—and leave you at peace with your war.

(WALDO is in genuine pain. He glances at his wife.)

WALDO *(after a pause).* All right, my young conscience. What shall I do?

HENRY. Declare yourself!

(Another pause)

WALDO. I will. Absolutely. The next time the occasion arises—

HENRY *(fiercely).* NOW! A year ago was too late! I'll get you an audience. This afternoon. At Concord Square!

(HENRY strides out of the light. WALDO, troubled, looks at LYDIAN in silence. The light falls away on the EMERSONS. A bell-rope drops from the flies[11] as the light comes up on the thrust. HENRY springs up, grasps the rope, and swings on it. A bell from above peals, a reverberating command. People begin to assemble, curious and excited.)

FARMER *(running on).* Fire someplace?

WOMAN. What's the news? Is the war over?

SAM. What you doin' up there, Henry? What's goin' on?

(There is a growing babble of voices as the crowd gathers. HENRY lets go of the rope as the swinging bell dies away.)

HENRY. Dr. Emerson's coming. To speak. He's promised to make a statement! Now. Right here. Can't wait!

---

11. fly, the space above the stage, often used for storage

The Night Thoreau Spent in Jail by Jerome Lawrence & Robert E. Lee

MOTHER (*rushing on*). Oh, David Henry! Are you riling everybody up again?

HENRY. Emerson is going to rile up the whole country. And you're going to hear it first!

FARMER. Is he going to say something or give a sermon?

(HENRY *laughs, jubilantly.*)

HENRY. Both! God willing!

(*Others are gathering.*)

SAM. Dr. Emerson gonna speak now?

HENRY. I just left him! He's on his way.

(*There is a babble of anticipation. One man—probably a local newspaperman—draws out a pad and pencil, prepared to write.*)

VOICE. And no lecture charge, neither!

(*There is a pause as they wait. They're getting a little restless.*)

WOMAN. Well, where is he?

(*Several start to go. The reporter puts away his pad.*)

HENRY (*confidently*). Don't worry! He's coming. He'll be here!

(LYDIAN *enters slowly, her head down. The crowd falls back to let her through. She comes up to* HENRY. *Silently she looks into his face. She clears her throat.*)

LYDIAN. Dr. Emerson has asked me to tell you—

HENRY (*gray*). Yes?

LYDIAN. —that he wants more time to meditate on these matters. (HENRY *does not move, merely stares at her.*) So that he can write a careful essay setting forth his position.

HENRY. And he gave his wife the happy job of coming here to tell us? Like a walking written-excuse to a schoolmaster, saying: "So sorry, Johnny cannot come today, he's in bed with the croup"?

(LYDIAN *shares* HENRY's *feeling, but her loyalty to her husband is unshakable.*)

LYDIAN. Waldo wants to collect his thoughts.

HENRY (*outraged*). What is this, the winter of our *content*? By the time he "collects his thoughts," they'll be dead as dandelions under the snow.

(*The crowd is restless and begins to disintegrate.*)

FARMER. Well, we come running to the fire, but nobody lit it. That's Henry for ya.

(*As the crowd wanders off,* HENRY *stares at* LYDIAN. *Slowly, he turns away from her and starts to go, too.*)

LYDIAN (*stopping him*). Henry—my husband loves you—as much as any man can love another man   . . .

(HENRY *stops, but his back is still to* LYDIAN.)

HENRY (*shaking his head*). My God, he was my god! No more! If he is the Deity, I am a doubter!

LYDIAN. Why do you enjoy hurting him?

HENRY (*wheeling on her*). He hurts *me!*

(*They are both talking at once, their speeches overlapping.*)

LYDIAN. He cares what you think, and so he gets excited and overstates himself—

HENRY. Patronizing, that's what he is. I won't sit at the foot of his pulpit!

LYDIAN. When he talks to you—

HENRY. He never talks to me! Was he talking to me just now? *(Bitterly)* He was in England, pontificating with Carlyle!

LYDIAN. You widen the distance—

HENRY. It's a waste of breath, talking to your husband. Trying to have a sane discussion with him. I lose my time, almost my identity—

LYDIAN. I hear you both. You wrangle and tussle like boys in a cricket match. Hitting and pushing and kicking each other—not for the sake of the idea, just playing to *win!*

HENRY *(coldly).* Your husband, Mrs. Emerson, has the misfortune of being a gentleman. And famous. And he is drowning in his own success.

LYDIAN. My husband's best friend doesn't even know who my husband *is!* You've drawn some ideal in your mind, some imaginary Waldo—the way you want him to be. Please, Henry, give him the same liberty he gives you—to be what you are.

(HENRY looks down, doesn't answer. Everyone has gone now. LYDIAN would like to say, "I'm sorry, HENRY, I wish I could comfort you"— but she doesn't. Quickly, LYDIAN moves off. HENRY looks around at the empty square which was recently so full of people.)

HENRY *(shouts).* Citizens of Concord!— *(But he is talking to the wind. Frustrated, he casts about for some way to reach the ears of a deaf public. He sees the dangling bell-rope, leaps up to ring it—and though he swings on it with the weight of his whole body, there is no sound whatsoever! THE BELL DOES NOT RING!*

Stunned, he pulls more frantically. Nothing.) How do we make a sound? How do we break the silence?

*T**he light falls away on the discouraged and disheartened* HENRY. *The bell-rope vanishes in the flies. He throws himself on his cot in the cell.*

The sky goes red. HENRY *writhes on the cot. There is a cannon blast—and the sky seems ripped apart by psychedelic splatterings of shrapnel.*

A snare drum snarls a military cadence. A drummer boy marches on, turns smartly front. The face is EDWARD EMERSON's. *A* SERGEANT *comes on, in the Federal uniform of the 1840's. It is* SAM STAPLES.

SERGEANT (SAM) *(as if drilling troops).*
Forward to Mexico . . . March!

Hate-two-three-four!

Hate-two-three-four!

Hate-two-three-four!

(The SERGEANT *prods* BAILEY *awake with a rifle butt.* BAILEY *staggers to attention. The* SERGEANT *puts a military cap on* BAILEY *and flings a musket into his hands. With the eternal imprecision of the civilian-soldier,* BAILEY *marches around the thrust to the insistent beat of the snare drum. The* FARMER, *uniformed, becomes part of the marching company.* BALL *appears, in a* GENERAL's *epaulets and gold braid. He mounts the box, as if it were a military reviewing stand.)*

GENERAL (BALL) *(In the drum-cadence).*
Learn to kill!

Learn to kill!

Learn to kill

so you won't be killed!

(This entire sequence has the blurred and overlapping quality of a nightmare, Goya-esque. It is a Walpurgisnacht[12], a bad trip, a surrealistic mixing of hallucinations. Time, space, sound are wrenched awry.)

BAILEY *(out of the rhythm).* I ain't gonna shoot at them; they done nothin' to me!

(All turn on BAILEY.*)*

VARIOUS VOICES. Coward!

Slacker!

Traitor!

Deserter!

GENERAL (BALL). Heathen!

SERGEANT (SAM). Vagrant!

(There is a great explosion of gunfire, and all drop to their bellies for cover. Shouts and confusion.)

GENERAL (BALL) *(Pointing to* HENRY *on his cot).* Why doesn't that man have a gun?

SERGEANT (SAM) *(shaking* HENRY*'s shoulder).* Wake up, Henry. I got somethin' here for ya. Wake up!

HENRY. I don't want it!

(But the SERGEANT *forces a musket into his hands. Dazed, as if walking through syrup,* HENRY *comes to his feet. He holds the musket at arm's length distastefully.)*

GENERAL (BALL). The purpose of this action is to stop the enemy from protecting themselves from the enemy.

HENRY *(helplessly defiant).* I won't go!

MOTHER. That's a good boy, David Henry. Always do the right thing. Even if it's wrong.

(The snare drum has continued, building snappishly. But HENRY *moves arhythmically,*

his march out of sync with all the rest.)

SERGEANT and **SOLDIERS** *(whispered).* Hate-two-three-four! Hate-two-three-four!

(The PRESIDENT *appears in a morning coat and striped pants. It is* WALDO.*)*

GENERAL (BALL). Mr. President, the military advises that we conquer the entire territory. Level them all to rubble! Are you prepared to go along?

ALL VOICES *(a kind of demoniac glee).*

Go along!

Go along!

Go along!

Go along!

*(*HENRY *rushes up to the* PRESIDENT. *He tries to talk, excitedly, urgently. But although his mouth is working, no sound comes out.)*

PRESIDENT (WALDO) *(loftily, to the* GENERAL*).* Is this man saying something? I can't hear him.

*(*HENRY *tries to stop the other marchers, one by one; but no one pays any attention.)*

GENERAL (BALL). *What are your instructions, Mr. President?*

PRESIDENT (WALDO). I wish more time to collect my thoughts. So I am going to appoint a committee to appoint a committee to appoint a committee.

---

12. . . . Goya-esque. It is Walpurgisnacht, Spanish painter Francisco Goya (1764-1828) created powerful, gut-wrenching images of war. Walpurgisnacht is a mythical German event in which the dead emerge and romp the eve before the feast day of St. Walpurgis.

(Cheers)

Get to the bottom of this, so the top will know what to do!

(A swarthy Mexican soldier [WILLIAMS] comes on with a Mexican flag.)

SERGEANT (STAPLES). There he is, boys, there's the enemy!

(All muskets swing toward the Mexican; he is like a trapped animal.)

HENRY *(shouts).* Run, Henry Williams! Run for it!

(The Mexican soldier [WILLIAMS] leaps into the midst of the Federal troops, darts a zig-zag path among them, brandishing his banner. Rifles crack at him, shots ring wildly, the smoke continues to rise. Then WILLIAMS jumps off the thrust and disappears.)

VOICE. He got away!

HENRY *(jubilant).* He's safe!

(All of the Federal troops turn toward HENRY accusingly. At the same time, they realize that the drumbeat has stopped. The little drummer boy [EDWARD] has fallen wounded across his drum. HENRY runs to the stricken boy, lifting him like the Pietà.[13] Then he looks toward the statuesque PRESIDENT [WALDO].)

HENRY. Mr. President! He only wanted to pick huckleberries!

(The PRESIDENT is still benign, impervious to the confusion and the smoke.)

PRESIDENT (WALDO). I proposed to write a careful essay, setting forth my position.

(The rumbling of cannon and the crack of muskets continue. HENRY flings the musket away, then casts about pleading to the air with his empty hands.)

HENRY. Please! Somebody say something! Somebody speak out!

UNSEEN VOICE. Mr. Speaker. Gentlemen of the Congress! *(Everything on stage freezes, in whatever tortured position it is, as in stopped action. HENRY listens with animal intentness.)* "This unnecessary war was unconstitutionally commenced by the President, who may be telling us the Truth—but he is not telling the *Whole* Truth. He has swept the war on and on, in showers of blood. His mind, taxed beyond its powers, is running about like some tortured creature on a burning surface!" *(With passion)* Stop the war, Mr. President! For the love of God, *stop this war!*

(The figures of the battlefield begin to move again in weird, grotesque slow motion, as if mired and helpless in quicksand. But on HENRY's face there is a look of vast relief: someone has spoken!)

HENRY. I do not know you, Mr. Congressman. I doubt if the people of Illinois will re-elect you, because you refused to "go along." But *I* shall remember who you are, Congressman Lincoln.

(Deafening artillery fire peaks in volume. There are great flashes of light, the arcing of mortar shells, the staccato splattering of bullets. The Federal troops form into a ragged line of attacking infantrymen. They point their muskets front and move slowly forward, advancing on the audience as if it were the enemy. HENRY wanders, aghast at the bloodshed.)

---

13. the Pietà, a Christian image of a seated Mary holding the dead Jesus across her lap. The artist Michelangelo (1475–1564) created the scene in a famous marble sculpture, now in the Vatican in Italy.

On a bellowed command from the SERGEANT [SAM STAPLES] *all the troops drop to one knee, and raise their rifles to fire. Then we see, for the first time, in the second rank of troops a familiar face: it is* HENRY's *brother* JOHN, *in full Federal uniform. When* HENRY *sees* JOHN, *he pushes his way through the troops to run to him.)*

HENRY. John! John! (*And just as he reaches* JOHN, *there is a fusillade of shots, a ricocheting bullet.* JOHN *is hit. He flings his arms to the sky in pain, and falls. The troops crash about in all directions, scattering to clear the area, leaving* HENRY *with the dying* JOHN *on the battlefield in the stagnant smoke. Utterly shattered,* HENRY *cradles* JOHN's *head in his arms.)* Don't die! Not again, God—don't let him die!

(The whole stage fades into darkness.)

(Six chimes from the bell tower. Across the sky there is the faint gray line of dawn. BAILEY *is on his cot,* HENRY *lies in twisted, restless sleep as* SAM STAPLES—*no longer a sergeant—enters with mugs and tin plates, which he puts on the box. From now on, all are in their customary clothing.* STAPLES *shakes* HENRY's *shoulder.)*

SAM. Wake up, Henry. I got something here for ya. Wake up.

*(*HENRY *thrashes, still half-dreaming.)*

HENRY. I don't want it!

SAM. Well, the porridge ain't very good. But the cocoa's hot.

HENRY (*coming painfully awake).* Oh. Morning, Sam. Is it morning?

SAM. Yeah. Here's yer pint of chocolate. Ya heard the news?

HENRY. What news?

SAM. It's finished.

HENRY. The war?

SAM. That wire they been stretchin' clean to Texas. And it works. Now a fella in New York can send words down there 'lectric—fast as he can talk.

HENRY (*as he sips his chocolate thoughtfully).* But Sam, what if nobody in New York has anything to say to anybody in Texas?

SAM. I just thought you'd be happy to know. Another thing—uh—(*Clearing his throat)*—uh—you can leave, Henry. Any time you're a mind to.

HENRY. Leave?

SAM. During the night yer tax got paid up.

HENRY. Who did it?

SAM. Hain't material fer me to say.

HENRY. Waldo! Did Dr. Emerson pay it?

SAM. No sir.

HENRY. My mother.

SAM. No.

HENRY. Did you?

SAM. I offered, Henry. You flat refused.

HENRY. Mrs. Emerson. Did she come and pay it?

SAM. Now stop pokin' around tryin' to get me to tell. I promised your Aunt Louisa I wouldn't open my—

HENRY (*disgusted).* Aunt Louisa! (BAILEY *is beginning to stir.)* I am cursed with the charity of my mother's sister! (*Shouting offstage to her)* Aunt Louisa, why couldn't you leave your nose and your false teeth out of my life! I hereby EXCOMMUNICATE YOU FROM THE MILKY WAY!

(SAM *swings the jail door open, hands* HENRY *a paper.*)

SAM. Been nice havin' ya with us, Henry. Here's the receipt.

(HENRY *ignores the paper.*)

HENRY. I don't want it. You can't accuse *me* of paying my tax!

SAM. It's been paid!

HENRY. Not by me. I'm still guilty.
(HENRY *sits on the cot, doggedly.*)

SAM. Henry, a man's got no right to stay in jail if they's no charge ag'in him. I can't even bring you lunch.

BAILEY (*a bit wistfully*). You goin' already?

SAM. He's goin'!

HENRY. No!

SAM. Law put you in here. The law says when you're out.

BAILEY. Gonna be God-a'mighty quiet around here ... (HENRY *stares intensely at* BAILEY.) What's wrong?

HENRY (*softly*). Everything's wrong— when a man only thinks about himself. (*Wheeling sharply on* SAM) Sam! You know what *quid pro quo* means?

SAM (*pained*). That one of them Harvard words?

HENRY. It means if you see to it that Bailey gets his trial—not in another three months, or another three weeks, but now, right away—why, then maybe I'll favor your law by walking out onto the sidewalk. Not before.

SAM. It ain't in my power. I don't make decisions like that.

(HENRY *gets back into his cot, pulls the blanket over himself.*)

HENRY. Goodnight, Sam.

SAM (*suffering*). It's morning, Henry.

HENRY. Not for me. Not until you let Bailey out.

SAM. I'll do everything I kin. I'll talk to the Judge and the Selectmen.

HENRY. Tell them unless Mr. Bailey's trial is right away, they'll have another eating, non-paying guest in their jail—permanently!

(SAM *goes out, almost wishing he were a soldier in Mexico.* BAILEY *is moved. Nobody in his life has ever stood up for him like this.*)

BAILEY. Thankee. I ain't ever gonna fergit this night here. And—when I'm out—I'm gonna come visit you, if you don't mind—at your pond place.

(*The sound of the flute reenters, but there is no leafy projection—only the mounting flames of dawn. Pause.* HENRY *is making a difficult decision. He comes down, staring far off, toward Walden.*)

HENRY. I may not be there at the "pond place," Bailey. Seems to me I've got several more lives to live. And I don't know if I can spare any more time for *that* one.

BAILEY. Sounds to me like it's just about perfick.

HENRY. That's the trouble. If I live there much longer, I might live there forever. And you have to think twice before you accept heaven on terms like that. (*Abruptly*) You ever take a boat trip, Bailey?

BAILEY. Riverboat only.

HENRY. When you buy a cabin ticket for an ocean passage, they give you the liberty of the whole ship. It's a privilege that should be *used*. Man shouldn't stay the whole voyage just in one place, below decks, no matter how dry and cozy it is. And warm. *(Simply)* I think I'll have to roam the whole ship. Go before the mast! Stand out there on the foredeck. *(The flute melody falls away.)* Bailey, I tried to escape. But escape is like sleep. And when sleep is permanent, it's death. *(A pause. He moves closer to the imagined downstage window, so the morning sun fills his face.)* I must leave Walden. *(The words are painful to him.* BAILEY *goes toward* HENRY *as if to comfort him, raising a hand toward his shoulder; but* BAILEY *is helpless.)* It's not necessary to be there in order to *be* there.

*(*BAILEY *moves to the window, prompted by the growing light on* HENRY*'s face. He looks out, awed.)*

BAILEY. Bright morning. Gonna be a fine July day out there.

HENRY. Sometimes the light gets so bright it puts your eyes out. And then it's just darkness all over again. *(He looks up. The sky is really brilliant with the sunlight now.)* But there is more day to dawn. The sun is only a morning star.

(He shakes hands with BAILEY, *starts out, remembers something: his shoe. He gets it from under the bed, salutes* BAILEY *with it.*

In the doorway, HENRY *stops, looks up sharply.*

From a distance, he hears an eccentric, non-military drummer.

He moves into Concord Square ablaze with morning light. Suddenly the drumbeat comes from a different direction, growing in volume. It is like thunder all around him.

His eyes follow the arc of the sky. He seems to grow in stature, lifted and strengthened by a greater challenge.

He waves to BAILEY, *who waves back warmly from the cell window.*

With determination, HENRY *leaps from the stage and strides up the aisle of the theatre to the sound of his own different drummer.*

No curtain falls. The lights do not fade, but grow brighter. During the curtain calls, and as the audience leaves the theatre, HENRY*'s distinctive and irregular drum-cadence builds and resounds.)*

The Night Thoreau Spent in Jail

Responding to the Play

1. How would you describe Henry's beliefs?
2. Do you think Henry was justified in refusing to pay his taxes? Why or why not?
3. How are Henry and Waldo alike? How are they different?
4. Deacon Ball represents Concord society. How would you characterize him?
5. Draw a thumbnail sketch of the set you envision for this play.

More About Thoreau

Henry David Thoreau (1817-1862) was born in Concord, Massachusetts, where this play is set. He returned there after graduating from Harvard, and worked as a lead-pencil maker, teacher, tutor, and surveyor. He also published a few poems, a travel book, and an essay entitled "Civil Disobedience" (1849), which argued the right of citizens to withhold taxes in protest against government policies. He is best known, however, for undertaking a life in the woods at Walden Pond, just outside Concord.

Thoreau wrote a book about his two-year stay at Walden, where he built himself a hut, did some farming, and explored the surrounding wildlife. He called it *Walden, or Life in the Woods.* His writings from Walden Pond offered a direct challenge to the cultural values and materialism of established society.

In 1854, when *Walden* was published, it attracted little attention. But in the years since, it has come to be known as a philosophical and literary classic. Today, Thoreau ranks among America's most respected philosophers, naturalists, and ecologists.

Creating and Performing

1. Improvise the scene in which John asks Ellen to marry him.
2. Use cardboard, foam board, or wood to make a model of the coffin/boat/box used in the play.
3. Read about an important decision or action taken by an historical figure or a person in the news. Then write and perform a monologue in which the person discusses his or her actions.

The Play as Literature: Stereotype

The joke begins, "a yuppie and a farmer were sitting in a lifeboat." When you hear it, you know, or think you know, what to expect of each character. That's because stories in general, and comedies in particular, often use *stereotypes,* or broad generalities about people, as a sort of shorthand. Chances are that no real person fulfills all the characteristics of a stereotype. Yet the composite picture it provides can offer writers a quick way to comment on a profession, a social class, or a way of life.

As you read *The Love Doctor,* be aware of the stereotypes the play employs and the ways in which they are used to poke fun at human foibles.

The Play as Theatre: Physical Comedy

Comedy is a way for both playwrights and audience members to deal with the ridiculous side of life. Its power comes from the unexpected: the foolish emperor, the servant in charge, the sleek aristocrat who falls on his face.

Physical comedy is the most immediate and accessible form of comedy; people of all ages and backgrounds understand what it is to trip over a shoelace, swat at a fly and miss, or save themselves  from falling by performing a series of ridiculous stunts. Physical comedy calls for broad movement and lots of expression.

WARM UP!

With your classmates, come up with a list of easily stereotyped professions and social situations. Then form small groups. Take turns trying to perform scenes that include a profession or situation on the list—without resorting to stereotypes.

THE LOVE DOCTOR

by Molière

Adapted by Marvin Kaye

CHARACTERS

SGANARELLE
LUCINDA, Sganarelle's daughter
LISETTE, Lucinda's maid
CLITANDER, Lucinda's lover
LUCRECE, Sganarelle's niece
MADEMOISELLE AMINTE, Sganarelle's neighbor
REDEW, merchant
LAPIDARE, merchant
DOCTORS BLABBER, BLEEDER, GRUMBLE,
MUMBLE and LASTGASP
A QUACK
A NOTARY

SGANARELLE *is discovered at his home in Paris with* LUCRECE, *his niece; his neighbor* AMINTE; *and the merchants,* REDEW *and* LAPIDARE. SGANARELLE *is frantically pacing.*

SGANARELLE. What am I going to do? I only had one wife and now she's dead.

REDEW. But you only get one at a time.

SGANARELLE. And now I don't have any. True, I argued with her all the time. If she walked into the room right now, in two seconds we'd be fighting. But still, I miss her. What's worse, my daughter Lucinda is so down in the dumps, I'm worried for her health. That's why I asked you all to stop by—*(Indicating each in turn)*—my niece Lucrece, neighbor Aminte, and you, my fellow merchants. Tell me how to cheer up my daughter.

REDEW. Fix up her room. Redecorate it tastefully.

LAPIDARE. Better yet, buy her some jewels.

AMINTE. Don't be silly. She's mooning over that chap, Clitander. Marry them off.

LUCRECE. What a horrible idea! My cousin's too frail. Childbirth would kill her. Send her to a convent, uncle, if you want to save her life.

SGANARELLE. Why, you scoundrels! Redew, you tell me to redecorate, and you're an upholsterer. *(To* LAPIDARE*)* "Buy her jewels," you say, Lapidare, and guess what business you're in? *(To* AMINTE*)* Your lover is interested in my daughter. No wonder you tell me to marry her to Clitander! *(To* LUCRECE*)* And you, my own flesh and blood, you're worst of all! You know I have no intention of letting my daughter marry anybody, but that's not good enough for you, is it? You think if she were exiled to a convent, you might have a chance of becoming my heir. You're all rascals and scavengers! Get out of my house! (*The four swiftly exit,* SGANARELLE *muses alone.*) I'm baffled. How can I help my poor child? (*Enter* LUCINDA) Ah, there you are. (*She sighs.*) Sad, Lucinda? What's wrong? Is there anything I can do? (*She sighs.*) You're breaking my heart, child! Tell Daddy what's wrong. I'll make it better. (*She heaves her deepest sigh yet, which makes him lose his temper.*) Now cut that out! I'm not a mindreader. Tell me what's wrong and Daddy will try to fix it! (*She maintains a sullen silence.*) Is there anything I can buy you, Lucinda, to make you feel better? The necklace you liked last week? (*She shakes her head.*) Maybe your bedchamber's too drab? Would you like it redecorated? (*She shakes her head. He grows angry.*) What if I pack you off to the Convent of the Sad Virgin?

LUCINDA (*gasping*). No!

SGANARELLE (*slyly*). I don't suppose it's just that you'd like to get married? (*She nods vigorously.*) No, I didn't think that was it.

(*Enter* LISETTE, LUCINDA'*s maid*)

LISETTE. Well, master, have you figured out what ails her?

SGANARELLE. No. She's driving me crazy.

LISETTE. Let me give it a try. Mistress Lucinda, maybe you're too shy to talk to your father, but you can't be afraid to talk to me. Just whisper what's wrong. (LUCINDA *murmurs in her ear.*) I thought so. The secret's out, master. She's as good as cured—

SGANARELLE (*interrupting*). I understand what's wrong. She's an ungrateful wretch. Nothing I do is good enough for her. Let her act stubborn, then.

LUCINDA. But, Daddy—

SGANARELLE. I don't want to hear any more.

LISETTE. But, master, all she wants—

SGANARELLE. All she wants is to worry me to death.

LISETTE. All she wants is a man.

SGANARELLE (*pretending not to hear*). I've had enough of her moods.

LISETTE. All she wants is a man.

SGANARELLE. I'm really angry at her.

LISETTE. A man.

SGANARELLE. Extremely upset.

LISETTE. A man!

SGANARELLE. Even if she changes her mind and decides to tell me what's wrong, it's too late now—

LISETTE. A *man!*

SGANARELLE. I positively refuse to listen. (*He exits.*)

LISETTE (*shouting after him*). A *man!* A MAN! A *MAN!*

LUCINDA. Save your breath. I told you Daddy doesn't want to hear a word about my marrying Clitander.

LISETTE. Well, after all, he *is* a stranger.

LUCINDA. With the most eloquent eyes! The first time we saw each other, Lisette, we fell in love.

LISETTE. He told you so?

LUCINDA. We've never spoken a word.

LISETTE. Then how can you possibly know—

LUCINDA (interrupting). Because Clitander asked for my hand in marriage, only Daddy told him no. See why I'm upset?

LISETTE. Yes, but cheer up, mistress, I'm going to help you.

LUCINDA. How? There's no talking to my father.

LISETTE. Leave him to me. *I'll* handle him.

LUCINDA. How?

LISETTE (under her breath). God only knows. (Aloud) Let's go to your room . . . I'll figure something out.

(As they exit, SGANARELLE re-enters.)

SGANARELLE (to the audience). I worked too hard all my life making a fortune and raising a daughter to hand them both over to the first clown who asks for them. Sometimes it's smart to play dumb.

Lisette *runs in, seemingly upset. She pretends she doesn't see* SGANARELLE.

LISETTE (running about frantically). O tragedy! O horror!

SGANARELLE (trying to catch her). Good God, what's wrong?

LISETTE (same business). My poor master!

SGANARELLE (same). What's wrong?

LISETTE (same). Unhappiest of fathers!

SGANARELLE (catching up with her). What happened to Lucinda?

LISETTE. Sorrow, sorrow!

SGANARELLE. What's wrong?!

LISETTE. Calamity, calamity!

SGANARELLE. *What's wrong*?!!

LISETTE. Disaster, di—

SGANARELLE (furiously). WHAT IN HOLY HELL IS WRONG?!!!

LISETTE. Ah, master, your daughter, overcome by grief, ran to her room and opened up the window. You know the one I mean—the window high above the river!

SGANARELLE. No!

LISETTE. Yes! "Daddy is angry at me," she said. "I'm too wicked to live." Then she threw herself—

SGANARELLE. Into the river?!

LISETTE. Onto her bed. She began to cry. Suddenly, her piteous tears stopped. Her eyes closed, her face went white. Her broken heart stopped beating—

SGANARELLE. Lucinda is dead?

LISETTE. I shook her hard and brought her back to life. But if we don't help her right away, she won't last long.

SGANARELLE. Send for a doctor immediately!

LISETTE. I already thought of that—

SGANARELLE (not hearing her). One is not enough! Quick—bring as many doctors as you can find! (To audience) Is there a doctor in the house? (Runs out) Help!

LISETTE (with a shrug). This is going to be harder than I thought . . .

(SGANARELLE hurries back in, followed by four physicians: DOCTORS BLABBER, BLEEDER, MUMBLE, and LASTGASP.)

SGANARELLE. Walk this way, gentlemen. *(He indicates exit* LUCINDA *used. They cross and exit, imitating his walk.)*

LISETTE. Four doctors! Why four doctors?

SGANARELLE. Four times the chance of saving my daughter's life.

LISETTE. Four times as good a chance of killing her.

SGANARELLE. Doctors don't kill people!

LISETTE. Wait and see.

SGANARELLE. Oh, be still, you foolish girl! *(The doctors re-enter.)* Well, gentlemen, what's the matter with my child?

BLEEDER. We've examined the patient. She's absolutely foul.

SGANARELLE. Foul? My daughter *foul*?!

BLEEDER. Harrumph! Her system is foul. She's sick as a dog.

SGANARELLE. Oh, dear!

BLEEDER. My colleagues and I must hold a consultation.

SGANARELLE. Lisette, hurry up and bring chairs.

LISETTE *(She does so.)* A chair for you, Dr. Bleeder—

SGANARELLE. How do you know this doctor's name?

LISETTE. I met him a few days ago at your niece's house.

BLEEDER. That's right. I treated your niece's coachman.

LISETTE. Treated him to a coffin.

BLEEDER *(offended)*. I beg your pardon?

LISETTE. He's dead.

BLEEDER. He can't be dead! The illness I treated him for lasts two to three weeks. He's only been in bed six days.

LISETTE *(shaking her head)*. Mm-mmm. Four days. The other two—*(She points downward.)*

BLEEDER *(furious)*. I'll have you know, the treatment I gave him was recommended by Hippocrates!

LISETTE. The coachman's probably giving *him* hell right now.

SGANARELLE. That's enough sauce, Lisette! Go tend to your mistress! *(To* THE DOCTORS*)* We'll give you privacy to consult. *(One of the doctors coughs meaningfully.)* Oh, I almost forgot . . . *(He pays each doctor then, taking* LISETTE *by the ear, steers her out. A long silence. Each* DOCTOR *coughs importantly.)*

LASTGASP. It's getting harder and harder to make my rounds.

BLEEDER. I know what you mean. Paris is getting too big.

LASTGASP. I've got a great horse. That's how I get around.

BLEEDER. A horse? Bah. I use a mule. It's incredible how far he can carry me in a day.

LASTGASP. My horse can go just as far and twice as fast.

BLEEDER. Possibly. But what do you think about the brouhaha between Doctor Thunderhoney and Doctor Blight? The whole faculty's taking sides.

LASTGASP. I support Doctor Blight.

BLEEDER *(nodding)*. So do I. Thunderhoney had no business disputing the opinion of a colleague with seniority.

LASTGASP. He was right, though.

The Love Doctor by Molière adapted by Marvin Kaye **101**

BLEEDER. So what? Blight was the physician of record. His treatment killed the patient, but that's beside the point. It's a matter of professional courtesy!

(SGANARELLE *re-enters.*)

SGANARELLE. Gentlemen, my daughter's fading fast! How do you propose to treat her?

BLEEDER (*nodding to* LASTGASP). I defer to you, Doctor Lastgasp.

LASTGASP. No, no, Doctor Bleeder, you speak first.

BLEEDER. After you, sir.

LASTGASP. After you.

BLEEDER (*indicating the others*). Perhaps Doctor Blabber or Doctor Mumble would care to go first . . .

SGANARELLE. Will somebody please say *something*?! (*All four doctors talk at once, ad lib.*) ONE AT A TIME!!!

BLEEDER. My opinion is, your daughter's blood is too hot. We have to bleed her.

LASTGASP. I don't think so. She's got bad things inside her.

SGANARELLE. How do we get them out?

LASTGASP. We have to make her throw up.

BLEEDER. I wouldn't do that. It might kill her.

LASTGASP. Well, bleeding would certainly finish her off.

BLEEDER. Nonsense!

LASTGASP. You bled that coachman.

BLEEDER. What about that lad you sent to his Maker yesterday?

LASTGASP. I don't have to sit here and take this. (*To* SGANARELLE) I gave you my advice. Induce vomiting.

BLEEDER. If you do, your daughter will be dead by tomorrow morning. Bleed her! (*Storms out*)

LASTGASP. If you do, she won't make it to morning. (*Exits*)

SGANARELLE. Now what do I do? (*To the remaining doctors*) I'm not a doctor. How am I supposed to know which treatment will save my daughter? Gentlemen, help me out here!

MUMBLE (*speaking v-e-r-y slowly*). We-e-e-e-ell, if you ask me—and you are—asking me—it's my considered opinion (and practice)—in cases like this—to proceed cautiously—carefully. Never do anything in haste. That's how to avoid making fatal mistakes.

SGANARELLE (*addressing* BLABBER). Do you agree with that?

BLABBER (*swiftly, but with a bad stutter*). A-a-a-a-absolutely! You've g-g-g-g-got to be v-v-very care-care-care-care-care-ful. M-m-m-make one f-f-f-f-false m-m-move and it's b-b-b-b-bye-bye p-p-patient! You've g-g-g-got to th-th-think this over v-v-very care-care-care—

SGANARELLE. I get the message!

MUMBLE (*same*). We-e-e-e-ell, since you've asked my opinion—it's my considered opinion—that your daughter's condition is chronic—and if you don't do anything about it—dangerous.

SGANARELLE. But what should I do?

BLABBER. In m-m-my opinion, we've g-got to l-l-loosen her up.

SGANARELLE. How?

BLABBER. G-g-g-g-give her an em-em-em-em-em-

SGANARELLE. An emetic?

BLABBER *(shaking his head).* An em-em-em-em-em-

SGANARELLE. An enema?

BLABBER *(blurting it out).* Emulsion! In a little syr-syr-syr-

SGANARELLE. Syringe?

BLABBER. Syrup.

MUMBLE *(same as before).* I agree—with Dr. Blabber's treatment. But do understand—your daughter—still—might—die.

BLABBER. B-b-but at least you'll know you d-d-d-did everything you c-c-c-could for her.

SGANARELLE *(ironically).* We-e-e-e-ell, since you've given me your opinion—it's my c-c-c-considered opinion—that you should both go to Hell!!! *(The doctors exit in a huff. To the audience.)* How do you like that? Their advice isn't worth beans . . . and I paid good money for it!

(A QUACK *enters the theatre, singing.)*

THE QUACK.
I'm a curator of skills.
I will cure you of your ills
With my inexpensive pills—they are priceless!
I've an elixir that will ease any virulent disease—
If you rub it on your cheese you'll be miceless!
I can cure you, dinna doubt,
Of the vapors, cough or gout,
So just haul your money out:
Buy a box or bag or bottle.

If a minor ache you'd nix, buy a little of *this* mix;
If a major pain you'd fix, then buy a lottle! *(Exits)*

SGANARELLE *(chasing after him).* Wait! I'll buy whatever you've got . . . one of everything!

nter DOCTORS BLEEDER, GRUMBLE, *and* LASTGASP.

GRUMBLE. You two should be ashamed of yourselves, arguing in front of a patient! It's bad enough that anybody can read the history of medicine and see how many disagreements there were amongst physicians of antiquity. All we've got is our pose. Lose that and what's left? Not that you're hurting me. I've had a profitable career and salted away a tidy sum, but if you want to do the same, remember, people have got to trust us. That's how we make a buck.

BLEEDER. In principle, I agree, but in practice, I'm furious.

LASTGASP. Look, I'm willing to compromise. *(To* BLEEDER*)* If you'll back up my diagnosis this time, I'll agree with whatever you prescribe for your next patient.

GRUMBLE. That's a handsome offer, Bleeder.

BLEEDER. Good enough for me. *(To* LASTGASP*)* Let's shake on it. *(*LASTGASP *and* BLEEDER *shake hands.)*

LISETTE *(entering).* You doctors wouldn't look so pleased if you'd seen what I just saw.

The Love Doctor by Molière adapted by Marvin Kaye **103**

GRUMBLE. What was that?

LISETTE. A fight. A man died, and guess what?

GRUMBLE. What?

LISETTE. The man who killed him wasn't even a doctor! *(She laughs at them as they leave, incensed.)*

BLEEDER *(sticking his head back in).* Just you wait . . . we'll get YOU someday.

LISETTE. I'll die first! *(BLEEDER smiles at that notion and exits. LISETTE calls to someone offstage.)* Come on in—my master's busy talking to some quack. *(CLITANDER enters, dressed like a doctor.)*

CLITANDER. So how do I look, Lisette?

LISETTE. Terrific. My mistress fell for you one-two-three, and now I see why. I'm determined to liberate Lucinda from her father's tyrannic rule.

CLITANDER. How?

LISETTE. Easy . . . *(She whispers to him; he laughs.)* Here he comes now. Wait in the other room till I call you. *(CLITANDER exits as SGANARELLE re-enters.)*

SGANARELLE. Remarkable how cheap that fellow's remedies are.

LISETTE. Master, rejoice!

SGANARELLE. What?

LISETTE. Rejoice!

SGANARELLE. What for?

LISETTE. Rejoice, and I'll tell you.

SGANARELLE. Tell me some good news, and I'll rejoice.

LISETTE. No, rejoice first, then I'll tell you why.

SGANARELLE *(exasperated).* What do you expect, a song and dance?

LISETTE. That'd be nice.

SGANARELLE *(singing and dancing).*
I'm doing what you said I should
Despite the fact I'm tired.
Your reason why had best be good
Or else I swear you're fired!
(Stops) Now what am I so blankety-blank happy about?

LISETTE. Your daughter is cured!

SGANARELLE. Cured?!

LISETTE. As good as cured. I found a new doctor.

SGANARELLE *(disappointed).* I've had my bellyful of doctors.

LISETTE. Not like this one. He's different.

SGANARELLE. How?

LISETTE. I'll show you . . . *(LISETTE waves offstage. Enter CLITANDER.)* This is Doctor Love.

SGANARELLE. He's too young.

LISETTE. He's old enough. Talk to him.

SGANARELLE I've begun to think all doctors are scoundrels.

CLITANDER. I agree.

SGANARELLE. You do?

LISETTE. Except for him.

SGANARELLE. Hush! *(To CLITANDER)* My daughter is sick. I suppose you'll want to bleed her or purge her or—

CLITANDER *(shakes his head).* No, no, I don't employ such techniques. My treatment is entirely different.

SGANARELLE. In what way?

CLITANDER. I use the power of language to cure.

SGANARELLE. The—*what?*

CLITANDER. I weave a spell of words to charm the sufferer. A single dose restores the ecstasy of health.

SGANARELLE *(interested).* A single dose? That can't cost too much.

CLITANDER. "Who chooseth me must give and hazard all he hath."

SGANARELLE. I knew it! Another money-leech!

CLITANDER. Sir, I spoke metaphorically. I charge no fees.

SGANARELLE. From one extreme to the other! How do you survive?

CLITANDER. I was born wealthy. I justify it with public service.

SGANARELLE. Dangerous idea. It'll never catch on.

LISETTE. Look, master, here comes Lucinda! The mere presence in the house of this marvelous physician has prompted her to quit her bedchamber.

(LUCINDA enters.)

CLITANDER *(holding* SGANARELLE *'s wrist).* Hm. She's very sick.

SGANARELLE. How can you tell that from taking MY pulse?

CLITANDER. Father and daughter are one flesh.

LISETTE. Master, we'd better leave them alone with each other.

SGANARELLE. What for?

LISETTE. The doctor has to examine her . . . *(Coughs)* privately.

SGANARELLE *(embarrassed).* Oh . . . yes, of course. *(To* CLITANDER *)* I'll be close by, in case you need me. *(*CLITANDER *nods.* SGANARELLE *and* LISETTE *exit.)*

CLITANDER *(in a stage whisper).* I don't know what to say! When only our eyes spoke, I was eloquent. Now I'm dumb.

LUCINDA. Who needs words? *(They move nearer.)*

SGANARELLE *(peeping in).* Why's he so close to her?

LISETTE. He's about to palpate. Don't watch. *(She yanks him offstage.)*

CLITANDER. Will you always love me?

LUCINDA. Ever and ever. Will you?

CLITANDER. My whole life through! Kiss me! *(They kiss.)*

SGANARELLE *(re-entering).* So how's she doing? She looks lots better.

CLITANDER *(taking him aside; sotto voce).* That's just temporary. She's suffering from a debased urge to get married. Of course, that would be the worst thing you could let her do.

SGANARELLE *(to audience).* What a wise doctor!

CLITANDER. People afflicted with such a delusion will never relinquish it willingly. I had to pretend to her that I'm not a doctor, but a young man about to ask you for her hand in marriage. As soon as she thought she was going to be betrothed, her eyes brightened and her spirits soared.

SGANARELLE. But what happens when she learns there's not going to be a ceremony?

CLITANDER. Her condition is still too chancy for that. It would be dangerous for her to learn the truth.

SGANARELLE. What do you recommend?

CLITANDER. For now, we must encourage her notion that she and I are about to be wed. Once she's healthy again, I'll induce a long-range therapy to destroy her delusions.

SGANARELLE. Brilliant! (*To* LUCINDA) Child, this gentleman wants to marry you. I've told him it's all right.

LUCINDA. Oh, Daddy, truly?

SGANARELLE. Truly.

CLITANDER (*to* SGANARELLE). Note her color immediately improves.

LUCINDA (*to* CLITANDER). You really want to marry me?

CLITANDER. I certainly do.

LUCINDA. My father actually agrees?

CLITANDER (*to* SGANARELLE). Look at her eyes light up.

SGANARELLE. Yes, my darling daughter, yes!

LUCINDA. I'm afraid to believe this is true. (*To* CLITANDER) Why are you all dressed up like a doctor?

CLITANDER (*winking at* SGANARELLE). I've been in love with you for a long time, but didn't know how to reach you. These doctor's robes are just a trick to fool your father.

SGANARELLE (*to audience, laughing*). Have you ever seen such a smart doctor?!

LUCINDA (*to* CLITANDER). Now I understand. You're so clever!

SGANARELLE (*to audience, laughing*). Have you ever seen such a gullible girl?

CLITANDER (*on his knees*). Lucinda, will you marry me?

LUCINDA. If my father accepts you, how can I possibly refuse?

SGANARELLE (*dotingly to audience*). She's always been a good girl.

CLITANDER. With this ring, I thee wed. (*To* SGANARELLE) It has psychotherapeutic[1] properties.

SGANARELLE (*sagaciously*). Oh, of course!

LUCINDA. Now all we need is a notary.

SGANARELLE. A . . . what?

LUCINDA (*frowning*). A notary! To draft the marriage contract.

SGANARELLE. But . . . ahhh—

---

1. psychotherapeutic, treating bodily ills by dealing with emotional upsets

CLITANDER *(whispering to* SGANARELLE*).* She's growing pale again. We mustn't contradict her. She'll suffer a relapse.

SGANARELLE *(reluctantly).* Well, if it's absolutely necessary . . . *(Calls)* Lisette! *(*LISETTE *enters with a* NOTARY*.)*

LISETTE. Yes, master?

SGANARELLE. Go fetch a notary.

LISETTE. He's here.

SGANARELLE *(gaping at* NOTARY*, then regarding* CLITANDER *suspiciously).* What's going on here?

CLITANDER *(drawing him aside).* This young man works for me. I anticipated your daughter might do this, so rather than cause you the embarrassment—and expense—of sending for a real notary, if the need arose I instructed my apprentice to pose as one.

SGANARELLE *(to audience).* Have you ever seen such a marvelous doctor? *(To* NOTARY*)* So you're a notary, sir?

NOTARY. That's what I am. How may I serve you?

SGANARELLE. By drawing up a marriage contract right away.

NOTARY. Tell me the names of the bride and her father.

SGANARELLE *(to* NOTARY*, who writes).* L-U-C-I-N-D-A, daughter of *(Slowly)* S . . . G . . . uh—*(Hesitates)*

LISETTE *(swiftly).* A-N-A-R-E-L-L-E!

SGANARELLE. As a dowry, I give her half my estate. *(Winking at* CLITANDER*)* Write that down, Notary.

LUCINDA. Thank you, Daddy!

NOTARY. It's writ. I've got the bridegroom's signature already. As soon as you and the bride sign it, the wedding's official.

SGANARELLE *(taking contract, suddenly suspicious).* How did you manage to write so much so fast?

*(*LISETTE *claps a hand over* NOTARY*'s mouth.)*

CLITANDER *(drawing* SGANARELLE *aside).* He prepared it in advance.

SGANARELLE *(pointing to contract).* But it looks real.

CLITANDER. It is. I bought a blank contract from a real notary.

SGANARELLE. Why?

CLITANDER. Your daughter's too smart to be fooled by a fake one.

SGANARELLE. But how did you know before you even examined her—

LUCINDA. Oh! Oh! I'm feeling sick again!

LISETTE. Master, your daughter's going to faint!

CLITANDER. She's having a relapse!

SGANARELLE. My darling child! No!

CLITANDER. Quickly . . . sign the contract, before it's too late!

SGANARELLE. All right, I'm signing it! *(Runs to* LUCINDA *and puts the contract in her hands)* Lucinda, look! All you've got to do is sign this, and you're a bride!

LUCINDA. I . . . I don't . . . have . . . enough strength left.

SGANARELLE. Here, Daddy will help you . . . *(He guides her hand.)* There! *(Crooning)* Now you're all-ll-ll married!

LUCINDA *(jumping up and throwing her arms around* SGANARELLE*).* Oh, Daddy, thank you, thank you! You've made me the happiest woman in the world!

SGANARELLE *(overjoyed).* It's the cure of the century!

CLITANDER *(taking* LISETTE*'s hand).* Yes, but now it's time for the long-range therapy I told you about.

SGANARELLE *(to* LISETTE*).* To cure her of her romantic delusions.

LISETTE. Marriage will do that.

SGANARELLE *(to* LISETTE*).* Marriage? What are you talking about? This wasn't real.

CLITANDER. Come, my bride, our carriage is waiting.

SGANARELLE. A carriage? What for?

CLITANDER. Her long-range therapy begins abroad.

CLITANDER *exits with* LUCINDA, *who blows a kiss to her father and* LISETTE *as she goes.*

SGANARELLE *(calling after them).* Abroad? Abroad?! Who's paying for this trip?

LISETTE *(aside).* You are, master, with half of your estate.

SGANARELLE. What kind of therapy requires foreign travel?

LISETTE. I know all about it. It's a very old cure.

SGANARELLE. It is? What do you call it?

LISETTE. A honeymoon.

(SGANARELLE looks horrified.)

CURTAIN

The Love Doctor

Responding to the Play

1. How would you characterize Sganarelle's relationship with his daughter?
2. Do you think Lisette and Lucinda are justified in tricking Sganarelle? Why or why not?
3. Who do you think is the wisest person in this play? Who is the most foolish?
4. How would you costume Clitander to disguise him as a doctor, yet distinguish him from the "real" doctors in the play?
5. Design a poster to advertise a performance of the play.

About Molière

Born in 1622 to wealthy French parents, Molière grew up with an insider's view of society and court politics. Against his father's will, he began working in the theatre at age 21, first as an actor, then as a writer.

In 1658, after many years of debt and hardship, Molière found a bit of luck. *The Love Doctor* was performed to acclaim before the French court and established his reputation as a playwright.

While Molière's satirical wit delighted most courtiers, some people, who recognized themselves in his characters, were angered. Still, his reputation grew, and today, Molière is considered by many to be France's greatest playwright.

Creating and Performing

1. With two partners, choreograph and perform a scene that features the three doctors. Use stereotypical behavior to develop the scene's potential for physical and vocal humor.
2. Design a costume that shows Lisette to be pretty, clever, loyal, and loving.
3. Perform a scene featuring dialogue between Sganarelle and Clitander, with or without Lisette. Maintain the breakneck pace that confuses Sganarelle and wins Clitander his bride.

The Play as Literature: Flashback

Everyone likes to look back to the past now and again, even authors. And when authors present events that happened before the opening scene of their work, they are using the *flashback*. Flashbacks let us see characters at an earlier period in their lives.

Sometimes a flashback occurs when a character remembers an earlier event and tells us about it. Sometimes the entire scene is re-created for us just as it happened, as in the following play.

There are three flashbacks in *Haiku*. Pay attention to the dynamics of each. Think about how each relates to the scene that follows.

The Play as Theatre: Lighting

Lighting draws the viewer toward the stage. It illuminates the actors and the sets in a way that conveys the director's interpretation of the playwright's theme. Lighting creates mood and establishes a sense of time and place.

Bright light can create a mood of sunlight, warmth, and good feeling, but overdo it and the scene will seem intense, jarring, and oppressive. Dim lighting can create an aura of mystery, romance, or sadness. Cool colors can create a strange or alien atmosphere. A red spotlight will make a character look cruel or aggressive, while warm colors such as yellow or orange can have a comic effect. Purple creates a regal or dreamy effect. White creates a feeling of peace and integrity. The mood of the scene is also influenced by whether it is lit from above, from the side, or from below.

Warm Up!

To get the effect of different lighting on your face, use an ordinary flashlight. Look in a mirror and aim the light at the top of your head, pointing it downward. How do you look? Next, position the light below your chin. What do you look like now? Compare the differences in your face created by the different lighting. Make up a few lines for a character to go with each type of lighting.

Haiku

by Katherine Snodgrass

Setting	Characters	Time
A living room	NELL, fifties, mother of LOUISE and BILLIE LOUISE, twenties–thirties, NELL's youngest daughter BILLIE, twenties–thirties, NELL's eldest daughter	Present

The set is suggestive rather than realistic. The flashback sequences may be signaled by light changes or sounds or both. A bamboo flute or porcelain wind chime may be substituted for the autoharp and/or used to signal the flashbacks, but the sound should remain delicate, almost eerie.

At rise: The stage is black. We hear an autoharp. It goes from the top of the scale to the bottom. As lights come up, NELL *has an obvious bruise on her wrist, a pad of paper and black magic marker in her lap, and a magnifying glass on a chain around her neck.* LOUISE *has a bandage on her forehead and is wearing a football helmet. The lighting suggests a mystery.*

NELL. You were born in early winter. John and I planned it that way. I couldn't imagine having a baby in the summertime. It gets so sticky in August, humid. A breach baby. You tried to back into the world. I remember, the doctor had to pull you out. It was night when they finally brought you to me.

LOUISE.
November evening.
Blackbirds scull across the moon.
My breath warms my hands.

NELL (*writes haiku, then checks it with the magnifying glass*). John said you were too beautiful to live. It was true. You and Bebe together, you were like china dolls. Delicate, perfect. And then . . . that day I saw you through the window. Billie was on the swing set, and you were there. Outside. She was in red, and you had on that blue jumpsuit, the corduroy one with the zipper. The ball lay beside you. And that momma doll that winked. You were so quiet. You'd stared before, of course, when something fascinated you, as all children do when they . . . as all children do. But this time, you were . . . different. I called for you to come inside. *Lulu, come inside and have some lunch!* But you didn't hear me. *Bebe, bring Lulu and come inside!* I went out then. I had to get down on my knees beside you.

I touched your hair and then your face. I held up that momma doll, but you stared through it in a way that . . . Funny, I don't remember being afraid. I remember the look on your sister's face.

LOUISE.

Cold, chain-metal swings
Clang in the empty school yard.
Silent summer rain.

NELL. *(writes haiku, same process as before).* Do you know, I used to cry when school ended? It's true! I used to cry on the last day of school every year. My mother thought I was crazy. I'd come dragging my book bag over the fields, my face all wet. And my momma!

LOUISE. And my momma!

NELL. Nellie, she'd say . . .

LOUISE. Nellie, she'd say . . . you're the strangest girl I ever did see!

NELL. Yes, that's . . . What did you say?

LOUISE. That you're the strangest girl?

NELL. No, no. Before that. Are you tired?

LOUISE. Before that?

NELL. You are tired, and Billie's late.

LOUISE. Tell me again about John. Please. You haven't talked about John in a long time.

NELL. John. All right then. John was tall and thin like Icabod Crane, only not so scared.

LOUISE. John wasn't scared of anything.

NELL. He wasn't scared of anything, not John. He had a big, strong jaw and a tuft of yellow hair that stood up on his head, as yellow . . .

LOUISE. . . . as Mr. Turner's daffodils.

NELL. At least. And he would take you on his knee. Do you remember the song he used to sing? *(NELL clears her throat and sings)* Here come a Lulu! Here come a Lulu to the Indian dance. *(LOUISE joins in.)* All of them Indians, all of them Indians dance around Lulu's tent. *(Like a drum.)* *Here* come a Lulu! *Here* come a Lulu! *Here* come a Lulu! *(They laugh, remembering.)*

LOUISE.

Icy branches bend
And break over stones. I hear
My dead father . . . laugh.

(NELL writes haiku, same process as before.)

LOUISE. Wasn't there a story about a fox? Who had a bushy tail?

NELL. You remember that?

LOUISE. And John would rub Bebe's back until she went to sleep. He smelled of soap and something . . . sweet?

NELL *(dryly).* Sweet! Cigars from Havana.

LOUISE *(repeating with* NELL*'s exact inflection).* Cigars from Havana.

NELL. We'll stop now. *(During this next exchange,* NELL *fishes in her pocket for a bottle of pills and takes a pill out.)*

LOUISE. No! No, I want to do more.

NELL. Louise—

LOUISE. I'm not ready to go back. Please, not now.

NELL. But Billie's not here yet. We've got to be careful.

LOUISE. But I can do it! I promise.

Please, Momma, I hate to go back. It's like being smothered!

NELL. I know.

LOUISE. Everything is so dim, and I can't hear you properly. Or see you or touch you or . . . *(Seeing the bruise on* NELL*'s wrist—)* Did I do that?

NELL. It's not bad.

LOUISE. That was before I knew what to do. Please. I can stop it now, I know I can. You said so yourself.

NELL. I know what I said.

LOUISE. If you don't let me try, I'll never learn what to do.

NELL. We can talk to Bebe tomorrow. Today, it would be better—

LOUISE. Today, it would be better—if I saw Bebe first. Then I can stand it.

(During this next exchange NELL *tries to give* LOUISE *a pill.* LOUISE *refuses.* NELL *removes the helmet.)*

NELL. No. Not today!

LOUISE. Not today!

NELL. You're too tired.

LOUISE. I can control it.

NELL. Louise. I don't want to wait too long. You'll hurt yourself.

LOUISE. You'll hurt yourself. I mean, no! I won't. You promised I could talk to Bebe. You said I *had* to talk to her.

NELL. Yes, yes we will. Tomorrow. *(*NELL *holds out pill.)* I want you to take this now.

LOUISE. *(stubborn)* . . . You promised I could wait for Bebe.

NELL. I want you to—

LOUISE. I need some water. *(*NELL *is*

silent.) I do! I can't swallow.

NELL. Louise.

LOUISE. I can't swallow. My throat is dry.

NELL *(sighing)* . . . Yes, all right, just a minute. *(*NELL *exits.)*

LOUISE. Just a minute. Just a minute.

(A loud door slam startles LOUISE. *Abruptly, lights come full up as* BILLIE *enters with a suitcase and packages. There is a moment of recognition between* LOUISE *and* BILLIE. LOUISE *might say* BILLIE*'s name, but* NELL *enters with a glass of water. There is an awkwardness in this next exchange.* NELL *greets* BILLIE *and moves to* LOUISE *with the pill.)*

BILLIE. Nell, how are you? You look exhausted. I thought I'd never make it. The traffic at the airport is worse than ever.

NELL. You're here.

BILLIE. Yes, I'm here.

NELL. You're late.

BILLIE. I'm sorry. Are you all right? You sounded strange on the telephone.

NELL. I? Yes. *(Pause.* LOUISE *refuses to take the pill.)*

BILLIE. *(half-kidding).* Shall I leave again and come back?

NELL. No. No, of course not. We don't mind at all, do we, Lulu? *(Holding up pill, asking.)* Can you tell Bebe how we don't mind?

LOUISE. *(to Billie).* We don't mind.

NELL. *(putting pill away).* Michael's not with you?

BILLIE. No. No, he's not coming. *(Then quickly)* Look what I came across in a little shop in Boston. They had both of your books, is that unbelievable? And get this, they actually had them in the poetry section. I get so tired of searching through the books on Japanese culture. Do you need them, or can I keep them? You know, I really love the cover on this last one.

NELL. Oh, Billie, I wish you'd waited. I was going to send you a copy, but . . .

BILLIE. They're finally getting the hang of it at that place. Black and white photography is much closer to what you wanted all along, isn't it?

NELL. I've been so busy. I don't know how I could have forgotten to send you . . .

BILLIE. Of course, I had to see that lovely dedication. I'm such a pushover. It always gives me a little thrill to see my name in print even if it is after the fact.

NELL. Let me go upstairs and—

BILLIE. I was just so surprised to run across them, and I was really impressed with this new cover. Where did they find the photographer?

NELL. I'll give you your copy now.

BILLIE. No, Mother, Mother, really! This one's fine. Well, it's not as if I can't afford it. At least it's not one of those dry biographies you used to write, the lives of the saints or some such thing? Somehow with you I always feel like a groupie at the stage door. "Please, ma'am, it's a first edition and would you sign it, please?"

NELL. I've already signed your copy. But if you want me to sign this,

too . . . Why don't I do it later, all right? Let me do it later when Lulu's asleep. That way, we—

BILLIE. Fine, sure. Later is fine, whatever. Oh, I brought something for Lulu, too. (BILLIE *brings out package from her large bag and holds it out to* NELL. *It is wrapped in very shiny wrapping paper with a bright ribbon.*)

NELL. You did? Why, that was thoughtful. What is it?

LOUISE. What is it?

BILLIE. Open it. Oh hell, it's another music box.

LOUISE. Oh hell.

NELL. It's wrapped so prettily, why don't you let Lulu open it?

BILLIE. Do we have time before Easter?

NELL. Billie.

BILLIE. I'm sorry. Really. But she won't care what's inside. She just likes the wrapping paper.

NELL. That's not true. Lulu loves music.

LOUISE. Lulu loves music.

BILLIE. Lulu loves wrapping paper.

NELL (*to* BILLIE). Go on. You give it to her.

Flashback sequence begins. *They are children. Dolls are mimed.*

BILLIE. I have to give this to you. This is the baby doll, and this is the momma doll. Now you take the baby doll and rock her to sleep, like this. (*Singing.*) Rock-a-bye baby in the treetop. When the wind blows . . . That's right. You be the babysitter. And now the momma comes to play with the baby. Hello, baby.

LOUISE. Hello, baby.

BILLIE. My, you are sleeping so soundly I don't want to wake you up. How did my baby do today, Mrs. Lippoman? Was she a good baby?

LOUISE. Was she a good baby?

BILLIE. Let me see her. Isn't she the most beautiful baby in the whole— No, give it back. No you can't have the momma doll. You have the baby doll.

LOUISE. You have the baby doll.

BILLIE. No, let go.

LOUISE. No.

BILLIE. Give it back, you can't have both of them.

LOUISE. Both of them.

BILLIE *(new tactic).* All right then, give me the baby doll.

LOUISE. Give me the baby doll.

BILLIE. Give it to me. It's my momma doll, and it's my baby doll. Let go, let go . . . !

LOUISE. Let go, let go! *(Baby doll breaks.)*

BILLIE. You broke it! That was my baby doll. It was mine, and I'm going to tell on you, you . . .

LOUISE. You . . .

BILLIE. I didn't want to play with you anyway. You're stupid, stupid!

LOUISE. Stupid!

BILLIE. I'm going to tell, and then I'll never have to play with you again. Not ever! *(BILLIE shoves LOUISE's forehead with the palm of her hand.)*

LOUISE. Not ever! *(LOUISE begins hitting herself in the forehead.)*

BILLIE. Stop hurting yourself!

(Flashback sequence ends.)

BILLIE. Is she hurting herself again? What's that bandage for?

NELL. No, no, of course not. We just had a little accident.

BILLIE. Isn't the medicine working?

NELL. Of course, yes.

BILLIE. Let's look at it.

NELL. No, it's perfectly fine now. Almost healed.

BILLIE. Did you get that bruise at the same time?

NELL. Oh, this? It's nothing. I don't even remember where I got it.

LOUISE. *(holds up her hands for a hug).* Bebe.

BILLIE. Good lord. (LOUISE *and* BILLIE *hug.)*

NELL. That's new, isn't it?

BILLIE. What?

NELL. She's different than when you saw her last, isn't she?

BILLIE. Because she hugged me? We all know how much that means.

NELL. Billie, what will we do with you?

BILLIE. Well, they're supposed to get more affectionate as they get older. I might as well be a rag doll that she's fond of. But if that's what you mean, that she's more responsive, then yes, we can thank whatever gods there be that she's not gone the other way. At least the medicine is doing that for her.

NELL. The medicine.

BILLIE. Yes.

NELL. But don't you think she's getting better, though? Honestly, isn't she more alert?

BILLIE. Alert.

NELL. She knew you, Billie. She wanted to touch you.

BILLIE. Of course she knows me. I'm her sister. She's wanted to get her hands around my neck for years.

LOUISE. For years.

BILLIE (*laughing*). There, you see? All right, all right, let's try this. (*She takes wrapped present and holds it out to* LOUISE.) Ah, it's a lovely bow, isn't it? And look at that shiny wrapping paper. You love that, don't you? Look at her. I tell you, Nell, I wasted my money on the music box. This wrapping paper's going to be enough.

NELL. Let's just take this bow off. Here.

BILLIE. No fair, no fair helping.

NELL. Now this paper comes off.

(LOUISE *tears the paper off the music box. She opens the box as it tinkles out a song. She is enthralled.*)

NELL. There, now. There. Why, that's beautiful, isn't it, Lulu? That's beautiful. See, see how she loves the music?

BILLIE. Yes.

NELL. Look, look at her. And she unwrapped it herself.

BILLIE. Mother.

NELL. She knew exactly—

BILLIE. No.

NELL. —what to do. Don't you see a difference in her?

BILLIE (*During this speech,* BILLIE *takes the box, handing the shiny paper back to* LOUISE). You never change, do you? No, I don't see any difference. She's not more alert, and she's not getting any better. All right. All right, maybe she's a little more affectionate. Maybe. But that's natural. Most of them become more affectionate. They learn to feed themselves and to go to the bathroom and to hug their sisters when they come home to visit.

NELL. (*taking shiny paper from* LOUISE). You don't understand. You can't possibly know, you don't see her every day.

BILLIE. Yes, and you do, and you take every gaze out the window and rationalize it into some sort of normal reaction.

NELL. I don't rationalize. I don't need to. I see real change for the better!

BILLIE. Better, Momma?

Second flashback sequence. Again, they are children.

BILLIE. Better bring her inside, Momma. She's staring at the sun again. Maa-maa! (*There is no answer, so* BILLIE *uses a shiny necklace or a prism from around her own neck and holds it up for* LOUISE, *who is captivated with the shine. Singing.*) Twinkle, twinkle, little star, how I wonder who you are. Oooo, pretty twinkle, pretty twinkle. Maa-maa! (*She sings a song to the tune of "Frère Jacques."* LOUISE *hums some notes.*)

Where is Lulu? Where is Lulu?
Here I am, here I am.
How are you this morning?
Very well, I thank you

(BILLIE *pulls* LOUISE *to her feet.*)

Please stand up. Please sit down.

(BILLIE *pulls* LOUISE *back down.*)

Where is Booboo? Where is Booboo?

(*Pointedly.*)

Here you are, here you are.
How are you this morning?
Very well, I thank you.

(BILLIE *pulls* LOUISE *to her feet.*)

Please stand up. Please sit down.

(BILLIE *pulls Louise back down. She begins to substitute different sounds for* LOUISE's *name.* LOUISE *imitates, repeating only the last sounds.*)

Where is Poopoo? Where is—

LOUISE. —Poopoo (*Pause.*)

BILLIE. Where is . . . Bongbong?

LOUISE. Bongbong.

(BILLIE *gives up on the song and does the sounds rhythmically and playfully as* LOUISE *follows, repeating each set of sounds.* BILLIE *begins enjoying* LOUISE, *who mirrors even facial expressions. Different sounds may be repeated or substituted as the actors play.*)

BILLIE (*and* LOUISE *after, grunting*).
Ugghh-Ugghhh. (*Tongue out.*) Blah-blah. Eeeek-eeek. (*Like a villain.*) Heh-heh-heh. (*Rolling the tongue.*) Thrrrrrrhrrrr. (*Like a pig.*) Snort-snort. Snort-snort. Snort-snort. (*As the sounds become funny to her,* BILLIE *laughs.* LOUISE *laughs.* BILLIE *laughs again.* LOUISE *imitates. When she realizes that* LOUISE *is not playing with her but only repeating,* BILLIE *holds up the chain prism again.*)

BILLIE. Pretty twinkle, pretty twinkle. I wish . . . (*End of flashback sequence.*) I wish I could understand you, Momma.

NELL. I know you've never been able to understand. You were too young, I suppose. It was asking too much of you.

BILLIE. Was it? Strange. I don't remember being asked. Is that why you don't dedicate your books to Lulu?

NELL. What?

BILLIE. Yes, is that your way of asking me to understand now?

NELL. No, Bebe, I never—

BILLIE. Why not to Lulu? Because she can't *ever* understand?

NELL. No, that's not it at all. We've been wanting to talk to you. That's why I telephoned.

BILLIE. Because of the dedication?

NELL. Yes, and . . . and—

BILLIE. I thought it was because of your eyes.

NELL. Well, yes. That too.

BILLIE. How much can you see, anyway?

NELL. I can make out your shape, but it's getting worse.

LOUISE. It's getting worse. (*Silence.*)

BILLIE. All right, then. Will Daddy's trust fund cover a nurse for Lulu?

NELL. Even if it would, I don't want some stranger in the house caring for Lulu. I'll do it myself.

BILLIE. Yourself? Mother, how?

NELL. I'll manage. I've done it up until now.

BILLIE. But what if she dirties her clothes? What if she has a reaction? What if you were to fall? Lulu couldn't help you. She wouldn't know what to do. Why, she wouldn't even understand that anything was wrong.

NELL. I do not have to have help.

BILLIE. Then why did you ask me—?

NELL. I've managed this long, and besides . . .

BILLIE. Yes?

NELL. Lulu understands more than you know.

LOUISE. More than you know.

BILLIE. Lulu understands what *you want* her to understand. Momma, you can't go on ignoring Lulu's illness.

NELL. I'm not ignoring—

BILLIE. Mother, listen to me. Put her in a hospital where she can be taken care of properly. No, wait, I can help you. Please. Michael and I have talked it over, and . . . Really. I'd be happy if you'd come live with us. I thought that's what you wanted. You can visit Lulu every day if you want to. You can sit with her. Please. It's not as if she's going to know where she is.

NELL. Of course she knows where she is! What are you talking about? You haven't heard what I've been trying to say.

BILLIE. What haven't I heard?

NELL. That she's different. She's changed.

BILLIE. Changed how? And if you say she's more affectionate—

NELL. It's not just that. It's more. Much more. I haven't told you before this because I knew you wouldn't believe me. But you don't live with her,

Billie, you don't see. You asked why I dedicate the haiku to you and never to Louise. It's because . . . I don't write the haiku.

BILLIE. What?

NELL. It's Louise.

LOUISE. It's Louise. *(Silence.)*

BILLIE. No.

NELL. It's true.

BILLIE. That's impossible.

NELL. No, I swear it.

LOUISE. I swear it.

BILLIE. Momma.

NELL. . . . It started three years ago after we changed to that new medication.

BILLIE. . . . What started?

NELL. . . . I was reading a book. Very absorbed. Lulu was sitting, as she always does, next to the window. Suddenly, I realized that I had forgotten to give her the afternoon pill. I glanced up, and she was sitting forward in her chair, leaning on the sill. *(LOUISE does this as NELL speaks.)* It was odd. I knew she wouldn't notice me, but I said her name, *Lulu?* And she turned to me and looked at me, *really looked at me,* for the first time. She asked me to forgive her. Hah! As if there was anything to forgive. She was so frightened, so frightened. Bebe, it's as if she's trapped, trapped in a maze, and everything's all white, like cotton, or clouds, and . . . and she can't get out. Everything moves so slowly. And when she tries, sounds come in to distract her. They pull her away, and she can't concentrate. She can't be herself. But she was there. She is. *Louise* is there.

LOUISE. Can't concentrate.

BILLIE. You mean she's . . . normal . . . without the medication, or—?

NELL. No, it's not that. She still—Well, she can't go on without the medicine. I have to give her the medicine. She needs it.

BILLIE. Then what—?

NELL. Because it was late! The medicine has to be late. I don't understand it. I don't pretend to.

BILLIE. Wait. Are you saying that now you deliberately hold back her medicine?

NELL. Yes, yes! She can't get out without my help!

BILLIE. Dear God.

NELL. I used to think I was making it up.

BILLIE. I can imagine.

NELL. But I'm not. I'm not. The haiku is real. Louise is real.

BILLIE. Why didn't you tell me this before?

NELL. I didn't dare believe it myself. Then when we started working, we decided it was better if no one knew for the time being.

BILLIE. Why?

NELL. It was so fragile, don't you see? So delicate. It doesn't happen all the time. Sometimes when her medicine is late. But even then, not every day. And she only stays for a little before we have to take the medicine.

BILLIE. I see. And she speaks . . . in poetry.

NELL. No, no. We were at the window. It was October and just about dusk. Mr. Turner was burning leaves in his incinerator out back. I said, "Look how beautiful the colors are. Late autumn." And she said, "Late autumn evening/Swallows circle overhead/Wood smoke curling up." By concentrating on what we could see through the window, we'd make a haiku together. After that, she began making them up on her own. I simply sit and talk, and . . . Billie, it's as if she sees my thoughts, my innermost feelings, and translates them into images.

BILLIE. Almost as if she were you.

NELL. Yes.

BILLIE. What do you talk about?

NELL. Nothing important. Memories. The past. But she'll take the most ordinary event and make it so personal somehow.

BILLIE. Yes. How long do you talk?

NELL. Not long.

BILLIE. *How* long?

NELL. Half an hour at the most. But she's trying very hard. She wants to practice. She wants to be . . .

BILLIE. You want her to be normal.

NELL. No. More than that. Extraordinary. And she is.

BILLIE. Mother, if this is true . . . I mean, *when* this happens . . . Why haven't you told the doctors?

NELL. No doctors and no more hospitals. They brought on this problem in the first place. If I hadn't rushed her to the doctors so quickly, maybe she would have come out of it. No! We don't know! If they didn't have her taking all these drugs . . . Nobody knows what might have happened!

LOUISE. Nobody knows.

BILLIE. All right, if you mean that, then take her off the drugs entirely.

NELL. We can't do that.

BILLIE. Why not?

NELL. She hurts herself. She could—!

BILLIE. Momma, if that's what you believe, take her off the drugs. We could put her in the hospital and have the drug levels monitored.

NELL. No. I told you no hospitals.

BILLIE. But they could even wean her off the drugs slowly, and then we could—

NELL. No!

BILLIE. *Why not?*

LOUISE. *Why not?*

NELL. She needs the drugs. She's not herself yet. She needs them to . . . to protect her until . . . It's a question of will power.

BILLIE. Whose, yours?

NELL. I knew you wouldn't understand. I warned her, but no! She said she wanted to let you in. She said we *had* to tell you.

BILLIE. *She* said that?

NELL. . . . She loves you, Bebe. The way she hugged you today was only a tiny indication of that.

BILLIE. Why did you ask me here?

NELL. I can barely see to write the words anymore. Don't you understand?

BILLIE. I'm sorry.

NELL. I need your help, Bebe. We need you.

*F*lashback sequence. BILLIE *is teaching* LOUISE *about makeup. The lipstick, mirror, etc., is mimed.* BILLIE *pushes hair back from* LOUISE'*s forehead.*

BILLIE (*to* LOUISE). You need to keep your hair out of your face. Okay, now, you take the lipstick and you put in on like . . . that. See? Okay. Pucker up. (BILLIE *puckers, and* LOUISE *imitates her as* BILLIE *applies lipstick to* LOUISE'*s mouth, then to her own.*) Mmmm, luscious pink!

LOUISE. Mmmm.

BILLIE. Now then, you take this pencil. And *don't* put it in your eye!

LOUISE. *Don't* put it in your eye!

BILLIE (*to mirror*). You draw around the eye . . . underneath . . . above . . . but not too much. There. See?

LOUISE. *Don't* put it in your eye!

BILLIE. Right. And now for the shadow. What color shall we use? Let's use turquoise or . . . What about this purple? Yeah, let's use the purple!

LOUISE. Yeah, let's use the purple!

(BILLIE *puts it on for the mirror while* LOUISE *picks up the turquoise and draws big circles over her neck, her face, her cheeks, and forehead.*)

BILLIE. And we put it above the crease of the eye, not just on the lid. Then we take this black pencil and we draw it out, just like Elizabeth Taylor did in *Cleopatra.* Now, then, what's next?

LOUISE. Now, then, what's next? (BILLIE

looks at LOUISE *and reacts as* NELL *enters.*)

BILLIE. Oh . . . !

NELL. Billie, how could you!

LOUISE. How could you!

NELL. *(begins wiping off the makeup).* I thought you knew better than this. What were you thinking of? Oh, Lulu, such a mess.

LOUISE. Mess!

NELL. Her face is as red as a fire engine. And this turquoise! It'll take days for these colors to wear off. Why on earth . . . ?

(LOUISE *begins slapping her legs.*)

NELL. Now you've done it! Here, hold her hands. This is not the first time this has happened, but by God it will be the last. For the final time, do not take it upon yourself to teach her. You leave that to me, or you can leave this house! Do you understand? (BILLIE *lets go of* LOUISE*'s hands.*) Oh, now I've got it all over me. Lulu, be still! *(Surprisingly,* LOUISE *is still.)* Bebe *(End of flashback sequence.)*

NELL. Bebe.

BILLIE. What do you want me to do?

NELL. I want for you, I *need* for you to listen to her and believe in her so that she can be who she is. If we believe, she can get well. We can help her, I know it. Let us show you. Louise? Louise, Billie's here.

BILLIE. She's not listening.

NELL. Billie's here, and you wanted to talk to her. Remember? (LOUISE *looks at* BILLIE.) You see? There. Now, Bebe, say something to her. Go on.

BILLIE. Mother, don't make me do this.

NELL. Lulu. It's Billie.

LOUISE. Bebe.

BILLIE. Lulu.

NELL. Ask her something.

BILLIE. Mother.

NELL. Ask her.

BILLIE. Alright. Lulu. Is it really you?

LOUISE. Is it really you?

BILLIE. Yes, it's really me. Is it true?

LOUISE. . . . True?

BILLIE. *(looks back at* NELL *for encouragement;* NELL *is insistent)* . . . It's been a long time since I've seen you, Lulu. It's been months and months, I think. How . . . how are you?

LOUISE. . . . How are you?

BILLIE. . . . I've been fine, but how are you? *(Pause.)*

LOUISE. I've been fine.

BILLIE. She's just repeating, Mother.

NELL. She's tired. We were writing just before you got here. It's hard, but she can do it. Concentrate, Lulu. This is important. It's Billie. *(To* BILLIE.) Ask her about the poems.

BILLIE. Yes, I've read the poems. They're lovely.

LOUISE. We were writing just before you got here.

NELL. You see?

BILLIE. Momma told me. I want so much to believe it's true.

LOUISE. Believe it's true.

BILLIE. No, no, say something else. Say anything else. Make up a poem. Can you do that for me? Make up a poem. Please do that.

LOUISE. Make up a poem?

BILLIE. Yes, yes, please.

NELL. Look out the window. Describe it to her.

BILLIE (*to* LOUISE). Look, look out there. Winter's nearly over. Mr. Turner's daffodils are in bloom. And the hydrangea bushes we planted that year Daddy died. Remember? They're big now. Why, they cover the whole side of the porch. Momma's already put out that old bird feed—I can't do this.

NELL. Keep going, she's listening.

BILLIE. She's not. You are, Momma.

NELL. Please.

BILLIE. Well then . . . (*To the window*) It's almost sunset. The sky is . . . red.

NELL. Yes. Red sky at dusk.

LOUISE. Red sky at dusk.

BILLIE. One gray cloud . . . lies just . . . over the trees . . .

LOUISE. Over the trees . . . one gray cloud lies—

BILLIE. She's mimicking me.

LOUISE. —in my sister . . .

BILLIE. (*comforting*). That's right, I am your sister, aren't I?

LOUISE. (*grabbing* BILLIE's *hand*). —in my sister's . . . sister's—

NELL. In my—

LOUISE (*gesturing*). —sister's—

NELL (*prompting*). —sister's . . .

BILLIE. Mother.

NELL (*understanding*). . . . eyes!

LOUISE. —eyes!

NELL. There. (NELL *claps.*) Bravo, Lulu! Good girl!

BILLIE. Stop it!

NELL. What.

BILLIE. She's repeating.

NELL. No.

LOUISE. No.

BILLIE. She's repeating what I say and what you say.

NELL. No, no! Louise, help me now.

BILLIE. Don't put us through this.

NELL. Louise?

BILLIE. I can't bear it.

LOUISE. I can't bear it.

NELL. Try a little harder, baby.

BILLIE. Mother, listen to me!

NELL. Concentrate now.

BILLIE. Please, don't!

LOUISE. Listen to me!

BILLIE. Mother, you have got to—

NELL. Louise, look at me and—

BILLIE. *Mother, stop!*

(LOUISE *is startled by the shout and begins screaming and banging her head. Both* NELL *and* BILLIE *shout over the screaming.* BILLIE *gets the football helmet but can't get it onto* LOUISE.)

NELL. The helmet. Lulu, Lulu, there.

BILLIE. Where is her medicine?

NELL. Oh, my hand! Hold her arms!

(*Instead,* BILLIE *gets the music box and opens it for* LOUISE *to see.* LOUISE *immediately calms and focuses on the music.* NELL *gives* LOUISE *the pill and some water.* BILLIE *and* NELL *recover.*)

BILLIE. Will she be all right now?

NELL. Yes. If we can keep her quiet, the pill should take hold. We startled her.

BILLIE. How can you do this?

NELL. I hate to see her leave. I know what you're going to say. But every word I've told you is true. You didn't want to believe.

BILLIE. That's not true. I want to believe. Just don't ask me to see something that isn't there.

NELL. Then let us prove it to you. We'll try again tomorrow.

BILLIE. No, no. I don't want to try any-more. I've tried before. I can't keep trying and have it not be true.

NELL. It doesn't always happen, so I'm not promising anything.

BILLIE. No.

NELL. Bebe.

BILLIE. No, it hurts too much. You talk to her as if . . .

NELL. . . . as if she's real. As if she's there. And she is.

BILLIE. Yes. Yes.

NELL. She is. Let me try tomor—

BILLIE. No.

NELL. I'm not asking you to believe it.

BILLIE. Aren't you?

NELL. I'm only asking you to let me try. Wait and see.

BILLIE. Wait and see.

NELL. You'll do that, won't you? Just that? For me?

*S*ilence. LOUISE *has closed the music box. Lights slowly begin fading back to the setting with which we began the play.*

BILLIE. For you? Yes.

NELL. You'll wait.

BILLIE. I think I can do that.

NELL. That's my Bebe. You can stay as long as you like, you know. As long as you need to. *(Silence.)*

BILLIE. It's spring.

NELL. Yes. Finally. Did I ever tell you— when I was a girl, we had a cherry tree in the backyard. It was just big enough for me to sit in. The thickest branch was my backrest. It was curved, like a hammock, and I could lean back into that tree and rest my legs on either side of the trunk. In the spring and summer, I took books out there and devoured them along with the cherries. The Brontës, Alexander Dumas, Jane Austen, and I were surrounded by flowers. The perfume.

BILLIE. I was never very literary. I can't even make a good rhyme.

NELL. You're your father all over again.

BILLIE. He wasn't scared of anything, not John. But I am, Momma.

NELL. No, John wasn't scared of anything.

BILLIE. I wish Daddy could be here to . . . see his garden. *(Silence.* BILLIE *and* NELL *are together. They do not attend* LOUISE, *who is alone at the window, separate.)*

LOUISE.

Walking in his garden
Suddenly in the twilight—
White hydrangea.

Fade to blackout.

Haiku

Responding to the Play

1. Kate Snodgrass has written that "the last moment in the play is meant to be ambiguous." Describe the ambiguity and then discuss how you interpret the scene.
2. What is the conflict between Nell and Billie?
3. If you were casting the play, would you have Billie and Louise be played by children in the flashback sequences? Why or why not?
4. The playwright suggests using an autoharp, bamboo flute, or wind chime to create delicate sound effects. What other things might be used to create such a sound?
5. Use a graphic organizer to list details or draw a diagram that indicates how you would light the three flashbacks.

About Haiku

Haiku, a poem written in three lines of five, seven, and five syllables, originated in Japan in the seventeenth century. It is written in an attempt to achieve spiritual insight and to arouse emotion. Its subject is usually a scene from nature.

Western poets such as Thoreau, Wordsworth, and Pound have used the form, but it is very difficult to write haiku in English. The Japanese syllable is usually short and uniform, often simply a consonant and a vowel. Because English has so many more separate sounds than Japanese, the form tends to be overwhelmed by English pronunciations.

Creating and Performing

1. Read aloud one of the haiku from the play while a classmate interprets it through pantomime.
2. With a partner, perform a scene in which Billie and Louise interact as children, then as adults. Compare the scenes for the class.
3. Write a haiku based on your interpretation of the play.

Sorry, Right Number

The Play as Literature: Suspense

Science fiction, fantasy, horror, and action films are all known for their suspenseful moments. In truth, however, all effective dramas have moments of suspense. Suspense occurs whenever you anticipate and fear a particular outcome. It increases each time the author hints that the outcome will—or may—take place. As you read this play, look for the moments of uncertainty in the plot. Think about what you want to happen and what you fear. Then look for clues that point to the outcome.

The Play as Theatre: The Screenplay

A screenplay is like a stage play in that it identifies time and place and tells what each character says. It is unlike a stage play in the amount of visual detail it includes. In fact, most screenplays are presented in two columns. One column, labeled "Audio," includes dialogue and sound effects. The other column, labeled "Visual," includes information about the scene, the sets, lighting, and camera angles.

As you read, think about the ways in which camera angles and featured images help create suspense in *Sorry, Right Number.*

Warm Up!

Create a suspenseful story chain with the help of your classmates. Stand in a circle. Begin a story by describing a character and that character's biggest hope or fear. Set up a situation in which that hope or fear might be realized. Then break off your narrative just as something significant is about to happen. Let the person on your left finish your sentence, building to the next suspenseful moment. Continue until everyone has added to the story.

Setting	*Characters*	*Time*
Suburbia	**KATIE WEIDERMAN** **BILL WEIDERMAN** **JEFF, CONNIE, DENNIS, POLLY,** their children **DAWN,** Katie's sister **MINISTER** **GROUNDSKEEPER** **HANK** **ANNOUNCER**	The present

Act 1

Fade in on:

KATIE WEIDERMAN'S MOUTH, EXTREME CLOSE-UP (*She's speaking into the telephone. Pretty mouth; in a few seconds we'll see that the rest of her is just as pretty.*)

KATIE. Bill? Oh, he says he doesn't feel very well, but he's always like that between books . . . can't sleep, thinks every headache is the first symptom of a brain tumor . . . once he gets going on something new, he'll be fine.

SOUND, BACKGROUND: THE TELEVISION

(*The camera draws back. KATIE is sitting in the kitchen phone nook, having a good gab with her sister while she idles through some catalogues. We should notice one not-quite-ordinary thing about the phone she's on: it's the sort with two lines. There are lighted buttons to show which ones are engaged. Right now only one—KATIE's—is. As KATIE continues her conversation, the camera swings away from her, tracks across the kitchen, and through the arched doorway that leads into the family room.*)

KATIE (*voice, fading*). Oh, I saw Janie

Charlton today. Yes! Big as a house!
(*She fades. The TV gets louder. There are three kids:* JEFF, *eight,* CONNIE, *ten, and* DENNIS, *thirteen. Wheel of Fortune is on, but they're not watching. Instead they're engaged in that great pastime, Fighting About What Comes On Later.*)

JEFF. Come onnn! It was his first book!

CONNIE. His first gross book.

DENNIS. We're gonna watch *Cheers* and *Wings,* just like we do every week, Jeff.

(DENNIS *speaks with the utter finality only a big brother can manage. "Wanna talk about it some more and see how much pain I can inflict on your scrawny body, Jeff?" his face says.*)

JEFF. Could we at least tape it?

CONNIE. We're taping CNN for Mom. She said she might be on the phone with Aunt Lois for quite awhile.

JEFF. How can you tape CNN, for God's sake? It never stops!

DENNIS. That's what she likes about it.

CONNIE. And don't say God's sake, Jeffie—you're not old enough to talk about God except in church.

JEFF. Then don't call me Jeffie.

CONNIE. Jeffie, Jeffie, Jeffie.

(JEFF *gets up, walks to the window, and looks out into the dark. He's really upset.* DENNIS *and* CONNIE, *in the grand tradition of older brothers and sisters, are delighted to see it.*)

DENNIS. Poor Jeffie.

CONNIE. I think he's gonna commit suicide.

JEFF (*turns to them*). It was his first book! Don't you guys even care?

CONNIE. Rent it down at the Video Stop tomorrow, if you want to see it so bad.

JEFF. They don't rent R-rated pictures to little kids and you know it!

CONNIE (*dreamily*). Shut up, it's Vanna! I love Vanna!

JEFF. Dennis—

DENNIS. Go ask Dad to tape it on the VCR in his office and quit being such a totally annoying little booger.

(JEFF *crosses the room, poking his tongue out at Vanna White as he goes. The camera follows as he goes into the kitchen.*)

KATIE. . . . so when he asked me if Polly had tested strep positive, I had to remind him she's away at prep school . . . and God, Lois, I miss her . . .

(JEFF *is just passing through, on his way to the stairs.*)

KATIE. Will you kids please be quiet?

JEFF (*glum*). They'll be quiet. Now.

(*He goes up the stairs, a little dejected.* KATIE *looks after him for a moment, loving and worried.*)

KATIE. They're squabbling again. Polly used to keep them in line, but now that she's away at school . . . I don't know . . . maybe sending her to Bolton wasn't such a hot idea. Sometimes when she calls home she sounds so unhappy . . .

INTERIOR: BELA LUGOSI AS DRACULA, CLOSEUP

(*Drac's standing at the door of his Transylvanian castle. Someone has pasted a comic-balloon coming out of his mouth which reads:* "Listen! My children of the night! What music they make!" *The poster is on a door but we only see this as* JEFF *opens it and goes into his father's study.*)

INTERIOR:. A PHOTOGRAPH OF KATIE, CLOSE-UP

(*The camera holds, then pans slowly right. We pass another photo, this one of* POLLY, *the daughter away at school. She's a lovely girl of sixteen or so. Past* POLLY *is* DENNIS . . . *then* CONNIE . . . *then* JEFF.

The camera continues to pan and also widens out so we can see BILL WEIDERMAN, *a man of about forty-four. He looks tired. He's peering into the word-processor on his desk, but his mental crystal ball must be taking the night off, because the screen is blank. On the walls we see framed book-covers. All of them are spooky. One of the titles is* Ghost Kiss.

JEFF *comes up quietly behind his dad. The carpet muffles his feet.* BILL *sighs and shuts off the word-cruncher. A moment later* JEFF *claps his hands on his father's shoulders.*)

JEFF. BOOGA-BOOGA!

BILL. Hi, Jeffie.

(*He turns in his chair to look at his son, who is disappointed.*)

JEFF. How come you didn't get scared?

BILL. Scaring is my business. I'm case-hardened. Something wrong?

JEFF. Daddy, can I watch the first hour of *Ghost Kiss* and you tape the rest? Dennis and Connie are hogging everything.

(BILL *swivels to look at the book jacket, bemused.*)

BILL. You sure you want to watch that, champ? It's pretty—

JEFF. Yes!

INTERIOR: KATIE, IN THE PHONE NOOK

(*In this shot, we clearly see the stairs leading to her husband's study behind her.*)

KATIE. I really think Jeff needs the orthodontic work but you know Bill—

(*The other line rings. The other light stutters.*)

KATIE. That's just the other line, Bill will—

(*But now we see* BILL *and* JEFF *coming downstairs behind her.*)

BILL. Honey, where're the blank video-tapes? I can't find any in the study and—

KATIE (*to* BILL). Wait! (*To* LOIS) Gonna put you on hold a sec, Lo.

(*She does. Now both lines are blinking. She pushes the top one, where the new call has just come in.*)

KATIE. Hello, Weiderman residence.

SOUND: DESPERATE SOBBING

SOBBING VOICE (*filter*). Take . . . please take . . . t-t-

KATIE. Polly? Is that you? What's wrong?

SOUND: SOBBING. (*It's awful, heartbreaking.*)

SOBBING VOICE (*filter*). Please—quick—

SOUND: SOBBING (*. . . Then, click! A broken connection.*)

KATIE. Polly, calm down! Whatever it is can't be that b—

HUM OF AN OPEN LINE.

(JEFF *has wandered toward the TV room, hoping to find a blank tape.*)

BILL. Who was that?

(*Without looking at her husband or answering him,* KATIE *slams the lower button in again.*)

KATIE. Lois? Listen, I'll call you back. That was Polly, and she sounded very upset. No . . . she hung up. Yes. I will. Thanks.

(*She hangs up.*)

BILL (*concerned*). It was Polly?

KATIE. Crying her head off. It sounded like she was trying to say "Please take me home" . . . I knew that damn school was bumming her out . . . Why I ever let you talk me into it . . .

(*She's rummaging frantically on her little phone desk. Catalogues go slithering to the floor around her stool.*)

KATIE. Connie, did you take my address book?

CONNIE (*voice*). No, Mom.

(BILL *pulls a battered book out of his back pocket and pages through it.*)

BILL. I got it. Except—

KATIE. I know, damn dorm phone is always busy. Give it to me.

BILL. Honey, calm down.

KATIE. I'll calm down after I talk to her. She is sixteen, Bill. Sixteen-year-old girls are prone to depressive interludes. Sometimes they even k . . . just give me the damn number!

BILL. 617-555-8641.

As she punches the numbers, the camera slides in to CLOSE-UP.)

KATIE. Come on, come on . . . don't be busy . . . just this once . . .

SOUND: CLICKS. (*A pause. Then . . . the phone starts ringing.*)

KATIE (*eyes closed*). Thank You, God.

VOICE (*filter*). Hartshorn Hall, this is Frieda. If you want Christine the Sex Queen, she's still in the shower, Arnie.

KATIE. Could you call Polly to the phone? Polly Weiderman? This is Kate Weiderman. Her mother.

VOICE (*filter*). Oh, jeez! Sorry. I thought—hang on, please, Mrs. Weiderman.

SOUND: THE PHONE CLUNKS DOWN.

VOICE (*filter, and very faint*). Polly? Pol? . . . Phone call! . . . It's your mother!

INTERIOR: A WIDER ANGLE ON THE PHONE NOOK, WITH BILL

BILL. Well?

KATIE. Somebody's getting her. I hope.

(JEFF *comes back in with a tape.*)

JEFF. I found one, Dad. Dennis hid 'em. As usual.

BILL. In a minute, Jeff. Go watch the tube.

JEFF. But—

BILL. I won't forget. Now go on.

(JEFF *goes.*)

KATIE. Come on, come on, come on . . .

BILL. Calm down, Katie.

KATIE (*snaps*). If you'd heard her, you wouldn't tell me to calm down! She sounded—

POLLY (*filter, cheery voice*). Hi, Mom!

KATIE. Pol? Honey? Are you all right?

POLLY (*happy, bubbling voice*). Am I all right? I aced my bio exam, got a B on my French Conversational Essay, and Ronnie Hansen asked me to the Harvest Ball. I'm so all right that if one more good thing happens to me today, I'll probably blow up like the Hindenburg.

KATIE. You didn't just call me up, crying your head off?

(*We see by* KATE*'s face that she already knows the answer to this question.*)

POLLY (*filter*). Heck no!

KATIE. I'm glad about your test and your date, honey. I guess it was someone else. I'll call you back, okay?

POLLY (*filter*). 'Kay. Say hi to Dad!

KATIE. I will.

INTERIOR: THE PHONE NOOK, WIDER

BILL. She okay?

KATIE. Fine. I could have sworn it was Polly, but . . . she's walking on air.

BILL. So it was a prank. Or someone who was crying so hard she dialed a wrong number . . . "through a shimmering film of tears," as we veteran hacks like to say.

KATIE. It was not a prank and it was not a wrong number! It was someone in my family!

BILL. Honey, you can't know that.

KATIE. No? If Jeffie called up, just crying, would you know it was him?

BILL (struck by this). Yeah, maybe. I guess I might.

(She's not listening. She's punching numbers, fast.)

BILL. Who you calling?

(She doesn't answer him. SOUND: PHONE RINGS TWICE. Then:)

OLDER FEMALE VOICE (filter). Hello?

KATIE. Mom? Are you . . . (She pauses.) Did you call just a few seconds ago?

VOICE (filter). No, dear . . . why?

KATIE. Oh . . . you know these phones. I was talking to Lois and I lost the other call.

VOICE (filter). Well, it wasn't me. Kate, I saw the prettiest dress in La Boutique today, and—

KATIE. We'll talk about it later, Mom, okay?

VOICE (filter). Kate, are you all right?

KATIE. I have . . . Mom, I think maybe I've got diarrhea. I have to go. 'Bye.

(She hangs up. BILL hangs on until she does, then he bursts into wild donkey-brays of laughter.)

BILL. Oh boy . . . diarrhea . . . I gotta remember that the next time my agent calls . . . oh Katie, that was so cool—

KATIE (almost screaming). This is not funny!

(BILL stops laughing.)

INTERIOR THE T.V. ROOM

(JEFF and DENNIS have been tussling. They stop. All three kids look toward the kitchen.)

INTERIOR: THE PHONE NOOK, WITH BILL AND KATIE

KATIE. I tell you it was someone in my family and she sounded—oh, you don't understand. I knew that voice.

BILL. But if Polly's okay and your mom's okay . . .

KATIE (positive). It's Dawn.

BILL. Come on, hon, a minute ago you were sure it was Polly.

KATIE. It had to be Dawn. I was on the phone with Lois and Mom's okay so Dawn's the only other one it could have been. She's the youngest . . . I could have mistaken her for Polly . . . and she's out there in that farm-house alone with the baby!

BILL (startled). What do you mean, alone?

KATIE. Jerry's in Burlington! It's Dawn! Something's happened to Dawn!

(CONNIE comes into the kitchen, worried.)

CONNIE. Mom? Is Aunt Dawn okay?

BILL. So far as we know, she's fine. Take it easy, doll. Bad to buy trouble before you know it's on sale.

(KATIE punches numbers and listens.)

SOUND: THE DAH-DAH-DAH OF A BUSY SIGNAL.

(KATIE hangs up. BILL looks a question at her with raised eyebrows.)

KATIE. Busy.

BILL. Katie, are you sure—

KATIE. She's the only one left—it had to be her. Bill, I'm scared. Will you drive me out there?

(BILL takes the phone from her.)

BILL. What's her number?

KATIE. 555-6169.

(BILL dials. Gets a busy. Hangs up and punches 0.)

OPERATOR *(filter).* Operator.

BILL. I'm trying to reach my sister-in-law, operator. The line is busy. I suspect there may be a problem. Can you break into the call, please?

INTERIOR: THE DOOR TO THE TV ROOM

(All three kids are standing there, silent and worried.)

INTERIOR: THE PHONE NOOK, WITH BILL AND KATIE

OPERATOR *(filter).* What is your name, sir?

BILL. William Weiderman. My number is—

OPERATOR *(filter).* Not the William Weiderman that wrote *Spider Doom?*

BILL. Yes, that was mine. If—

OPERATOR *(filter).* Oh my God, I just loved that book! I love all your books! I—

BILL. I'm delighted you do. But right now my wife is very worried about her sister. If it's possible for you to—

OPERATOR *(filter).* Yes, I can do that. Please give me your number, Mr. Weiderman, for the records. *(She giggles.)* I promise not to give it out.

BILL. It's 555-4408.

OPERATOR *(filter).* And the call number?

BILL *(looks at* KATIE*).* Uh . . .

KATIE. 555-6169.

BILL. 555-6169.

OPERATOR *(filter).* Just a moment, Mr. Weiderman . . . *Night of the Beast* was also great, by the way. Hold on.

SOUND: TELEPHONIC CLICKS AND CLACKS

KATIE. Is she—

BILL. Yes. Just . . .

(There's one final CLICK.*)*

OPERATOR *(filter).* I'm sorry, Mr. Weiderman, but that line is not busy. It's off the hook. I wonder if I sent you my copy of *Spider Doom*—

(BILL *hangs up the phone.)*

KATIE. Why did you hang up?

BILL. She can't break in. Phone's not busy. It's off the hook.

(They stare at each other bleakly.)

EXTERIOR: A LOW-SLUNG SPORTS CAR PASSES THE CAMERA, NIGHT

INTERIOR: THE CAR, WITH KATIE AND BILL

(KATIE*'s scared.* BILL, *at the wheel, doesn't look exactly calm.)*

KATIE. Hey, Bill—tell me she's all right.

BILL. She's all right.

KATIE. Now tell me what you really think.

BILL. Jeff snuck up behind me tonight and put the old booga-booga on me. He was disappointed as hell when I didn't jump. I told him I was case-hardened. *(Pause)* I lied.

KATIE. Why did Jerry have to move out there when he's gone half the time? Just her and that little tiny baby? Why?

BILL. Shh, Kate. We're almost there.

KATIE. Go faster.

EXTERIOR: THE CAR

(He does. That car is smokin'.)

INTERIOR: THE WEIDERMAN TV ROOM

(The tube's still on and the kids are still there, but the horsing around has stopped.)

CONNIE. Dennis, do you think Aunt Dawn's okay?

DENNIS (*thinks she's dead, decapitated by a maniac*). Yeah. Sure she is.

INTERIOR: THE PHONE, POINT OF VIEW FROM THE TV ROOM

(*Just sitting there on the wall in the phone nook, lights dark, looking like a snake ready to strike*)

Fade out

Act 2

EXTERIOR: AN ISOLATED FARMHOUSE

(*A long driveway leads up to it. There's one light on in the living room. Car lights sweep up the driveway. The* WEIDERMAN *car pulls up close to the garage and stops.*)

INTERIOR: THE CAR, WITH BILL AND KATIE

KATIE . I'm scared.

(BILL *bends down, reaches under his seat, and brings out a pistol.*)

BILL (*solemnly*). Booga-booga.

KATIE (*total surprise*). How long have you had that?

BILL. Since last year. I didn't want to scare you or the kids. I've got a license to carry. Come on.

EXTERIOR: BILL AND KATIE

(*They get out.* KATIE *stands by the front of the car while* BILL *goes to the garage and peers in.*)

BILL. Her car's here.

(*The camera tracks with them to the front door. Now we can hear the TV, playing loud.*

BILL *pushes the doorbell. We hear it inside. They wait.* KATIE *pushes it. Still no answer. She pushes it again and doesn't take her finger off.* BILL *looks down at:*)

EXTERIOR: OF THE LOCK, BILL'S POINT OF VIEW

(*Big scratches on it*)

EXTERIOR: BILL AND KATIE

BILL (*low*). The lock's been tampered with.

(KATIE *looks, and whimpers.* BILL *tries the door. It opens. The TV is louder.*)

BILL. Stay behind me. Be ready to run if something happens. God, I wish I'd left you home, Kate.

(*He starts in.* KATIE *comes after him, terrified, near tears.*)

INTERIOR: DAWN AND JERRY'S LIVING ROOM

(*From this angle we see only a small section of the room. The TV is much louder.* BILL *enters the room, gun up. He looks to the right . . . and suddenly all the tension goes out of him. He lowers the gun.*)

KATIE (*draws up beside him*). Bill . . . what . . .

(*He points.*)

INTERIOR: THE LIVING ROOM, WIDE, BILL AND KATIE'S POINT OF VIEW

(*The place looks like a cyclone hit it . . . but it wasn't robbery and murder that caused this mess; only a healthy eighteen-month-old baby. After a strenuous day of trashing the living room, Baby got tired and Mommy got tired and they fell asleep on the couch together. The baby is in* DAWN'*s lap. There is a pair of Walkman earphones on her head. There are toys—tough plastic Sesame Street and*

PlaySkool stuff, for the most part—scattered hell to breakfast. The baby has also pulled most of the books out of the bookcase. Had a good munch on one of them, too, by the look. BILL *goes over and picks it up. It is* Ghost Kiss.)

BILL. I've had people say they just eat my books up, but this is ridiculous.

(He's amused. KATIE *isn't. She walks over to her sister, ready to be mad . . . but she sees how really exhausted* DAWN *looks and softens.)*

INTERIOR: DAWN AND THE BABY, KATIE'S POINT OF VIEW

(Fast asleep and breathing easily, like a Raphael painting of Madonna and Child. The camera pans down to: the Walkman. We can hear the faint strains of Huey Lewis and the News. The camera pans a bit further to a Princess telephone on the table by the chair. It's off the cradle. Not much; just enough to break the connection and scare people to death.)

INTERIOR: KATIE

(She sighs, bends down, and replaces the phone. Then she pushes the STOP button on the Walkman.)

INTERIOR: DAWN, BILL, AND KATIE

*(*DAWN *wakes up when the music stops. Looks at* BILL *and* KATIE, *puzzled.)*

DAWN *(fuzzed out).* Well . . . hi.

(She realizes she's got the Walkman phones on and removes them.)

BILL. Hi, Dawn.

DAWN *(still half asleep).* Shoulda called, guys. Place is a mess.

(She smiles. She's radiant when she smiles.)

KATIE. We tried. The operator told Bill the phone was off the hook. I thought something was wrong. How can you sleep with that music blasting?

DAWN. It's restful.

(Sees the gnawed book BILL'*s holding.)*

Oh, my God, Bill, I'm sorry! Justin's teething and—

BILL. There are critics who'd say he picked just the right thing to teethe on. I don't want to scare you, beautiful, but somebody's been at your front door lock with a screwdriver or something. Whoever it was forced it.

DAWN. Gosh, no! That was Jerry, last week. I locked us out by mistake and he didn't have his key and the spare wasn't over the door like it's supposed to be. He was mad because he had to take a whiz real bad and so he took the screwdriver to it. It didn't work, either—that's one tough lock. *(Pause)* By the time I found my key he'd already gone in the bushes.

BILL. If it wasn't forced, how come I could just open the door and walk in?

DAWN *(guiltily).* Well . . . sometimes I forget to lock it.

KATIE. You didn't call me tonight, Dawn?

DAWN. Gee, no! I didn't call anyone! I was too busy chasing Justin around! He kept wanting to eat the fabric softener! Then he got sleepy and I sat down here and thought I'd listen to some tunes while I waited for your movie to come on, Bill, and I fell asleep—

(At the mention of the movie BILL *starts visibly and looks at the book. Then he glances at his watch.)*

BILL. I promised to tape it for Jeff. Come on, Katie, we've got time to get back.

KATIE. Just a second.

(She picks up the phone and dials.)

DAWN. Gee, Bill, do you think Jeffie's old enough to watch something like that?

BILL. It's network. They take out the blood-bags.

DAWN *(confused but amiable).* Oh. That's good.

INTERIOR: KATIE, CLOSE-UP

DENNIS *(filter).* Hello?

KATIE. Just thought you'd like to know your Aunt Dawn's fine.

DENNIS *(filter).* Oh! Cool. Thanks, Mom.

INTERIOR: THE PHONE NOOK, WITH DENNIS AND OTHERS

(He looks very relieved.)

DENNIS. Aunt Dawn's okay.

INTERIOR: THE CAR, WITH BILL AND KATIE

(They drive in silence for awhile.)

KATIE. You think I'm a hysterical idiot, don't you?

BILL *(genuinely surprised).* No! I was scared, too.

KATIE. You sure you're not mad?

BILL. I'm too relieved. *(Laughs)* She's sort of a scatterbrain, old Dawn, but I love her.

KATIE *(leans over and kisses him).* I love you. You're a sweet man.

BILL. I'm the boogeyman!

KATIE. I am not fooled, sweetheart.

EXTERIOR: THE CAR

(passes the camera and we dissolve to:)

INTERIOR: JEFF, IN BED

(His room is dark. The covers are pulled up to his chin.)

JEFF. You promise to tape the rest?

(Camera widens out so we can see BILL, sitting on the bed.)

BILL. I promise.

JEFF. I especially liked the part where the dead guy ripped off the punk rocker's head.

BILL. Well ... they used to take out all the blood-bags.

JEFF. What, Dad?

BILL. Nothing. I love you, Jeffie.

JEFF. I love you, too. So does Rambo.

(JEFF holds up a stuffed dragon of decidedly unmilitant aspect. BILL kisses the dragon, then JEFF.)

BILL. 'Night.

JEFF. 'Night. *(As BILL reaches his door)* Glad Aunt Dawn was okay.

BILL. Me too.

(He goes out.)

INTERIOR: TV, CLOSEUP

(A guy who looks like he died in a car crash about two weeks prior to filming [and has since been subjected to a lot of hot weather] is staggering out of a crypt. The camera widens to show BILL, releasing the VCR pause button.)

KATIE *(voice).* Booga-booga.

(BILL looks around companionably. The camera widens out more to show KATIE, wearing a sexy nightgown.)

BILL. Same to you. I missed the first forty seconds or so after the break. I had to kiss Rambo.

KATIE. You sure you're not mad at me, Bill?

(*He goes to her and kisses her.*)

BILL. Not even a smidge.

KATIE. It's just that I could have sworn it was one of mine. You know what I mean? One of mine?

BILL. Yes.

KATIE. I can still hear those sobs. So lost . . . so heartbroken.

BILL. Kate, have you ever thought you recognized someone on the street, and called her, and when she finally turned around it was a total stranger?

KATIE. Yes, once. In Seattle. I was in a mall and I thought I saw my old roommate. I . . . oh. I see what you're saying.

BILL. Sure. There are sound-alikes as well as look-alikes.

KATIE. But . . . you know your own. At least I thought so until tonight.

(*She puts her cheek on his shoulder, looking troubled.*)

KATIE. I was so positive it was Polly . . .

BILL. Because you've been worried about her getting her feet under her at the new school . . . but judging from the stuff she told you tonight, I'd say she's doing just fine in that department. Wouldn't you?

KATIE. Yes . . . I guess I would.

BILL. Let it go, hon.

KATIE (*looks at him closely*). I hate to see you looking so tired. Hurry up and have an idea, you.

BILL. Well, I'm trying.

KATIE. You coming to bed?

BILL. Soon as I finish taping this for Jeff.

KATIE (*amused*). Bill, that machine was made by Japanese technicians who think of damned near everything. It'll run on its own.

BILL. Yeah, but it's been a long time since I've seen this one, and . . .

KATIE. Okay. Enjoy. I think I'll be awake for a little while. (*Pause*) I've got a few ideas of my own.

BILL (*smiles*). Yeah?

KATIE. Yeah.

(*She starts out, showing a lot of leg, then turns in the doorway as something else strikes her.*)

KATIE. If they show that part where the punk's head gets—

BILL (*guiltily*). I'll edit it.

KATIE. 'Night. And thanks again. For everything.

(*She leaves.* BILL *sits in his chair.*)

INTERIOR: TV, CLOSE-UP

(*A couple is necking in a car. Suddenly the passenger door is ripped open by the dead guy and we dissolve to:*)

INTERIOR: KATIE, IN BED

(*It's dark. She's asleep. She wakes up . . . sort of.*)

KATIE (*sleepy*). Hey, big guy—

(*She feels for him, but his side of the bed is empty, the coverlet still pulled up. She sits up. Looks at:*)

INTERIOR: A CLOCK ON THE NIGHT TABLE, KATIE'S POINT OF VIEW:

(*It says 2:03 A.M. Then it flashes to 2:04.*)

INTERIOR: KATIE

(Fully awake now. And concerned. She gets up, puts on her robe, and leaves the bedroom.)

INTERIOR: THE TV SCREEN, CLOSEUP

(Snow)

KATIE *(voice, approaching).* Bill? Honey? You okay? Bill? Bi—

INTERIOR KATIE, IN BILL'S STUDY

(She's frozen, wide-eyed with horror.)

INTERIOR: BILL, IN HIS CHAIR

(He's slumped to one side, eyes closed, hand inside his shirt. DAWN was sleeping. BILL is not.)

EXTERIOR: A COFFIN, BEING LOWERED INTO THE GRAVE

MINISTER *(voice).* And so we commit the earthly remains of William Weiderman to the ground, confident of his spirit and soul. "Be ye not cast down, brethren . . ."

EXTERIOR: GRAVESIDE

(All the WEIDERMANS are ranged here. KATIE and POLLY wear identical black dresses and veils. CONNIE wears a black skirt and white blouse. DENNIS and JEFF wear black suits. JEFF is crying. He has Rambo the Dragon under his arm for a little extra comfort.

Camera moves in on KATIE. Tears course slowly down her cheeks. She bends and gets a handful of earth. Tosses it into the grave.)

KATIE. Love you, big guy.

EXTERIOR: JEFF

(Weeping)

EXTERIOR: LOOKING DOWN INTO THE GRAVE

(Scattered earth on top of the coffin)

DISSOLVE TO:

EXTERIOR: THE GRAVE

(A groundskeeper pats the last sod into place.)

GROUNDSKEEPER. My wife says she wishes you'd written a couple more before you had your heart attack, mister. *(Pause)* I like Westerns, m'self.

(The groundskeeper walks away, whistling.)

DISSOLVE TO:

EXTERIOR: A CHURCH DAY

TITLE CARD: FIVE YEARS LATER

(The wedding march is playing. POLLY, older and radiant with joy, emerges into a pelting shower of rice. She's in a wedding gown, her new husband by her side.

Celebrants throwing rice line either side of the path. From behind the bride and groom come others. Among them are KATIE, DENNIS, CONNIE, and JEFF . . . all five years older. With KATIE is another man. This is HANK. In the interim, KATIE has also taken a husband.

POLLY turns and her mother is there.)

POLLY. Thank you, Mom.

KATIE *(crying).* Oh doll, you're so welcome.

(They embrace. After a moment POLLY draws away and looks at HANK. There is a brief moment of tension, and then POLLY embraces HANK, too.)

POLLY. Thank you too, Hank. I'm sorry I was such a creep for so long . . .

HANK *(easily).* You were never a creep, Pol. A girl only has one father.

CONNIE. Throw it! Throw it!

(After a moment, POLLY throws her bouquet.)

EXTERIOR: THE BOUQUET, CLOSE-UP, SLOW MOTION

(*Turning and turning through the air*)

DISSOLVES TO:

INTERIOR: THE STUDY, WITH KATIE, NIGHT

(*The word-processor has been replaced by a wide lamp looming over a stack of blueprints. The book-jackets have been replaced by photos of buildings. Ones that have first been built in* HANK's *mind, presumably.*

KATIE *is looking at the desk, thoughtful and a little sad.*)

HANK (*voice*). Coming to bed, Kate?

(*She turns and the camera widens out to give us* HANK. *He's wearing a robe over pajamas. She comes to him and gives him a little hug, smiling. Maybe we notice a few streaks of gray in her hair; her pretty pony has done its fair share of running since* BILL *died.*)

KATIE. In a little while. A woman doesn't see her first one get married every day, you know.

HANK. I know.

(*The camera follows as they walk from the work area of the study to the more informal area. This is much the same as it was in the old days, with a coffee table, stereo, TV, couch, and* BILL's *old easy-chair. She looks at this.*)

HANK. You still miss him, don't you?

KATIE. Some days more than others. You didn't know, and Polly didn't remember.

HANK (*gently*). Remember what, doll?

KATIE. Polly got married on the five-year anniversary of Bill's death.

HANK (*hugs her*). Come on to bed, why don't you?

KATIE. In a little while.

HANK. Okay. Maybe I'll still be awake.

KATIE. Got a few ideas, do you?

HANK. I might.

KATIE. That's nice.

(*He kisses her, then leaves, closing the door behind him.* KATIE *sits in* BILL's *old chair. Close by, on the coffee table, is a remote control for the TV and an extension phone.* KATIE *looks at the blank TV, and the camera moves in on her face. One tear rims one eye, sparkling like a sapphire.*)

KATIE. I do still miss you, big guy. Lots and lots. Every day. And you know what? It hurts.

(*The tear falls. She picks up the TV remote and pushes the ON button.*)

INTERIOR: TV, KATIE'S POINT OF VIEW

(*An ad for Ginsu Knives comes to an end and is replaced by a Star logo.*)

ANNOUNCER (*voice*). Now back to Channel 63's Thursday night Star Time Movie . . . *Ghost Kiss.*

(*The logo dissolves into a guy who looks like he died in a car crash about two weeks ago and has since been subjected to a lot of hot weather. He comes staggering out of the same old crypt.*)

INTERIOR: KATIE

(*Terribly startled—almost horrified. She hits the OFF button on the remote control. The TV blinks off.*

KATIE's *face begins to work. She struggles against the impending emotional storm, but the coincidence of the movie is just one thing too many on what must have already been one of the most emotionally trying days of her life. The dam breaks and she begins to sob . . . terrible heartbroken sobs. She reaches*

out for the little table by the chair, meaning to put the remote control on it, and knocks the phone onto the floor.)

SOUND: THE HUM OF AN OPEN LINE

(Her tear-stained face grows suddenly still as she looks at the telephone. Something begins to fill it . . . an idea? an intuition? Hard to tell. And maybe it doesn't matter.)

INTERIOR: THE TELEPHONE, KATIE'S POINT OF VIEW

(The camera moves in to EXTREME CLOSEUP . . . moves in until the dots in the off-the-hook receiver look like chasms.)

SOUND OF OPEN-LINE BUZZ UP TO LOUD

WE GO INTO THE BLACK . . . AND HEAR

BILL (voice). Who are you calling? Who do you want to call? Who would you call, if it wasn't too late?

INTERIOR KATIE

(There is now a strange hypnotized look on her face. She reaches down, scoops the telephone up, and punches in numbers, seemingly at random.)

SOUND: RINGING PHONE

(KATIE continues to look hypnotized. The look holds until the phone is answered . . . and she hears herself on the other end of the line.)

KATIE (voice; filter). Hello, Weiderman residence.

(KATIE—our present-day KATIE with the streaks of gray in her hair—goes on sobbing, yet an expression of desperate hope is trying to be born on her face. On some level she understands that the depth of her grief has allowed a kind of telephonic time-travel. She's trying to talk, to force the words out.)

KATIE (sobbing). Take . . . please take . . . t-t-

INTERIOR: KATIE, IN THE PHONE NOOK, REPRISE

(It's five years ago. BILL is standing beside her, looking concerned. JEFF is wandering off to look for a blank tape in the other room.)

KATIE. Polly? What's wrong?

INTERIOR: KATIE, IN THE STUDY

KATIE (sobbing). Please—quick—

SOUND: CLICK OF A BROKEN CONNECTION

KATIE (screaming). Take him to the hospital! If you want him to live, take him to the hospital! He's going to have a heart attack! He—

SOUND: HUM OF AN OPEN LINE

(Slowly, very slowly, KATIE hangs up the telephone. Then, after a moment, she picks it up again. She speaks aloud with no self-consciousness whatever. Probably doesn't even know she's doing it.)

KATIE. I dialed the old number. I dialed—

SLAM CUT TO:

INTERIOR: BILL, IN THE PHONE NOOK WITH KATIE BESIDE HIM

(He's just taken the phone from KATIE and is speaking to the operator.)

OPERATOR (filter, giggles). I promise not to give it out.

BILL. It's 555-

SLAM CUT TO:

INTERIOR: KATIE, IN BILL'S OLD CHAIR, CLOSEUP

KATIE (finishes). -4408.

INTERIOR: THE PHONE, CLOSE-UP

(KATIE's *trembling finger carefully picks out the number, and we hear the corresponding tones: 555-4408.*)

INTERIOR: KATIE, IN BILL'S OLD CHAIR, CLOSE-UP

(*She closes her eyes as the phone begins to ring. Her face is filled with an agonizing mixture of hope and fear. If only she can have one more chance to pass the vital message on, it says . . . just one more chance.*)

KATIE (*low*). Please . . . please . . .

RECORDED VOICE (*filter*). You have reached a non-working number. Please hang up and dial again. If you need assistance—

(KATIE *hangs up again. Tears stream down her cheeks. The camera pans away and down to the telephone.*)

INTERIOR: THE PHONE NOOK, WITH KATIE AND BILL, REPRISE

BILL. So it was a prank. Or someone who was crying so hard she dialed a wrong number . . . "through a shimmering film of tears," as we veteran hacks like to say.

KATIE. It was not a prank and it was not a wrong number! It was someone in my family!

INTERIOR: KATIE (PRESENT DAY) IN BILL'S STUDY

KATIE. Yes. Someone in my family. Someone very close. (*Pause*) Me.

(*She suddenly throws the phone across the room. Then she begins to sob again and puts her hands over her face. The camera holds on her for a moment, then dollies across to:*)

INTERIOR: THE PHONE

(*It lies on the carpet, looking both bland and somehow ominous. Camera moves in to* EXTREME CLOSE-UP—*the holes in the receiver once more look like huge dark chasms. We hold, then:*)

Fade to black

Responding to the Play

1. Look back over the script for *Sorry, Right Number* and identify the first scene you found suspenseful. Describe in writing what you hoped and what you feared would happen.
2. In order for a play to be suspenseful, the audience has to care about the characters. How did the author get you to identify with the characters in this screenplay?
3. How did the horror in *Ghost Kiss* differ from the horror in the message Katie received?
4. How do the camera angles effect the way in which viewers experience the telephone calls?
5. Humor often helps relieve tension. Identify a humorous moment that cuts the suspense in this play, and explain how it does so.

About Stephen King

Stephen King has written dozens of horror stories, many of which have been made into screenplays, including *Salem's Lot*, *The Shining*, *The Dead Zone*, *Cujo*, and *Dolores Claiborne*. His early novel, *Carrie*, about a tormented teenager, became a cult classic, inspiring a movie, a musical, and a comedy spoof. King has also written his own screenplays, most notably for *Cat's Eye*, *Creep Show*, *Pet Sematary*, and *The Stand*. His writing style is vibrant and suspenseful, lending itself easily to the screen.

Creating and Performing

1. Rewrite a page from this play in screenplay format, with separate columns for words and images.
2. The first scene of this play introduces a typical family. Perform a portion of the scene in which the children are bickering. Be sure to make each character likable and distinct from the others.
3. The scene featuring Bill's death and the scene featuring Katie's phone call are linked, though they take place five years apart. Write a set plan for each scene. Include similarities to establish links between the two sets and differences to indicate the passing of time.

Before Reading

DEATH KNOCKS

The Play as Literature: Dialogue

Dialogue is more than a simple recorded conversation. It performs important dramatic functions as well. Effective dialogue advances the plot of the play. It fills in details about events and characters and often supplies information about the past. It reveals the personality, interests, nationality, and status of characters. It can also make characters and events seem lifelike and real by allowing the characters to speak as real people might speak under the same circumstances.

As you read *Death Knocks*, be aware of the way in which dialogue helps define the characters, their circumstances, and the plot of the play. Notice how it makes the somber subject of death approachable and even funny.

The Play as Theatre: Comic Timing

Writers develop comedy by building tension and then releasing it in unexpected ways. Actors do the same thing. In addition to providing capable line readings, comic actors must provide surprises by responding quickly to each other, varying the pace at which they speak and act, and changing their tone at surprising moments.

Look carefully at the opening moments of this play. Where can you find opportunities for an actor to vary pace and tone in order to provide comic surprises?

WARM UP!

With a partner, take on two distinct roles. Then develop four or five lines of dialogue that offer clues to your characters' personalities, occupations, and status. Perform your dialogue for the class and see how many classmates can guess correctly who your characters are.

DEATH KNOCKS

by Woody Allen

The play takes place in the bedroom of the NAT ACKERMAN*s' two-story house, somewhere in Kew Gardens. The carpeting is wall-to-wall. There is a big double bed and a large vanity. The room is elaborately furnished and curtained, and on the walls there are several paintings and a not really attractive barometer. Soft theme music as the curtain rises.* NAT ACKERMAN, *a bald, paunchy fifty-seven-year-old dress manufacturer, is lying on the bed finishing off tomorrow's* Daily News. *He wears a bathrobe and slippers, and reads by a bed light clipped to the white headboard of the bed. The time is near midnight. Suddenly we hear a noise, and* NAT *sits up and looks at the window.*

NAT. What the hell is that?

Climbing awkwardly through the window is a sombre, caped figure. The intruder wears a black hood and skintight black clothes. The hood covers his head but not his face, which is middle-aged and stark white. He is something like NAT *in appearance. He huffs audibly and then trips over the windowsill and falls into the room.*

DEATH *(for it is no one else).* Jeez. I nearly broke my neck.

NAT *(watching with bewilderment).* Who are you?

DEATH. Death.

NAT. Who?

DEATH. Death. Listen—can I sit down? I nearly broke my neck. I'm shaking like a leaf.

NAT. Who *are* you?

DEATH. *Death.* You got a glass of water?

NAT. Death? What do you mean, Death?

DEATH. What is wrong with you? You see the black costume and the whitened face?

NAT. Yeah.

DEATH. Is it Halloween?

NAT. No.

DEATH. Then I'm Death. Now can I get a glass of water—or a Fresca?

NAT. If this is some joke—

DEATH. What kind of joke? You're fifty-seven? Nat Ackerman? One eighteen Pacific Street? Unless I blew it—where's that call sheet?

(He fumbles through pocket, finally producing a card with an address on it. It seems to check.)

NAT. What do you want with me?

DEATH. What do I want? What do you think I want?

NAT. You must be kidding. I'm in perfect health.

DEATH *(unimpressed)*. Uh-huh. *(Looking around)* This is a nice place. You do it yourself?

NAT. We had a decorator, but we worked with her.

DEATH *(looking at the picture on the wall)*. I love those kids with the big eyes.

NAT. I don't want to go yet.

DEATH. *You* don't want to go? Please don't start in. As it is, I'm nauseous from the climb.

NAT. What climb?

DEATH. I climbed up the drainpipe. I was trying to make a dramatic entrance. I see the big windows and you're awake reading. I figure it's worth a shot. I'll climb up and enter with a little—you know . . . *(Snaps fingers)* Meanwhile, I get my heel caught on some vines, the drainpipe breaks, and I'm hanging by a thread. Then my cape begins to tear. Look, let's just go. It's been a rough night.

NAT. You broke my drainpipe?

DEATH. Broke. It didn't break. It's a little bent. Didn't you hear anything? I slammed into the ground.

NAT. I was reading.

DEATH. You must have been really engrossed. *(Lifting newspaper* NAT *was reading)* "NAB COEDS IN POT ORGY." Can I borrow this?

NAT. I'm not finished.

DEATH. Er—I don't know how to put this to you, pal . . .

NAT. Why didn't you just ring downstairs?

DEATH. I'm telling you, I could have, but how does it look? This way I get a little drama going. Something. Did you read *Faust*?

NAT. What?

DEATH. And what if you had company? You're sitting there with important people. I'm Death—I should ring the bell and traipse right in the front? Where's your thinking?

NAT. Listen, mister, it's very late.

DEATH. Yeah. Well, you want to go?

NAT. Go where?

DEATH. Death. It. The Thing. The Happy Hunting Grounds. *(Looking at his own knee)* Y'know, that's a pretty bad cut. My first job, I'm liable to get gangrene yet.

NAT. Now, wait a minute. I need time. I'm not ready to go.

DEATH. I'm sorry. I can't help you. I'd like to, but it's the moment.

NAT. How can it be the moment? I just merged with Modiste Originals.

DEATH. What's the difference, a couple of bucks more or less.

NAT. Sure, what do you care? You guys probably have all your expenses paid.

DEATH. You want to come along now?

NAT *(studying him)*. I'm sorry, but I cannot believe you're Death.

DEATH. Why? What'd you expect—Rock Hudson?

NAT. No, it's not that.

DEATH. I'm sorry if I disappointed you.

NAT. Don't get upset. I don't know, I always thought you'd be ...uh ...taller.

DEATH. I'm five seven. It's average for my weight.

NAT. You look a little like me.

DEATH. Who should I look like? I'm your death.

NAT. Give me some time. Another day.

DEATH. I can't. What do you want me to say?

NAT. One more day. Twenty-four hours.

DEATH. What do you need it for? The radio said rain tomorrow.

NAT. Can't we work out something?

DEATH. Like what?

NAT. You play chess?

DEATH. No, I don't.

NAT. I once saw a picture of you playing chess.

DEATH. Couldn't be me, because I don't play chess. Gin rummy, maybe.

NAT. You play gin rummy?

DEATH. Do I play gin rummy? Is Paris a city?

NAT. You're good, huh?

DEATH. Very good.

NAT. I'll tell you what I'll do—

DEATH. Don't make any deals with me.

NAT. I'll play you gin rummy. If you win, I'll go immediately. If I win, give me some more time. A little bit—one more day.

DEATH. Who's got time to play gin rummy?

NAT. Come on. If you're so good.

DEATH. Although I feel like a game ...

NAT. Come on. Be a sport. We'll shoot for a half hour.

DEATH. I really shouldn't.

NAT. I got the cards right here. Don't make a production.

DEATH. All right, come on. We'll play a little. It'll relax me.

NAT (*getting cards, pad, and pencil*). You won't regret this.

DEATH. Don't give me a sales talk. Get the cards and give me a Fresca and put out something. For God's sake, a stranger drops in, you don't have potato chips or pretzels.

NAT. There's M&M's downstairs in a dish.

DEATH. M&M's. What if the President came? He'd get M&M's too?

NAT. You're not the President.

DEATH. Deal.

(NAT *deals, turns up a five.*)

NAT. You want to play a tenth of a cent a point to make it interesting?

DEATH. It's not interesting enough for you?

NAT. I play better when money's at stake.

DEATH. Whatever you say, Newt.

NAT. Nat. Nat Ackerman. You don't know my name?

DEATH. Newt, Nat—I got such a headache.

NAT. You want that five?

DEATH. No.

NAT. So pick.

DEATH (surveying his hand as he picks). Jesus, I got nothing here.

NAT. What's it like?

DEATH. What's what like?

(Throughout the following, they pick and discard.)

NAT. Death.

DEATH. What should it be like? You lay there.

NAT. Is there anything after?

DEATH. Aha, you're saving twos.

NAT. I'm asking. Is there anything after?

DEATH (absently). You'll see.

NAT. Oh, then I will actually see something?

DEATH. Well, maybe I shouldn't have put it that way. Throw.

NAT. To get an answer from you is a big deal.

DEATH. I'm playing cards.

NAT. All right, play, play.

DEATH. Meanwhile, I'm giving you one card after another.

NAT. Don't look through the discards.

DEATH. I'm not looking. I'm straightening them up. What was the knock card?

NAT. Four. You ready to knock already?

DEATH. Who said I'm ready to knock? All I asked was what was the knock card.

NAT. And all I asked was is there anything for me to look forward to.

DEATH. Play.

NAT. Can't you tell me anything? Where do we go?

DEATH. We? To tell you the truth, you fall in a crumpled heap on the floor.

NAT. Oh, I can't wait for that! Is it going to hurt?

DEATH. Be over in a second.

NAT. Terrific. (Sighs) I needed this. A man merges with Modiste Originals ...

DEATH. How's four points?

NAT. You're knocking?

DEATH. Four points is good?

NAT. No, I got two.

DEATH. You're kidding.

NAT. No, you lose.

DEATH. Holy Christ, and I thought you were saving sixes.

NAT. No. Your deal. Twenty points and two boxes. Shoot. (DEATH deals.) I must fall on the floor, eh? I can't be standing over the sofa when it happens?

DEATH. No. Play.

NAT. Why not?

DEATH. Because you fall on the floor! Leave me alone. I'm trying to concentrate.

NAT. Why must it be on the floor? That's all I'm saying! Why can't the whole thing happen and I'll stand next to the sofa?

DEATH. I'll try my best. Now can we play?

NAT. That's all I'm saying. You remind me of Moe Lefkowitz. He's also stubborn.

DEATH. I remind him of Moe Lefkowitz. I'm one of the most terrifying figures you could possibly imagine, and him I remind of Moe Lefkowitz. What is he, a furrier?

NAT. You should be such a furrier. He's good for eighty thousand a year. Passementeries.[1] He's got his own factory. Two points.

DEATH. What?

NAT. Two points. I'm knocking. What have you got?

DEATH. My hand is like a basketball score.

NAT. And it's spades.

DEATH. If you didn't talk so much.

(They redeal and play on.)

NAT. What'd you mean before when you said this was your first job?

DEATH. What does it sound like?

NAT. What are you telling me—that nobody ever went before?

DEATH. Sure they went. But I didn't take them.

NAT. So who did?

DEATH. Others.

NAT. There's others?

DEATH. Sure. Each one has his own personal way of going.

NAT. I never knew that.

DEATH. Why should you know? Who are you?

NAT. What do you mean who am I? Why—I'm nothing?

DEATH. Not nothing. You're a dress manufacturer. Where do you come to knowledge of the eternal mysteries?

NAT. What are you talking about? I make a beautiful dollar. I sent two kids through college. One is in

---

1. passementerie, trimming of braid, bead, or cord

Death Knocks by Woody Allen

advertising, the other's married. I got my own home. I drive a Chrysler. My wife has whatever she wants. Maids, mink coat, vacations. Right now she's at the Eden Roc. Fifty dollars a day because she wants to be near her sister. I'm supposed to join her next week, so what do you think I am—some guy off the street?

DEATH. All right. Don't be so touchy.

NAT. Who's touchy?

DEATH. How would you like it if I got insulted quickly?

NAT. Did I insult you?

DEATH. You didn't say you were disappointed in me?

NAT. What do you expect? You want me to throw you a block party?

DEATH. I'm not talking about that. I mean me personally. I'm too short, I'm this, I'm that.

NAT. I said you looked like me. It's a reflection.

DEATH. All right, deal, deal.

They continue to play as music steals in and the lights dim until all is in total darkness. The lights slowly come up again, and now it is later and their game is over. Nat tallies.

NAT. Sixty-eight ... one-fifty ... Well, you lose.

DEATH (*dejectedly looking through the deck*). I knew I shouldn't have thrown that nine. Damn it.

NAT. So I'll see you tomorrow.

DEATH. What do you mean you'll see me tomorrow?

NAT. I won the extra day. Leave me alone.

DEATH. You were serious?

NAT. We made a deal.

DEATH. Yeah, but—

NAT. Don't "but" me. I won twenty-four hours. Come back tomorrow.

DEATH. I didn't know we were actually playing for time.

NAT. That's too bad about you. You should pay attention.

DEATH. Where am I going to go for twenty-four hours?

NAT. What's the difference? The main thing is I won an extra day.

DEATH. What do you want me to do— walk the streets?

NAT. Check into a hotel and go to a movie. Take a *schvitz*.[2] Don't make a federal case.

DEATH. Add the score again.

NAT. Plus you owe me twenty-eight dollars.

DEATH. *What?*

NAT. That's right, buster. Here it is— read it.

DEATH (*going through pockets*). I have a few singles—not twenty-eight dollars.

NAT. I'll take a check.

DEATH. From what account?

NAT. Look who I'm dealing with.

DEATH. Sue me. Where do I keep my checking account?

---

2. *schvitz,* from *schvitzbud,* sweat bath, a kind of bath in which the bather sweats in a steam room, showers, and then has a massage or rubdown

NAT. All right, gimme what you got and we'll call it square.

DEATH. Listen, I need that money.

NAT. Why should you need money?

DEATH. What are you talking about? You're going to the Beyond.

NAT. So?

DEATH. So—you know how far that is?

NAT. So?

DEATH. So where's gas? Where's tolls?

NAT. We're going by car!

DEATH. You'll find out. *(Agitatedly)* Look—I'll be back tomorrow, and you'll give me a chance to win the money back. Otherwise I'm in definite trouble.

NAT. Anything you want. Double or nothing we'll play. I'm liable to win an extra week or a month. The way you play, maybe years.

DEATH. Meantime I'm stranded.

NAT. See you tomorrow.

DEATH *(being edged to the doorway).* Where's a good hotel? What am I

talking about hotel, I got no money. I'll go sit in Bickford's. *(He picks up the* News.*)*

NAT. Out. Out. That's my paper. *(He takes it back.)*

DEATH *(exiting).* I couldn't just take him and go. I had to get involved in rummy.

NAT *(calling after him).* And be careful going downstairs. On one of the steps the rug is loose.

(And, on cue, we hear a terrific crash. NAT *sighs, then crosses to the bedside table and makes a phone call.)*

NAT. Hello, Moe? Me. Listen, I don't know if somebody's playing a joke, or what, but Death was just here. We played a little gin . . . No, *Death.* In person. Or somebody who claims to be Death. But, Moe, he's such a *schlep!*[3]

---

3. *schlep,* person who is unusually awkward, bumbling, or slow

CURTAIN

DEATH KNOCKS

Responding to the Play

1. At what point in the play did Death first make you laugh? Why was this moment funny?
2. Is Nat Ackerman like anyone you know? Explain.
3. How is Death like Nat? How is he different?
4. How long do you think Nat can win out over Death? Explain.
5. Draw a sketch personifying death as you see it.

About Woody Allen

Woody Allen was born in 1935. He is a prominent writer, actor, director, and comedian who has directed more than twenty-five movies. He began his career as a comic writer for magazines, television, and film. Allen launched his film career In 1965, when he co-wrote and acted in a farcical comedy called *What's New, Pussycat?*

Allen's early films were broad physical comedies in which he played a prominent character. Often, these comedies had elements of social satire and romance. Later, he broadened his style to include serious, introspective films and sophisticated comic dramas. His comedies have been more popular than his serious work.

Allen has also written comic essays and stories, and two plays, *Don't Drink the Water* (1966) and *Play It Again, Sam* (1969), both of which were adapted for film. He won Academy Awards for directing and writing *Annie Hall* (1977) and for writing *Hannah and Her Sisters* (1986).

CREATING AND PERFORMING

1. With a few partners, write a short, serious scene. Then make changes to create humor.
2. Design a costume for Death.
3. Improvise a comic scene based on the lines of dialogue you wrote in the Warm Up.

The Actor's Nightmare

The Play as Literature: Style

What's your style? Whether it's bold or bashful, it's part of who you are—and a signature by which people know you. The same is true for writers. Writers each have their own style, characterized by the vocabulary, sentence structure, diction, and literary tools they use.

In *The Actor's Nightmare*, Christopher Durang presents his own wacky style alongside parodies of other playwrights such as William Shakespeare, Noel Coward, and Samuel Beckett. (You can read more about parody on p. 169.) As you read the play, try to pick out features that characterize each author's style.

The Play as Theatre: Costumes

Costumes, like sets, help establish the time and place in which the action of a play occurs. In addition, costumes contribute to the mood and overall style of a production. They can also provide clues to the personalities of the characters.

Costuming can illuminate a character's status, suggesting his or her physical, emotional, and economic condition. Costumes can also show alliances with other characters and provide clues about choices that a character will make.

What do their costumes tell you about these characters?

A play like *The Actor's Nightmare* offers a wide range of costuming opportunities—and challenges. As you read the play, think about how you would costume a character for a role that spans roughly 400 years and five distinct styles.

Warm Up!

In order to practice acting in a variety of styles, form groups of three. Each person should take a turn introducing the other two people in the group to each other. With each introduction, the speaker should invent a new and different identity for the other two. Challenge this pair to act and speak in a style that fits the way in which they were introduced.

The Actor's Nightmare

by Christopher Durang

Setting	Characters	Time
A stage	GEORGE SPELVIN MEG SARAH SIDDONS ELLEN TERRY HENRY IRVING	The present

Scene—Basically an empty stage, maybe with a few set pieces on it or around it. GEORGE SPELVIN, *a young man (20 to 30), wanders in. He looks baffled and uncertain where he is. Enter* MEG, *the stage manager. In jeans and sweatshirt, perhaps, pleasant, efficient, age 25 to 30 probably.*

GEORGE. Oh, I'm sorry. I don't know how I got in here.

MEG. Oh, thank goodness you're here. I've been calling you.

GEORGE. Pardon?

MEG. An awful thing has happened. Eddie's been in a car accident, and you'll have to go on for him.

GEORGE. Good heavens, how awful. Who's Eddie?

MEG. Eddie *(He looks blank.)* Edwin. You have to go on for him.

GEORGE. On for him.

MEG. Well, he can't go on. He's been in a car accident.

GEORGE. Yes I understood that part. But what do you mean "go on for him"?

MEG. You play the part. Now I know you haven't had a chance to rehearse it exactly, but presumably you know your lines, and you've certainly seen it enough.

GEORGE. I don't understand. Do I know you?

MEG. George, we really don't have time for this kind of joshing. Half-hour. *(Exits)*

GEORGE. My name isn't George, it's . . . well, I don't know what it is, but it isn't George. *(Enter* SARAH SIDDONS, *a glamorous actress, perhaps in a sweeping cape)*

SARAH. My God, did you hear about Eddie?

GEORGE. Yes, I did.

SARAH. It's just too, too awful. Now good luck tonight, George darling, we're all counting on you. Of course, you're a little too young for the part, and you are shorter than Edwin so we'll cut all the lines about bumping your head on the ceiling. And don't forget when I cough three times, that's your cue to unzip the back of my dress and then I'll slap you. We changed it from last night. *(She starts to exit.)*

GEORGE. Wait, please. What play are we doing exactly?

SARAH *(stares at him).* What?

GEORGE. What is the play, please?

SARAH. Coward.

GEORGE. Pardon?

SARAH. Coward. *(Looks at him as if he's crazy)* It's the Coward. Noel Coward. *(Suddenly relaxing).* George, don't do that. For a second, I thought you were serious. Break a leg, darling. *(Exits)*

GEORGE *(to himself).* Coward. I wonder if it's *Private Lives.* At least I've seen that one. I don't remember rehearsing it exactly. And am I an actor? I thought I was an accountant. And why does everyone call me George? *(Enter* DAME ELLEN TERRY, *younger than* SARAH, *a bit less grand)*

ELLEN. Hello, Stanley. I heard about Edwin. Good luck tonight. We're counting on you.

GEORGE. Wait. What play are we doing?

ELLEN. Very funny, Stanley.

GEORGE. No really. I've forgotten.

ELLEN. *Checkmate.*

GEORGE. *Checkmate?*

ELLEN. By Samuel Beckett. You know, in the garbage cans. You always play these jokes, Stanley, just don't do it onstage. Well, good luck tonight. I mean, break a leg. Did you hear? Edwin broke *both* legs. *(Exits)*

GEORGE. I've never heard of *Checkmate.* *(Reenter* MEG*)*

MEG. George, get into costume. We have 15 minutes. *(Exits)* *(Enter* HENRY

IRVING, *age 28 to 33, also somewhat grand)*

HENRY. Good God, I'm late. Hi, Eddie. Oh, you're not Eddie. Who are you?

GEORGE. You've never seen me before?

HENRY. Who the devil are you?

GEORGE. I don't really know. George, I think. Maybe Stanley, but probably George. I think I'm an accountant.

HENRY. Look, no one's allowed backstage before a performance. So you'll have to leave, or I'll be forced to report you to the stage manager.

GEORGE. Oh, she knows I'm here already.

HENRY. Oh. Well, if Meg knows you're here it must be all right I suppose. It's not my affair. I'm late enough already. *(Exits)*

MEG *(off-stage).* Ten minutes, everybody. The call is 10 minutes.

GEORGE. I better just go home. *(Takes off his pants)* Oh dear, I didn't mean to do that. *(Enter* MEG*)*

MEG. George, stop that. Go into the dressing room to change. Really, you keep this up and we'll bring you up on charges.

GEORGE. But where is the dressing room?

MEG. George, you're not amusing. It's that way. And give me those. *(Takes his pants)* I'll go soak them for you.

GEORGE. Please don't soak them.

MEG. Don't tell me my job. Now go get changed. The call is 5 minutes. *(Pushes him off to dressing room; crosses back the other way, calling out)* 5 minutes, everyone. 5 minutes. Places.

(A curtain closes on the stage. Darkness. Lights come up on the curtain. A voice is heard.)

VOICE. Ladies and gentlemen, may I have your attention please? At this evening's performance, the role of Elyot, normally played by Edwin Booth, will be played by George Spelvin. *(Sound of audience moans)* The role of Amanda, normally played by Sarah Bernhardt, will be played by Sarah Siddons. The role of Kitty the bar maid will be played by Mrs. Patrick Campbell. Dr. Crippin will play himself. The management wishes to remind the audience that the taking of photographs is strictly forbidden by law, and is dangerous as it may disorient the actor. Thank you.

The curtain opens. There is very little set, but probably a small set piece to indicate the railing of a terrace balcony. Some other set piece [a chair, a table, a cocktail bar] might be used to indicate wealth, elegance, French Riviera.

SARAH SIDDONS *is present when the curtain opens. She is in a glamorous evening gown, and is holding a cocktail glass and standing behind the terrace railing, staring out above the audience's head. There is the recorded sound of applause.*

After a moment GEORGE *arrives onstage, fairly pushed on. He is dressed as Hamlet—black leotard and large gold medallion around his neck. As soon as he enters, several flash photos are taken, which disorient him greatly. When he can, he looks out and sees the audience and is very taken aback. We hear music.*

SARAH. Extraordinary how potent cheap music is.

GEORGE. What?

SARAH. Extraordinary how potent cheap music is.

GEORGE. Yes, that's true. Am I supposed to be Hamlet?

SARAH *(alarmed; then going on).* Whose yacht do you think that is?

GEORGE. Where?

SARAH. The Duke of Westminster, I expect. It always is.

GEORGE. Ah, well, perhaps. To be or not to be. I don't know any more of it. *(She looks irritated at him; then she coughs three times. He remembers and unzips her dress; she slaps him.)*

SARAH. Elyot, please. We are on our honeymoons.

GEORGE. Are we?

SARAH. Yes. *(Irritated, being over-explicit)* Me with Victor, and you with Sibyl.

GEORGE. Ah.

SARAH. Tell me about Sibyl.

GEORGE. I've never met her.

SARAH. Ah, Elyot, you're so amusing. You're married to Sibyl. Tell me about her.

GEORGE. Nothing much to tell really. She's sort of nondescript, I'd say.

SARAH. I bet you were going to say that she's just like Lady Bundle, and that she has several chins, and one blue eye and one brown eye, and a third eye in the center of her forehead. Weren't you?

GEORGE. Yes. I think so.

SARAH. Victor's like that too. *(Long pause)* I bet you were just about to tell me that you travelled around the world.

GEORGE. Yes I was. I travelled around the world.

SARAH. How was it?

GEORGE. The world?

SARAH. Yes.

GEORGE. Oh, very nice.

SARAH. I always feared the Taj Mahal would look like a biscuit box. Did it?

GEORGE. Not really.

SARAH (*She's going to give him the cue again.*) I always feared the Taj Mahal would look like a biscuit box. Did it?

GEORGE. I guess it did.

SARAH (*again*). I always feared the Taj Mahal would look like a biscuit box. Did it?

GEORGE. Hard to say. What brand biscuit box?

SARAH. I always feared the Taj Mahal would look like a biscuit box. Did it? (*Pause*) Did it? Did it?

GEORGE. I wonder whose yacht that is out there.

SARAH. Did it? Did it? Did it? Did it? (*Enter* MEG. *She's put on an apron and maid's hat and carries a duster, but is otherwise still in her stage manager's garb.*)

MEG. My, this balcony looks dusty. I think I'll just clean it up a little. (*Dusts and goes to* GEORGE *and whispers in his ear; exits*)

GEORGE. Not only did the Taj Mahal look like a biscuit box, but women should be struck regularly like gongs. (*Applause*)

SARAH. Extraordinary how potent cheap music is.

GEORGE. Yes. Quite extraordinary.

SARAH. How was China?

GEORGE. China?

SARAH. You travelled around the world. How was China?

GEORGE. I liked it, but I felt homesick.

SARAH (*Again this is happening; gives him cue again.*) How was China?

GEORGE. Lots of rice. The women bind their feet.

SARAH. How was China?

GEORGE. I hated it. I missed you.

SARAH. How was China?

GEORGE. I hated it. I missed . . . Sibyl.

SARAH. How was China?

GEORGE. I . . . miss the maid. Oh, maid!

SARAH. *How was China?*

GEORGE. Just wait a moment please. Oh, maid! (*Enter* MEG) Ah, there you are. I think you missed a spot here. (*She crosses, dusts, and whispers in his ear; exits.*)

SARAH. How was China?

GEORGE (*with authority*). Very large, China.

SARAH. And Japan?

GEORGE. (*doesn't know, but makes a guess*). Very . . . small, Japan.

SARAH. And Ireland?

GEORGE. Very . . . green.

SARAH. And Iceland?

GEORGE. Very white.

SARAH. And Italy?

GEORGE. Very . . . Neapolitan.

SARAH. And Copenhagen?

GEORGE. Very cosmopolitan.

SARAH. And Florida?

GEORGE. Very . . . condominium.

SARAH. And Perth Amboy?

GEORGE. Very . . . mobile home, I don't know.

SARAH. And Sibyl?

GEORGE. What?

SARAH. Do you love Sibyl?

GEORGE. Who's Sibyl?

SARAH. Your new wife, who you married after you and I got our divorce.

GEORGE. Oh were we married? Oh yes, I forgot that part.

SARAH. Elyot, you're so amusing. You make me laugh all the time. *(Laughs)* So, do you love Sibyl?

GEORGE. Probably. I married her. *(Pause. She coughs three times, he unzips her dress, she slaps him.)*

SARAH. Oh, Elyot, darling, I'm sorry. We were mad to have left each other. Kiss me. *(They kiss. Enter* DAME ELLEN TERRY *as* SIBYL, *in an evening gown.)*

ELLEN. Oh, how ghastly.

SARAH. Oh, dear. And this must be Sibyl.

ELLEN. Oh, how ghastly. What shall we do?

SARAH. We must all speak in very low voices and attempt to be civilized.

ELLEN. Is this Amanda? Oh, Elyot, I think she's simply obnoxious.

SARAH. How very rude.

ELLEN. Oh, Elyot, how can you treat me like this?

GEORGE. Hello, Sibyl.

ELLEN. Well, since you ask, I'm very upset. I was inside writing a letter to your mother and wanted to know how to spell apothecary.

SARAH. A-P-O-T-H-E-C-A-R-Y.

ELLEN *(icy)*. Thank you. *(Writes it down;* SARAH *looks over her shoulder.)*

SARAH. Don't scribble, Sibyl.

ELLEN. Did my eyes deceive me, or were you kissing my husband a moment ago?

SARAH. We must all speak in very low voices and attempt to be civilized.

ELLEN. I was speaking in a low voice.

SARAH. Yes, but I could still hear you.

ELLEN. Oh. Sorry. *(Speaks too low to be heard)*

SARAH *(speaks inaudibly also)*

ELLEN *(speaks inaudibly)*

SARAH *(speaks inaudibly)*

ELLEN *(speaks inaudibly)*

SARAH. I can't hear a bloody word she's saying. The woman's a nincompoop. Say something, Elyot.

GEORGE. I couldn't hear her either.

ELLEN. Elyot, you have to choose between us immediately—do you love this creature, or do you love me?

GEORGE. I wonder where the maid is.

ELLEN and SARAH *(together, furious)*. Forget about the maid, Elyot! *(They look embarrassed.)* You could never have a lasting relationship with a maid. Choose between the two of us.

GEORGE. I choose . . . Oh, God, I don't know my lines. I don't know how I got here. I wish I *weren't* here. I wish I had joined the monastery like I almost did right after high school. I almost joined, but then I didn't.

SARAH *(trying to cover).* Oh, Elyot, your malaria is acting up again and you're ranting. Come, come, who do you choose, me or that baggage over there.

ELLEN. You're the baggage, not I. Yes, Elyot, who do you choose?

GEORGE. I choose . . . *(To* SARAH*)* I'm sorry, what is your name?

SARAH. Amanda.

GEORGE. I choose Amanda. I think that's what he does in the play.

ELLEN. Very well. I can accept defeat gracefully. I don't think I'll send this letter to your mother. She has a loud voice and an overbearing manner and I don't like her taste in tea china. I hope, Elyot, that when you find me hanging from the hotel lobby chandelier with my eyes all bulged out and my tongue hanging out, that you'll be very, very sorry. Goodbye. *(Exits)*

SARAH. What a dreadful sport she is.

GEORGE *(doing his best to say something his character might).* Poor Sibyl. She's going to hang herself.

SARAH. Some women should be hung regularly like tapestries. Oh, who cares? Whose yacht do you think that is?

GEORGE *(remembering).* The Duke of Westminster, I exp—

SARAH *(furious).* How dare you mention that time in Mozambique? *(Slaps him)* Oh, darling, I'm sorry. *(Moving her cigarette grandly)* I love you madly!

GEORGE *(gasps).* I've inhaled your ciga-rette ash. *(He coughs three times.* SARAH *looks confused, then unzips the front of his Hamlet doublet. He looks confused, then slaps her. She slaps him back with a vengeance. They both look confused.)*

SARAH. There, we're not angry any-more, are we? Oh, Elyot, wait for me here and I'll pack my things and we'll run away together before Victor gets back. Oh, darling, isn't it extra-ordinary how potent cheap music can be?

(She exits; recorded applause on her exit. GEORGE *sort of follows a bit, but then turns back to face the audience. Flash photos are taken again;* GEORGE *blinks and is disori-ented. Lights change, the sound of trumpets is heard, and* HENRY IRVING, *dressed in Shakespearean garb, enters and bows grand-ly to* GEORGE.*)*

HENRY. Hail to your Lordship!

GEORGE. Oh hello. Are you Victor?

HENRY. The same, my Lord, and your poor servant ever.

GEORGE. This doesn't sound like Noel Coward.

HENRY. A truant disposition, my good Lord.

GEORGE. You're not Victor, are you?

HENRY. My Lord, I came to see your father's funeral.

GEORGE. Oh yes? And how was it?

HENRY. Indeed, my Lord, it followed hard upon.

GEORGE. Hard upon? Yes, I see. *(Enter* MEG*)* Oh, good, the maid. *(She whis-pers to him.)* Thrift, thrift, Horatio. The funeral baked meats did coldly furnish forth the marriage tables.

What does that mean? *(MEG exits.)* Ah, she's gone already.

HENRY. My Lord, I think I saw him yesternight.

GEORGE. Did you? Who?

HENRY. My Lord, the king your father.

GEORGE. The king my father?

HENRY. Season your admiration for a while with an attent ear till I may deliver upon the witness of these gentlemen this marvel to you.

GEORGE. I see. I'm Hamlet now, right?

HENRY. Sssssh! *(Rattling this off in a very Shakespearean way:)*:
Two nights together had these gentlemen,
Marcellus and Bernardo, on their watch
In the dead waste and middle of the night
Been thus encountered. A figure like your father,
Arméd at point exactly, cap-a-pe,
Appears before them and with solemn march
Goes slow and stately by them. Thrice he walked
By their oppressed and fear-surprised eyes
Within his truncheon's length, whilst they, distilled
Almost to jelly with the act of fear,
Stand dumb and speak not to him. This to me
In dreadful secrecy impart they did,
And I with them the third night kept the watch,
Where, as they had delivered, both in time,
Form of the thing, each word made true and good,
The apparition comes. I knew your father.
These hands are not more like.

GEORGE. Oh, my turn? Most strange and wondrous tale you tell, Horatio. It doth turn my ear into a very . . . *(At a loss)* Merry . . . bare bodkin.

HENRY. As I do live, my honored Lord, tis true, and we did think it writ down in our duty
To let you know of it.

GEORGE. Well, thank you very much. *(Pause)*

HENRY. Oh yes, my Lord. He wore his beaver up.

GEORGE. His beaver up. He wore his beaver up. And does he usually wear it down?

HENRY. A countenance more in sorrow than in anger.

GEORGE. Well I am sorry to hear that. My father was a king of much renown. A favorite amongst all in London town. *(Pause)* And in Denmark.

HENRY. I war'nt it will.

GEORGE. I war'nt it will also.

HENRY. Our duty to your honor. *(Exits)*

GEORGE. Where are you going? Don't go. *(Smiles out at audience. Enter SARAH dressed as QUEEN GERTRUDE.)* Oh, Amanda, good to see you. Whose yacht do you think that is?

SARAH. O Hamlet, speak no more.
Thou turn'st mine eyes into my very soul,
And there I see such black and grainéd spots
As will not leave their tinct.

GEORGE. I haven't seen Victor. Someone was here who I thought might have been him, but it wasn't.

SARAH. Oh, speak to me no more. These words like daggers enter in mine ears. No more, sweet Hamlet.

GEORGE. Very well. What do you want to talk about?

SARAH. No more! *(Exits)*

GEORGE. Oh, don't go. *(Pause; smiles uncomfortably at the audience)* Maybe someone else will come out in a minute. *(Pause)* Of course, sometimes people have soliloquies in Shakespeare. Let's just wait a moment more and maybe someone will come. *(The lights suddenly change to a dim blue background and one bright, white spot center stage. GEORGE is not standing in the spot.)* Oh, dear. *(He moves somewhat awkwardly into the spot, decides to do his best to live up to the requirements of the moment.)* To be or not to be, that is the question. *(Doesn't know any more)* Oh, maid! *(No response; remembers that actors call for "line")* Line. Line! Ohhhh. Oh, what a rogue and peasant slave am I. Whether tis nobler in the mind's eye to kill oneself, or not killing oneself, to sleep a great deal. We are such stuff as dreams are made on; and our lives are rounded by a little sleep. *(The lights change. The spot goes out, and another one comes up stage right. GEORGE moves into it.)* Uh, thrift, thrift, Horatio. Neither a borrower nor a lender be. But to thine own self be true. There is a special providence in the fall of a sparrow.

Extraordinary how potent cheap music can be. Out, out, damn spot! I come to wive it wealthily in Padua; if wealthily, then happily in Padua. *(Sings)* Brush up your Shakespeare; start quoting him now; Da da . . . *(Lights change again. That spot goes off; another one comes on, center stage, though closer to audience. GEORGE moves into that.)* I wonder whose yacht that is. How was China? Very large, China. How was Japan? Very small, Japan. I pledge allegiance to the flag of the United States of America and to the republic for which it stands, one nation, under God, indivisible with liberty and justice for all. Line! Line! Oh, my God. *(Gets idea)* O my God, I am heartily sorry for having offended thee, and I detest all my sins because I dread the loss of heaven and the pains of hell. But most of all because they offend thee, my God, who art all good and deserving of all my love. And I resolve to confess my sins, to do penance, and to amend my life, Amen. *(Friendly)* That's the act of contrition that Catholic school children say in confession in order to be forgiven their sins. Catholic adults say it too, I imagine. I don't know any Catholic adults. Line! *(Explaining)* When you call for a line, the stage manager normally gives you your next line, to refresh your memory. Line! The quality of mercy is not strained. It droppeth as the gentle rain upon the place below, when we have shuffled off this mortal coil. Alas, poor Yorick. I knew him well. Get thee to a nunnery. Line. Nunnery. As a child, I was taught by nuns, and then in high school I was taught by Benedictine priests. I really rather liked the nuns, they were sort of warm, though they were fairly crazy too. Line. I liked the priests also. The school was on the grounds of the monastery, and my junior and senior years I spent a few weekends joining in the daily routine of the monastery—prayers, then breakfast, then prayers, then lunch, then prayers, then dinner, then prayers, then sleep. I found the predictability quite attractive. And the food was good. I was going to join the monastery after high school, but they said I was too young and should wait. And then I just stopped believing in all those things, so I never did join the monastery. I became an accountant. I've studied logarithms, and cosine and tangent . . . *(Irritated)* Line! *(Apologetic)* I'm sorry. This is supposed to be *Hamlet* or *Private Lives* or something, and I keep rattling on like a maniac. I really do apologize. I just don't recall attending a single rehearsal. I can't imagine what I was doing. And also you came expecting to see Edwin Booth and you get me. I really am very embarrassed. Sorry. *Line!* It's a far, far better thing I do than I have ever done before. It's a far, far better place I go to than I have ever been before. *(Sings the alphabet song)* a,b,c,d,e,f,g,h,i,j,k,l,m,n,o,p,q,r,s,t . . . *(As he starts to sing, enter* ELLEN TERRY, *dragging two large garbage cans. She puts them side by side, gets in one.)* Oh, good. Are you Ophelia? Get thee to a nunnery. *(She points to the other garbage can, indicating he should get in it.)* Get in? Okay. *(He does.)* This must be one of those modern Hamlets. *(Lights change abruptly to "Beckett lighting.")*

ELLEN. Nothing to be done. Pause. Pause. Wrinkle nose. *(Wrinkles nose)* Nothing to be done.

GEORGE. I guess you're not Ophelia.

ELLEN. We'll just wait. Pause. Either he'll come, pause pause pause, or he won't.

GEORGE. That's a reasonable attitude. Are we, on a guess, waiting for Godot?

ELLEN. No, Willie. He came already and was an awful bore. Yesterday he came. Garlic on his breath, telling a lot of unpleasant jokes about Jews and Polacks and stewardesses. He was just dreadful, pause, rolls her eyes upward. *(She rolls her eyes.)*

GEORGE. Well, I am sorry to hear that. Pause. So who are we waiting for?

ELLEN. We're waiting for Lefty.

GEORGE. Ah. And is he a political organizer or something. I seem to recall?

ELLEN. Yes, dear, he is a political organizer. He's always coming around saying get involved, get off your behinds and organize, fight the system, do this, do that, uh, he's exhausting, he's worse than Jane Fonda. And he has garlic breath just like Godot, I don't know which of them is worse, and I hope neither of them ever comes here again. Blinks left eye, blinks right eye, closes eyes, opens them. *(Does this)*

GEORGE. So we're really not waiting for anyone, are we?

ELLEN. No, dear, we're not. It's just another happy day, pause, smile, pause, picks nit from head. *(Picks nit from head)*

GEORGE. Do you smell something?

ELLEN. That's not your line. Willie doesn't have that many lines. *(Louder)* Oh, Willie, how talkative you are this morning!

GEORGE. There seems to be some sort of muck at the bottom of this garbage can.

ELLEN. Mustn't complain, Willie. There's muck at the bottom of everyone's garbage can. Count your blessings, Willie. I do. *(Counts to herself, eyes closed)* One. Two. Three. Are you counting, Willie?

GEORGE. I guess so.

ELLEN. I'm up to three. Three is my eyesight. *(Opens her eyes)* Oh, my God, I've gone blind. I can't see, Willie. Oh, my God. Oh, what a terrible day. Oh, dear. Oh, my. *(Suddenly very cheerful again)* Oh, well. Not so bad really. I only used my eyes occasionally. When I wanted to see something. But no more!

GEORGE. I really don't know this play at all.

ELLEN. Count your blessings, Willie. Let me hear you count them.

GEORGE. All right. One. Two. Three. That's my eyesight. Four. That's my hearing. Five, that's my . . . Master Charge. Six, that's . . .

ELLEN. Did you say God, Willie?

GEORGE. No.

ELLEN. Why did you leave the monastery, Willie? Was it the same reason I left the opera?

GEORGE. I have no idea.

ELLEN. I left the opera because I couldn't sing. They were mad to have hired me. Certifiable. And they were certified shortly afterward, the entire staff. They reside now at the Rigoletto Home for the Mentally Incapacitated. In Turin. Pause. Tries to touch her nose with her tongue. *(Does this)*

GEORGE. The Duke of Westminster, I expect.

VOICE. Ladies and gentlemen, may I have your attention please?

ELLEN. Oh, Willie, listen. A voice. Perhaps there is a God.

VOICE. At this evening's performance, the role of Sir Thomas More, the man for all seasons, normally played by Edwin Booth, will be played by George Spelvin. The role of Lady Alice, normally played by Sarah Bernhardt, will be played by Sarah Siddons. The role of Lady Margaret, normally played by Eleanora Duse, will be read by the stage manager. And at this evening's performance the executioner will play himself.

GEORGE. What did he say?

ELLEN. The executioner will play himself.

GEORGE. What does he mean, "the executioner will play himself"?

(Lights change to Man for All Seasons *general lighting. Enter* SARAH *as Lady Alice [Sir Thomas More's wife], and* MEG *with a few costumed touches but otherwise in her stage*

manager's garb and carrying a script as Lady Margaret [Sir Thomas More's daughter.])

MEG. Oh, Father, why have they locked you up in this dreadful dungeon; it's more than I can bear.

SARAH. I've brought you a custard, Thomas.

MEG. Mother's brought you a custard, father.

GEORGE. Yes, thank you.

MEG. Oh, Father, if you don't give in to King Henry, they're going to cut your head off.

SARAH. Aren't you going to eat the custard I brought you, Thomas?

GEORGE. I'm not hungry, thank you. *(Sudden alarming crash of cymbals, or something similarly startling musically occurs. The* EXECUTIONER *appears upstage. He is dressed as the traditional headsman—the black mask, bare chest and arms, the large axe. The more legitimately alarming he looks, the better. He can be played by the same actor who plays Henry Irving if his build and demeanor are appropriate. If not, it is possible to have a different actor play this role.)* Oh, my God, I've got to get out of here.

MEG. He's over here. And he'll never give in to the King.

GEORGE. No, no, I might. Quick, is this all about Anne Boleyn and everything?

MEG. Yes, and you won't give in because you believe in the Catholic Church and the infallibility of the Pope and the everlasting life of the soul.

GEORGE. I don't necessarily believe in any of that. *(To* EXECUTIONER*)* Oh, sir, there's been an error. I think it's fine if the King marries Anne Boleyn. I just want to wake up.

MEG. Oh, don't deny God, Father, just to spare our feelings. Mother and I are willing to have you dead if it's a question of principle.

SARAH. The first batch of custard didn't come out all that well, Thomas. This is the second batch. But it has a piece of hair in it, I think.

GEORGE. Oh, shut up about your custard, would you? I don't think the Pope is infallible at all. I think he's a normal man with normal capabilities who wears gold slippers. I thought about joining the monastery when I was younger, but I didn't do it.

ELLEN *(waking up from a brief doze)*. Oh, I was having such a pleasant dream, Willie. Go ahead, let him cut your head off, it'll be a nice change of pace. *(The* EXECUTIONER, *who has been motionless, now moves. In a sudden gesture, he reveals the cutting block that waits for George's head.)*

GEORGE. That blade looks very real to me. I want to wake up now. Or change plays. I wonder whose yacht that is out there. *(*SARAH *offers him the custard again.)* No, thank you. A horse, a horse! My kingdom for a horse!

EXECUTIONER. Sir Thomas More, you have been found guilty of the charge of High Treason. The sentence of the court is that you be taken to the Tower of London, thence to the place of execution, and there your head shall be stricken from your body, and may God have mercy on your soul. (MEG *helps* GEORGE *out of the garbage can.*)

GEORGE. All this talk about God. All right, I'm sorry I didn't go to the monastery, maybe I should have, and I'm sorry I giggled during Mass in third grade, but I see no reason to be killed for it.

ELLEN. Nothing to be done. That's what I find so wonderful. (MEG *puts* GEORGE*'s head on the block.*)

GEORGE. No!

EXECUTIONER. Do I understand you right? You wish to reverse your previous stand on King Henry's marriage to Anne and to deny the Bishop of Rome?

GEORGE. Yes, yes, God, yes. I could care less. Let him marry eight wives.

EXECUTIONER. That's a terrible legacy of cowardice for Sir Thomas More to leave behind.

GEORGE. I don't care.

EXECUTIONER. I'm going to ignore what you've said and cut your head off anyway, and then we'll all pretend you went to your death nobly. The Church needs its saints, and school children have got to have heroes to look up to, don't you all agree?

ELLEN. I agree. I know I need someone to look up to. Pause smile picks her nose. (*Does this*)

GEORGE. Yes, yes, I can feel myself waking up now. The covers have fallen off the bed, and I'm cold, and I'm going to wake up so that I can reach down and pull them up again.

EXECUTIONER. Sir Thomas, prepare to meet your death.

GEORGE. Be quiet, I'm about to wake up.

EXECUTIONER. Sir Thomas, prepare to meet your death.

GEORGE. I'm awake! (*Looks around him.* SARAH *offers him custard again.*) No, I'm not.

SARAH. He doesn't know his lines.

EXECUTIONER. Sir Thomas, prepare to meet your death.

GEORGE. Line! Line!

MEG. You turn to the executioner and say, "Friend, be not afraid of your office. You send me to God."

GEORGE. I don't like that line. Give me another.

MEG. That's the line in the script, George. Say it.

GEORGE. I don't want to.

MEG. Say it.

ELLEN. Say it, Willie. It'll mean a lot to me and to generations of school children to come.

SARAH. O Hamlet, speak the speech, I pray you, trippingly on the tongue.

EXECUTIONER. Say it!

GEORGE. Friend, be not afraid of your office. You send me . . .
Extraordinary how potent cheap music is.

MEG. That's not the line.

GEORGE. Women should be struck regularly like gongs.

MEG. George, say the line right.

GEORGE. They say you can never dream your own death, so I expect I'll wake up just as soon as he starts to bring the blade down. So perhaps I should get it over with.

MEG. Say the proper line, George. *(GEORGE breaks down.)*

GEORGE. Friend, be not afraid of your office. *(EXECUTIONER raises his axe.)*

ELLEN. Goodbye, Willie.

SARAH. Goodbye, Hamlet.

MEG. Goodbye, George.

EXECUTIONER. Goodbye, Sir Thomas.

GEORGE. You send me to God. *(EXECUTIONER raises the axe to bring it down. Blackout. Sound of the axe coming down.)*

EXECUTIONER *(in darkness).* Behold the head of Sir Thomas More.

ELLEN *(in darkness).* Oh I wish I weren't blind and could see that, Willie. Oh well, no matter. It's still been another happy day. Pause, smile, wrinkles nose, pause, picks nit from head, pause, pause, wiggles ears, all in darkness, utterly useless, no one can see her. She stares ahead. Count two. End of play. *(Music plays. Maybe canned applause. Lights come up for curtain calls. The four take their bows {if Henry Irving does not play the* EXECUTIONER, *he comes out for his bow as well}.* SARAH *and* ELLEN *have fairly elaborate bows, perhaps receiving flowers from the* EXECUTIONER. *They gesture for* GEORGE *to take his bow; but he seems to be dead. They applaud him, and then bow again, and lights out.)*

Responding to the Play

1. Do you think this play accurately represents a nightmare? Why or why not?
2. How is George's style distinct from that of any other character in this play?
3. Based on what you read in this play, how would you characterize Noel Coward's style?
4. Based on what you read in this play, how would you characterize Shakespeare's style?
5. Sketch an appropriate costume for Sarah, Ellen, or Henry.

More About Parody

Parody is a form of satire in which a writer pokes fun at a well-known author's work. To write a successful parody, a writer must determine the stylistic elements and the ideas that make the author's work unique, then exaggerate them to shocking or humorous proportions.

Like the parodies found in this play, most parodies pay homage to respected masters of writing. But the form can also be used to ridicule writers or their ideas. Sometimes, writers and actors extend their use of parody beyond the literary realm. They use the principles of parody to poke fun at prominent politicians, business leaders, and celebrities.

Creating and Performing

1. Write a parody of the style in a favorite book or movie. Share it with classmates and see whether they can recognize the target of your parody.
2. Design a basic costume that can be easily altered to represent different characters and historical periods.
3. Write and perform a scene between two favorite fictional or historical characters from different eras. Use diction, vocabulary, and other elements of style to point up the differences between the worlds the two characters inhabit.

The Play as Literature: Theme

All theatrical works, from the earliest ritual entertainments to the most experimental forms of performance art, have something in common, and that something is a *theme.* The theme of a piece is its central or most important idea. In short, it is the reason the piece exists.

As you read *The Post Office,* you will notice that many of the characters have completely different personalities, motivations, and activities to perform. They are united by the character of Amal—and by the fact that they all contribute to the theme of the play. Read the play carefully to discover the theme. At what point does it become clear to you?

The Play as Theatre: Ensemble Acting

Sometimes casual viewers of theatre think that acting is about cultivating stardom. But in most cases, the success of a play depends on the ability of the actors to act as one body—an ensemble—devoted to the reality of the play. In ensemble acting, the actors put the overall effect of the play above their own potential celebrity. They tailor their characterizations to match the style of the play so that their characters help bring out, but do not overwhelm, the play's message. As you read this play, note how each character plays a part in creating the play's message.

WARM UP!

To practice acting as an ensemble, play the "spectator game." Get together in groups of three and pretend to watch an imaginary sport-

ing event. At first your team is losing, but then one of your players makes a spectacular play . . . and scores! Then the other team steals the ball. Oh, no! You must convince the audience you are watching a game, while also interacting with your fellow actors. Work out the scenario with your group, and then share it with the class.

THE
POST OFFICE

by Rabindranath Tagore

SETTING	CHARACTERS	TIME
India	**MADHAV DUTTA** **AMAL**, a small boy and MADHAV'S adopted child **DOCTOR** **CURDSELLER** **WATCHMAN** **THAKURDA**, a wanderer **FAKIR** **VILLAGE HEADMAN**, a bully **SHUDHA**, a flower girl **VILLAGE BOYS** **RAJA'S (KING'S) HERALD** **RAJA'S (KING'S) PHYSICIAN**	1911

ACT ONE

MADHAV's *house*

MADHAV DUTTA. What a mess I'm in. Before he came, he meant nothing to me—I had no worries. Then he came here out of nowhere and filled my entire home; if he leaves me now, this house will no longer seem like my home. Doctor, do you think he will—

DOCTOR. If the child is fated for long life, then he shall have it, but it is written in the *Ayurveda*[1] that—

MADHAV. What? Please tell me!

DOCTOR. The scriptures say, "Bile and fever, palsy and phlegm all—"

MADHAV. Stop, stop, please don't recite those *slokas;*[2] they just make me more anxious. Tell me instead what must be done.

DOCTOR *(taking snuff).* Great care must be observed.

MADHAV. That I know, but what kind of care? You must tell me.

DOCTOR. I have told you before: On no account should he be allowed out-of-doors.

MADHAV. But he's so young! To keep him inside all day is really cruel.

DOCTOR. What choice do you have? The autumn sun and wind are both like venom to the boy, for as the scriptures say, "In epilepsy, fever, or

---

1. *Ayurveda,* an ancient system of medicine recorded in the *Vedas,* the oldest writings of India
2. *sloka,* couplet or verse taken from classical or folk literature

wheezing fit; in jaundice or in swelling—"

MADHAV. Enough, that's enough scripture. So we have to shut him indoors—is there really no other cure?

DOCTOR. None at all, for in the wind and the sun—

MADHAV. Oh cease with your "this, that, and the other." Please, stop it—just tell me what I have to do. Your remedies are so harsh. The poor boy is already putting up with a lot without complaining—but it breaks my heart to see how your prescription makes him suffer further.

DOCTOR. The greater the suffering, the happier the outcome. As the great sage Chyabana says, "In medication as in good counsel, the bitterest remedy brings the speediest results." Well, I must be going, Mr. Dutta.

(He goes.)

*(*THAKURDA *enters.)*

MADHAV. Oh no, Thakurda's back! Looks like trouble.

THAKURDA. Why? Why should a fellow like me scare you?

MADHAV. Because you make children run wild.

THAKURDA. You are not a boy, you have no child in your house, and you are past the age for running away—why do you worry?

MADHAV. Because I have brought a child to the house.

THAKURDA. Indeed!

MADHAV. My wife wanted to adopt a boy.

THAKURDA. I've known that for a long time, but I thought you didn't want to.

MADHAV. You know, I was making a lot of money by hard work, and I used to think how terrible it would be if some boy turned up and wasted all my money without any effort. But this one has somehow charmed me so much that—

THAKURDA. —that no wealth is too much for him. And you now feel that the more you spend, the merrier your money's fate.

MADHAV. Before, I was addicted to making money—I couldn't help myself. But now my reward is the knowledge that whatever I earn will be his.

THAKURDA. And where did you find him?

MADHAV. He's a sort of nephew of my wife through some village connection. He lost his mother very early, poor boy. And just recently, he lost his father, too.

THAKURDA. How sad! Maybe I could be of some help to him.

MADHAV. The doctor says that he is so sick with fever that there isn't much hope. Now the only cure is somehow to keep him inside, away from the autumn sunshine and breezes. But you always come along and gaily lead children outside—that's why you scare me.

THAKURDA. Yes, I admit it, I have become a free spirit, like the autumn sun and wind. But I also know how to play games indoors. Let me finish a few errands of mine, then I will make friends with this boy of yours.

(*He goes.*)

(AMAL *enters.*)

AMAL. Uncle!

MADHAV. What is it, Amal?

AMAL. Can't I even go out into the courtyard?

MADHAV. No, Amal.

AMAL. Look, over there, where Auntie is grinding lentils, there's a squirrel, balancing on its tail and munching the broken bits between its paws—can't I please go and see?

MADHAV. No, my son.

AMAL. I wish I could be a squirrel—Uncle, why can't I go out?

MADHAV. The doctor says that if you go out, you will get ill.

AMAL. How does the doctor know that?

MADHAV. What do you mean, Amal? Of course he knows! He has read so many huge old books.

AMAL. Does reading make you know everything?

MADHAV. Of course! Don't you know?

AMAL (*with a sigh*). I have not read a single book, so I guess I don't know anything.

MADHAV. But you are just like the greatest of pundits—you know, they never leave their houses.

AMAL. Don't they?

MADHAV. No, they don't; how can they? They only sit and read books, and never glance in any other direction. Amal, young fellow, you, too, will become a pundit—you will sit and read all those books,

and everyone will gaze at you in wonder.

AMAL. No! Uncle, please no, I beg you, I don't want to be a pundit. I don't want to be one, Uncle.

MADHAV. Why not, Amal! If I could have been a pundit, my life would have been totally different.

AMAL. I want to see everything—everything there is to see.

MADHAV. What are you talking about? See what?

AMAL. Those faraway hills, for instance, which I can see from my window—I would so love to cross over them.

MADHAV. What a crazy idea! Just like that, for nothing, on a whim, you want to cross those hills? You are not talking sense. Those hills stand up so tall because they are forbidding you to go beyond them—otherwise, why would stone have been piled upon stone to form such a huge heap?

AMAL. Uncle, are you sure they are really forbidding us? To me, it looks like the earth is mute, and so she is raising up her hands toward the sky and calling us. Distant people sitting beside their windows in the heat of midday are also hearing the call. Don't the pundits hear it?

MADHAV. They are not mad like you—they don't want to listen.

AMAL. Yesterday, I met someone as mad as me.

MADHAV. Really? Tell me.

AMAL. There was a bamboo pole across one of his shoulders. At the top of it was tied a small bundle. He held a small brass pot in his left hand.

There was an old pair of curly-toed slippers on his feet, and he walked along the path through the fields toward the hills. I called out, "Where are you going?" He said, "I don't know—wherever I happen to go." So I asked him, "Why are you going?" And he replied, "I'm seeking work." Uncle, does everybody have to seek work?

MADHAV. Of course. People are always looking for work.

AMAL. All right, I'll be like them and go searching for work, too.

MADHAV. What if you seek and don't find?

AMAL. I will keep on searching. When the man with the slippers walked away, I watched him from our doorway. Not far off, where the stream flows past the fig tree, he put his pole down and gently washed his feet. Then he opened his sack, took out some maize flour, kneaded it with water, and ate *chhatu*. When he was finished, he picked up the sack again and put it on his shoulder, hitched up his clothes, waded into the stream, and made his way across. I said to Auntie that I'm going to go to the stream sometime and eat *chhatu*.

MADHAV. What did she say?

AMAL. She said, "Get well first, then I myself will take you to the stream and feed you with *chhatu*." When will I get better?

MADHAV. It won't be much longer, young fellow.

AMAL. Not long? You know, as soon as I get well I must be off.

MADHAV. Where to?

AMAL. There are so many winding streams I want to dip my feet in. And at noontime, when everyone is resting behind shuttered doors, I want to walk and walk in search of work, farther and farther.

MADHAV. All right, but first get better, then you—

AMAL. You won't tell me to become a pundit, Uncle, will you?

MADHAV. What will you become then?

AMAL. I can't think of anything yet—I will tell you when I've thought.

MADHAV. But you shouldn't talk to strangers like that.

AMAL. I like strangers very much.

MADHAV. What if one were to snatch you away?

AMAL. That would be fun. But no one ever takes me away; everyone wants me to sit right here.

MADHAV. I have some work to do, so I must go. But son, don't wander outside, all right?

AMAL. I won't. But Uncle, you must let me sit here in this room next to the road.

(MADHAV *goes.*)

ACT TWO

MADHAV's *house*

CURDSELLER. *Dai, dai,* good *dai!*

AMAL. Daiwallah,[3] Daiwallah, oh Daiwallah!

———
3. daiwallah, a curdseller (*dai* means curds)

CURDSELLER. What do you want? To buy some *dai*?

AMAL. How can I? I have no money.

CURDSELLER. What kind of child are you? If you're not buying, why are you wasting my time?

AMAL. I just want to walk with you.

CURDSELLER. With me?

AMAL. When I hear your cry in the distance, it makes me so restless.

CURDSELLER (*unhitching his harness*). Young fellow, what are you doing, sitting there like that?

AMAL. The doctor's forbidden me to go outdoors, so I must sit here all day, every day.

CURDSELLER. You poor child. What's wrong?

AMAL. I don't know. I haven't read any books, so I can't know what is the matter with me. Daiwallah, where do you come from?

CURDSELLER. I come from our village.

AMAL. Your village. Is it far away?

CURDSELLER. Our village is at the foot of the Panchmura Hills, beside the Shamli River.

AMAL. Panchmura Hills, Shamli River— I think I've seen your village, although I don't remember when.

CURDSELLER. You have been there? Have you been to the foot of the hills?

AMAL. No, I've never been there. But I feel as if I have. Doesn't your village lie beneath some ancient sprawling trees, next to a red road?

CURDSELLER. You are right, son.

AMAL. And there are cows grazing on the hillside.

CURDSELLER. Right again! In our village, cows do graze, yes indeed.

AMAL. And women come to fetch water from the river and carry it in pitchers on their heads—and they wear red saris.

CURDSELLER. Yes, yes, that's it. All of our dairywomen come to the river for their water. But not all of them wear red saris. You must have visited the place sometime.

AMAL. No, I assure you, I have never been there. As soon as the doctor lets me go out, will you take me to your village?

CURDSELLER. Of course I will, with pleasure.

AMAL. Teach me how to sell *dai*, as you do—walking all those far-off roads with your harness across your shoulder.

CURDSELLER. But my son, why sell *dai*? You should read books and become a pundit.

AMAL. No, no, I will never become a pundit. I will take some *dai* from your village beneath the old banyan tree beside the red road, and I will sell it in distant villages. How does your call go? *"Dai, dai, good dai!"* Teach me the tune, won't you, please?

CURDSELLER. Heavens! Is such a tune worth teaching?

AMAL. Don't say that. I like it. You know when you hear a hawk shrieking high up in the sky, the cry gives you a strange feeling? Well, your distant call—which seems to float through the trees from some far bend in the road—has the same effect on me.

CURDSELLER. Son, please have a pot of my *dai*.

AMAL. But I have no money.

CURDSELLER. It doesn't matter, don't mention money. I would be ever so pleased if you ate some of my *dai*.

AMAL. Have I delayed you much?

CURDSELLER. No, not at all, son, it's no loss at all. For you have shown me the joy in selling *dai*.

(He goes.)

AMAL *(chanting). Dai, dai,* good *dai! Dai* from the dairies beside the Shamli River in the Panchmura Hills. *Dai— dai!* Every dawn the dairywomen milk the cows under the trees, and every evening they set the *dai*—and what *dai* it is! *Dai, dai, dai-i,* delicious *dai!* Ah, look, there's the watchman doing his rounds. Watchman, oh Watchman, won't you come and listen to me for just a minute?

(WATCHMAN enters.)

WATCHMAN. What's all this shouting for? Aren't you afraid of me?

AMAL. Why should I be afraid of you?

WATCHMAN. What if I arrest you, take you away?

AMAL. Where will you take me? Far away, over the hills?

WATCHMAN. I might take you straight to the Raja!

AMAL. To the Raja! Would you really?! But the doctor has forbidden me to go out. No one can take me anywhere. I must just sit here all day and night.

WATCHMAN. Doctor's orders? Ah, I can see your face is quite pale. There are dark rings under your eyes. The veins are sticking out in both of your arms.

AMAL. Are you going to sound your gong?

WATCHMAN. The time is not yet right.

AMAL. Some people say, "time flies," while others say that "time is not yet ripe." But if you strike your gong, won't the time be right?

WATCHMAN. How so? I sound the gong only when the time is right.

AMAL. I do like your gong. I love listening to it, especially at noon after everyone's eaten and my uncle has gone out somewhere to work and Auntie dozes off reading the *Ramayana,*[4] and our small dog curls up into its tail in some shadow of the courtyard—then I hear your gong strike, *dhong, dhong, dhong dhong dhong!* But why do you strike it?

WATCHMAN. It tells everyone that time does not stand still, that time always moves onward.

AMAL. Where is time going? To what land?

WATCHMAN. Nobody knows that.

AMAL. You mean nobody's been there? I would love to run away with time to this land that nobody knows.

WATCHMAN. All of us will go there one day, young man.

AMAL. Me, too?

WATCHMAN. Of course.

---

4. *Ramayana,* one of two ancient epics of India, the other being the *Mahabharata*

AMAL. But the doctor has forbidden me to go out.

WATCHMAN. Someday perhaps the doctor will hold your hand and take you there.

AMAL. No, you don't know him, all he does is keep me locked up here.

WATCHMAN. But there is a greater doctor than he, a doctor who can set you free.

AMAL. When will this Great Doctor come for me? I'm so tired of staying here.

WATCHMAN. Shouldn't say such things, son.

AMAL. But I have to sit here all the time never going out, doing as I am told, and when your gong goes *dhong dhong dhong* I feel so frustrated. Watchman—?

WATCHMAN. What is it?

AMAL. Over there, across the road, that big house with a flag on top, with lots of people going in and out of it—what is it?

WATCHMAN. It's the new post office.

AMAL. Post office? Whose post office?

WATCHMAN. The Raja's, of course—who else could have a post office? *(Aside)* He's a strange boy.

AMAL. Do letters come to the post office from the Raja himself?

WATCHMAN. Yes, of course. Someday, there may even be a letter addressed to you.

AMAL. A letter with my name on it? But I am only a child.

WATCHMAN. The Raja sends his littlest letters to children.

AMAL. Really? When will I get my letter? And how do you know that he's going to write to me?

WATCHMAN. Why else would he bother to set up a post office with a splendid golden flag outside your open window? *(Aside)* But I rather like the boy.

AMAL. When the Raja's letter comes, who will give it to me?

WATCHMAN. The Raja has many messengers—surely you have seen them running about with gold badges pinned to their chests?

AMAL. Where do they go?

WATCHMAN. From door to door, country to country. *(Aside)* The boy's questions really are amusing.

AMAL. When I grow up, I want to be a Raja's messenger.

WATCHMAN. Ha, ha, ha! A Raja's messenger! Now there's a responsible job. Come rain, come shine, among rich, among poor, wherever you are you must deliver your letters—it's a tremendous job!

AMAL. Why are you smiling that way? It's the best job there could be. Oh, I don't mean that your job isn't good, too—you strike your gong during the heat of noon, *dhong dhong dhong,* and also in the dead of night—sometimes I suddenly wake up and find that the lamp has gone out and I hear a deep, dark *dhong dhong dhong!*

WATCHMAN. Uh-oh, here comes the big boss—time to run. If he catches me chatting with you, he's sure to cause trouble.

AMAL. Where's the boss, which one is he?

WATCHMAN. Over there, way down the road. Don't you see his big umbrella—the one made of palm leaves—bobbing up and down?

AMAL. Has the boss been appointed by the Raja?

WATCHMAN. Oh, no—he's been appointed by himself. But if you don't obey him, he'll cause endless difficulties—that's why people are afraid of him. Our Headman's entire job seems to be troublemaking, for everyone. So that's enough talk for today, time to leave. I'll be back tomorrow morning to bring you the news of the town.

(He goes.)

AMAL. If I receive a letter every day from the Raja, that would be wonderful. I'll sit here by the window and read them. Oh, but I don't know how to read. I wonder who could read them for me? Auntie reads *Ramayana.* Maybe she can read the Raja's writing. If nobody can read the letters, I'll keep them and read them all later, when I grow up. But what if the Raja's messengers don't know about me? Mr. Headman, oh dear Mr. Headman, could I talk to you for a minute?

HEADMAN. Who's this? Bellowing at me in the road! Who's this monkey?

AMAL. You are the Headman. I hear that everyone pays attention to you.

HEADMAN *(flattered).* Yes, yes, they do. They do, or else.

AMAL. Do the Raja's messengers listen to you, too?

HEADMAN. Of course! Would they dare to ignore me?

AMAL. Will you tell the messengers that my name is Amal, and that I am always here, sitting by the window?

HEADMAN. Why should I do that?

AMAL. In case there is a letter addressed to me.

HEADMAN. A letter for you! Who would write *you* a letter?

AMAL. If the Raja writes to me then—

HEADMAN. Well now, aren't you a mighty fellow! Ho, ho, ho! So the Raja will write to you, will he? Of course he will, for you are his dear friend. In fact, he's getting sadder by the day because he's not seen you lately, so I hear. Well, your waiting's almost over; I bet that your letter will come any day now.

AMAL. Mr. Headman, why is your voice so harsh? Are you angry with me?

HEADMAN. Goodness me. Why should I be angry with you? Could I be so bold? After all, you are a correspondent of the Raja. *(Aside)* I can see that Madhav Dutta thinks he can drop the names of rajas and maharajas, just because he has made a little money. We'll soon see that he gets his comeuppance— Yes, my lad, you'll soon get a royal letter at your house, I shall see to it myself.

AMAL. No, no, please, you don't have to go to any trouble for me.

HEADMAN. And why not? I will tell our Raja about you, and I am sure he will not keep you waiting long. In fact, I bet he will send a footman at once to hear your news. (*Aside*) Really, Madhav Dutta's arrogance is too much. Just as soon as this reaches the ears of the Raja, there'll be trouble, that's for sure.

(*He goes.*)

AMAL. Who is that, with her jingling anklets? Please stop awhile.

(*A* GIRL *enters.*)

GIRL. How can I stop? The day's already passing.

AMAL. You don't want to stop, even for a moment—and I don't want to sit here a moment longer.

GIRL. To look at you reminds me of the fading morning star. What's the matter with you, tell me?

AMAL. I don't know, but the doctor has forbidden me to go out.

GIRL. Then don't go out; obey Doctor's words—if you don't, people will say you are naughty. I can see that just looking outside makes you restless. Let me close this window a bit.

AMAL. No, no, don't close it! Everything is closed to me except this window. Tell me who you are. I don't seem to know you.

GIRL. I am Shudha.

AMAL. Shudha?

SHUDHA. Don't you know? I am the daughter of the local flower seller.

AMAL. And what do you do?

SHUDHA. I fill a wicker basket with plucked flowers and make garlands. Just now I'm off to pick some.

AMAL. You're going to pick flowers? Is that why your feet are so lively, and your anklets go *jingle-jangle* with each step? If I could go with you, I would

pick flowers for you from the highest branches, beyond your sight.

SHUDHA. Would you now?! So you know where the flowers are better than I do?

AMAL. Yes, I know a lot. For example, I know all about the seven *champak*[5] flower brothers. If I were well, I would go deep into the forest where there is no path to be seen. There I would blossom as a *champak* flower on the tallest tip of the thinnest twig, where the hummingbird gets drunk on honey. Will you be Parul[6], my *champak*-flower sister?

SHUDHA. How silly! How could I be your Parul *didi*?[7] I am Shudha, daughter of Shashi, the flower seller. Everyday I have to string many flower garlands. If I could spend the day sitting like you, then I would be very happy.

AMAL. What would you do if you had all day?

SHUDHA. First, I would play with my *bene-bou*[8] doll and marry her off, and then there's my pussycat, Meni. I would love to—but it's getting late, and there won't be any flowers left if I dawdle here.

AMAL. Please talk to me a little longer. I'm enjoying it.

SHUDHA. All right, if you are a good boy and stay here quietly, on my way back with the flowers I'll stop for another chat.

---

5. *champak*, a species of magnolia, well known in Bengali folk literature
6. parul, a species of trumpet flower
7. *didi*, older sister
8. *bene-bou*, a common clay doll of rural Bengal

AMAL. Will you bring me a flower?

SHUDHA. How can I? Can you pay?

AMAL. I'll pay you when I grow up, when I've gone out seeking work beyond the stream over there—then I'll repay you.

SHUDHA. I accept.

AMAL. So you will return after picking flowers?

SHUDHA. I will return.

AMAL. Promise?

SHUDHA. I promise.

AMAL. You won't forget me? My name is Amal. Will you remember it?

SHUDHA. No, I won't forget. You will be remembered.

(She goes.)

(Some BOYS *enter.)*

AMAL. Brothers, where are you going? Stop for awhile.

BOYS. We're off to play.

AMAL. What game are you going to play?

BOYS. The ploughman's game.

FIRST BOY *(waving a stick).* This is our ploughshare.

SECOND BOY. And we two will be the oxen.

AMAL. Will you play all day?

BOYS. Yes, the entire day.

AMAL. After that, will you come back home along the path by the river?

A BOY. Yes, we will, when it's evening.

AMAL. Please drop by here, in front of my house.

A BOY. You can come with us now, come and play.

AMAL. Doctor's ordered me not to go out.

A BOY. Doctor! Why do you listen to him? Come on, let's go, it's getting late.

AMAL. Please, friends, won't you play in the road outside my window, just for a little while?

A BOY. But there's nothing here to play with.

AMAL. All my toys are lying right here, take them all. It's no fun playing indoors all alone—the toys are just lying here, doing nothing, scattered in the dust.

BOYS. Oh, what wonderful toys! Look at this ship! And this one with the matted hair is the old witch, Jatai. And here's a terrific *sepoy*[9] to play soldiers with. Are you really giving us these? Won't you miss them?

AMAL. No, I won't miss them, you can have them all.

A BOY. So we don't have to give them back?

AMAL. No, you don't need to.

A BOY. Nobody will scold you?

AMAL. No, nobody will. But promise me that you will come and play with them outside my house for awhile each morning. When they get worn out, I'll get you some new ones.

A BOY. All right, friend, we'll come and play here every day. Now let's take the *sepoys* and have a battle. Where can we get muskets? Over there, there's a large piece of reed—that'll do if we cut it up into pieces. But friend, you are dozing off!

---

9. *sepoy,* Indian soldier under European (especially British) discipline

AMAL. Yes, I'm very sleepy. Why I feel sleepy so often, I don't know. But I've been sitting up a long time and I can't sit any longer; my back is aching.

A BOY. It's only the beginning of the day—why are you sleepy already? Listen, there goes the gong.

AMAL. Yes—*dhong dhong dhong;* it lulls me to sleep.

BOYS. We're going now, but we'll be back in the morning.

AMAL. Before you go, let me ask you something. You go about a lot. Do you know the Raja's messengers?

BOYS. Yes, we do; quite well.

AMAL. Who are they? What are their names?

BOYS. One's called Badal, another's called Sharat, and there are others.

AMAL. Well, if a letter comes for me, will they know who I am?

A BOY. Why not? If your name is on the letter, they will certainly find you.

AMAL. When you come back in the morning, please ask one of them to stop by and meet me, will you?

BOYS. Yes, we will.

ACT THREE

AMAL, *in bed*

AMAL. Uncle, can't I even sit near the window today? Doctor really forbids it?

MADHAV. Yes, he does. He says that sitting there every day is making your illness worse.

AMAL. But Uncle, that's not right—I don't know about my illness, but I know I feel better when I sit there.

MADHAV. Sitting there you have become friends with half the town—young and old alike. The area outside my door looks like a fairground. How will you stand the strain? Look at your face today—so wan!

AMAL. If my friend the fakir[10] comes by my window, he will miss me and go away again.

MADHAV. Who is this fakir?

AMAL. Every day he drops in and tells me tales of lands far and wide; he's so much fun to listen to.

MADHAV. I don't know of any fakir.

AMAL. He usually comes along about now. Uncle, I beg you, please ask him to come and sit with me.

(THAKURDA *enters, dressed as a* FAKIR.)

AMAL. There you are, Fakir. Come and sit on my bed.

MADHAV. What! Is that your—

THAKURDA (*winking*). I am the fakir.

MADHAV. Of course you are.

AMAL. Where have you been this time, Fakir?

THAKURDA. To the Island of Parrots. I just got back.

MADHAV. Parrot Island, eh?

THAKURDA. Why so skeptical? Am I like you? When I travel, there are no expenses. I can go wherever I please.

AMAL (*clapping in delight*). You have so much fun. When I get well, you promised I could be your disciple, remember?

---

10. fakir, a Hindu or Muslim holy man

THAKURDA. Of course. I will initiate you in my travel *mantras,*[11] so that neither ocean nor mountain nor forest will bar your way.

MADHAV. What is all this crazy talk?

THAKURDA. Dearest Amal, there is nothing in mountain or ocean that frightens me—but if the doctor and your uncle get together, my *mantras* will be powerless.

AMAL. You won't tell Doctor about all of this, will you Uncle? Now I promise I will lie here, sleep, and do nothing. But the day I get well I will swear by Fakir's *mantras,* and then I shall cross the rivers, mountains, and oceans.

MADHAV. Hush, son, don't keep on talking about leaving—just to hear you makes me feel so sad.

AMAL. Tell me, Fakir, what is Parrot Island like?

THAKURDA. It's a rather weird place, a land of birds without any human beings. The birds do not speak or come to land, they only sing and fly around.

AMAL. How fantastic! And is there ocean all around?

THAKURDA. Yes, of course.

AMAL. And are there green hills?

THAKURDA. Yes, in the hills, the birds make their nests. In the evening, as the rays of the setting sun make the green hillsides glow, the parrots flock to their nests in a green swarm—and then the hills and the parrots become one single mass of green. It's indescribable.

AMAL. And what about streams and waterfalls?

THAKURDA. Absolutely! How could there not be?! They flow like molten diamonds, and how the drops dance! The small pebbles in the streams hum and murmur as the waters gush over them, until finally they plunge into the ocean. No one, not even a doctor, can restrain them for even a single second. I tell you, if the birds did not ostracize me as a mere man, I would make myself a small hut among the thousands of nests beside some waterfall and pass my days watching the waters and the ocean waves below.

AMAL. If I were a bird then—

THAKURDA. Then there would be a problem. I hear you have already arranged with the daiwallah to sell *dai* when you grow up. I don't think your business would do too well among parrots. Who knows, you might even take a loss.

MADHAV. I can't take this nonsense any longer! You two will drive me crazy. I am going.

AMAL. Uncle, has my daiwallah come and gone yet?

MADHAV. Of course he has. He won't make ends meet by carrying things for you and your fancy fakir friend, or by flitting around Parrot Island, will he? But he left a pot of *dai* for you, and he said to tell you that his youngest niece is getting married in his village—so he's rather busy, because he has to go and book the flute players from Kalmipara.

---

11. *mantra,* word or phrase used in meditation, believed to possess spiritual powers

AMAL. But he promised that his youngest niece would marry me.

THAKURDA. Now we are in trouble.

AMAL. He said she would be a delicious bride, with a nose ring and a red-striped sari. With her own hands she would milk a black cow in the mornings and bring me an earthenware bowl full of frothy, fresh milk. And at evening time, after taking a lamp to the cowshed, she would settle down with me and tell me tales of the seven *champak*-flower brothers.

THAKURDA. Well, she sounds like a wonderful bride. Even a fakir like me feels tempted. But don't lose heart, my child, let him marry off this niece. I give you my word that when your time comes, there will be no shortage of nieces in his family.

MADHAV. Be off with you! This time you really have gone too far.

(MADHAV *goes.*)

AMAL. Fakir, now that Uncle's gone, tell me secretly—has the Raja sent a letter in my name to the post office?

THAKURDA. I hear that his letter has been dispatched—it is on its way.

AMAL. On its way? Which way? Is it coming by that path through the dense forest that you see when the sky clears after rain?

THAKURDA. Yes. You seem to know it.

AMAL. I know a lot, Fakir.

THAKURDA. So I see—but how?

AMAL. I can't say. I can see everything before my eyes, as if I have really seen it many times, but long ago—how long ago I cannot recall. Shall I describe it to you? I can see the Raja's messenger coming down the hillside alone, a lantern in his left hand and on his back a bag of letters, descending for days and nights; and then at the foot of the hills, where the waterfall becomes a winding stream, he follows the footpath along the bank and walks on through the corn; then comes the sugarcane field and he disappears into the narrow lane that cuts through the tall stems of sugarcanes; and then he reaches the open meadow where the cricket chirps and where there is no one to be seen, only the snipe wagging their tails and poking at the mud with their beaks. I can picture it all. And the nearer he gets, the gladder I feel.

THAKURDA. Though I do not have your fresh vision, still I see it.

AMAL. Tell me, Fakir, do you know the Raja?

THAKURDA. I certainly do, I often go to his court to seek alms.[12]

AMAL. Really? When I get better I will go with you and seek alms from him. Can I go with you?

THAKURDA. Son, you do not need to seek—he will give without your asking.

AMAL. But I would rather seek. I'll go to the road outside his palace chanting "Victory to the Raja!" and begging alms—maybe I will also dance with a cymbal. What do you think?

THAKURDA. It sounds good; and if I accompany you, I will receive gifts, too. What will you ask him for?

---

12. alms, charity; often something (money, food, a blessing, etc.) given to help one in need

AMAL. I will ask him to make me a Raja's messenger, who will go all over the land with a lantern in his hand delivering messages from door to door. You know, Fakir, someone has told me that as soon as I am well, he will teach me how to beg. I will go out begging with him wherever I please.

THAKURDA. And who is this person?

AMAL. Chidam.

THAKURDA. Which Chidam?

AMAL. Blind and lame Chidam. Every day he comes to my window. A boy just like me pushes him around in a cart with wheels. I've often told Chidam that when I'm better, I will push him around, too.

THAKURDA. That would be interesting, I can see.

AMAL. He is going to teach me all about begging. I tell Uncle that we should give Chidam something, but Uncle says that he's not really blind or lame. Perhaps he is not totally blind, but I know he does not see very well—I am sure of that.

THAKURDA. You are right. Whether you call him blind or not, it is true that he does not see very well. But if he gets no alms from you, why does he like to sit with you?

AMAL. Because he hears all about different places from me. The poor fellow cannot see, but he listens when I tell him about all the lands that you tell me about. The other day you told me of the Land of No Weight, where everything weighs nothing and even a tiny hop will

send you sailing over a hill. He really liked hearing about that place. Fakir, how do you reach that land?

THAKURDA. There's an inner road, but it's hard to find.

AMAL. Since the poor man is blind, he will never see any place, and will have to go on begging alms. Sometimes he moans to me about it, and I tell him that at least he visits a lot of places as a beggar—not everyone can do that.

THAKURDA. Son, why do you feel so sad to stay at home?

AMAL. Not sad, not now. Until now, my days did drag endlessly—but I have seen the Raja's post office and I am happier. I even like sitting indoors. I know my letter will come, and the thought keeps me company, so I wait quite happily. But I have no idea what the Raja will write in his letter.

THAKURDA. You do not need to know. As long as your name is there, that is enough.

(MADHAV *enters.*)

MADHAV. Do you realize what trouble you have gotten us into?

THAKURDA. Why, what's up?

MADHAV. Rumor has it that you are saying that the Raja has built his post office only to correspond with you.

THAKURDA. So?

MADHAV. And so the Headman has sent an anonymous letter about this to the Raja.

THAKURDA. We all know that most things reach the Raja's ears.

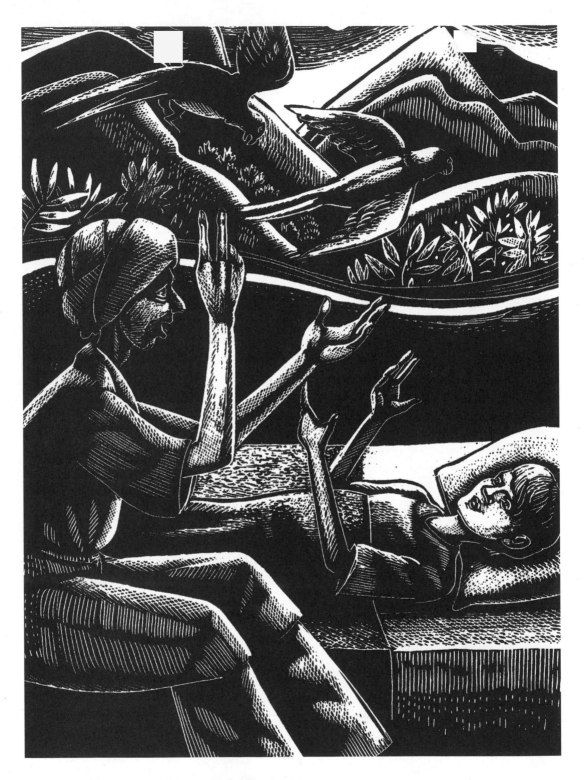

186   *The Post Office* by Rabindranath Tagore

MADHAV. Then why didn't you watch yourself? Why did you take the names of rajas and maharajas in vain?! You'll pull me in, too.

AMAL. Fakir, will the Raja be angry?

THAKURDA. Who says so? Why should he be? How can he rule his kingdom with majesty if he becomes mad at a child like you and a fakir like me?

AMAL. You know, Fakir, since this morning there has been a kind of darkness in my mind; sometimes things look as if in a dream. I feel like being totally silent. I don't want to talk anymore. Won't the Raja's letter ever come? Just now, this room seemed to vanish, as if everything— as if all . . .

THAKURDA (*fanning* AMAL). It will come, my dear, the letter will come today.

(DOCTOR *enters.*)

DOCTOR. So how do you feel today?

AMAL. Doctor, I am now feeling comfortable; all my pain seems to be going away.

DOCTOR (*aside to* MADHAV). I don't like the look of that smile very much. When he says he feels better there is danger in store. As the great Chakradhar Dutta says—

MADHAV. *Please* Doctor, spare me Chakradhar Dutta. Just tell me, what is the matter?

DOCTOR. It looks as if we cannot hold onto him much longer. I recommended certain precautions, but he seems to have been exposed to the outside air.

MADHAV. No, Doctor, I have done my utmost to keep him from such exposure. He has been kept indoors, and most of the time the place was kept shut.

DOCTOR. The air has turned rather strange today, and I notice a severe draft blowing through your door. That is not at all good. You must shut the door at once. Try not to have any visitors for a few days. If people drop in, they can come through the back door. And you should get rid of this glare that comes through the window when the sun sets—it disturbs the patient's mind.

MADHAV. Amal's eyes are closed. I think he's asleep. When I look at his face, it's as if—oh, Doctor! This child who is not my own, but whom I have loved as my own, will he be taken from me?

DOCTOR. Who's coming now? It's the Headman, coming here. Drat! I must go, my friend. Go inside and shut your door tight. When I get home, I'll send over a strong dose—give it to the boy. If he can resist its power, he may yet pull through.

(DOCTOR *and* MADHAV *go.*)

(HEADMAN *enters.*)

HEADMAN. Hey, boy!

THAKURDA (*suddenly standing up*). Ssh ssh . . . be quiet!

AMAL. No, Fakir, you thought I was sleeping, but I wasn't. I heard everything. And I also heard faraway talk; my parents were talking beside my bed.

(MADHAV *enters.*)

HEADMAN. So, Madhav Dutta, these days you are rubbing shoulders with people in high places!

MADHAV. What do you mean, Headman? Don't make fun of us. We are very humble folk.

HEADMAN. But isn't your boy awaiting a letter from the Raja?

MADHAV. He's a mere child, and sick and confused at that. Why do you listen to him?

HEADMAN. On the contrary. Where else could our Raja find a worthier correspondent than your boy? That must be why he has built his new royal post office outside your window. Hey little fellow, there is a letter from the Raja addressed to you.

AMAL *(startled).* Really?

HEADMAN. And why not?—with your royal friendship! *(Hands him a blank sheet)* Ha, ha, ha. Here's your letter.

AMAL. Are you teasing? Fakir, Fakir, tell me, is it really the letter?

THAKURDA. Yes, my boy, you have your Fakir's word, it is indeed the letter.

AMAL. But my eyes can't see anything— everything looks blank to me! Headman, sir, tell me what's in the letter.

HEADMAN. His Majesty writes, "I will be visiting your home shortly. Prepare me a meal of puffed rice and parched paddy with molasses. I don't like to stay in the palace one minute more than I have to." Ha, ha, ha!

MADHAV. *(with folded hands).* I beg you, sir, I implore you, do not ridicule us.

THAKURDA. Ridicule! What ridicule? Who would dare to ridicule!

MADHAV. What! Thakurda, are you out of your mind?

THAKURDA. Maybe I am. But I also see letters on this sheet. The Raja writes that he will personally visit Amal, and that his royal physician will accompany him.

AMAL. Fakir—it is true! I hear his herald! Can you hear the call?

HEADMAN. Ha, ha, ha! Let him become a bit more demented, then he'll hear it!

AMAL. Headman, sir, I thought that you were angry with me, that you disliked me. I never imagined that you would bring me the Raja's letter—it never occurred to me. I must wash the dust from your feet.

HEADMAN. Well, I'll say this much, the boy certainly has good manners. Not too bright, but he has a good heart.

AMAL. The day is nearly over, I can feel it. There goes the evening gong— *dhong dhong dhong, dhong dhong dhong.* Has the evening star appeared yet, Fakir? Why don't I see it?

THAKURDA. They have shut all your windows. I will open them.

(A banging at the outside door)

MADHAV. What's that! Who's there? What an annoyance!

(From outside). Open the door.

MADHAV. Who are you?

(From outside). Open the door.

MADHAV. Headman, could it be robbers?

HEADMAN. Who's there? This is Panchanan Morhal, Headman, speaking. Aren't you scared? *(To* MADHAV*)* Listen! The banging has stopped. Even the toughest thieves know to fear Panchanan's voice!

MADHAV (looking out the window). Look! They have smashed the door, that's why the banging has ceased!

(RAJA'S HERALD enters.)

RAJA'S HERALD. His majesty will arrive tonight.

HEADMAN. Disaster!

AMAL. When in the night, Herald? At what hour?

HERALD. In the dead of night.

AMAL. When my friend the watchman strikes his gong at the town's Lion Gate, *dhong dhong dhong, dhong dhong dhong*—at that hour?

HERALD. Yes, at that hour. In the meantime, the Raja has sent his finest physician to attend to his little friend.

(RAJA'S PHYSICIAN enters.)

RAJA'S PHYSICIAN. What's this? All closed up?! Open up, open up, open all the doors and windows. (*He feels* AMAL's *body.*) How are you feeling, young fellow?

AMAL. Quite well, very well, Doctor. My illness is gone, my pain is gone. Now everything is open—I can see all the stars, shining on the far side of darkness.

PHYSICIAN. When the Raja comes in the dead of night, will you rise and go forth with him?

AMAL. I will, I have the will. I long to go forth. I will ask the Raja to show me the Pole Star in the heavens. Perhaps I have seen it many times, and have not recognized it.

PHYSICIAN. The Raja will show you all things. (*To* MADHAV) Please make the room clean and decorate it with flowers to greet our Raja. (*Pointing to the* HEADMAN) That man should not be permitted here.

AMAL. Oh no, Doctor, he is my friend. Before you came, he brought me the Raja's letter.

PHYSICIAN. All right, my boy, since he is your friend, he may remain.

MADHAV (whispering in AMAL's ear). My son, the Raja loves you, and he is coming here in person. Please entreat him to give us something. You know our condition—we are not well off.

AMAL. Uncle, I have already thought about it—do not worry.

MADHAV. What will you request?

AMAL. I will beg him to make me a royal messenger in his post office. I will deliver his messages to homes everywhere.

MADHAV (striking his forehead). Alas, such is my fate!

AMAL. Uncle, when the Raja comes, what shall we offer him?

HERALD. The Raja has commanded a meal of puffed rice and parched paddy with molasses.

AMAL. Headman, those were your very words! You knew everything about the Raja, and we knew nothing!

HEADMAN. If you would send someone to my house, we will endeavor to provide his Majesty with good—

PHYSICIAN. No need for it. Now you must all be calm. It is coming, coming; his sleep is coming. I will sit beside his pillow as he drifts off. Blow out the lamp; let the starlight come in; his sleep has arrived.

MADHAV (*to* THAKURDA). Thakurda, why so hushed, with your palms pressed together like a statue? I feel a kind of dread. These do not seem like good omens. Why has the room been darkened? What use is starlight?

THAKURDA. Be quiet, unbeliever! Do not speak.

(SHUDHA *enters.*)

SHUDHA. Amal?

PHYSICIAN. He has fallen asleep.

SHUDHA. I have brought flowers for him. Can I put them in his hand?

PHYSICIAN. Yes, you may give him your flowers.

SHUDHA. When will he awake?

PHYSICIAN. When the Raja comes and calls him.

SHUDHA. Will you whisper a word in his ear for me?

PHYSICIAN. What shall I say?

SHUDHA. Tell him, "Shudha has not forgotten you."

THE POST OFFICE

Responding to the Play

1. Do you think Amal benefited or suffered from sitting by the open window? Explain.
2. Why do you think Amal inspired affection from people as diverse as the Curdseller, Shudha, and the Raja's Herald?
3. What do you think this play says about desire?
4. What is the significance of the post office?
5. The window at which Amal sits is a central location of the play. Create a design for the scenery outside the window.

About Rabindranath Tagore

Rabindranath Tagore (1861–1941) is arguably India's greatest writer. He won the Nobel Prize for Literature in 1913, as well as many other honors and awards. Many of his works have been published in English translation. In addition to being a poet, Tagore was also an essayist, fiction writer, and playwright. He published more than forty plays, most of which he wrote for his students to perform in the open air. *The Post Office,* which has both realistic and symbolic elements, has remained a perennial favorite.

Like Gandhi, Tagore wrote and preached against the caste system in India, and *The Post Office* reflects his respect for people from all walks of life. It brings to life the values of simplicity and naturalness for which Tagore is known.

CREATING AND PERFORMING

1. At the end of this play, Amal has brought together many characters from different levels of society. Write a farewell speech for him in which he praises the value of each character.
2. Many of the characters in this play change upon contact with Amal. With a partner, perform a scene between Amal and one character. Allow Amal's gentle nature to have an influence on the other character in the scene.
3. Design a simple set for all the acts of the play.

The Play as Literature: Magical Realism

"My most important problem was destroying the lines of demarcation that separate what seems real from what seems fantastic." South American author Gabriel García Márquez described in this way what writers of magical realism strive for. A narrative technique that blurs the separation between reality and fantasy, magical realism is characterized by equal measures of ordinary life and unearthly apparition. It fuses everyday and surrealistic images in order to examine the character of human society. (For more about magical realism see p. 223.)

In the play you are about to read, hard reality is mixed with the lyrical and mystic to create a work full of vibrancy and power.

The Play as Theatre: Sound

What kind of sound might be used to accompany this couple on stage?

In order to give dramatic presentations richness and depth, sound production must go beyond simply enhancing the voices of the actors. The sound equipment used to make the actors' voices louder also provides a wealth of other effects (such as the sound of a tractor roaring in a field or the rushing of water). Sound production also supplies music that sets the mood for the play.

In professional theatres, sound is enhanced by microphones, amplifiers, and speakers. Engineers sit at a sound control board to control all of these devices, as well as tapes, CDs, and records used in the production. Amateur and school productions are often limited in the sound production equipment they have. Sometimes a few microphones, a tape recorder, and creative thinking must do the trick.

WARM UP!

Think of two ordinary situations that happen to you on a weekly basis. Write a short paragraph about these situations. Now take these same two situations and add a magical element that converts them from the familiar to the strange. Write a new paragraph.

THE MIGRANT FARMWORKER'S SON

by Silvia Gonzalez S.

ACT 1

SCENE 1: 1970

Eerie blue light. Sounds of a tractor going across a field. Silhouette light, chest up, on OLIVERIO looking blankly out. BLUE MEXICAN PEASANTS cut lettuce off the ground and bag them. [This is like a dance.] MOM and DAD also work the ground. [They are younger.] After a few moments, rough sounds from a tractor trying to stop in the distance are heard. Lights dim out on OLIVERIO. The PEASANTS look in the opposite direction. In awe, MOM and DAD and the PEASANTS start to move towards the sound, then stop. Sounds of a tractor, losing control, followed by music.)

BLUE MEXICAN PEASANT (religious). Aye, Dios mio.
(The men take off their hats and the women cover their heads with their rebozos and turn away sadly. Eerie light. Slow blackout.)

SCENE 2: 1972

(A young GIRL enters in a ruffled dress and hair in braids. She is playful and full of charm. The light is slightly on her. Purple shadows behind her. She is talking to a baby in a crib, but it is not seen.)

GIRL. Bay-bee. Leetle bay-bee. Cahm here, leetle baby. That's how Mommy called you . . . I'm going to sing you a little song. Itzy bitzy spider, went up the water spout. Down came the rain and . . . But, Daddy, I learned the song in school. Down came the rain and washed the spider out . . . Daddy, I like to . . . It's pretty . . . Out came the sun and . . . (Long pause) Don't, Daddy, please.

SCENE 3: 1985

(DAD enters with a crate of oranges. He's wearing field clothes and is quite weathered. He puts the crate aside. Then exits and enters with a Nintendo game. He sets it up to play.

MOM *enters. She has already changed from working in the fields. She has a nice clean appearance. She is drying her hair.)*

MOM. What's that?

DAD. Nintendo.

MOM. Where's the telephone? What did I say to do after work?

DAD. It's for Enrigue.

MOM. *Henry?*

DAD. *Enrigue.* His name is Enrigue. You keep forgetting your own son's name.

MOM. What about the telephone?

DAD. Look how they put a game in the TV and you can play. Right here on the sofa. It's new. Everybody is getting one.

MOM. How much did that cost?

DAD. Practically nothing. Beto had to get rid of it. He was getting too addicted to it. It was taking all his beer time. We all forced him to sell it to me.

MOM. So the money is gone? Last time you were supposed to get a new carburetor, and instead, you gave the money to your brother.

DAD. He needed it to pay rent.

MOM. Does he ever return favors?

DAD *(looks at her with extreme sadness, returns to game).* He did one time. *(Long moment)*

MOM *(softly).* Play your game.

DAD *(recuperating well).* They say Mario is Italian, but I think he's a Mexicano. *(Pause)* Aye, Mario hit a wall.

*(*HENRY *enters with headphones.* HENRY *is much like a boy of today, in manner and dress. The clash of the cultures is obvious.* HENRY *will attempt to make lighter many moments until a certain point.)*

HENRY. Wow! Dad bought a Nintendo. All right! Give me the controls.

DAD. No. *Todavia no.* (MOM *exits.)*

HENRY. Hey, Mom? What's the matter with her?

DAD. Ah! She's mad at me.

HENRY. For what?

DAD. Nothing. Women.

HENRY. Yeah, women.

DAD. Don't let a woman work. She'll think she's wearing the pants in the house.

MOM *(off).* I do. And I'm a harder worker than you in the fields.

DAD. You are working there because you want to. If we lived in Mexico, they would shame me for letting her work. A real man doesn't allow that.

HENRY. Then why do you cook, Dad?

DAD. Sh! That's a family secret. Never tell anyone what goes on in this house. Understand? I told you that before. It's not the way. *(Back to Nintendo)* Look at that funny guy. He's a cartoon.

*(*MOM *enters with a basket of clothes.)*

MOM. You're a cartoon.

DAD. She wouldn't talk like that to me if we lived over there. And your Spanish would be better. *(Pause)* I'm ready to go tomorrow to get my dignity back.

MOM. They already stepped on it and tossed it out into the gutter. You know I am not going back. And you're not going back either. Your dad's been talking like this for fifteen years. *(HENRY hasn't been listening. He is wearing his Walkman.)*

DAD. Are you making fun of me?

MOM. You're not going back. You would die of starvation over there.

DAD. I don't believe it.

MOM. I do. Why do you think you're here?

DAD. There's death in this dirt. *(MOM turns away. HENRY looks as if he is used to this situation, even though he's not sure what they are talking about. There is silence for awhile.)*

MOM. Henry wouldn't make it over there. And why should I go back?

DAD. Is there another man?

MOM. What?

DAD. Do you have a man to take care of you already?

MOM. No. You don't need a man in the United States.

DAD *(to HENRY).* See that. She's becoming more *gringa* every day. *(HENRY's not listening. DAD knocks HENRY's headphones off.)* Want to go with me to Mexico?

HENRY. Of course not.

DAD. Why not?

HENRY. Like you said, I don't speak Spanish well.

DAD. You used to speak Spanish when you were a child. Why did she have it in her head you would do better in life with only English? Now look at you. You don't understand half the things I say. This is a conspiracy to take you away from me and from the mother country.

HENRY. Dad, I like everything the way it is.

DAD. Ah! What do you know?

MOM. I'm his mother and I look after his education.

DAD. You took my son away. *(Silence)*

HENRY. I'm not like you, Dad. We're different. Sorry.

MOM. That's not what's bothering him. You don't like it that I am learning too.

DAD. *Basta.*

MOM. I like to learn.

DAD. It's a waste of time for a woman to learn.

HENRY. Dad, you got to stop living in the stone age.

DAD. *¿Que?*

HENRY. Let her be. *(DAD looks at HENRY with inexplicable rage. He often does this.)*

MOM. Go, Henry. I'll take care of this.

DAD. Come here, *pocho.*[1] *(DAD motions for HENRY to approach. DAD touches his belt as a threat to HENRY, but MOM doesn't see this action.)*

HENRY. We live in America, Dad. You can't do that.

DAD. You must respect your father.

HENRY. Who is going to respect me? *(MOM directs HENRY out to get DAD a beer. MOM stares at DAD.)*

DAD *(softening).* I did the same to my father. He is growing up.

MOM. And what did he do?

----

1. *pocho,* SLANG. Someone who is neither Mexican nor American

DAD. Enrigue's very first words, between the tears and pooping in his pants, were *"Hola papá."*

MOM. It was *"Hola mamá."*

(HENRY re-enters.)

HENRY. And before that I was a one-cell swimmer.

DAD. You didn't swim. You were born here. *(HENRY sits.)*

HENRY. You don't understand, Dad. Can I play the game now? *(Long pause)* Thanks. *(Sounds of Nintendo game. All stare at the screen.)* Where did you get the money for this?

MOM. He used some of the money for the telephone connection.

HENRY. Man, no phone? Messed up.

DAD. Not everything. I sold his bike.

HENRY. What? Mom!

DAD. What do you need a bike for? You're too old for it.

HENRY. How will I get around?

DAD. You have two feet.

HENRY. I can't believe this. Without asking me?

DAD. Respect me. Respect me. *(HENRY looks at him with so much anger he can't take it.)* In the ranch, we had nothing. And you cry for a bike? *(HENRY rushes out of the house. A long silence between MOM and DAD after HENRY goes. MOM has an understanding expression on her face even though she disapproves greatly of what DAD did. DAD looks at her and becomes a little boy. He is really not the pillar of strength he tries to be. Softening.)* You know I love him.

MOM. Then tell him.

DAD. Who told me? *(DAD goes to the Nintendo game and starts playing. He glances at MOM several times. MOM exits.)*

SCENE 4: LATE THAT EVENING

(HENRY is by himself in a field. OLIVERIO is watching him from a distance. MOM approaches HENRY. OLIVERIO disappears.)

MOM. Henry.

HENRY. Mom.

MOM. Don't be angry with your father.

HENRY. I can't stand him.

MOM. Now God will punish you for saying that.

HENRY. We don't go to church.

MOM. I go. *(Pause)* He's had a hard life.

HENRY. *I've* had a hard life.

MOM. I'll get your bike back.

HENRY. Forget it, Mom. I think I just saw some kid riding it and he looked too happy.

MOM. You'll drive the car then.

HENRY. That piece of crap. I'd be embarrassed.

MOM. That's a way of life for a lot of people. There's nothing wrong with being poor.

HENRY. I want to be alone, Mom.

MOM. *No, you don't.* You don't want to be alone. No one does.

HENRY. Yes, I do. *(MOM hesitates, then leaves quietly. HENRY sits there.)*

(Crossfade to DAD near a canal in the background. He sits there staring at the water. He looks across and sees GIRL smiling at him. She then disappears.)

DAD. Why did you go *hija*? I don't like being alone. *(Blackout)*

SCENE 5: THE NEXT DAY

(DAD enters the house. He is covered with mud from the canal. MOM is trying to play Nintendo.)

DAD. I saw her.

MOM. You didn't see anybody.

DAD. I see her every time I clean out the canals. *(Silence. DAD is distraught again.)*

MOM. I don't know why I listened to you. No pictures, no talking about her. As if she was never alive. You even made me bury her far away.

DAD. I wanted her in Mexican soil.

MOM. This was once Mexican soil.

DAD. I have no worth here, so she couldn't stay.

MOM. Tell Henry about her now.

DAD. No. You know how I get. He'll think I'm weak.

(HENRY enters. DAD stares at him. HENRY eyes DAD's muddy appearance.)

HENRY. How come when I come in *that* dirty, I get in trouble? *(Silence. HENRY looks around.)* The silent treatment.

MOM. I'll get some towels. *(MOM exits. HENRY and DAD stare at each other.)*

HENRY. Hi, Pop.

DAD. Pop? What happened to papá?

HENRY. Yeah, what happened to you?

DAD. What do you got in that bag?

HENRY. Fish.

DAD. From where?

HENRY. The canal.

DAD. I told you not to go to the canals.

HENRY. Dad, this toxic waste could be dinner.

DAD. Don't go over there.

HENRY. Okay. I won't go there . . . today.

DAD. What did you say?

HENRY *(puts his Walkman headphones on)*. Rap with me.

DAD. I'll rap your face. Stop that! *(HENRY keeps dancing.)* ¡Ya! *(DAD grabs HENRY.)* I want you to say thank you for breaking my back for you. ¡Dilo!² For a roof over your head, for food on the table. Give me appreciation for all that I do for you!

HENRY. Is it Father's Day or something?

DAD. *¡Dilo!*

(MOM re-enters.)

MOM. *¡Dejalo!*³

DAD. *¡Diga!*⁴

HENRY. Thanks, *Dad.*

DAD. *¡Papá!*

HENRY. Thanks, *Papá!*

DAD. The rest!

MOM. Stop it, you two.

HENRY. I know you work hard.

DAD. No, you don't. Your mother tells you.

MOM. Leave him alone. *(DAD lets go of HENRY. HENRY sits on the table and picks up a hardened tortilla. He breaks the tortilla.)*

HENRY. Look, I'm abusing a tortilla.

DAD. What did he say?

MOM. He's being funny.

DAD. Being funny while we work in the fields.

---

2. *dilo,* say it
3. *dejalo,* leave him alone
4. *diga,* speak

MOM. Get your father a beer.

HENRY. Gladly. (HENRY *puts his headphones back on to escape. He starts moving to the beat. He gets the beer from the refrigerator and continues dancing with a beer in hand, absentmindedly.* MOM *and* DAD *are unaware of his movement with the can of beer for they are talking quietly with each other. Then* HENRY *stops to adjust his headphones, and* DAD *looks up.*)

DAD. You have my beer?

HENRY. Here, Dad.

DAD (*correcting him*). *Papá.* (*He opens the beer and it squirts all over his face.* DAD *runs after* HENRY *and catches him by the ear.*)

MOM. Stop it!

HENRY. OW! Dad, you're making a Van Gogh out of me.

DAD. Hear that! He told *me to go!* No respect!

HENRY (*breaks away*). *Van Gogh.* He lost an ear. Well, he cut it off.

MOM. Go out, Henry.

HENRY. Glad to. (*He exits to the bedroom.*)

DAD. He has no respect for me. The children born here are spoiled.

MOM. We came here to spoil our children.

DAD (*softens*). Not like this.

MOM. You are jealous of your own son.

(HENRY *enters and heads for the front door.*)

HENRY. I don't need this.

MOM. Henry!

HENRY. What?!

MOM. Come back here.

HENRY. When you stop arguing!

MOM. Who's arguing? This is how we make love.

HENRY. Funny, Mom. I'm not in the mood.

MOM. Talk to your son! *Andale.*

DAD. You'll never do what I do. Never will you cut lettuce or pick from the trees, or anything.

HENRY. No problem!

DAD. *Understand? Understand!?*

HENRY. Who's going to pick the oranges in the tree out back? A wetback like you, Dad?

(DAD *is about to reach for his belt when several* BLUE MEXICAN PEASANTS *[only seen by the audience] enter and restrain him. The* PEASANTS *finally let* DAD *go and they exit with* HENRY.*)

DAD (*softening*). If I had all the money in the world, I would give that boy everything. I would give my wife the world. (*Pause*)

MOM (*softly*). Don't work in the canals, anymore. It brings bad memories to you. It turns you into this monster.

DAD. Sometimes, bad memories make the monster happy.

SCENE 6: LATE AT NIGHT

(*Nighttime. Stars in the sky.* OLIVERIO, *a farmworker, stands in a field. White doves fly around him. He is smiling and enjoying the stars. He then starts shoveling dirt.* HENRY *walks by holding his ear.* OLIVERIO *notices.*)

OLIVERIO. Something in your ear? Hey! I'm talking to you. Something in your ear like your finger? Then take your finger out.

HENRY. I thought it was bleeding.

OLIVERIO. *El corazon sangra . . . (Waits for a response)* Only the heart bleeds, idiot.

HENRY. My Spanish isn't that good.

OLIVERIO. Pity. Where are you going?

HENRY. Nowhere.

OLIVERIO. Then you are in the right place.

HENRY. You work here?

OLIVERIO. I work all the time. And you?

HENRY. I don't work all the time. I'm too young.

OLIVERIO. I started working when I was this high. I had a rifle at the age of seven.

HENRY. To protect yourself?

OLIVERIO. To shoot my food. Jack rabbits. Sometimes a squirrel. Whatever came my way. I was sent off to herd the sheep and fend for myself. Sometimes it was months before I saw another person. Sometimes I forgot what I looked like. *No mirror in my pocket.* And I should have had one. I was very good-looking. Well, I needed to remind myself of that.

HENRY. You killed for your own food, at seven?

OLIVERIO. Or eight years old. I can't remember now. Once I ate a 'possum. It tasted very good. The tail wasn't good. Felt like a snake in your mouth. The eyes were good. Well, when you are in the middle of nowhere and you are not sure you'll get a chance to kill for food again, everything tastes good.

HENRY. Would you eat 'possum again?

OLIVERIO. Eh, no . . . What's your name?

HENRY. Henry.

OLIVERIO. Mine's Oliverio. Like Oliver, but only better.
El señor de la tierra
El señor de poesias
El señor muy amable
Con poesias mas allegres que tu.

HENRY. What are you doing here?

OLIVERIO. Look at that. Don't you see it? Staring at the stars cleanses the soul. You should try it. Maybe it'll clean out that ear of yours. Look, there's the North Star.

HENRY. Great, I'm standing here with an old man that stares at stars.

OLIVERIO. And I'm standing with an idiot who holds his ear. I recognize that look on your face . . . Once, I picked up a lemon from the ground and put it in my pocket. It came from a man who was selling them. He saw the bulge in my pocket and rushed me to my father by the shirt collar. My father beat me up so much. Everyone saw him whipping me in the street. He wanted to teach me a lesson I would never forget.

HENRY. You didn't steal the lemon. You just picked it up.

OLIVERIO. And put it in my pocket. Same thing. My father was very determined I learn respect for the hard-working man.

HENRY. My father is a hard-working man. Hard at work in smacking me.

OLIVERIO. Maybe you deserved it.

HENRY. I didn't deserve that. Did you? *(Pause)*

OLIVERIO. See that star. That one is mine. And that one over there. That one. That belongs to your family. Do you want a star to give away?

HENRY. A *what*?

OLIVERIO. Humor me.

HENRY. All right. Then, that one belongs to my girlfriend. Well, the one girl I really like.

OLIVERIO. Oh, you have a girlfriend. That's nice. Much too young to fall in love. Don't you know what love does to you. It makes you love more. It makes you hurt more. It makes you crazy. Of course I've forgotten that part.

HENRY. *Que viejito.* What else do you have to amuse me?

OLIVERIO. *(He smiles, then picks up some dirt and lets it sprinkle to the ground slowly.)* Look at this. This is my family. All of them. My uncles, my aunts, my father, mother, brothers, sisters, and my grandparents, and all the greats before them. But not the grandchildren or my wife. They are still alive and live well enough.

HENRY. Where are your children?

OLIVERIO. Lost. Like you.

HENRY. And the rest of the family is dirt?

OLIVERIO. The darker ones are mud. They're dust. Don't say dirt, sounds impersonal. Say dust. Say it like this, DUST.

HENRY. Okay, "DUST."

OLIVERIO. Dust. We are all simply dust. *Muchacho,* look at your shoes. You've been stepping on my mother. And that right there sticking to your pants, is one of my ancestors. She was an Aztec Indian. Okay. Take them home and introduce them to your family. *(HENRY starts to exit.)* So soon? Then go. But come back again.

HENRY. I should stay. I'll probably get my other ear smacked.

OLIVERIO *(looks at the stars).* No you won't.

SCENE 7: THE NEXT DAY

(BLUE MEXICAN PEASANTS enter. From their bags they take out tomatoes, onions, and some oranges and put them on the kitchen table. One peasant puts a carton of eggs and a package of tortillas by the stove. Another peasant opens one end of the tortilla package. Another goes to the shelf and gets the Mazola oil and sets it near the stove, and then picks up a dollar bill he knows is payment and puts it in his pocket. DAD enters and starts dicing up the ingredients for migas.[5] He tears a tortilla into bits and throws it in with the tomato and onion to fry. He then adds eggs.)

DAD *(while cooking happily).* Migas, migas, migas. Que sabrosas. Tomate, cebolla, y huevos. ¿Y que mas?

(He looks into the refrigerator and pulls out a pan of beans to put in the mixture. GIRL appears. DAD accepts her presence.)

DAD. *Hija.*

GIRL. Hi, Daddy.

DAD. *Que bonita te miras.*

GIRL *(curtsies).* Thank you, Daddy.

DAD. *Papá.* Remember what I told you. *Papá.*

GIRL. Okay, Daddy.

DAD. *¿Tienes hambre, mija?*

---

5. *migas,* fried bread crumbs and eggs

GIRL. Yes, Daddy.

DAD. *Diga, si papá.*

GIRL. *Si, papá.*

DAD. *Muy bien. Tengo migas. Que sabrosas. ¿Te gustan? Huelelas.*

GIRL. Smells good, Daddy.

DAD (*correcting her*). *Papá.*

GIRL. Daddy.

DAD. *Sí, mona.*

GIRL. I want to take my bike out. Can I borrow your keys?

DAD. Keeyz?

GIRL. Yeah. The keys. I need the keys to take my bike out of the shed. You locked it in there. So I want the keys.

DAD. The keeyz?

GIRL. Yeah. The keys.

DAD. Okay. (DAD *puckers up and makes a smoochy kiss noise.*) There.

GIRL. No, not a kiss, the keys.

DAD. Oh, I thought you said a keeyz.

GIRL. You do that all the time. Okay, *las llaves. Presteme las llaves.*

DAD. *Mejor. Aqui estan.* (*He takes the keys out of his pocket.*) *¿Otra cosa?*

GIRL. Can I have a quarter?

DAD. Me no speak English.

GIRL. Daddy!

DAD. *Cuando hablas Español.*

(GIRL *exits as* HENRY *enters.*)

HENRY. Hey, Dad. I want to borrow the car. Can I borrow the keys?

DAD. Keeyz?

HENRY. Yeah. I want to see my friends over at the high school. I won't be long.

DAD. Yule want the keeyz?

HENRY. Yeah. That's what I said. Can I have the keys?

DAD. Okay. (DAD *puckers up to make a smoochy kiss noise.*)

HENRY. Oh, Dad! Not a kiss, the keys!

DAD. OH! . . . No.

HENRY. Ah, come on. There's going to be a pep rally.

DAD. A what?

HENRY. A pep rally. Cheerleaders will be there.

DAD. Girls?

HENRY. Yeah.

DAD (*thinks*). You go.

HENRY. The keys, Dad. You sold my bike.

DAD. All right. One hour.

HENRY. One hour! That's not enough.

DAD. Then give me back the keeyz.

HENRY. Man . . . What can I do to stay out a bit longer? Get you a beer?

DAD. Respect me.

HENRY. I do, Dad.

DAD. No you don't. You don't know what it means.

HENRY. *Por favor.*

DAD. Go for an hour and a half.

HENRY. Dad, listen. It's exciting. There's dancing. Music. Everyone is happy. It's fun, Dad. Want to go?

DAD. Me? No. You go. Go for two hours. Maybe three.

HENRY. *Gracias Papá.*

DAD. You should learn Spanish. It's good for you. If you forget the language, you'll be lost. You'll never know yourself, or your history.

HENRY. *No hablo Español.*

DAD. *¡Vete!*

HENRY *(laughing).* *Adios, Papá.*

DAD *(long moment later, under his breath).* Go kill yourself. *(Slow blackout.)*

SCENE 8: TWO DAYS LATER

(DAD and MOM are sitting at the table with bills and statements scattered about. MOM does the bill paying as DAD watches. Then MOM puts money in an envelope and that in a Zip-lock bag. She then puts it in a secret place: a hole in the wall under the sink.)

DAD. My friend's children speak the language so beautifully. I understand them. They have respect. I don't understand Enrigue.

MOM. Henry will do better with—

DAD *(overlapping on "better").* Enrigue.

MOM. Henry.

DAD *(pause).* Mothers and sons always stick together and gang up on the father.

MOM. Why don't you go to school and learn English yourself? That's the secret to success.

DAD. Why waste my time? I'm going to die in Mexico.

MOM. You're not going back.

DAD. Yes, I am. I have to be buried in the soil that speaks my language. If I don't, then I'll truly feel like a foreigner.

MOM. You don't feel anything when you are dead.

DAD. I will.

MOM *(pause).* You want that boy to succeed, you let him speak the language of this country. You'll see that I am right. The schools here—

DAD *(overlapping on "here").* Help families lose their children. He talks to me about things I don't know. Like pepto, pepto bees-mo.

MOM. What?

DAD. He invited me to go to the school for the pepto-algo. I don't know. The girls, cheerleaders.

MOM. Oh, the pep rally.

DAD. Yes. How did you know that's what it's called?

MOM. If we both take a class, we would learn English very well. And you would understand your son better.

DAD. Take a class to understand my son? I refuse to be made an idiot in public.

MOM. It's a school. You go there because you are an idiot. *(DAD looks at her. Long moment. Softly.)* Do you like Salinas better?

DAD. In Salinas I can forget about her. Here, I think I see her all the time.

MOM. Try to forget. Then the misery will leave you. *(MOM exits. DAD sits silently. A blue arm opens the kitchen window and slips several school books onto the sink counter. Moments later DAD takes one of the books and tries to read it. He covers one eye in an attempt to better see the page. He then puts the book down and exits.)*

SCENE 9: LATER THAT DAY

(Near a canal HENRY is assembling a fishing pole. DAD enters.)

HENRY. Dad. Ah, there's a bunch of fish in there. I saw them swimming. I borrowed the fishing pole and . . . Are you mad?

DAD. What are you doing here?

HENRY. Fishing?

DAD. *¿Como?*

HENRY. With a fishing pole.

DAD. Ah. You don't need a fishing pole. In the ranch, all you needed was some line and a hook. *Mira.* I'll show you. Get this fishing line and wrap it around something. A rock, or a little stick. Then put a hook at the end. *Aqui.* Now put it in the water. This end with the stick, you put in your pocket, but first twist the middle of the line around the button of your *camisa. Asi.* When you feel your shirt moving, you got a fish.

HENRY. You can catch a fish that way?

DAD. *Pescados grandes.*

HENRY. Get out of town. You won't catch a thing.

DAD. *Vamos aver.* (DAD *waits for the fish. Suddenly, his shirt tugs and a fish splashes up.*)

HENRY. I don't believe it.

DAD. Watch it. Watch it. Aye. You let it get away! *Bueno.* That's what it's all about.

HENRY. That's totally amazing. I've never seen anything like that. Cool. So utterly cool.

(GIRL *appears from across the canal.* DAD*'s mood becomes somber.*)

HENRY. Let's do it again over here. Kind of embarrassing in a way, but who cares. We're catching fish. Dad, let's . . . Dad? What's the matter? Dad? *¿Papá?* Hey. Come on. Don't

stop, now. This is the best fun we've had in a long time. Dad? (DAD *is staring at* GIRL *smiling at him.* HENRY *can't see* GIRL.)

DAD *(slowly).* I miss Mexico.

HENRY. Dad. It's not too far.

DAD. *Vamanos.*

HENRY. Dad. Geesh. (*Under his breath*) Man, get it together. (DAD *exits.* GIRL *watches* HENRY *gather the fishing gear and start to go.*)

SCENE 10: THE SAME DAY

(MOM *is listening to a "Learn the English Language" tape.*)

TAPE. I am hungry.

MOM. I am hungree.

TAPE. I am hungry.

MOM. I am hungry.

TAPE. Repeat. I am hungry.

MOM. Repeat I am hungry.

TAPE. What would you like to eat?

MOM. Apple pie and coffee.

TAPE. I am not hungry.

(HENRY *enters.*)

HENRY. Mom.

MOM. Sh!

TAPE. I am not hungry.

HENRY. Mom.

MOM *(turns off tape).* I'm practicing my English. You're bothering me. Making me nervous.

HENRY. You speak good enough.

MOM. Oh no. People stare at me when I talk. I have to get rid of the accent.

HENRY. It's all right, Mom.

MOM. I want to speak properly. No accents.

HENRY. Mom, even in the English language there are different accents.

MOM. That's not true.

HENRY. Yes, it is.

MOM. Well, then, it all sounds the same to me.

HENRY. But it isn't. Listen to me. Here's one accent. *(Southern California accent)* Killer dude. Totally awesome. Freakster. And here's another one. *(Boston accent)* Where's da ca? Or this. *(Chicago south-sider accent)* Hey, I'a breaka your face.

MOM. It all sounds the same to me.

HENRY. Ma. I'm sure it's like that over there. Regional Spanish?

MOM. Well, yes. Different accents. But I liked the first one. I'll speak like that. That accent sounded good.

HENRY. The California talking?

MOM. Keeler doode. I like that. What does that mean?

HENRY. Nothing.

MOM. How can something mean nothing?

HENRY. Put the tape away.

MOM. No. I want to be educated. *You can be educated.*

HENRY. I have enough skills to make it in life.

MOM. That's not good enough. Go to college.

HENRY. We've talked about this before and you said you'd stop. I want to rap.

MOM. Then go rap and I'll study. *(Pause)* You're stubborn like your father.

HENRY. Where is he?

MOM. He went his way and I went mine. *Hombre tan sonso.*

HENRY. Most would leave, Mom.

MOM. I can't leave my husband. I'm Catholic. Besides, we were taught not to leave a man if he has some good in him. Anyway, I have to help him.

HENRY. Help him do what?

MOM. *Nada.*

HENRY. What's wrong with him? Is he sick?

MOM. No. Go rap.

HENRY. What's the matter then?

MOM. I have to listen to my tape. Go. I'll study for the both of us.

HENRY. Mom. I'm old enough to know what's going on.

MOM. No, you're not. *(Pause)* Go. You are making this hard on me.

HENRY. Sure. I don't want to be a burden. (HENRY *exits.* MOM *sits there quietly for a long moment. She then turns on the tape.)*

TAPE RECORDER (MOM's *voice*). Everyone is a burden. Even memory becomes a burden. The memory of it brings you down. Tears you to pieces. Best to forget and remember only when you are alone. If the mind was more powerful you could tell it to erase things. Then record a different message over it. And play what you want to hear again and again.

TAPE. I am thirsty.

MOM. I am thirstee.

TAPE. I am thirsty. Repeat.

MOM. Repeat.

(MOM *turns off the recorder, but it still continues. We hear "repeat, repeat, repeat" in a strange way for a while longer. Then the "repeat" fades away.* MOM *walks over to a shoe box. Inside the shoe box are several ruffled hair ribbons that belonged to* GIRL. *There is also a small school picture of* GIRL. MOM *stares at the picture. She then goes to the refrigerator. As she opens the door, a* BLUE MEXICAN PEASANT*'s face is inside and looks out.* MOM *takes a beer and closes the refrigerator door. She then takes some paper out of the shoe box and walks over to the trash can. As she is ready to toss the paper, a blue arm reaches out of the trash can and takes the paper, then crumbles it and disappears into the trash can with it. Moments later* MOM *goes to the sink and slices a lime. Outside of the window are several* BLUE MEXICAN PEASANTS *looking miserable. They stare at* MOM. *She doesn't see them. She goes to the table and squeezes the lime slice into the beer. She continues to look at the picture. She licks her side wrist, sprinkles salt on it, and licks the salt off. She then drinks her beer. A group of* BLUE MEXICAN PEASANTS *enter and surround her. They have devastated looks on their faces.* MOM *continues looking at the picture. She starts to cry and the* PEASANTS *back off.* MOM *quickly regains control of herself, and the* PEASANTS *approach again. They stare at her as if to tell her something, but then give up and exit. Crossfade to darkness.*)

SCENE 11: THE SAME DAY

(GIRL *is at the window. She opens it and looks in. Moments later* HENRY *walks past and exits. A bit later,* DAD *enters, gets his boots, and exits.* MOM *enters and sits at the table to sew a dress.*)

GIRL. Mommy. Mommy, can you hear me? Mommy! Mommy, why don't you open the door? I was out there and you didn't even hear me. Where did Dad go? He can hear me. You're too busy to hear me. Daddy always hears me. He really listens when I speak Spanish. What are you doing? Mommy! I'm talking to you. I know, I know, you're too busy. *(Pause)* Why do you and Daddy fight? It's no good to fight. Why do you let him be mean to my brother? You're not mean. *(Pause)* Mommy, don't go to Salinas without me again. I have to stay here all by myself when you go. I get scared. I get so scared. Mommy, you never listen to me. Listen to me. Listen to me. I hate you. I hate you. (MOM *starts to cry.*) I'm sorry, Mommy. Don't cry. I'll be good. I'll be quiet. I'll go outside to play. I'm so sorry. (MOM *stops crying.* GIRL *feels better. Crossfade.*)

SCENE 12: THE NEXT DAY

(DAD *enters with a few cantaloupes in his arms. He puts them down and turns on the radio and hears rap music. He quickly changes it to a Spanish radio station. He listens for a moment and then slices a cantaloupe.* MOM *enters.*)

DAD. *Aye querida.*

MOM. You're in a good mood.

DAD. I am. Look. I want to talk to you. Have some of this.

MOM. What is it?

DAD. Melon!

MOM. I know. What do you want to tell me?

DAD. Guess.

MOM. You quit smoking.

DAD. No.

MOM. Well, you should. You stink up the house.

DAD. Guess again.

MOM. You quit drinking.

DAD. NO.

MOM. Then it's not good news.

DAD. I got a job.

MOM. You got a job?

DAD. A better one than the fields.

MOM. Is that why you left so early.

DAD. I had to.

MOM. They were asking me where you were. I told them you were urinating. You still didn't come back so I told them you had infection on your *"pito."*

DAD. Why did you tell them that?

MOM. I had to.

DAD. Anyway, I did go to urinate, then I saw Julio.

MOM. Julio!?

DAD. He's starting a business.

MOM *(suspicious). What kind of business?*

DAD. A restaurant. He wants me to be a partner.

MOM. He wants you to put all the money in. You know I don't trust him.

DAD. Neither do I, but it's a chance.

MOM. A chance for what? To lose what you already have?

DAD. What do I have? I have nothing. How can I lose nothing? The Salvadorians are taking the field work from us. They do the work for practically nothing. Soon they'll be doing all the work. There's so many of them who are trying to survive like us.

MOM. What are you going to do in that restaurant, wash dishes?

DAD. I did that before. This time, I get to be in charge. I'll be the boss. If I only give Julio money today to—

MOM *(overlapping on "money").* We have no money.

DAD. We have some hidden.

MOM. That's not ours.

DAD. We'll use a little and then replace it.

MOM. It's not ours. We're giving it to Henry when he decides to go to college.

DAD. It came from our suffering. Think about our future. He will benefit from it.

MOM. I didn't come to this country to steal from my child.

DAD. He doesn't know he has it. He's not serious about school. He won't be for a long time and by that time, I'll have replaced it two times over.

MOM. No. My son means more to me than that stupid restaurant.

DAD *(overlapping on "than").* Than me?

MOM. Than that restaurant.

DAD. What about me? What about me? *(Long tension-filled silence.* DAD *goes to the shoe box. He throws out the contents and holds a picture of* GIRL.*)* Do it for her!

MOM. Julio will make you eat dirt.

DAD. Give it to me.

MOM. He's not doing anything for you. Only for himself.

DAD. It's a chance! . . . It's a chance. Listen to me, *querida.* We have to work together the way the Koreans do. You know when they come to this country they have nothing. Just like us, nothing. Then all the members of the family put their money together and buy one store. They all work it, bumping into each other, day and night, saving all the profits, until they pay for the store. Then they buy another store, and together work that one until they have enough to buy another one, then another one, then another one. Finally, all the members who put their money in for the first store, get their own store at the end. They do this all the time. That's how they have all the grocery stores. And we're grateful for at least they are selling tortillas.

MOM (*pause*). None of those Koreans went into partnership with Julio. It's with their own families they do such things. No one cheats a family member and if they do, the whole family tells him to go to hell.

DAD. My family is all over and they are more miserable than me! That is why I am going to use the money with Julio.

MOM. No, you're not.

DAD. Yes, I am.

MOM. No, you're not.

DAD. *Querida.* This time you are wrong.

MOM. Our son is our only chance for self respect.

DAD. Because I didn't give it to you?

MOM. We are immigrants to this country. I didn't come with high expectations. It's foolish to have—

DAD (*overlapping on "foolish"*). Foolish to have high expectations of this country, or me?

MOM. Not with my son's college money.

DAD. Then with what? (MOM *covers her ears to avoid listening.* DAD *looks at her wedding ring. She notices this, and after a long moment slips off the ring and gives it to* DAD. DAD *then starts to exit.*) You are a strong woman for doing this. (*Pause*) Julio also thanks you. (*He exits.*)

MOM. Julio is a loser. And so are you.

SCENE 13: A FEW DAYS LATER

(OLIVERIO *is pushing a wheelbarrow across the field.* DAD *walks by holding a plastic bag with money inside.*)

OLIVERIO. *Estrellas, estrellas, estrellas. Muchas estrellas.*

(HENRY *comes on and sneaks up to scare* OLIVERIO.)

OLIVERIO. *Ep-pa.*

HENRY. Scared you.

OLIVERIO. Scared me like a ghost.

HENRY. I got good news. Remember that girl I told you about?

OLIVERIO. No.

HENRY. Yeah, you remember, old man. She's going to Mesa College. It's a good way to get the hell out of here if you got the money.

OLIVERIO. Those *gringos* like to use Spanish names for everything now. One time, everything here was named in Spanish. They changed them to English, and now back to Spanish to sell it as high real estate. Hal-ci-en-da Heights, ugh. La Play-zza di May-yo, ehh. Yor-ba Lin-da. *Es yerba linda.* Such a travesty to corrupt a beautiful language. At least their gardeners say the names correctly. Ah! A beautiful night. Oh, look. Isn't that beautiful? Let's see how smart you are. What is it?

HENRY. A star.

OLIVERIO. What is it really?

HENRY. A meteorite?

OLIVERIO. No. It's a mass with gas. That's what we are. And, we are all the same. Should be no names, no labels, no political affiliation. All those things make war. Understand? *(No answer)* Someday you will. *(They see a falling star.)* See that one going down? . . . Has a lot of gas. Too many tacos. (HENRY*'s not amused.)* What's the matter? Life can be fought with a smile and a little joking. For that matter, death. When you're my age, you won't care about too many things. Too much effort. Will give you ulcers. *(Burps)*

HENRY. How old are you?

OLIVERIO. Why do you want to know? Isn't it enough to see the gray hair and the wrinkles running into each other? *(Smiles)* Did you know that the tears of the clown are so true.

HENRY. What?

OLIVERIO. He cries.
There's tears painted on his face, but he cries.
He cries from what he feels inside.
"Las lagrimas"

It's painted on the face
But he smiles
Do you know why he smiles? . . .
He smiles because he learned that he has to face a situation, with the opposite.

(No response) I've learned that true wisdom comes with death. *(No response)* Your girlfriend is going to college? Go yourself. Maybe what I learned in the fields someone with a degree can teach you.

HENRY. Money problems, *hombre.* Plus why should I? Where's it going to take me?

OLIVERIO. At least to show that some dirt can mix with the white sand. Look, my boy, someday you'll find that money doesn't make you happy. It's the work. If you like what you do, then you'll care less about the money and the things you can get with it.

HENRY. That's what you're trying to tell me? My parents are picking for me? Give me a break.

OLIVERIO. No. They're picking for everybody.

*(*HENRY *looks at* OLIVERIO *for a long moment, then exits. At that moment,* GIRL *appears.* OLIVERIO *sees* GIRL *and goes to her.)*

OLIVERIO. Are you ready?

GIRL. In English?

OLIVERIO. Will you interrupt?

GIRL. I don't know.

OLIVERIO. You always do. All right. Ready? In the eyes of a child.

GIRL. The child sees so much.

OLIVERIO. Rainbows never pass without mention.

GIRL. Ooohh. I liked that one.

OLIVERIO. The face brightens
in peaceful acknowledgment of
the colors
The cheeks of a child
soft, soft
soft pillows of joy
When pressed against a parent's face
Brings more colors of happiness
and even more joy.

GIRL. Can I sing?

OLIVERIO. And from the tenderness of
the lips
A voice so pure exists
Making all who have saddened
A temporary haven
One that will only continue
If you insist
The baby cries
And sounds so demanding
Deciding quickly what the child
needs

GIRL *(interrupts on "child")*.
I have a little brother. His name is
Enrigue. That's what my father said
was his name. I told you, teacher.
Enrigue. His name is Enrigue. She
said, "Henry. His name is Henry."
Your name is Henry.

OLIVERIO. He needs everything.
Mother, father, soil, all the tools to
begin.

GIRL. I'm going to teach him English.
So they don't make fun of him. He'll
be good in school, like me.

OLIVERIO. Pity those who don't
understand.

*(OLIVERIO exits as a group of BLUE MEXICAN
PEASANTS enter and sit around GIRL.)*

GIRL. Okay everyone. Are you ready?
Itzy bitzy spider, went up the water
spout. Down came the rain and
washed the spider out.

*(The PEASANTS then gently grab GIRL as she
goes limp, they toss her in the movement of
water going through an irrigation canal. In
this stylized dance of "water rushing" they
exit with GIRL. DAD enters and runs toward
them. He doesn't reach GIRL in time.)*

DAD. ¡HIJA!

SCENE 14: THE NEXT DAY

*(Lights up on HENRY. He is watching DAD in
the distance. They are both being watched by
the BLUE MEXICAN PEASANTS. DAD drops to
his knees. Crossfade to OLIVERIO and HENRY.)*

HENRY. You like to pick?

OLIVERIO. I like the life on the farm.

HENRY. It's degrading.

OLIVERIO. To you maybe, but to me, it's
wonderful. Seeing how God makes a
seed grow from a soil that is black
like hell.

HENRY. It's hell, all right.

OLIVERIO. Feeling the sun that can
silently peel your skin from its
intense rays.

HENRY. I only tan on a beach.

OLIVERIO. From water that comes all
the way from the mountains in the
north, then through these canals.
Canals that hold life. They can also
hold death. Are you afraid to die?

HENRY. No.

OLIVERIO. Death is a blanket. It stops
life, yet it's the beginning of something else. Go home now. Your
parents need you.

HENRY. Maybe I will go away. Just leave with twenty cents in my pocket and make a life.

OLIVERIO. Sounds familiar.

HENRY. My dad said he did that.

OLIVERIO. I had ten cents in my pocket. Will you follow your father's footsteps?

HENRY. What do you think?

OLIVERIO. I think you made up your mind. Go then.

HENRY (hesitates). I will.

OLIVERIO. Get what you need for the road, but travel light. Good luck.

HENRY. I'm going. Don't rush me.

OLIVERIO. What kind of work will you find?

HENRY. What do you mean, what kind of work?

OLIVERIO. You have to survive. I worked in the fields for money to pay for food. Don't tell me you have an American Express card?

HENRY. I'll rap.

OLIVERIO (confused). How much they pay you?

HENRY. Thousands of dollars if you're good. That's the profession I want. I want to feel important.

OLIVERIO. The oldest profession in the world is just as important.

HENRY. The oldest profession in the world?

OLIVERIO. Without it, there would be no population.

HENRY. The oldest profession in the world is—

OLIVERIO. Farming. That's the oldest profession in the world. Think about it.

HENRY. I will. (HENRY *walks to his own home.* DAD *is there waiting for him.*)

DAD. Enrigue. I'll need your help in the restaurant.

HENRY. What restaurant?

MOM. Your father bought a partnership with Julio.

HENRY. He's a drunk, Dad.

DAD. I'll be running the business. You work as a busboy.

HENRY. No way.

DAD. *¿Por que no?*

HENRY (hesitates). 'Cause I'm going to school.

DAD. What school?

HENRY. The junior college. Mesa College.

MOM. I want you to go to the state college.

DAD. You're not even serious about life. How are you going to go?

HENRY. What if I get a scholarship?

MOM. This is wonderful. I knew it. Henry, I want to show you something. Oh, your father and I worked hard for this. We've managed to scrape some money together for you. I've been sewing for ladies to add to it. I hope you'll appreciate it. We obligated ourselves to save it for you. So your life would be better. It's not that much, but at least you can pay for a few classes, books and—(As she speaks she reaches for the envelope in the hole. The BLUE MEXICAN PEASANTS *look through the window.* MOM *doesn't find the Zip-lock bag with the envelope of money. She turns to* DAD.) You took it!

DAD. Julio needed more. I had to do it. No more dirt on my fingers. No

The Migrant Farmworker's Son by Silvia Gonzalez S. **211**

more getting my hands moist from the *"canales de muerte."* You know how I hate working *los canales,* as well as the fields.

MOM. He's our only hope.

DAD. What about me? You're married to me, not to him.

MOM. You took the money that belonged to him. (HENRY *runs out.* OLIVERIO *catches him and they embrace.*)

DAD. Everything that comes into this house is mine. I can do whatever I want with it. (MOM *and* DAD *stare at each other as the lights turn blue, then they exit.*)

(*The* BLUE MEXICAN PEASANTS *enter wearing skull masks. They strip the house of all its furniture. They place a microwave in the room. "Itzy Bitzy Spider" is heard faintly in the distance.*)

(*End of Act One*)

ACT 2

SCENE 1: THREE MONTHS LATER

(HENRY *is by himself in a field.* OLIVERIO *is watching him from a distance.* MOM *approaches* HENRY. OLIVERIO *disappears.*)

HENRY. Mom. Mom. Have you used the microwave? I was lucky. I won it at the school raffle. I never win anything and I got it. I wanted the bike, but the microwave was the second prize. You can cook tortillas in it. (DAD *is cursing in the other room.*) What's his problem? (*No answer*) You two keep things from me. I wish I had a sibling to team up with me against you two. *Sibling.* What a funny word. Sounds like a chicken.

MOM (*stunned, then threatens to strike*). I'm going to break your mouth.

HENRY. Why? What I do?

MOM. Get out of my sight, you snake in

the grass. *(About to strike* HENRY *but he grabs her arm)*

HENRY. I'm not a snake! Call me anything but that.

MOM. Oh, my God. I'm turning into your father.

HENRY. Some kind of compulsion. Beat the kid.

MOM. Enrique. He stopped it, didn't he? I told him NO MORE OF THAT BEHAVIOR. *(*HENRY *starts rapping with sound effects.)*

*(*DAD *enters.)*

DAD. *Que esta pasando aqui. Tu sabes que no me gusta rap.*

MOM *(exploding).* You said Julio knew what to do.

DAD. He had the place rented for two months.

MOM. He strings people along.

HENRY. How much did Julio take you for?

MOM. Even your own son knows about Julio.

HENRY. Everyone knows about Julio. He stands in front of the school waiting to gyp someone. If he thinks you got something, he goes after you. When I was coming home with the microwave, he tried to give me a ring for it. I told him to get lost.

MOM. Did you see the ring?

HENRY. No. He said he had it in a safe place.

DAD. Why didn't you tell me this before?

HENRY. Because you never asked.
(Silence. HENRY *then goes to the refrigerator and gets three beers. He gives one to* MOM *and* DAD, *and one for himself. He pops open his beer. Slow blackout.)*

SCENE 2: THE SAME DAY

(In the fields. A glimmer of stars. The BLUE MEXICAN PEASANTS *walk across holding baskets of fruit, a baby bundle, and a television set. A somber* MOM *follows them with the shoe box. They exit. Much later,* OLIVERIO *enters to see the stars.* HENRY *then enters. He sees* OLIVERIO, *but wants to walk past, avoiding him.)*

OLIVERIO. Where are you coming from and where are you going? Come on. Relax. Soon life will be over and all that has preoccupied you will not be that important anymore. Ignoring me? Fine. Then I'll talk to myself. I'll make up a poem right here as you walk away.
El espiritu te envia
El corazon se enternece
La vida se va
Sin todos los muebles.

HENRY. What does that mean?

OLIVERIO. How the hell should I know?

HENRY. But you said it.

OLIVERIO. I only speak from the heart. A lot of times I don't know what it means.

HENRY. That doesn't make sense.

OLIVERIO. Oh, but it does. It's much later when I figure them out. But by that time, it's too late. I've already lost the original feeling of the poem and feel something else. Then there comes a new poem, and I have to figure that out, too. It gets to be too much, but I write a lot of poems that way. I mean it. Where are you going?

HENRY. I don't know. I have to get away.

The Migrant Farmworker's Son by Silvia Gonzalez S. **213**

OLIVERIO. From what?

HENRY. From everything. From my parents. I'm going crazy with them. I don't know who they are or what they want from me. You know, I don't always understand the way they talk. How come they don't talk like you?

OLIVERIO. Poetry?

HENRY. No. In simple English so I can understand. I get bits and pieces and I know I miss the rest. They know too, but say nothing.

OLIVERIO. Henry. Language doesn't mean a thing. It's what's here, in the heart, that speaks. *(Long moment)* There's your girlfriend's star. Have you seen her lately?

HENRY. Yeah. She made me mad by touching my arm. So I hit her.

OLIVERIO. Oh, boy. You're a handful. Why I got you, I'll never know.

HENRY. What?

OLIVERIO. Look at that star.

HENRY. I have no more stars to look at.

OLIVERIO. Then look at the moon. The moon looks so innocent, and at times it realizes it's not. So it goes away for a while to think things out. And then it returns to try again. Each time it fails, but it keeps coming back to try again. A new poem.

La luna no sabe
Como todos la miran
Ella siempre va y viene
Para que todos la admiran.

HENRY. What the hell does that mean?

OLIVERIO. I just recite them, I don't explain them. Anyway, if I did tell you, it would lose its mystery. It's not what the words mean. It's how the language makes you feel. If you feel the meaning, then why do you need to know the words?

HENRY. Because, if you don't know the words, you get hit.

OLIVERIO. There's meaning even behind that. Don't always listen to the sounds of the whip. Feel the meaning behind it.

HENRY. I'll never understand you, or them!

OLIVERIO. You will always think about us. Even when you are far away. Even if you run away up here, you'll think about us. See those stars. You think about them even when you don't see them, especially on those foggy nights. You'll think, "Where are the stars? I know they are there." Another poem.

¿Donde estan las estrellas?
Los quiero con toda mi alma
Brillan orgullosas
Aun cuando nos dormimos.
(HENRY *exits.*)
Where are the stars
I love them, will all my life
They shine with pride
Even when we sleep.

Boy, that sounds awful in English.

(With some passion)
Cuando ellas brillan
Mi tristeza resultan
Y mis lagrimas caen
Quiero decirle a mi gente
Que no se vayan muy lejos
Y siempre recuerdan
de las mañanitas allegres.

SCENE 3: THAT EVENING

(HENRY *is at the kitchen table doing his home-work.* DAD *enters and stands there, staring at him.*)

HENRY. Dad, I have homework to do. (*No response. Still more staring.*) Dad, leave me alone. I'm doing *tarea.*

DAD. *Tarea. ¡Digalo bien!*

HENRY. *Tengo ser me tarea. Adesso.*

DAD. *¿Adesso? Eso es Italiano.*

HENRY. I like Italian. And for your information, that's where I'll go if I'm going to travel. There, or Egypt. See, I already know about Mexico.

DAD. No, you don't. I thought I knew everything about the United States, and when I came here, I was mistaken. Where's your mother?

HENRY. She went to class.

DAD. I told her not to go.

HENRY. Give her a break.

DAD. She's planning to leave me. (*Long pause*) In this house, *vamos hablar puro Español, des de ahora.*

HENRY. Speak in Spanish only? Not in your life.

DAD. You're going to write your home-work in Spanish. And if you don't, out you go.

HENRY. I'll go! (HENRY *gets up, but* DAD *grabs him and throws him on the chair.*) I'll fail if I write this in Spanish.

DAD. I failed, too! *Comiensa su tarea en Español.*

HENRY. Dad!

DAD. *¡En este momento! ¡Andale!* (DAD *pushes* HENRY *off the chair.*)

HENRY. Go to hell!

(DAD *pulls out his belt. A* BLUE MEXICAN PEASANT *appears. He is holding a belt and watches the action.*)

DAD. *Venga aqui. Lloron.* You baby.

HENRY. Baby? I saw you near the canal crying! *Crying.* You are a grown man who cries near the canal! Macho, macho, macho.

DAD. I'm going to kill you.

HENRY. Go ahead and do it! It just doesn't hurt me anymore!

DAD. If your mother could hear you talking to me in this way.

HENRY. If I told her you never stopped, she'd leave you! And you would be *solo! ¡Muy solo!*

DAD. So you think I'm an animal?

HENRY. No, Dad. I think you're crazy. (DAD *is about to strike* HENRY, *but* HENRY *protects himself by picking up a basket of laundry and throwing it towards* DAD.)

DAD. You run from *su papá* and I'll beat you harder.

HENRY. *¡Tu no eres mi papá!*

DAD. *Venga aqui.*

HENRY. No. You're going to hit me.

DAD. I'll hit you harder if you don't come *en este momento.*

HENRY. You'll hit me anyway. (DAD *stares at* HENRY *for a long time.* HENRY *weakens to* DAD*'s authority. He approaches* DAD, *stops, and turns around to get hit.*)

DAD. I'll kill you.

HENRY. Go ahead. Being dead is better than this.

DAD. *En Español.*

HENRY. No.

(DAD *raises the belt and at the top, freezes. Other* BLUE MEXICAN PEASANTS *appear and start swinging belts in slow motion during* HENRY'S *monologue.* HENRY *will be stoic as he speaks, staring straight out.*)

HENRY. See, Dad. It was bound to happen. I got used to it. I got used to all the beatings. Ever wonder if that would happen? This is not how you get respect. If only I had brothers and sisters to share in this delightful activity. If only they'd been here to either take it with me, or help me in telling you how wrong you are in doing this. Ever since I was little I had to cover what you did to me. I had to have a smile on my face and pretend nothing happened. So no one would suspect. Never see my shame. Never let anyone know what happens in this house. Keep hitting me, Dad, if it makes you feel better. After all, this is your house. I am a snake in the grass for not understanding you. For being too young and stupid to know why you hurt. I will always remember the beatings with pity for you, because the scars of this, will be a lot deeper for you.

DAD (*unfreezes*). ¡LLORA! ¡LLORA! (*As he unfreezes, the* PEASANTS *stop whipping the air. They express silent pain.* DAD *ends his swing.*) Ya. You will respect your father. (HENRY *exits.* DAD *stands there staring at the belt for a long time. He then goes to the refrigerator for a beer.*)

(*Mexican waltz music as* GIRL *enters.* DAD *sees her and they come together to dance.* DAD *is enjoying his dance with his daughter. They continue dancing on the next lines.*)

GIRL. *Papi.*

DAD. *Sí, mija.*

GIRL. Love me?

DAD. With all my heart.

GIRL. Love Enrigue?

DAD (*breaks down*). *Sí.* (*They continue dancing. Then girl stops and exits.* DAD *calls out, softly.*) No! Come back. Come back to me! (*Sobbing*) Aye, hija. Why do you keep leaving me? Why did you go? I miss you so much. I missed you when I was at work. I missed you when you started to grow from a baby. You were so independent. Strong like your mother. Nothing could hurt you. Then you started to mistreat me by learning a language I couldn't understand. You came home to sing songs that had no meaning to me. I couldn't understand. In my own home. I couldn't understand your voice. I couldn't learn. I was too busy in the fields. You don't talk to anyone when you work the fields. You have no time. As each day passed, you became a stranger to me. I gave you life. (*Attempting to be in control*) It would have been nice if you said a few words in *Español* before you . . . Forgive me for punishing you on the day you died. I will never lose that guilt.

(DAD *sees* MOM *and* HENRY *in a light in the background.* HENRY *is covered with large bruises.*)

DAD. I hit him only because I needed to make a man out of him. It's true, Henry. (MOM *takes a breath.*) I'm preparing him for what will happen out there. (*Lights fade out on* MOM *and* HENRY.) Is everyone leaving me? Is everyone leaving this man who has nothing? Nothing but misery? You think the devil is me? I'll wrestle with the devil. I'll take him by the neck and force him to get away from me. At night, he comes and tells me what a failure I am. I wake up and see that he is right.

(BLUE MEXICAN PEASANTS *enter. They are wearing hideous masks. The one wearing the devil mask coaxes* DAD *to fight with him.*)

DAD. I drink so I'd be too drunk to go with you. I know why you do this to me. No matter how foolish my decisions are, I'm a good man, and you can't stand that. *(Pause)* It's not my fault. This is what I was taught. To make them good. She didn't listen to me, and dirtied her dress. The dress her mother and I worked so hard to buy. I hit her for dirtying her dress. She ran to the canal to wash it, and then, she fell. She ended up washing her dress with tears. And my tears have never stopped. *(Slow blackout)*

SCENE 4: THE NEXT DAY

(HENRY *has the rap music very loud, and is on the furniture dancing to it. The* BLUE MEXICAN PEASANTS *are dancing, too.* MOM *enters after a few moments, not too surprised at his acting out his frustration. She's frustrated too. The* PEASANTS *exit.*)

MOM. Henry, get down.

HENRY. No.

MOM. Don't punish me, get down. *(He won't.)* Henry. Henry. Henry!

HENRY *(with the rap).* I'm black and blue. I'm black and blue.

MOM. Stop it.

HENRY. Don't you get it, Mom? It's an English expression.

MOM. Stop it.

HENRY. You just don't get it. I'm black and blue!

MOM *(turns off the music).* Stop it, Enrigue.

HENRY. No, I'm E.B.J.

MOM. No, you are my son and I want you to sit down. I want to explain something to you.

HENRY. Explain what to me? Why I get beat?

MOM. Henry! He only gets this way when he's frustrated.

HENRY. I'm frustrated. I'm suffering here worse than that tearful Madonna. And what have you done? Stand there while it was happening. You closed your eyes, Mom, and I can't forgive you.

MOM. I didn't close my eyes. I told him to stop.

HENRY. He didn't, Mom.

MOM. He said he would.

HENRY. He didn't.

MOM. Then why didn't you tell me?

HENRY. Because I thought I loved you.

MOM. Henry!

HENRY. WHAT?

MOM *(losing her temper).* Don't talk to me like that. Don't you talk to me like that. I'm your mother. You don't know what I do for you. Both of you blaming me!? I'm stuck between two stubborn boys who are fighting. Don't you think I get tired of this? Do you think I'm made of stone? Don't you see how I mourn for the way you two behave? I'm sick and tired of going between you and your father. Never appreciation from the two of you. You think I'm on your father's side when I ask you to have pity for him. He thinks I'm on your side when I ask him to let you be a teenager. It is impossible to be both judge and lawyer. The two of you have been spoiled by my understanding attitude. Let me make this clear today and at this moment. I'm finished with protecting you both from each other. At this point, I could care less if you kill each other. Go ahead. I don't have a family. I lost it a long time ago. I have animals living in here and I've had it! *(She exits.)*

HENRY *(starts rapping sounds)*. Now you know, Now you know, Now you know, Why I'm black and blue. *(Ends with rapping sounds)*

SCENE 5: THAT EVENING

(HENRY is in the field rapping. OLIVERIO hears him and goes to him.)

HENRY. Yo.
And my name is Eee
E.B. Jay
I'm here to find the only way
To tell you who, who I really am
But first,
I'm no fool
Stop messing with my mind
Or I'll give you a fight
Yo
Word to your mother. Olé.

OLIVERIO. *Dios mio.* If this is poetry, I'm getting out of town.

HENRY. I am. As soon as I get my act together, I'm gone. *Hasta la vista.* Word to your mother.

OLIVERIO. You're stepping on her. If you need help with your poetry, you knew I was here.

HENRY. I need no help from you.

OLIVERIO. What is E.B.J? Sounds like some disease you get from mosquitoes. You need help with the words. Right now, it sounds like you put them together with spit. I put the words together with dust.

HENRY. Stop with the dust business. I'm bored of it. All right?

OLIVERIO. So you want to be a poet.

HENRY. A rapper.

OLIVERIO. A clapper?

HENRY. A RAP-PER. Get out of here, man.

OLIVERIO. Your verse stinks.

HENRY. Go away.

OLIVERIO. What's the first line?

HENRY. What?

OLIVERIO. To that ugly thing you were singing.

HENRY. Damn. I think I said "yo."

OLIVERIO. Yo?

HENRY. Yo. It's not Spanish.

OLIVERIO. What does it mean?

HENRY. It's how you say it.

OLIVERIO. *Las palabras dicen mucho.*

HENRY. What are you doing?

OLIVERIO. *Pero lo que dicen, no es todo la verdad.*

HENRY *(translating reluctantly)*. The words say a lot. But it's not what they say that is, that is, happening.

OLIVERIO. *Cuando me siento mal.*

HENRY (more into it). But when I feel very sad.

OLIVERIO. *Necessito su paciencia.*

HENRY. All I really want is your patience. Patience? When I'm black and blue?

OLIVERIO. People share their hopes and pains. That's part of life. Don't expect things to change so fast. Unnatural when it does. Are you going to be a clapper?

HENRY. You mean a rap-per? I don't know.

OLIVERIO (picks up a clump of grass). You got to be patient. Sometimes the plant takes its time. Other times, the weeds choke it. But the plant still sucks water from the ground, pollinates, and feeds the people. That's a beautiful plant for you. Look. A worm is hiding in between the roots. Get out, little fellow. Find another place to rest your body. Then come back and nourish the soil. Go. Go churn the ground with your friends so it's ready for the seeds.

HENRY. A bird is going to eat that worm.

OLIVERIO. It has to take his chances.

HENRY (pause). Maybe he needs a star.

(OLIVERIO disappears and MOM enters. She gives HENRY the picture of GIRL.)

MOM. Go to your father. He's finally ready to explain her to you. (HENRY looks at the picture then at MOM. He exits.)

SCENE 6: THE SAME EVENING

(HENRY is by himself in a field. OLIVERIO is watching him from a distance. MOM approaches HENRY. OLIVERIO disappears.)

(HENRY enters and sees DAD. HENRY is outraged. He holds out the picture of GIRL. DAD drops his head in pain.)

HENRY. Who is she, Dad? (DAD won't look at the picture.) WHO IS SHE? She's someone you're ashamed of? Someone you've been hiding? I get it. I get the whole picture. It comes as a shock, Dad, but I should have figured it out. You had a child from some other woman, and the guilt has been eating you up inside. (DAD is silent. He is almost suffocating with grief.) Come on! Come on!

(DAD won't move. He is frozen. Finally HENRY pulls out his belt and is about to smack DAD with it when the BLUE MEXICAN PEASANTS enter, wagging their index fingers and shaking their heads "no." GIRL enters. Her eyes meet DAD's.)

GIRL. Daddy?

DAD. *Mija.* (GIRL exits.) NO!!!!

HENRY. WHO IS SHE? (DAD looks all around and can't find GIRL. In desperation, he grabs the picture and then looks at HENRY holding the belt. They look at each other for a long time, then DAD turns away. HENRY drops the belt after seeing the look in DAD's eyes.)

DAD (softly). If you ever want to kill me, I give you permission. Why would I want to live anyway? I'm no good. I hurt the people I love. I can't give you a better life. I am ashamed of myself at every turn. I make mistakes every single day. This picture is the next most beautiful thing to your mother. I never wanted to tell you about this because I didn't want you to suffer like me . . . (Pause) You and your mother have a connection I envy. We wanted two children. A son for her and a daughter for me. We had made plans to spoil each one in our own private way. Then she went away . . . I had the love of a daughter and she went away. She is your sister. One year after you were born, she was taken away from me. From your mother and I. I have not been able to forget her. Do you know what kind of pain is in your stomach when you see a child you've given life to sink to the bottom of the water? . . . No. You don't understand my pain. No one does. Your mother is a strong woman and she let God have her fifteen years ago. But I couldn't let her go. I want to hold her every day. I want to touch her hair and the ruffles on her dress. I DIDN'T GET A CHANCE TO LOVE HER . . . To think she would have been married by now. (HENRY *has been retreating.*) I blame myself. I am a stupid man . . . Come back here with your belt and *dame shingasos.* I deserve it for what I have done to you. I let misery take me away. This house and the one in Salinas have had misery imprinted on the walls. It's time to wash it away. (*Silence*)

HENRY. Dad. You have a son left. (*They hesitate, then hug.*)

SCENE 7: TWO MONTHS LATER

(*In darkness, rap music is playing loudly. Light on a sofa chair.* DAD *is sitting there listening to the rap music. The expression on his face alternates from: Rap isn't too bad, I'll give it a chance, It's okay, There's some good in it, etc.* HENRY *enters, wearing glasses and holding a book bag.*)

HENRY. Dad? Dad! You like that?

DAD (*nods his head with the beat, then*). I like it. I like rap. Spanish, English, whatever. (HENRY *smiles as he watches* DAD*'s head nod up and down with the beat. He starts to exit and passes* MOM. MOM *has huge pieces of paper stuffed in her ears.* HENRY *waves to her and she waves back smiling. He exits.*)

SCENE 8: THAT EVENING

(OLIVERIO *is in the field staring at the stars.* HENRY *enters.*)

HENRY. Hey.

OLIVERIO. Hello.

HENRY. Where've you been?

OLIVERIO. Where've you been?

HENRY. No place. Just doing a little studying, and . . . Hanging out with my dad. Can you believe it?

OLIVERIO. What about the clapping?

HENRY. Rapping? Nothing . . . I came to tell you that—

OLIVERIO (*overlapping on "you"*). I already know. (HENRY *smiles and turns to leave.*) You ever get a chance, stop at a field that is about to get picked. Look at all the vegetables and tell them you respect them. Then, come and watch the pickers, and tell them you respect them. Doing those two things is like thanking the guy above.

HENRY. I came to say—

OLIVERIO. Goodbye? I already said goodbye.

HENRY. You did?

OLIVERIO. You say goodbye every day. To the dust. To the stars,

HENRY. To the moon . . .

To the worms.
To the vegetables
   picked by my father and mother
Their sweat
   to give us fruit to eat
Their sacrifice
   For the love of their son
Their dreams
A small step
   towards happiness.

OLIVERIO. Not bad. *(Challenging)*
Children of the dust

HENRY. Following the crops of their parent's frown

OLIVERIO. Families canvassing the land of land

HENRY. Walking across patches of striped earth

OLIVERIO. Green, beige and brown

HENRY. Heavy boots, callused hands

OLIVERIO. Machetes swinging on tough plants

HENRY. Children watching parents work
From the trailers with broken doors.

OLIVERIO. Very nice. I like how you say it.

HENRY. Oliverio, where do you live?

OLIVERIO. I live nowhere, and I live here on the field.

HENRY. How poetic.

OLIVERIO. "Yo." You better believe it.

(OLIVERIO smiles and waves goodbye to HENRY. HENRY turns to go home. The BLUE MEXICAN PEASANTS enter. They smile and walk up to OLIVERIO.)

OLIVERIO. You don't have to force me to go with you. I've known you all my life. I only do what I can to change the pain. So I laugh as you all finally smile.

(GIRL appears.)

OLIVERIO. And I hold the hand of the most precious gift there is. The love of a child. *(OLIVERIO and GIRL exit.)*

(HENRY enters his home and sees MOM and DAD in the kitchen. DAD hands HENRY an envelope filled with money.)

DAD. For your school.

MOM *(sing-song)*. Julio will kill you for it.

DAD. I would kill for my family.

MOM. What about the ring? *(DAD shakes his head.)* Julio is a crook.

DAD. Julio's a crook.

HENRY. I can't take the money. I'll work for it myself.

MOM. Take the money, before your father spends it again.

HENRY. I'd even work in the fields for extra money. It would be good for me, so I'd respect.

DAD. No. You saw your parents pick, you have enough to be humble about.

HENRY. *La luna no sabe*
Como todos la miren
Ella siempre va y viene
Para que todos la admiren.

(MOM and DAD stare at HENRY.)

MOM. Where did you learn that?

HENRY. It's one of Oliverio's poems.

MOM. Whose poems?

DAD. *Era de Oliverio.*

MOM *(to DAD)*. What does this mean?

HENRY. He doesn't explain them. He only recites them. *(HENRY smiles, then looks out the window.)* Hey. Look at the stars. Aren't they beautiful. Mind if I go outside and take a look? Come out and see them with me. (HENRY *goes out the door. He looks up at the stars. There is a sense of hope.* MOM *and* DAD *stare at each other for a long moment, in bewilderment.*)

DAD. Oliverio used to recite them when he was . . . alive.

MOM. It can't be. He rolled over in the tractor fifteen years ago. He's dead.

DAD. Yes, but the spirit never dies.

MOM. We must tell Henry. (DAD *smiles and is about to shake his head "no" when a blackout occurs.*)

END OF PLAY

THE MIGRANT FARMWORKER'S SON

Responding to the Play

1. Do you think Henry and his father will be more understanding of one another in the future? Why or why not?
2. What do the Blue Mexican Peasants represent?
3. Discuss one element of magical realism in the play.
4. What role does Oliverio play in Henry's life?
5. What kind of music would you use as background sound for this play? Why?

More About Magical Realism

The origins of magical realism may have sprung from the art world. Magical realism was also a term used by German art critics to describe paintings in the late 1920's that attempted to show reality in a new way. An Italian critic later applied the term to Latin American literature. Later still, Nobel Prize-winning novelist Miguel Angel Asturias used it to describe his novels. Long associated with Latin American writers, elements of magical realism have been used by writers as diverse as Toni Morrison (in *Beloved*), Franz Kafka (in *Metamorphosis*), and Umberto Eco (in *Foucault's Pendulum*).

CREATING AND PERFORMING

1. Henry's father is a guilt-ridden, tormented man whose frustrations often explode into anger. Think of ways an actor might capture his pain physically. Share your ideas with the class.
2. Henry's mother tries hard to protect her son and husband from one another. Think about the tone of voice she would use with each of them. Share your ideas by reading a few of her lines to the class.
3. Henry is a good young man trying to make his way in a difficult situation. List the various emotions he experiences throughout the play and portray one of them for the class.

The Migrant Farmworker's Son by Silvia Gonzalez S.　**223**

The Janitor

The Play as Literature: Allusion

Allusion is a reference to an historical or literary figure, happening, or object. Artists use allusion to draw on our memories and to stir up our emotions. The associations we make with the allusions an author creates bring emotional impact to our experience of the piece.

Playwrights and authors often use Biblical allusions in their plays and stories, and August Wilson is no exception. In *The Janitor,* Wilson alludes not only to the Bible, but also to a cartoon strong man, mottoes, axioms, and clichés—many of which you will probably recognize and understand. Think about the meaning each allusion holds for you. (Read more about August Wilson on p. 229.)

The Play as Theatre: Character Analysis

To play a character in a believable manner, you must find a way to understand or identify with that character. Ask yourself the following questions about any character you wish to portray.

- How does my character see himself or herself?
- What is my character's background?
- How does my character sound and move?
- What does my character think about the other characters in the play?
- How does my character change from the beginning to the end of the play?

How do you think these characters see themselves and one another?

Warm Up!

Think of a well-known fairy tale character and draw a relationship diagram for the character. The character's name appears in the center. Around the name are other character names with a positive or negative sign indicating their relationship toward the main character. Cinderella, for example, would be surrounded by her stepsisters (-), stepmother (-), fairy godmother (+), and the prince (+).

The Janitor

by August Wilson

Setting	Characters	Time
A hotel ballroom	**SAM** **MR. COLLINS**	The present

SAM *enters, pushing a broom near the lectern. He stops and reads the sign hanging across the ballroom.*

SAM. *NATIONAL . . . CONFERENCE . . . ON . . . YOUTH.*

(He nods his approval and continues sweeping. He gets an idea, stops, and approaches the lectern. He clears his throat and begins to speak. His speech is delivered with the literacy of a janitor. He chooses his ideas carefully. He is a man who has approached life honestly, with both eyes open.)

I want to thank you all for inviting me here to speak about youth. See . . . I's fifty-six years old and I knows something about youth. The first thing I knows . . . is that youth is sweet before flight . . . its odor is rife[1] with speculation, and its resilience[2]—that means bounce back—is remarkable. But it's that sweetness that we victims of. All of us. Its sweetness . . . and its flight. One of them fellows in that Shakespeare stuff said, "I'm not what I am." See. He wasn't like Popeye. This fellow had a different understanding. "I am not what I am." Well, neither are you. You are just what you have been . . . whatever you are now. But what you are now ain't what you gonna become . . . even though it is with you now . . . it's inside you now this instant. Time . . . see, this is how you get to this . . . Time ain't changed. It's just moved. Or maybe it ain't moved . . . maybe it just changed. It don't matter. We are all victims of the sweetness of youth and the time of its flight.

See . . . just like you, I forgot who I am. I forgot what happened first. But I know the river I step into now . . . is not the same river I stepped into twenty years ago. See, I know that much. But I have forgotten the name of the river . . . I have forgotten the name of the gods . . . and like everybody else I have tried to fool them with my dancing . . . and guess at their faces. It's the same with everybody. We don't have to mention no names. Ain't nobody innocent. We are all victims of ourselves. We have all had our hand in the soup . . . and made the music play just so.

See now . . . this is what I call wrestling with Jacob's angel. You lay down at night and that angel come to wrestle with you. When you wrestling with that angel, you bargaining for your future. See. And what you need to bargain with is that sweetness of youth. So . . . to

---

1. rife, full; abounding
2. resilience, ability to spring back; elasticity

the youth of the United States I says . . . don't spend that sweetness too fast! 'Cause you gonna need it. See. I's fifty-six years old and I done found that out. But it's all the same. It all comes back on you . . . just like sowing and reaping.[3] Down and out ain't nothing but being caught up in the balance of what you put down. If you down and out and things ain't going right for you . . . you can bet you done put down a payment on your troubles. Now you got to pay up on the balance. That's as true as I'm standing here. Sometimes you can't see it like that. The last note on Gabriel's horn always gets lost when you get to realizing you done heard the first. So, it's just like—

MR. COLLINS (*entering*). Come on, Sam . . . let's quit wasting time and get this floor swept. There's going to be a big important meeting here this afternoon.

SAM. Yessuh, Mr. Collins. Yessuh. (*He goes back to sweeping, as the lights go down to black.*)

---

3. reap, gather a crop

The Janitor

Responding to the Play

1. If you could ask Sam one question, what would it be?
2. Create a character analysis of Sam. Answer the five questions presented on page 224.
3. Write a short description of Mr. Collins based on his appearance in the play.
4. List the meanings of as many of the allusions Sam uses as you can.
5. Draw a picture based on a line from the play.

More About August Wilson

When August Wilson was in high school, a teacher accused him of cheating on his homework. He left school that day and never went back, continuing his education at a local library. Wilson began to write poetry and later started the Black Horizons Theatre Company of St. Paul, Minnesota. His first play, *Jitney,* was written in 1982, followed by *Ma Rainey's Black Bottom* in 1985, *Fences* in 1986, *Joe Turner's Come and Gone* in 1988, *The Piano Lesson* in 1990, *Two Trains Running* in 1992, and *Seven Guitars* in 1997.

Creating and Performing

1. Perform a portion of Sam's monologue for the class. Be sure that your tone and speech are true to the character.
2. With a partner, improvise another encounter between Mr. Collins and Sam. Think seriously about how the two men would relate to one another.
3. Sam's speech could easily be titled "This I Believe." Write a paragraph telling what you believe is important in life.

The Lottery

The Play as Literature: Symbolism

It's hard to imagine life without symbols. What would a valentine mean? A wink? A wedding band? A symbol is anything that has impact above and beyond its ordinary meaning. An author uses symbols to telegraph emotions and ideas straight to the heart of the reader.

To help you understand the symbols in *The Lottery,* pick out the most important items in the play and think about what each suggests—the black box, for instance, or the lottery itself.

The Play as Theatre: Movement

An actor has more than lines to think about on stage. How, where, and when to move is also a major consideration. When *you* are onstage, always be aware of your position in relation to other actors. Where you position yourself tells the audience something about the importance of your character in the scene as well as your relationship to the other characters.

The actor who is moving or talking is generally the one the audience focuses on, so if you are not the dominant character in the scene try not to move. If you are directed to move, you should do so behind the dominant actor. Make eye contact with the audience only if the script or director tells you to do so.

Always sit, stand, and move naturally and with good posture. Try to move in character while maintaining a natural balance. Practice shifting your weight smoothly as you move.

Warm Up!

To help you with body awareness and movement, play the "shadow game." Stand behind a partner. The person who is designated "the mover" slowly makes a broad movement, such as lifting one leg or raising both arms. The "follower" must duplicate the movement as though he or she were the mover's shadow.

Shirley Jackson's *The Lottery* dramatized by Brainerd Duffield

The Lottery

by Shirley Jackson

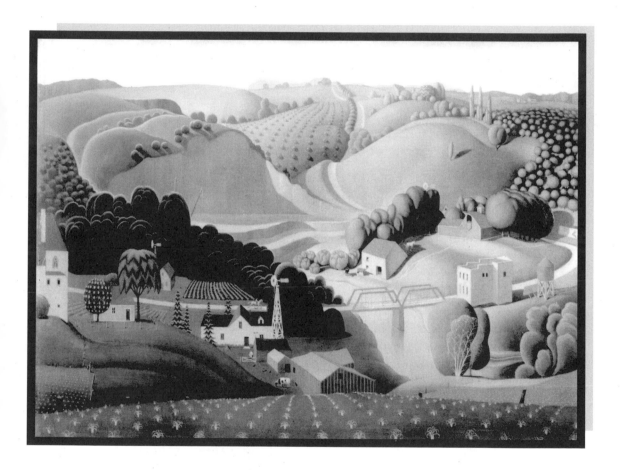

Dramatized by Brainerd Duffield

SETTING	CHARACTERS	TIME
A village square	TOMMY DICKIE MARTIN DELACROIX HUTCHISON MRS. DUNBAR MRS. WATSON MISS BESSOM JACK WILKINS OLD MAN WARNER BELVA SUMMERS JOE SUMMERS TESSIE HUTCHISON EXTRAS: LITTLE GIRL, DAVY, VILLAGERS	This year. The 27th of June

SCENE: *A bare stage with a few stones lying here and there. No scenery whatsoever is necessary, although curtains can be used.*

AT RISE OF CURTAIN: The stage is in darkness. Gradually a pool of amber light comes up at C stage. Two boys, TOMMY *and* DICKIE, *enter L, looking about on the ground. From time to time, one of them picks up a stone and puts it in his pocket. The search should continue for about a minute before either of them speaks.*

TOMMY. I'm keepin' the best ones right in my pocket.

DICKIE. Me, too.

TOMMY *(indicating R stage).* We oughta make an extra pile over here. Then we could take turns guardin'.

DICKIE. Sure. Then if some other kids tried to swipe any, we'll be ready for 'em. *(He and* TOMMY *cross R and begin to build a stockpile of stones at R.)*

(A GIRL *somewhat younger enters UL and crosses to watch them, but the boys ignore her. During this leisurely pantomime, a steeple bell has begun to chime, and the amber light widens, gradually illuminating the full stage.)*

DICKIE *(muttering).* Girls always got to be hangin' around.

TOMMY. I know it. They spoil everything. *(The little girl has attempted to assist* DICKIE *and* TOMMY *by adding a stone or two to pile, but they turn their backs on her and, feeling hurt,* GIRL *goes out R.)*

(During the preceding, two men, MARTIN *and* DELACROIX, *enter DL and cross to C, conversing quietly.)*

MARTIN (*glancing over R*). Children are always the first to gather.

DELACROIX. Sure—but everybody'll be comin' now, soon as they hear the bell.

MARTIN (*scanning sky*). Beautiful day for it.

DELACROIX. Yes, fine. I don't care if it is my hometown, we got the purtiest village green of any in the state.

(*Another man*, HUTCHISON, *has entered UL, leading his small son*, DAVY, *by the hand. They cross to join the others at C.*)

DELACROIX (*to* HUTCHISON). How are you, Bill?

HUTCHISON. Fred . . . Horace . . . (*Shakes hands with both men.*) Good to see you. You both know Davy?

MARTIN (*patting* DAVY *on head*). Well, I should hope so. How are you, Davy? (*To* HUTCHISON) This is his first year, ain't it?

HUTCHISON. That's right. Never seen a Lottery before, have you, Dave? (*DAVY nods.*)

MARTIN. Gonna grow up and be a good farmer like your dad? (*DAVY nods.*) That's the boy.

DELACROIX (*amiably*). My son, Chester, wants to go off to the Agriculture School and learn a lot of book rubbish. I tell him he'd do better to stay home and learn of his father, same as I did of mine.

MARTIN. That's right, too. Pitch in and help pay the taxes.

DELACROIX. I told him a farmer don't need to develop his mind, long as he builds up his muscles.

HUTCHISON. A strong back, that's what you need when you take up farmin'.

DELACROIX. Where's the wife, Bill?

HUTCHISON (*slight pause*). Oh, she'll be along. (*Frowns and looks about anxiously*)

(MRS. DUNBAR *and* MRS. WATSON *enter DL and cross toward DRC. The men continue to talk in pantomime.*)

MRS. DUNBAR (*as they cross*). How does the weather suit you, Myrtle?

MRS. WATSON. Couldn't be better.

MRS. DUNBAR. We always seem to get good weather for the twenty-seventh. Never knew it to fail.

MRS. WATSON. Been right cold and wet for June.

(MISS BESSOM *enters DR and starts toward DRC.*)

MRS. DUNBAR. Oh, that rain done us lots of harm. (*Shakes her head*) Too *much* rain!

MRS. WATSON. Guess the Lottery ought to change our luck.

MRS. DUNBAR. That's how the sayin' goes. (*Sees* MISS BESSOM) Look who's here. Howdy, Miss Bessom. Why, you ain't changed a particle!

MISS BESSOM (*slightly piqued*). Who ever said I had?

MRS. DUNBAR (*scrutinizing her*). They told me you were gettin' real fleshy, and it ain't so.

MRS. WATSON. Course it ain't. Hear you had a weddin' in the family.

MISS BESSOM. Yes—my sister Nina's girl got married to young Sam Gilliatt over to Rigby township.

MRS. WATSON. I s'pose that means she'll be drawin' over there from now on?

MISS BESSOM. Oh, sure! She's got to draw with *his* family now. (*To* MRS. DUNBAR) I declare, Hazel, it's been a month of Sundays since I seen you. Don't you never come into town?

MRS. DUNBAR. Not if I can help it. Ain't been further than m'own chicken yard—not since Decoration Day, and that's a fact.

MRS. WATSON. One thing about the Lottery, it does bring everyone out, like it or not.

MISS BESSOM. Well, Hazel's got Clyde to wait on, too. How's he makin' out?

MRS. DUNBAR. Oh, he'll be fine! Except he's terrible mad to have to stay home and miss the excitement.

MISS BESSOM. I'll bet. (*She and* MRS. WATSON *cluck sympathetically, and the women continue to converse silently.* DICKIE *and* TOMMY *have drifted off R by now to continue their search for stones offstage. The group at C stage, conversing in pantomime, have worked down to a position at DLC.*)

Other VILLAGERS *now drift in UL and UR, taking positions ULC and URC. They chat ad lib, building to a general murmur.*

MARTIN (*on spoken cue, "I'll bet."*). Now I got that tractor, I was figurin' I might make the switch from grass to hay silage.

HUTCHISON. Costs about the same to harvest an acre, don't it?

MARTIN. Just about. Cattle don't seem to mind what they're eatin', and I thought I could get away from the risk of bad weather—

DELACROIX (*slight chuckle*). Don't you fret about the weather, Horace. "Lottery in June, corn be heavy soon."

HUTCHISON (*nodding, with a faint smile*). That's what they always told us, ain't it, Fred? (DELACROIX *nods.*)

MISS BESSOM (*glancing about*). Don't see Tessie Hutchison any place, do you?

MRS. WATSON. No, I don't. Bill's standin' right there, though, and little Davy, too.

MISS BESSOM. Got a recipe I borrowed and want to give back to her. It's for the watermelon pickles she won a prize with at the social.

(JACK WILKINS *enters DR and nods to the ladies.*)

JACK. 'Scuse me, ladies. Hi, Miz Dunbar. How's Clyde doin'?

MRS. DUNBAR. Fine, thanks, Jack. Doctor's goin' to take the cast off next week.

JACK. How's he goin' to get the news today?

MRS. DUNBAR. I promised to send Tommy runnin', soon as the drawin's over.

JACK (*grinning*). That's good. (*Goes DLC to join other men. Women DRC beam at one another.*)

MISS BESSOM. *Such* a nice boy—Jack Wilkins.

MRS. WATSON. He's got his mother's looks and that's a blessin'.

MRS. DUNBAR. So many of the young ones seem to drift away. This place's gettin' smaller every year.

MISS BESSOM. I know it. Joe Summers

told me there's less'n two hundred names on the registration this time.

MRS. DUNBAR. You don't mean it?

MRS. WATSON. Isn't that awful?

OLD MAN WARNER *has made a slow entrance from UR, crossing to C. The* VILLAGERS *URC have a greeting for him as he passes. Now the group DLC hails his arrival.*

DELACROIX. Well, here's old man Warner, lookin' spry as ever!

HUTCHISON. How're you feelin', Mr. Warner?

WARNER. Not so bad. *(Winks)* Rheumatism comes and goes.

MARTIN. How's it seem to be the oldest citizen?

WARNER. You don't hear *me* complainin'.

HUTCHISON *(chuckling).* How many Lotteries does this make?

WARNER. I'm eighty-one last November. Seen my first at the age of five. You figure it out.

DELACROIX. Never missed one in all those years!

JACK. He hears very good, too, don't he?

DELACROIX. Oh, he's a marvel!

WARNER. And I'll be comin' back for a few more!

JACK *(grinning).* You tell 'em, old-timer!

MARTIN *(calling across to women DRC).* Hear that? Old man Warner says he's good for a few more! *(General murmur of approval from others on stage)*

MRS. WATSON. He's seen seventy-six of them.

MRS. DUNBAR. Imagine!

WARNER *(joining group DLC).* Oh, you fellers ought to been here in the old days. Not like now. Lottery meant somethin' when I was a boy.

(BELVA SUMMERS *has entered DL and stops just inside the entrance. She wears black, and carries some knitting with her, at which she works during the following action. She remains by herself, content to speak to no one.)*

MISS BESSOM. Almost time to get started.

MRS. WATSON *(crossing up to RC and looking off toward UL).* Guess we're goin' to, Miss Bessom. There's Joe Summers now, on the post office steps. *(MRS. DUNBAR and MISS BESSOM join MRS. WATSON at RC)*

MRS. DUNBAR. He's bringin' out the box.

MISS BESSOM. Where's his sister? She here?

MRS. DUNBAR *(nodding DL).* There she is. Off by herself, as usual.

MISS BESSOM *(looking at BELVA, DL).* Beats me how he can stay so cheerful with that one to put up with.

MRS. WATSON. I'd hate to have her in *my* house.

(*The murmur of the* VILLAGERS *swells.* DICKIE *and* TOMMY *have entered again from R. They start to C, see a stone and both grab simultaneously for it. They tussle with each other to gain possession of the stone.)*

TOMMY. You didn't, neither! I seen it first!

DICKIE. You give that back!

TOMMY. The heck I will! *(Shoves him)*

DICKIE. Cut it out, will you? Watch who you're shovin'—(*There is a tussle again.* MRS. DUNBAR *comes forward and grasps* TOMMY *by the wrist.*)

MRS. DUNBAR. You stop that!

TOMMY. Leggo, Ma! I seen it first, honest!

MRS. DUNBAR. Never you mind. You got stones a-plenty! (MRS. WATSON *attempts to collar* DICKIE, *but he escapes to DLC.*)

MRS. WATSON. You come here to me. Wait till I get you home.

MARTIN (*sharply, to* DICKIE). Obey your mother. Mind what I say.

DICKIE (*dutifully*). Yes, Uncle Horace. (*Crosses to* MRS. WATSON, *unwillingly.* MRS. WATSON *and* MRS. DUNBAR *move back to RC with* TOMMY *and* DICKIE.)

JACK (*pointing off L with gesture of thumb*). Joe Summers is comin'. It won't be long now.

DELACROIX (*good-humoredly*). We'd better line up by families and wait for the bad news. (VILLAGERS *begin to shift and reassemble according to family groups.*)

HUTCHISON (*to* DAVY). Now, Davy, stick close to me. There's nothin' to be a-scared of. (*Leads* DAVY URC)

(JOE SUMMERS *enters UL, crossing to UC. He is carrying a large black wooden box and a wooden paddle. A townsman follows with a high stool, on which* JOE *places the black box in a dignified and solemn manner.*)

JOE. Thank you, Norbert. (*During* JOE*'s entrance, there has been a growing murmur from* VILLAGERS.)

VILLAGERS (*ad libbing upon* JOE*'s entrance*). Here he comes. Howdy, Mr. Summers.

There's the head man comin'. He's got the old black box. Howdy, Joe. Let's get goin'.

(JOE *takes a sheaf of papers from his hip pocket and places them on box. He pauses now to mop his forehead with a handkerchief. Most of the* VILLAGERS *are in small groups covering right half of stage and ULC. The remainder of the left side of stage is clear, except for* BELVA, *DL.*)

JOE (*brightly*). Little late today, folks. (*Waves to* JACK) Here, you! The Wilkins boy. Give me a hand and stir these names up. Stir 'em good and hard. (JACK *comes UC and stirs box with paddle, which* JOE *hands him. Then* JOE *turns to* TOWNSMEN.) Norbert, you hold it steady for him. Better use both hands. (TOWNSMAN, *using both hands to steady box, helps* JACK *with stirring business.* JOE *now finds his way to RC, checking over his lists as he does so. He notices* BELVA *DL, and moves toward her, passing others en route.*) How are you, folks?

VILLAGERS. Mr. Summers! Howdy, Joe. How are you? (BELVA, *occupied with her knitting, awaits him with an enigmatic smile. During scene which follows between* JOE *and* BELVA, VILLAGERS *converse in pantomime.*)

BELVA (*drily*). Almost ready, are you, Joe? Hope you haven't forgotten, and left my name out.

JOE. No, Belva. You're down there. I just been checkin' the list.

BELVA (*looking over his shoulder*). Oh, you got a long ways to go yet. A terrible responsibility. Everybody says so. (*Shakes head with mock sympathy*) Poor Joe Summers. Doin' his duty. And with that naggin' sister, too.

JOE (*grimly*). Well, if everybody says so, Belva, there must be somethin' to it.

BELVA (*knitting as she talks*). I must say I enjoy myself. Watchin' an important man at work. Joe Summers—up there runnin' things—devotin' all his time and energy to civic activities. And how you love it!

JOE (*glancing over at* VILLAGERS). You'd oblige me, Belva, by lowerin' your voice a little.

BELVA (*smiling*). Why should I? Nobody asked you to come over and speak to me.

JOE. You might give a thought to the neighbors. . . .

BELVA (*contemptuously*). The neighbors! If everybody wasn't so scared of their neighbors, maybe we'd give up some heathen customs that don't make sense anymore. Half the young folks growin' up don't have the faintest notion what a Lottery stands for.

JOE (*turning away*). Oh, what's the use of talkin' to you! . . .

BELVA. There's no tellin' these days where the wisdom stops and superstition begins.

JOE (*turning back to her*). The Lottery has got to be taken serious. People get set in a way of doin' things and you can't change 'em. It's human nature.

BELVA (*stops knitting, speaking softly, but with intensity*). I don't like this town nor anybody in it. But you're the worst of 'em, Joe Summers. You drove him away. Our own brother and you drove him away.

JOE. It was more your doin' than mine. You're the one brought him up to be a weaklin' and a coward. You started him goin' out on the street and preachin' against tradition.

BELVA. You call that cowardly? It takes a brave man to say what he thinks, when every hand is against him.

JOE (*doggedly*). He left of his own accord. I didn't send him.

BELVA. It takes real courage to fight prejudice on your own doorstep. (*With contempt*) It's you and the rest of 'em that are the cowards.

JOE. Every day of my life I have to listen to your craziness. If you want to go off lookin' for him, Belva, I'll give you the money. Take the mornin' train. I'll even draw alone in the Lottery from now on. There—I couldn't offer more'n that, could I?

BELVA. I'm not goin' anywhere. I'm goin' to stay right here and wait. (*Looks up and straight at him*) Because sooner or later your name might come up. I wouldn't want to miss that day. (JOE *turns away abruptly and goes back UC.* BELVA *stands motionless for a moment or two and then resumes her knitting.*)

JOE. All right, Jack, that's good enough, I'm sure.

JACK. Glad to do it, Mr. Summers.

JOE (*to nearby* WOMEN VILLAGERS). Think it's stirred enough, ladies?

MRS. WATSON (*chuckling*). Don't worry, Joe. We trust you.

MRS. DUNBAR. Oh, Joe knows what he's doin' all right. (*General laughter from* WOMEN VILLAGERS)

WARNER. Hear those women hollerin' and cacklin'. They never would have stood for that in the old days.

DELACROIX. Seen some changes, ain't you, Mr. Warner?

WARNER. Bad enough to see Joe Summers up there crackin' jokes. Nobody shows respect for the ceremony. Just go through the motions nowadays. (JACK *has crossed to where* WARNER *is standing.*)

JACK. How was it different, Mr. Warner?

WARNER. Oh, it was *some* different. Everybody had to stand just so. And before the drawin', the head man spoke his piece real solemn-like. Had a regular recitation went with it.

HUTCHISON (*scanning* VILLAGERS). Now where in tarnation is my wife? (*Chuckle from those near him*)

MARTIN. Bill Hutchison lost his better half.

HUTCHISON (*to* MRS. DUNBAR). Hazel, you seen her?

MRS. DUNBAR. No, I ain't, Bill, and I been lookin', too.

MARTIN. Guess she ain't gonna make it.

MISS BESSOM. Late for the Lottery. Can you beat that?

HUTCHISON. I don't know what's got into the woman. (*Crosses to* ULC, *still leading* DAVY *by hand.*)

DELACROIX. That black box has seen a lot of service.

WARNER. Yessir. That box was here

afore I was born, and afore my father was.

JACK. Just imagine.

WARNER. Story goes it was made out of the pieces of the first box that ever was used.

DELACROIX. Makes you think, don't it?

WARNER. Goes way back to the days when they first settled down to make a village here.

JACK. Seems like we ought to be ready to build us a new one.

WARNER (*shocked*). No, boy! Don't say that. Not even jokin'.

DELACROIX. No, Jack. We don't want to upset tradition more'n we have to. Long as it holds together, we ain't gonna change it.

WARNER. I can recollect when they used to use wooden chips, 'stead of paper to write the names on.

JACK. What do you know? Wooden chips!

WARNER (*nodding*). I was real little, but I remember.

(JOE *has been busy checking his list, looking about and making notations on the sheets of paper. Occasionally he consults with one of the* VILLAGERS *close by him.*)

JOE (*raising voice*). Now, folks, I'm just about ready to declare this Lottery open. But you know how I always got this last-minute fussin' to do. Want to make sure the list is accurate—with all the heads of families and members of each household in each family.

MRS. DUNBAR. You go right ahead, Mr. Summers.

MRS. WATSON. Joe never made a mistake yet.

(TESSIE HUTCHISON, *wearing an apron over her house dress, enters DR and crosses toward RC.*)

MRS. DUNBAR. Why, Tessie! Where you been?

TESSIE. Clean forgot what day it was. *(Other women close by laugh softly.)* Thought Bill was out back stackin' wood. But I looked out the window and seen little Davy was gone. Then I remembered it was the twenty-seventh—and come a-runnin'. *(She is drying her hands on her apron as she speaks.)*

MRS. DUNBAR. You made it all right, though. Joe is still checkin' his list.

TESSIE. Seems like there's no time at all between Lotteries any more. Seems like we barely got through with the last one.

MRS. DUNBAR. Time sure goes fast.

TESSIE *(glancing around).* Where's Bill at? Oh, I see him. 'Scuse me, Hazel. (VILLAGERS *make way for her as she moves to join* HUTCHISON *ULC.)*

VILLAGERS. Hey, Hutchison! Here she comes! Here's your missus, Bill! Look, Bill! She made it after all!

TESSIE *(bending down, to* DAVY). Give Mama a kiss. (DAVY *kisses her.)* That's my good boy. *(Looks at* HUTCHISON *for a moment. He smiles faintly and takes her hand.)*

HUTCHISON. So you got here, did you?

JOE *(calling amiably).* Thought we were goin' to have to get on without you, Tessie.

TESSIE *(with forced pleasantness).*

Wouldn't have me leave my dishes in the sink, would you, Joe?

JOE. No, Ma'am. (*General ripple of laughter from* VILLAGERS)

HUTCHISON. You stay put, Dave, while I talk with your mother. (DAVY *joins other children at RC, as* HUTCHISON *brings* TESSIE *to DLC, where they talk somewhat apart from other* VILLAGERS. *He is not angry, but seems deeply concerned and worried.*) What ever kept you?

TESSIE. I don't know, Bill. I just wasn't thinkin', I guess.

HUTCHISON. That story's all right for the women. I know better. You knew the Lottery was today.

TESSIE. Well, it don't matter now. So long as I'm here.

HUTCHISON. What about Davy? Why'd you try to hide him?

TESSIE. Hide him? I didn't hide him. What makes you say that?

HUTCHISON. I found him in the stable loft. He said you told him to wait there—

TESSIE. Yes, but I was goin' to get him, Bill. I was goin' to bring him— honest.

HUTCHISON. What reason did you have to put him there?

TESSIE. Oh, Bill, he's such a little boy! And his birthday just last month. I hate to see the children takin' part in grown-up ructions before they've even put aside their toys.

HUTCHISON. I went through it when I was little.

TESSIE. I know, Bill. I guess I was born and brought up with it, same as yourself.

HUTCHISON. Then how did you think you could get away with such a thing? You know Davy's name has to be there along with ours. And you know how careful Joe Summers is. Why, we'd have been a laughin'-stock in front of everybody.

TESSIE. But I told you I intended to bring him. You got to believe me, Bill.

HUTCHISON. Talkin' a lot of sentimental tommyrot. I always gave you credit for more sense than some of these other females. What's come over you lately, anyway?

TESSIE. I told you—nothin'.

HUTCHISON. Next thing you'll be sayin' we ought to give up Lotteries altogether—like poor Joe Summers' sister.

TESSIE. Well, I've not come to that yet. But some places have given them up. Lots of little towns up to the north—

HUTCHISON. No good'll come of it, either. You wait and see.

TESSIE. I don't say it will. No, I reckon the Lottery serves its useful purpose. When a custom's been handed down from generation to generation, there must be good in it.

HUTCHISON (*wagging head, grinning*). Then you shouldn't be so cussed busy, findin' fault. (*Crosses to RC with* TESSIE, *and* DAVY *joins them.*)

JOE (*clearing throat*). Well, now, guess we better get started—get this over with—so's we can get back to work. Anybody ain't here?

VILLAGERS. Dunbar! Clyde Dunbar! Dunbar ain't here!

JOE *(glancing at list).* Clyde Dunbar—that's right. He's broke his leg, hasn't he? Who's drawin' for him?

MRS. DUNBAR. Me, I guess.

JOE. Wife draws for husband. Don't have a grown boy to do it for you, Hazel?

MRS. DUNBAR. Ralph's not but sixteen yet. Guess I got to fill in for the old man this year. *(Mild chuckle from* VIL-LAGERS *)*

JOE *(making note).* Right. Jack Wilkins, you're drawin' this year?

JACK *(blinking nervously).* Yessir. I'm drawin' for my mother and me.

MARTIN. Good fellow, Jack. Glad to see your mother's got a man to do it.

JOE. Well, I guess that's everyone. *(With a wink)* Old man Warner make it?

WARNER *(raising hand).* Here!

JOE *(nodding).* Knew you would. *(Raps on box)* All ready? *(Whisper runs through* VILLAGERS; *then a hush follows. Everyone is quite serious now. There is no more laughter.)* Now, I'll read off the names—heads of families first—and the men come up and take a paper out of the box. Keep the paper folded in your hand without lookin' at it until everyone has had a turn. Everything clear? *(VILLAGERS are silent, but nervous, wetting their lips, not looking around or moving.* JOE *reads from list.)* Adams. *(A man disengages himself from crowd, comes forward, reaches into black box and takes out a folded paper.* JOE *greets him.)* Hi, Steve. *(Holding paper firmly, the man goes back to his place and stands, not looking down at his hand.* JOE *calls next name.)* Allen. *(Another man comes to box, repeating same business.)* How are you, Mr. Allen? *(Now, as scene continues,* JOE *continues to call out names. Each time, someone comes forward, reaches into box, takes out folded piece of paper and returns to his place, not looking down at hand holding paper. As dialogue of* VILLAGERS *breaks into scene, overlapping* JOE's *voice, calling of the names becomes less distinct, becoming sort of a muted background to* VILLAGERS' *dialogue.)* Appleby . . . Barrows . . . Burgess . . . Caswell . . . Collins . . .

DELACROIX. They do say that over in the north village, they're talkin' of givin' up the Lottery.

WARNER. Pack of crazy fools! Listenin' to the young folks—nothin's good enough for *them.* Next thing you know, they'll want to go back to livin' in caves—nobody work any more—live *that* way for a while.

DELACROIX. That's right, Mr. Warner.

WARNER. First thing you know we'd all be eatin' stewed chickweed and acorns. There's *always* been a Lottery.

JOE. Dunbar . . .

MRS. WATSON. Go on, Hazel. That's you.

MISS BESSOM *(as* MRS. DUNBAR *crosses to draw).* There she goes . . .

JOE. Foster . . . Graves . . . Hutchison . . .

MRS. WATSON. Where do they keep the black box in between times?

MISS BESSOM. It varies. Sometimes one place—sometimes another.

MRS. WATSON. I heard it spent one whole winter in Mr. Graves' barn.

MISS BESSOM. Another year, Clem Martin put it on a shelf in his grocery and left it set there.

MRS. WATSON. Yep. I recall that time.

JOE. Tatum . . . Townsend. . . .Tuttle . . . Vincent . . .

MRS. DUNBAR (*to* TOMMY). I wish they'd hurry.

TOMMY. They're almost through, Ma.

MRS. DUNBAR. You get ready to run and tell Dad.

JOE. Warner . . . Howdy, Mr. Warner. (WARNER *takes slip and returns to his place.*)

WARNER. Got mine. Seventy-seventh year I been in the Lottery.

JOE. Watson . . . Hi, Myrtle.

MRS. WATSON (*drawing*). Hi, Joe.

JOE. Wilkins . . .

MISS BESSOM (*as* JACK *crosses to draw*). Don't be nervous, Jack.

JOE (*kindly*). Take your time, son.

JACK (*drawing*). Thanks, Mr. Summers.

JOE (*checking off list*). Now, that's all. (*A breathless pause.* JOE *draws and holds up his hand with his slip of paper in it.*) All right, fellows. (*For a moment, no one moves; then there is a rustle as all the slips are opened.*)

VILLAGERS (*whispering*). Who is it? Who's got it? Is it the Dunbars? Is it the Watsons? (*Then, louder ad libs are heard, building to an excited climax.*) It's Hutchison! It's Bill! Bill Hutchison's got it! Hutchison! (*The* HUTCHISONS *break away from others and form a small group at LC.*)

MRS. DUNBAR (*excitedly*). Go tell your father! (TOMMY *takes a last awestruck look at* BILL HUTCHISON, *where he stands quietly LC, flanked by* TESSIE *and* DAVE, *then* TOMMY *runs out DR.* HUTCHISON *is staring at bit of paper in his hand.* VILLAGERS *are silent again, all eyes on* HUTCHISON *family.*)

TESSIE (*shouting suddenly*). Joe Summers! You didn't give him time enough to take any paper he wanted. I saw you. It wasn't fair!

MRS. WATSON. Be a good sport, Tessie.

MISS BESSOM. All of us took the same chance.

HUTCHISON. You hush up, Tessie.

JOE. Well, everyone, that was done pretty fast, and now we've got to be hurryin' a little more to get done in time. (*Consulting list*) Bill, you draw for the Hutchison family. You got any other households in the Hutchisons?

TESSIE (*shrilly*). There's Don and Eva! Make them take their chance!

JOE (*gently*). Daughters draw with their husbands' families. You know that as well as anyone, Tessie.

TESSIE. It wasn't fair!

HUTCHISON. I guess there's just the three of us, Joe. Eva draws with her husband. That's only as it should be.

JOE. Then, as far as drawin' for families is concerned, it's you, and, as far as drawin' for households is concerned, that's you, too. Right?

HUTCHISON. Right.

JOE. How many kids, Bill?

HUTCHISON. Just the one. Little Davy

here. Bill, Jr., he died when he was a baby.

JOE. All right then. Jack, you got some blank tickets back? (JACK *holds up two blank slips of paper which he has taken from some of the villagers.*) Put them in the box, then. Take Bill's and put it in. (JACK *does so.*)

TESSIE (*out of the ensuing silence*). I think we ought to start over. (*As quietly as she can*) I tell you, it wasn't fair! You didn't give him time enough to choose. Everybody saw that. (*Appealing*) Listen, everybody! . . . (JACK *has stepped back from box. Other* VILLAGERS *have crumpled their own slips and let them drop to ground.*)

JOE. Ready, Bill? (HUTCHISON *takes a quick glance at his wife and son and then nods.*) Remember, take the slips and keep them folded until each of you has taken one. Jack, you help little Davy. (JACK *takes* DAVY's *hand and leads him to box.*) Take a paper out of the box, Dave. Take just one paper. (DAVY *does so.*) That's right. Jack, you hold it for him. (JACK *takes paper and holds it carefully.*) Tessie next. (TESSIE *hesitates for a moment, looking around defiantly, then she sets her lips and goes to box. She snatches out a paper, crosses back to LC, and holds it behind her.*) Bill . . . (HUTCHISON *reaches into box and brings out last slip of paper and joins* TESSIE. *The* VILLAGERS *are silent and tense.*)

MISS. BESSOM (*breaking silence*). I hope it isn't little Dave. (VILLAGERS *begin to whisper.*)

WARNER (*clearly*). It's not the way it used to be. People ain't the same way they used to be.

JOE. All right. Open the papers. Jack, you open little Dave's. (JACK *opens paper, holds it up, and a sigh of relief goes through villagers as they see that it is blank.* JOE *turns to* TESSIE.) Tessie . . . (*There is a pause.* TESSIE *does not move to open her slip of paper.* JOE *turns to* HUTCHISON, *who unfolds his paper and shows it. It is blank.* JOE *speaks to* TESSIE *in a hushed voice.*) It's Tessie. Show us her paper, Bill. (HUTCHISON *turns to* TESSIE *and forces her slip of paper out of her hand. It has a black spot on it. He holds it up. A murmur goes through* VILLAGERS. JOE *comes forward.*) All right, folks. Let's finish quickly. (JACK *carries black box, paddle and stool off UL and presently returns to rejoin* VILLAGERS.)

MRS. WATSON (*excitedly*). Come on, Hazel. Hurry up! Come on, Miss Bessom.

MISS BESSOM. I can't move as fast as I used to. (VILLAGERS *move downstage, some of them picking up stones as they come.* DICKIE *gives little* DAVY *a fistful of stones. As* VILLAGERS *shift about,* TESSIE *backs away, like a trapped animal, until she is alone at the center of a cleared space UC.* VILLAGERS *are grouped downstage at both sides of stage. Now,* TESSIE *holds out her hands in a desperate appeal, as* VILLAGERS *turn to face her and begin slowly to close in.*)

TESSIE. It isn't fair! It wasn't done fair!

HUTCHISON. Be quiet, Tess. We got to do this. (*Throws a stone, and* TESSIE *flinches, putting her hand to her brow.*) Come on. Come on, everyone. (DAVY *throws his fistful of stones.* TESSIE *utters a cry and sinks to her knees.* VILLAGERS *pantomime throwing stones.)*

TESSIE. It isn't fair! It isn't right! *(Shields her face as* VILLAGERS *continue to throw stones at her.* BELVA *has crossed from DL to DR, thrusting* JOE *aside in passing. She goes out DR without looking at spectacle on stage. By now,* VILLAGERS *have hemmed in the victim, cutting her off from view. The clamor of voices builds, as does the ferocity of the stone-throwing.)*

VILLAGERS. Come on! Get it over with! Hit her! That's the way! Hit her, everybody! Get it over! *(Lights dim out, and with darkness comes a low rumble of thunder. Voices of the* VILLAGERS *stop abruptly. Silence.)*

Curtain

Reader Response

1. At what point in the play did you have an idea this was no innocent gathering? Explain.
2. Why do you think the stage directions indicate that this play takes place in a village square this year, the 27th of June, and not fifty years ago or more?
3. What do you think the lottery symbolizes?
4. How do you think the villagers should move as the stoning of Tessie Hutchison is played out? Why?
5. Write a news article for the local paper about the lottery of June 27th. Be sure to keep in mind that newspapers generally reflect the culture of their readership.

More About Shirley Jackson and *The Lottery*

"The number of people who expected Mrs. Hutchison to win a Bendix washer would amaze you." So said author Shirley Jackson only half jokingly about her short story "The Lottery," upon which this play was closely based. By story's end, it is quite apparent that a washing machine is the farthest thing from the mind of poor Mrs. Hutchison.

From the time it was first published in *The New Yorker* magazine in 1948 to the present, reaction to Jackson's story has ranged from awe to outrage. *The New Yorker* received hundreds of puzzled and abusive letters about the story, and the government of South Africa once banned it. Even today, there are schools that refuse to put this classic tale on their reading lists.

Creating and Performing

1. How would you characterize the following people? Write a short sketch of each:
   a) Tessie Hutchison   b) Joe Summers   c) Old Man Warner
2. If you were cast as Belva Summers, how would you play her? Why?
3. With several classmates, pick a scene from the first half of the play and work on it together. Present it to the class.

Shirley Jackson's *The Lottery* dramatized by Brainerd Duffield   **245**

The Play as Literature: Plot

Plot, a series of events that occur in a literary work, is as necessary to literature as walls are to a house. A good plot presents events that seem natural and inevitable to the reader. Plot usually begins with a conflict that builds to a turning point, or climax, which leads to a resolution. See the diagram below.

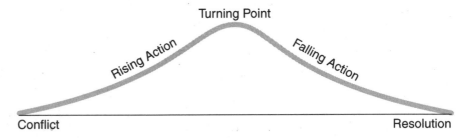

Turning Point

Rising Action

Falling Action

Conflict

Resolution

The Play as Theatre: Camera Shots

Survival was written as a television drama. TV productions can play with time, space, and action in a way that live dramatic presentations on stage cannot—and the camera holds the key to it all. Below are terms used in television scripts to describe camera shots.

Fade in	a scene that begins dark slowly becoming visible
Fade out	a scene that becomes darker and darker, then black
Pan	a slow movement of the camera from one side of the scene to another, capturing a 180-degree angle
Dissolve	simultaneous fade-out of one image and fade-in of another
Close-up	when an actor's face fills the screen

Warm Up!

With a partner, decide the kinds of camera shots you would use for the following scenes:

- a horse galloping over a plain
- the end of a television courtroom drama
- the beginning of a musical comedy film
- a man in the middle of a painful confession

Survival

by Alfred Brenner

Setting	Characters	Time
A rooming house and courtroom in Philadelphia, with some suggested scenes at sea	DAVID HOLMES LANDLADY TWO POLICEMEN PAT ASKIN ARMSTRONG CLERK JUDGE DALLAS FRANK ASKIN MARY O'BRIEN THOMAS ABLE LORNA QUINN STENOGRAPHER CAPTAIN AMOS TILTON MRS. RESTON FOREMAN OF THE JURY	1842

Act One

Fade in

A street in Philadelphia near the water front, 1842. A single street lamp drops a vague puddle of light on the cobbles. All we can see are the fronts of several buildings, some barrels, a coil of rope. DAVID HOLMES, *a thick, heavy-set seaman with hard, worried eyes, about thirty, carrying a seabag over his shoulder, is walking slowly along past buildings.*

NARRATOR *(over).* This story is based on a real case. It was tried in the U.S. Circuit Court[1] in the City of Philadelphia, on the 13th of April, 1842. It bears the title U.S. versus Holmes.

*(*HOLMES *halts abruptly at the door of a house over which hangs a sign:*

> ## THE JOLLY REST
> Rooms For Seamen
> And Their Guests

He knocks on door. We hear footsteps within, a rusty lock turns; then door opens a crack and we see a LANDLADY *in nightdress, holding a candle, looking out suspiciously.)*

LANDLADY *(looking him up and down).* Rent's two dollars a week . . . in advance . . . (HOLMES *reaches for his*

---

1. circuit court, the court of general jurisdiction in a state

money bag, takes out several coins, drops them into her hand. She counts them quickly, glances up at him again.) This way . . . (He enters a hallway, follows her a few steps to a door. She opens it, goes into a small dingy room containing a bed, small table, and chair. He steps in after her.) You just come off ship? (He nods.) What's yer name?

HOLMES (throwing bag down, feeling bed). Holmes . . .

LANDLADY (examining him carefully). Say, you ain't the one who brought in that longboat, saved all them women? (HOLMES glances at her swiftly, stiff, tense.) Wait'll I tell Mrs. Brannigan I got a *hero* boardin' with me . . .

HOLMES (leaping toward her, grabbing her throat, hissing). You don't tell nobody who you got! Nobody!

(He slowly drops his hands. They stare at each other. An awkward silence. Suddenly she turns on her heels, leaves. He stands there, staring after her, exhausted. Abruptly he shakes it off, bends down beside his seabag, opens it, takes out several sheets of paper, pen, ink, goes to desk, sits down and begins to write. He writes slowly, painfully. There is no sound except the scratching of the pen. Camera pans away from him, moves slowly around room.)

(Dissolve to: HOLMES slumped across desk, asleep. A partly addressed envelope is lying beside him. A shaft of sunlight lights up his face. It is morning. There is a knock on the door. His eyes open. He starts up, suddenly awake, springs to his feet.)

HOLMES. Who is it?

(Door opens, two POLICEMEN, followed by LANDLADY enter.)

FIRST POLICEMAN. David Holmes, we have a warrant for your arrest . . . (Grabs HOLMES' arm)

HOLMES (pulls away stiffly). Take your hands off me!

(He walks toward door almost proudly, exits. POLICEMEN follow him out quickly. LANDLADY glances around room, notices something on the table. The letter HOLMES wrote is still there. She picks up envelope, looks at it.

Cut to: close-up of envelope. We read the name "Pat Askin" on it.

Dissolve to: PAT ASKIN, an attractive girl in her twenties, standing somewhat nervously among a small knot of men and women outside a pair of paneled doors on which is printed:

U.S. CIRCUIT COURT FOR THE THIRD EASTERN DISTRICT OF PENNSYLVANIA

A buzz of excited conversation rises from the men and women. Suddenly PAT sees someone. Her whole body stiffens. The others, following her eyes, turn, stare at HOLMES, who has just arrived. Beside him is his attorney, ARMSTRONG, a well-dressed man in his forties holding a brief case under his arm. HOLMES catches sight of PAT, halts, stiffens. But ARMSTRONG quickly grabs his arm, pulls him through paneled doors, into courtroom.

Cut to: HOLMES and ARMSTRONG inside courtroom coming down the aisle. Suddenly HOLMES stops, his eyes fixed on something just ahead, an old weather-beaten longboat. We are able to read the name, William Brown, printed on the side of a boat near the bow.)

ARMSTRONG (*glancing at* HOLMES).
Exhibit A for the prosecution.

(*He leads* HOLMES *to defense table. They sit down.*)

I tried to get a postponement . . .

HOLMES (*becoming angry*). Who said I wanted a postponement?

ARMSTRONG. If I did everything you wanted, Holmes, there'd be a noose around your neck right now.

HOLMES. I'm gonna plead guilty.

ARMSTRONG. No!

HOLMES (*defiantly*). I did everything they said I did! I'm not gonna deny it. Armstrong, you didn't have to come all the way down here from Boston to defend me . . . Why did you?

ARMSTRONG. I'm not sure. Maybe it's because I've never seen Philadelphia before. (PAT ASKIN *is coming down the aisle.*)

HOLMES (*snapping*). I told you the facts—

ARMSTRONG. I understand the facts! What I need to understand is you! (*But* HOLMES *is not listening. He is staring out toward spectators.* ARMSTRONG, *following his eyes, sees* PAT. *She takes a seat among six or seven girls in first row.*) What about Pat Askin?

HOLMES (*turning on him angrily*). Listen, Armstrong! Why don't you let them sentence me and be done with it?

(*The rapping of the gavel interrupts him.*)

CLERK (*calling out*). Oyez! Oyez! The United States Circuit Court for the Third Eastern District of Pennsylvania is now in session. The United States versus Holmes. Will everyone rise.

(*Everyone rises.* JUDGE *enters, sits on bench. All are seated.*)

JUDGE. Is the accused ready for trial?

(ARMSTRONG *motions for* HOLMES *to rise.*)

HOLMES (*on his feet*). Yes, sir . . .

CLERK (*reading aloud from paper in his hands*). "In that David Holmes, ordinary seaman, on or about April 20, 1841, did commit manslaughter by unlawfully and feloniously[2] making an assault upon and casting Frank Askin, a passenger, from a longboat belonging to the merchant ship, the *William Brown*, into the Atlantic Ocean, by means of which Askin was suffocated and drowned . . ." David Holmes, you have heard the charge against you: how say you, guilty or not guilty?

HOLMES (*A pause. He looks around hesitantly.*) I . . . Not guilty . . .

PAT (*crying out*). He's lying! I saw him! He . . .

(PAT *leaps to her feet. She breaks, sobbing. Several other girls move to her side quickly, hold and comfort her. Sounds of excited conversation . . . confusion in the courtroom.*)

JUDGE (*pounding the gavel*). Order! Order in the Court!

(*Noise gradually ceases. He turns to prosecutor.*) Mr. Dallas, the United States District Attorney, will present the case for the people.

DALLAS (*rises, steps toward jury*). Gentlemen of the Jury, four months ago an American merchant ship, the *William Brown*, set sail from Liverpool,

---

2. **feloniously**, having to do with a serious crime or felony

England . . . *(His voice fades. Dissolve to:* DALLAS *from a different angle, still addressing jury. His jacket is open now, and he is loosening his collar and mopping his brow. He has been talking for a while and is beginning to wind up his address . . .)*

Although the members of the crew and the mate have all disappeared and have still not been reached, fortunately there are a number of witnesses present who were on that longboat, who saw these horrible deeds with their own eyes . . . *(He turns toward women sitting in first row, who are watching, listening intently.)* Why did Holmes do such a thing? I suggest, gentlemen, you will find the reason—the motive, if you will—in the character of the man himself . . .

(We see HOLMES *sitting in his chair, his right hand clenched on the table. He is motionless, expressionless.* ARMSTRONG *keeps glancing at him.)*

A man who in a moment of panic exploded, and sent not only Frank Askin, but eleven of his fellow passengers to their death!

*(*DALLAS *turns, walks slowly back to his seat.* JUDGE *looks questioningly at* ARMSTRONG. ARMSTRONG *says something to* HOLMES, *who does not react. Finally he rises.)*

ARMSTRONG. Your Honor, the defense will not address the jury at this time. *(He is seated.)*

JUDGE *(looks at him questioningly, then to* DALLAS*).* Prosecution will proceed . . . .

CLERK. Miss Pat Askin will take the stand . . . . *(*PAT *crosses up aisle to stand.* HOLMES *watches her carefully.)* Raise your right hand. Do you solemnly swear that the testimony you are about to give will be the truth, the whole truth, and nothing but the truth, so help you God?

PAT. I do.

CLERK. State your name.

PAT. Patricia Askin.

DALLAS *(approaches).* You are the sister of Frank Askin who was thrown off a longboat and drowned in the Atlantic Ocean on April 20 of this year?

PAT. Yes.

DALLAS. Were you on that same longboat at that time?

PAT. I was.

DALLAS *(points to boat).* Is that the longboat?

PAT. Yes . . .

DALLAS. Miss Askin, did you see the defendant, David Holmes, forcibly throw your brother, Frank, out of *this* longboat and thus cause him to drown?

PAT. Yes . . . I did.

(Murmuring, voices from courtroom. JUDGE *bangs gavel.)*

JUDGE. Did I hear an objection, Mr. Armstrong?

ARMSTRONG *(from far away).* What . . . ? No, Your Honor.

JUDGE *(to* DALLAS*).* Proceed.

DALLAS *(to* PAT*).* You and Frank were not the only passengers aboard the ship, the *William Brown*, were you, Miss Askin?

PAT. No . . . there were about thirty others with us.

DALLAS. Where were you coming from?

PAT. Ireland.

DALLAS. Why did you decide to come to America?

PAT. Well . . . it was the famine[3] . . . my father died . . . Frank and I decided to sell our little plot and seek a better life in this country.

DALLAS. Miss Askin, please tell the Court what happened on the night of April 19th.

PAT. An iceberg hit the ship.

DALLAS. Would you describe the circumstances.

PAT. Well, I was asleep when it happened. When I opened my eyes, everyone was in their nightclothes screaming . . . Someone was yelling: "On deck! Into the boats!" We piled up the hatchway with the seas crashing down. Some climbed into the little jollyboat. But most of us got into the longboat . . . Soon after the two boats were lowered into the sea, the ship went down . . .

DALLAS. Miss Askin, I am now going to ask you to step down from the stand and get into the longboat, taking the exact position you were in that night.

(DALLAS begins to help her out of stand.)

JUDGE. One moment—would the prosecutor please explain his purpose?

DALLAS. If it please the Court. It is necessary to show Miss Askin's position in the boat in order to show that she could see what was going on.

JUDGE. You may proceed.

(DALLAS leads PAT to longboat, helps her inside.)

DALLAS. Is this where you were sitting?

PAT. Yes.

DALLAS. What were you doing?

PAT. Bailing . . .

DALLAS *(over).* Bailing? There was water in the boat?

PAT. Oh, a great deal.

(Super: film, sound of sea, winds up)

PAT *(continues).* Besides, we had sprung a leak . . . My clothes were soaked and I was exhausted. My brother was sitting in front of me. Then I saw Holmes. Beside him were two seamen. He had a terrible look as he faced my brother.

(We are in close, can almost see what PAT is describing.)

Frank asked him what was happening. For a moment there was no reply—then Holmes took my brother by the shoulders and said, "It's your turn, Frank. You've got to go."

(There is a look of horror on FRANK's face.)

Then they threw my brother over the side. *(She screams.)* Leave him be! Leave him be!

(We are in for a close-up of her face.)

(Sound of storm down and out. We hear nothing but PAT's sobbing. Lights come up on DALLAS in courtroom.)

DALLAS. On that night, your brother as well as other male passengers were thrown over—Miss Askin, were any of the crew thrown overboard?

PAT. No.

---

3. famine, a time of starving. In 1845, disease ruined Ireland's potato crops, causing the Irish Potato Famine. A million people died, and over a million fled Ireland.

DALLAS. No further questions. *(Begins to help her down.)*

ARMSTRONG *(rising).* You may remain where you are, Miss Askin. You just stated that none of the crew members were thrown overboard. Could you tell me why?

PAT. Well . . . they . . . Holmes said they were needed to row.

ARMSTRONG. No more questions.

(He turns away. Court attendant helps PAT down.)

JUDGE. Is that the extent of your cross-examination of this important witness, Mr. Armstrong?

ARMSTRONG. Miss Askin will be called as a witness for the defense, Your Honor.

JUDGE. For the *defense?*

ARMSTRONG. Yes, Your Honor.

(JUDGE stares at him, shrugs, turns toward CLERK.)

CLERK. Miss Mary O'Brien.

(MARY comes forward, glances angrily at HOLMES. He is gazing across at PAT. ARMSTRONG notices the look on his face.

Dissolve to: DALLAS at stand.)

DALLAS. Miss O'Brien, was Holmes in command of the longboat immediately after the ship went down?

MARY *(in stand).* No, sir, John Widdows was—the first mate.

DALLAS. Oh?

MARY. Holmes took over later.

DALLAS. Took over? Forcibly? Did he fight with the mate?

MARY. Not right away. But he started to argue with him.

DALLAS. What about, Miss O'Brien?

MARY. The direction we was to take . . . The mate told Holmes to head west for land. Holmes refused. He said our only chance was to head south where we might pick up a ship . . . Well, sir, that's what we did—we went south.

DALLAS. Then Holmes actually took command.

MARY. All night long I heard his voice shoutin', cussin', threatenin' . . . I tell you, I'm not a shrinkin' violet [4] of a woman, but I was scared of him . . . He's crazy!

DALLAS. Crazy?

MARY. Yes, sir.

DALLAS. Thank you, Miss O'Brien . . . . Your witness.

ARMSTRONG *(rising).* How would you describe a man who was crazy, Miss O'Brien?

MARY. Well . . . Out of his mind . . . You know.

ARMSTRONG. Would you say that a man who is crazy doesn't know what he's doing?

MARY. Yes, sir! That's it!

ARMSTRONG. You mean Holmes didn't know what he was doing on that longboat?

MARY. I didn't say that . . .

ARMSTRONG. Well . . . You said he was crazy.

MARY. Well . . . He wasn't exactly *crazy* . . . He . . .

ARMSTRONG. No more questions.

---

4. shrinking violet, a shy, timid person

(He goes back to table. Camera stays on him and HOLMES.*)*

CLERK *(over, calling).* Thomas Able.

(Dissolve to: Witness stand. THOMAS ABLE, *a little withered seaman, sitting there looking at* DALLAS, *who has just begun to question him.)*

DALLAS. Mr. Able, how long were you and Holmes members of the crew of the *William Brown?*

ABLE. Five years.

DALLAS. At the time of the sinking, where did you go?

ABLE. In the jollyboat.

DALLAS. When you heard what had happened aboard the longboat, were you surprised?

ABLE. No, sir. I wouldn't be surprised at anything Holmes did. He's capable of anything. He's like gunpowder, ready to explode at any time . . .

DALLAS. Had he ever done anything like that before?

ABLE. No, not exactly . . . but, well, he was proud . . .

DALLAS. Proud?

ABLE. Well, he always had to be the first one up on the crow's nest . . . even during the worst weather. I see him hanging on to the top of the mizzen-mast once with the ship practically layin' over on her side in the sea . . . and the mast all icy. An' when he came down later, his hands all bloody, he didn't say one word . . . even when some of the men slapped his shoulder and told him he did a nice job. He was crazy!

DALLAS *(smiles).* Did you like him as a shipmate?

ABLE. Nobody likes him.

DALLAS. Why not?

ABLE. Well, he was different . . . Kept apart . . . Never swapped a yarn . . . Never took a drink . . . I don't trust a man who don't take a drink . . . Not a seafarin' man . . .

DALLAS. Thank you, Mr. Able.

(He returns to table. ARMSTRONG *approaches stand.)*

ARMSTRONG. Tell me, Mr. Able, is Holmes a good seaman? In your opinion?

ABLE. Aye.

ARMSTRONG. A brave man?

ABLE. Aye, I guess he's got courage, but it's stupid . . .

ARMSTRONG *(sharply).* Would you just answer my questions, please! Now, Mr. Able, in all the years that you knew the defendant, did he ever willfully harm anyone?

ABLE. Well . . . no.

ARMSTRONG. No further questions.

(He turns away.)

DALLAS. That's all, Mr. Able.

*(*ABLE *steps down.)*

CLERK *(calling).* Miss Lorna Quinn.

*(*LORNA *rises from among row of women. As she does, we see* ARMSTRONG *at defense table making a few notes.* HOLMES *glances at him.)*

ARMSTRONG. That Tom Able reminds me of a man I once shipped with . . .

HOLMES. What did *you* ever wanna go to sea for? It was a stupid thing to do.

(Dissolve to: LORNA QUINN *on stand being questioned by* DALLAS. *She is nervous.)*

DALLAS. . . . Do you actually mean, Miss Quinn, that on the night of April 20th, the night following the sinking of the *William Brown,* you heard the defendant order the crew to throw the male passengers overboard?

LORNA. I even saw it happen. I saw Holmes and two of the crew go up to Riley and they told him to stand up . . . and when Riley stood up, they gave him a shove and he went right overboard.

DALLAS. How close were you to Riley when this happened?

LORNA. Well, no further than you are from me right now.

DALLAS. Then what happened?

LORNA. Well, they threw over Duffy next, then Charlie Conlin . . . Charlie offered Holmes five sovereigns if he'd spare his life, but Holmes wouldn't even listen to him . . . and, well, this went on until every one of the men passengers except Ed McKenzie and Patrick Whelan were thrown over. Holmes spared those two because their wives were aboard.

DALLAS. Are you able to tell the Court—from your observation—how many men were thrown overboard during that terrible night?

LORNA. Well, there was Riley, Duffy, Charlie Conlin, Frank Askin . . . There were twelve.

DALLAS (*turning away swiftly*). Your witness.

ARMSTRONG (*rises, approaches* LORNA). Miss Quinn, did you personally feel

safer—when you saw that the boat had been lightened by those men?

DALLAS. Objection!

JUDGE. You are placing the witness in a very difficult situation, Mr. Armstrong . . .

ARMSTRONG. If it please the Court, the defendant was faced with exactly the same difficult situation.

JUDGE (*after a pause*). Objection overruled.

ARMSTRONG. Miss Quinn, I asked you if you felt safer—more secure—when you saw that the boat had been lightened by those men. Remember, you're under oath.

LORNA (*almost in tears*). I . . . I . . . don't know . . .

ARMSTRONG. That's all, Miss Quinn.

(*He returns to defense table. She steps down.* DALLAS *comes forward.*)

CLERK. Miss Ann Flaherty.

ARMSTRONG (*rising*). If the Court please, I understand the United States Prosecutor intends to call at least ten survivors as witnesses . . .

DALLAS. That's correct . . .

ARMSTRONG. The defense agrees that the testimony of these witnesses will confirm the testimony already heard.

JUDGE. Mr. Armstrong, you are yielding a rather important point . . .

ARMSTRONG. Your Honor, the defense does not deny that Holmes was responsible for casting Frank Askin and other male passengers overboard . . .

JUDGE. Oh! (*He studies* ARMSTRONG. *A silence.*) Mr. Armstrong, the Court understands you came all the way down from Boston to conduct this defense . . .

ARMSTRONG. That's correct, Your Honor . . .

JUDGE. You attended college in Boston?

ARMSTRONG. Harvard College, Your Honor.

JUDGE. Do you have any personal interest in this case, Mr. Armstrong?

ARMSTRONG. Your Honor, the effect of maritime law is felt in Boston as well as in Philadelphia; on land as well as on sea. I believe that this trial has meaning for all who travel on the sea—seamen and passengers. That is my personal interest.

JUDGE. The prosecution will proceed.

(ARMSTRONG *is seated.*)

CLERK. Captain Amos Tilton.

(CAPTAIN TILTON, *lean, hard, tanned, in sea uniform, approaches.*

Cut to: ARMSTRONG *and* HOLMES. HOLMES *is tensely watching* PAT. *Then to* PAT.

Dissolve to: Witness stand. DALLAS *is questioning the* CAPTAIN.)

DALLAS. Captain Tilton, how long were you in command of the *William Brown?*

CAPTAIN. Eight years.

DALLAS. During her last voyage, how many had she on board?

CAPTAIN. A crew of thirteen and thirty-nine passengers, Scotch and Irish immigrants, as well as a heavy cargo.

DALLAS. What happened when she was hit by the iceberg?

CAPTAIN. Well, there was panic among the passengers, sir, but the crew with one exception handled themselves well. . . . The second mate, seven of the crew, two passengers, and myself got into the small jollyboat, while the first mate, four seamen, and thirty-seven passengers got into the longboat. We in the jollyboat were picked up six days later.

DALLAS. How many male passengers were in the longboat?

CAPTAIN. Sixteen, sir.

DALLAS. Captain, you just stated that you in the jollyboat were picked up six days later.

CAPTAIN. Yes, sir.

DALLAS. During those six days conditions were extremely difficult. There was the same storm, the same rough sea as that which the longboat met . . . and yet you brought your boat into safety with all aboard?

CAPTAIN. Yes, sir.

DALLAS. Now, Captain—had you instead of Holmes been in command of the longboat—would you have given the same order—in other words, would you have sacrificed the lives of any of the passengers, just to save your own life?

ARMSTRONG. Objection!

JUDGE (*quickly*). Overruled! The Court considers the captain an expert witness.

DALLAS. Well, Captain? Would you have committed manslaughter?

CAPTAIN. I . . . No, sir.

(*Uproar in crowd.*

Cut to: HOLMES *and* ARMSTRONG *for reaction. Both are deeply shaken. Uproar swells— Quick fade out.*)

Act Two

Fade in: *The courtroom. No time lapse.* CAPTAIN TILTON *is in the witness stand. Uproar continues.* JUDGE *is rapping for order.*

DALLAS. Your witness.

ARMSTRONG *(approaches stand).* Captain, in your testimony you stated that the crew with one exception handled themselves well. Please explain the exception.

CAPTAIN. John Widdows, first mate . . .

ARMSTRONG *(surprised).* The first mate?

CAPTAIN. I would have taken him out of the longboat, but it was impossible due to the storm—the panic and all.

ARMSTRONG. Why?

CAPTAIN. He was a coward.

ARMSTRONG. And so Holmes took over. (CAPTAIN *looks down at his hands.*) Captain Tilton, how many people could the longboat normally hold?

CAPTAIN. She was built to hold twenty, sir.

ARMSTRONG. And how many were aboard?

CAPTAIN. Forty-two.

ARMSTRONG. Captain Tilton, what was the condition of the longboat?

CAPTAIN. I felt she was in grave danger, sir . . .

ARMSTRONG. Captain, based upon your experience, how did you judge your chances of survival?

CAPTAIN. At the time? Not one chance in a hundred.

ARMSTRONG. Did the crew agree?

CAPTAIN. Yes, sir.

ARMSTRONG. When the jollyboat and the longboat were lowered into the water, where did you send Holmes?

CAPTAIN. To the jollyboat.

ARMSTRONG *(surprised).* The jollyboat? How did he get into the longboat? Did you order him to go?

CAPTAIN. No, sir. He offered.

ARMSTRONG. Do you mean he offered to go into the longboat, knowing that he was possibly going to his death?

CAPTAIN. Yes.

ARMSTRONG. Do you know why Holmes offered to go?

CAPTAIN. No, sir.

ARMSTRONG. Did you have a chance to watch the defendant at the time the *William Brown* was hit by the iceberg?

CAPTAIN. Yes, sir.

ARMSTRONG. How did he act?

CAPTAIN. His efforts to save the passengers were outstanding, sir. Without him I'm sure more lives would have been lost.

ARMSTRONG. Captain, is it possible that Holmes offered to go into the longboat because he thought he could save the boat?

DALLAS *(jumping up).* Objection! This is a guess, suggestion . . . It is not evidence . . .

JUDGE. Sustained.[5]

---

5. sustained, allowing the objection made by the prosecution.

ARMSTRONG. All right . . . Captain, the longboat did survive . . . in spite of all the odds against her, and she was finally picked up. How do you account for this? Would you say it was due to Holmes' seamanship?

CAPTAIN. Well, Holmes is a fine seaman. It was very likely due to—

ARMSTRONG (*quickly*). Due to the fact that the boat was lightened?

DALLAS (*shouting*). Objection!

ARMSTRONG. I am only asking for the captain's expert opinion, Your Honor. It is important to this case to show why this longboat stayed afloat.

JUDGE. It is a reasonable question. Objection overruled.

ARMSTRONG. Captain, in your opinion, was the lightening of the longboat by about a ton important to its survival?

CAPTAIN. I cannot answer a question . . .

JUDGE. This a court of law, not the deck of a ship. Answer the question!

CAPTAIN (*unwilling*). Yes, it was possible . . .

ARMSTRONG. Thank you, Captain.

(*He turns away.* CAPTAIN *starts to leave stand.*)

DALLAS (*rising*). One moment, Captain . . . (CAPTAIN *remains in stand.*) Could the longboat have survived without Holmes? If he had not lightened the boat by throwing twelve human beings to their doom? Was there any chance at all, Captain?

CAPTAIN. There are always miracles, sir . . .

DALLAS. Will you answer my question, please! Yes, or no?

CAPTAIN. It was possible, sir . . .

DALLAS (*turning away*). No further questions.

(CAPTAIN *rises, steps out of stand.*)

JUDGE. Captain Tilton, you may leave the stand.

(CAPTAIN *hurries away.*)

DALLAS. Prosecution rests.

JUDGE. Is defense ready to present its case?

ARMSTRONG (*rising*). Yes, Your Honor.

JUDGE. Proceed.

(ARMSTRONG *nods to* CLERK.)

CLERK (*calling out*). Mrs. Margaret Reston. Please take the stand.

(MRS. RESTON *rises, comes forward.*
Cut to: HOLMES *watching her.*
Dissolve to: Witness stand.)

ARMSTRONG. You have a daughter, Mrs. Reston?

MRS. RESTON. Aye . . . Isabel . . . She's nine years old.

ARMSTRONG. Mrs. Reston, will you please tell the Court what happened to your daughter on the night the *William Brown* was struck by the iceberg . . .

MRS. RESTON. Well, she was left behind on the sinking ship.

ARMSTRONG. What did you do when you discovered this?

MRS. RESTON. Well, I was like out of my mind . . . I cried out for help . . . And, praise God, one of the seamen, he climbed back on to the ship just as she was turning over and rescued my daughter. Oh, I'll never forget it. That seaman didn't even know me, yet he risked his life.

ARMSTRONG. Who was that seaman, Mrs. Reston?

MRS. RESTON. David Holmes.

ARMSTRONG. Thank you, Mrs. Reston. Your witness.

DALLAS. Mrs. Reston, I'm sure there was a great deal of bravery shown. The question is: Did he willingly and illegally take the life of a fellow creature? I therefore ask you: While you were in the longboat, did you see him cause any of the passengers to be thrown into the sea?

MRS. RESTON. I . . . I . . .

DALLAS (angrily). Well, Mrs. Reston?

MRS. RESTON. I . . . I . . . Please . . . Please don't ask me . . .

(She sobs. ARMSTRONG is on his feet.)

ARMSTRONG. Objection. Is it necessary to bully the witness, Your Honor?

DALLAS. Your Honor, I would like to reserve the right to reexamine this witness later when she is more capable of answering questions.

JUDGE. Permission granted.

DALLAS. No further questions.

(He turns away. MRS. RESTON comes down from stand.)

CLERK (calling out). Miss Patricia Askin.

(PAT rises nervously, comes forward, takes stand.)

ARMSTRONG. Miss Askin, when did you first meet the defendant?

PAT. On the William Brown. During the first week of the voyage.

ARMSTRONG. Can you describe the circumstances?

PAT. My brother introduced us.

ARMSTRONG. Oh, he knew Holmes then?

PAT. Well, he met him aboard ship, too.

ARMSTRONG. Did he and Holmes see a lot of each other during the voyage?

PAT. Well, yes . . .

ARMSTRONG. Your brother tilled the soil in Ireland, didn't he?

PAT. Yes. Farming was his whole life. His dream was to get some land in America.

ARMSTRONG. Looking back on it now, doesn't it seem unusual to you that your brother and Holmes should have struck up such a speedy friendship . . . considering the fact that Holmes is supposed to be such a difficult man to know, that he doesn't mix easily . . . and that his first love is the sea?

PAT. David Holmes' first love is not the sea.

ARMSTRONG. Oh, no, what is it then?

PAT. Farming.

ARMSTRONG. He told you that?

PAT. Yes . . . All he wanted was to own a farm.

ARMSTRONG. No one else on board ship was aware of Holmes' attitude toward farming. You must have been quite friendly for him to trust in you like that.

DALLAS. Objection! I can see no purpose in this line of questioning, Your Honor . . .

ARMSTRONG. If it please the Court, I am trying to show why Holmes offered to go into the longboat at the risk of his life. I believe he had good reason. To understand it, however, it is necessary to understand his relationship with Pat and Frank Askin.

JUDGE. Objection overruled.

ARMSTRONG. How friendly with the defendant were you, Miss Askin?

PAT. Well, we used to talk a lot . . . that's all . . .

ARMSTRONG *(quickly).* You liked Holmes, didn't you?

PAT. I was blind . . .

ARMSTRONG *(sharply).* Were you in love with him?

PAT *(bursting out).* I didn't say that!

ARMSTRONG. Were you?

PAT. Well . . . I . . . don't know . . .

ARMSTRONG. Was he in love with you?

PAT. I don't know! Ask him!

ARMSTRONG. He thought a great deal of your brother, didn't he?

PAT. I . . . don't know . . .

ARMSTRONG. Didn't his actions show it?

PAT. I don't know!

ARMSTRONG. Miss Askin, during the ocean crossing, did you or your brother make any plans for the future in which the defendant was included?

PAT *(her voice low, broken).* I made plans, hundreds of them . . . What good are they now?

ARMSTRONG. Miss Askin, on the morning of April 21st, the morning after that terrible night in which your brother and the others were thrown overboard . . . Did you think there was any chance of rescue?

PAT. No, I didn't care . . .

ARMSTRONG. Would you say that David Holmes—by his own efforts and at the risk of his own life—was responsible for saving that longboat?

DALLAS *(jumping up).* Objection!

JUDGE. Sustained!

ARMSTRONG *(turns away).* No further questions . . .

(JUDGE looks at DALLAS. DALLAS shakes his head.)

JUDGE. You may step down, Miss Askin. *(She does.)*

ARMSTRONG *(rises).* I call the accused.

(HOLMES stands.)

JUDGE. Does the accused request that he be permitted to testify?

HOLMES *(after a pause).* I do.

JUDGE. You have the right to do so. You also have the right not to take the stand. If you don't testify, that fact won't be held against you. If you do, you may undergo a severe cross-examination.

HOLMES. I understand, Your Honor. *(HOLMES goes to stand.)*

CLERK. Raise your right hand. *(He does.)* Do you solemnly swear that the evidence you are about to give shall be the truth, the whole truth, and nothing but the truth, so help you God?

HOLMES. I do. *(He is seated.)*

ARMSTRONG. David Holmes, how long have you been a seaman?

HOLMES. Since I was fourteen.

ARMSTRONG. Do you like the sea?

HOLMES. I hate it!

ARMSTRONG. Yet you have been a seaman all your life. Why?

HOLMES. I had no other occupation . . . no money to buy a farm . . .

ARMSTRONG. Is that your ambition in life? To own a farm?

HOLMES. Yes.

ARMSTRONG. Have you ever worked on a farm?

HOLMES. My father's farm.

ARMSTRONG. Where was this?

HOLMES. New York State. Near Albany.

ARMSTRONG. Did you like the life, the work?

HOLMES. For me it's the only life.

ARMSTRONG. Why did you leave?

(A long silence. HOLMES *doesn't answer.)*

Did you hear my question?

HOLMES *(to* JUDGE*).* Can I leave the stand?

JUDGE. Why?

HOLMES. I'm not gonna answer these questions!

(Reaction from jury)

ARMSTRONG. May it please the Court, I beg for an opportunity to speak to my client. A brief delay. Two minutes.

JUDGE *(raps gavel).* There will be a two-minute pause in the proceedings.

ARMSTRONG *(to* HOLMES *in a low tone, angry).* If you leave the stand now, I walk out.

HOLMES. Go ahead!

ARMSTRONG. Holmes, what are you afraid of? A little rough questioning? Or maybe you threw Frank Askin overboard because you were frightened!

HOLMES. No!

ARMSTRONG. Well, prove it then! If not to me, to Pat. Answer the questions I ask you before the whole world.

(He walks away from stand.)

JUDGE *(raps gavel).* Mr. Holmes, do you intend to submit to questioning, or do you wish to step down? *(There is a pause.* HOLMES *looks across at* ARMSTRONG.*)* You will not have another chance to change your mind.

HOLMES. I'll answer.

ARMSTRONG. Your father had a farm. Why did he leave it?

HOLMES. They took it away from my father.

ARMSTRONG. Why did they take it away?

HOLMES *(resisting).* I dunno! *(Then, after a silence, as* ARMSTRONG *watches him, with great effort)* He owed money on it . . . He never told anybody . . . He was too proud . . . When a man came to take it away, my father shot him dead. I saw it . . . Then more men came and took my father, and they got a rope . . . *(His voice chokes, remembering.)* I couldn't stand it . . . I ran away . . .

ARMSTRONG. Where did you go?

HOLMES. New York City.

ARMSTRONG. What did you do there?

HOLMES. I hung around the water front, slept in doorways . . . One night some men came. They beat me unconscious. When I came to I was in the hold of a ship.

ARMSTRONG. How old were you?

HOLMES. Fourteen.

ARMSTRONG. What happened on the ship? Did you become part of the crew?

HOLMES. The mate sent me up the mast the first day out. I couldn't stay there. I got dizzy . . . I fell. Musta been laying on the deck for hours.

But them seamen—they just laughed. We were at sea eighteen months and they kept laughing at me. I couldn't do anything right. I hated them. (HOLMES *is wound up, talking with difficulty.* ARMSTRONG *steps back, listens politely.*) I made up my mind then I'd show them. It took me a year, two, three . . . I don't know how long. I hated the sea, but I fought it . . . I fought them . . . I swore an oath to myself that I'd get my father's farm back. Someday I'd return. That's all I lived for . . . I saved my money . . .

ARMSTRONG. What money?

HOLMES. My pay . . .

ARMSTRONG. What is your pay?

HOLMES. Eleven dollars a month.

ARMSTRONG. You mean you thought you could save enough out of that to buy back your father's farm?

HOLMES *(triumphantly).* I did! The money is in a bank in New York City right now . . .

ARMSTRONG. How long did it take you to save that much money?

HOLMES. Thirteen years.

ARMSTRONG. Thirteen years? Is that why you never went ashore with your shipmates?

HOLMES. I couldn't afford to.

ARMSTRONG. Well, if you had all this money, why didn't you leave the sea?

HOLMES. After this trip I was gonna quit.

ARMSTRONG. David Holmes, during the last voyage of the *William Brown* you met Frank Askin. Explain the circumstances.

HOLMES. Well . . . I heard some of the passengers one night . . . I was on the lee'ard watch. Frank Askin was talking about farming . . . He seemed to know what he was talking about, and he spoke like it really meant something to him. So I sought him out and asked him questions.

ARMSTRONG. You became friends?

HOLMES. Yes.

ARMSTRONG. In the course of your friendship with him, did you often speak with his sister, Pat?

HOLMES. Yes.

ARMSTRONG. What was your relationship with her?

HOLMES. We got along.

ARMSTRONG. Is that all?

HOLMES. We got along!

ARMSTRONG. Did you ask her to marry you?

HOLMES. No!

ARMSTRONG. Did you think of asking her? *(As HOLMES hesitates)* Did you?

HOLMES. I thought of a lot of things!

ARMSTRONG *(reaches inside his jacket, takes out a letter, shows it to judge).* Your Honor, this has been recorded as Exhibit B for the defense. *(Turns to HOLMES)* Have you ever seen this letter before? David Holmes, did you write this letter? Is this your signature? *(Shows it to him)* It was given to me by Mrs. Althea Temple, landlady of the boarding house you stayed in on your first night ashore. It is addressed to Miss Pat Askin. Did you write this letter? *(HOLMES nods—unable to speak.)* Please read it to the Court. *(He hands it to him.)*

HOLMES *(choked).* I didn't know what I was doing when I wrote it . . . I . . .

ARMSTRONG. I understand that. Please read it.

HOLMES *(mumbling, hunched over, after a long pause, reading).* "Dear Pat. I am going to ship out on the first vessel. I have some money. I want you to have it. Don't think of it as mine. Think of it as Frank's, that he left it for you . . . Pat, I want you to know that I loved Frank, too. I know you hate me, but there was nothing else I could have done . . . I don't know if he told you . . ."

(HOLMES breaks. ARMSTRONG takes letter, continues reading.)

ARMSTRONG. "I don't know if he told you, but we planned to farm together, as partners. I had hoped you would be with us. I am going to ship out on the first vessel. David Holmes . . ." *(Silence. HOLMES is sitting there, his head bowed. ARMSTRONG looks at him gently.)* Thank you, David. Now can you tell the Court why you offered to go into the longboat?

HOLMES *(his voice low).* To save it. Everything I had was on that boat. *(Then crying out in pain)* I had to save it! And I did! I did what I could! God, what else could I do? But I had to do it. I had to. I loved them.

(Fade out)

Act Three

Fade in: The courtroom. HOLMES *still on stand.* DALLAS, *having just completed his re-examination, returns to* table. JUDGE *looks across at* ARMSTRONG *questioningly.*

DALLAS. No further questions.

ARMSTRONG. No re-examination. Your Honor, the defense rests.

JUDGE. You may leave the stand, Mr. Holmes. *(HOLMES steps down. There is a pause as* JUDGE *checks his notes, looks up.)* Gentlemen, are you ready for summation?

(The FOREMAN of the jury rises.)

FOREMAN. Just a minute! Your Honor!

(Commotion in the courtroom)

JUDGE *(pounding gavel).* What is the cause of this outburst?

FOREMAN. There's been a mistake in some of the testimony.

JUDGE *(stern).* Mistake?

FOREMAN. Your Honor, maybe if you could have a part of Captain Tilton's and Lorna Quinn's testimony that tells about the number of men thrown overboard . . .

JUDGE *(staring at* FOREMAN, *after a long pause, to steno[6]).* You may do as he asks.

STENO *(flipping through notes, reads).* "Question by Mr. Dallas to Miss Quinn: From your observation, are you able to tell the Court how many men were thrown overboard during that terrible night? Answer: Well . . . there was Riley, Duffy, Charlie Conlin, Frank Askin. There were twelve."

---

6. steno, stenographer, person who takes notes in a courtroom.

FOREMAN (*quickly*). Now could you read the part where Captain Tilton tells how many men passengers were on the longboat.

STENO (*flipping through notes, reads*). "Question by Mr. Dallas: How many male passengers were in the longboat? Answer by Captain Tilton: Sixteen, sir."

FOREMAN. There you are, sir! Since there were sixteen men passengers originally in the longboat, and twelve were thrown overboard, *four* must have survived. But according to Miss Quinn's testimony, only two men passengers survived. She said they were not thrown overboard because their wives were present. Well, Your Honor, that leaves two men not accounted for. I'd like to know what happened to them!

DALLAS (*rises*). If the Court please, both the defense and the prosecution are aware that two of the male passengers are not accounted for . . . the fact is, no one seems to know what happened to them . . . and it has no bearing on this case.

JUDGE. Gentlemen, the question you must decide involves only one point: is the defendant, David Holmes, guilty of the manslaughter of Frank Askin? Only Frank Askin. None other.

FOREMAN. But Your Honor! How can we come to a decision unless the evidence regarding those two men . . .

JUDGE. You're out of order, sir.

VOICE. Your Honor! Your Honor!
(*Everyone turns. We see* MRS. RESTON *extremely upset, coming forward. Suddenly she halts, frightened at the* JUDGE's *stern look.*) Excuse me, sir . . . I . . . Perhaps I can explain . . . I mean, about those two men.

JUDGE (*severely*). Do you know what happened to them?

MRS. RESTON. Yes. Yes.

(*Reaction from the court*)

ARMSTRONG (*rising*). Please the Court! I request that this witness be allowed to take the stand! I have no idea what she will say, but her evidence might have a bearing on this case . . .

JUDGE. Any objection, Mr. Dallas?

DALLAS. No objection.

JUDGE. Mrs. Reston, you may take the stand.

ARMSTRONG (*comes forward*). Now, Mrs. Reston, your testimony will bear directly upon the question which is disturbing the jury . . . It will include nothing else.

MRS. RESTON. Yes . . . (*Glancing across at* HOLMES *with difficulty*) I didn't say before; I didn't want to hurt anybody—I—but it is eating away inside me, and I must get it out or I will never be able to look anyone in the face again. It is something I saw . . .

ARMSTRONG. What did you see?

MRS. RESTON. It was just before dawn (*Hit film.*) after that awful night. I mean the night the men were cast over. The storm had quieted at that moment, and we were trying to rest when I noticed a movement beneath the canvas on the bottom of the boat . . . two of the men passengers were hidden. Their feet were sticking out.

I realized that they had hidden during the night to escape being thrown over. Just then I saw that two of the seamen had also noticed them. They didn't know that I was watching. They bent down and struck and struck, and then they threw the two unconscious bodies overboard. *(Film out)* They didn't have to do it. There was no need for it any more. Yet they threw those men over anyway. I sat there too frightened to say anything. *(She is sobbing.)*

ARMSTRONG. Thank you, Mrs. Reston.

(He crosses to defense table, sits beside HOLMES.*)*

HOLMES *(shocked deeply).* I didn't know . . . I didn't know . . .

JUDGE. Mr. Dallas?

DALLAS *(rises).* No questions, Mrs. Reston. *(She leaves stand.)* Your Honor, I waive my right to final summation and would like to address the jury now.

JUDGE. Mr. Armstrong?

ARMSTRONG. Agreed.

DALLAS. Please the Court, Gentlemen of the Jury. The act just described by Mrs. Reston is murder—vicious, stupid, unreasonable killing for its own sake. Why did those seamen cast two human beings into the sea, when any need for such an act was clearly at an end? Because they had been ordered to kill and because once they started to kill, all sense of right and wrong broke down. They couldn't stop. Who was responsible for it? The prisoner, David Holmes, for it was he alone who made the decision to take the lives of his fellow men! Did David Holmes have the right to give such an order? Did he have the right to place himself above his fellow men and select those who should die and those who should live? Does any man have that right? Gentlemen, this case does not deal only with the guilt or innocence of one man. In a sense we are all on that longboat, and at stake is a question of greatest importance. It is this: that *all* men's lives are sacred, of equal value . . . that in a crisis where some men have to die in order to save the rest, the decisions as to who will go cannot be left to one man but must be decided upon equally by all. Gentlemen, David Holmes not only committed manslaughter but he broke the law upon which our democracy rests! Therefore you have no choice . . . but to find the defendant GUILTY!

(Uproar of crowd. JUDGE *pounds gavel, courtroom becomes quiet. He looks toward* ARMSTRONG. ARMSTRONG *rises slowly now, approaches* JUDGE *and jury.)*

ARMSTRONG. Your Honor, Gentlemen of the Jury. As you sit here in the courtroom judging David Holmes . . . I ask you to look for one moment into your own hearts. What would YOU have done on the night of April 20th? A hundred leagues from land . . . a boat filled with water . . . women screaming, knowing that at any moment all may die . . . . What would you have done? Talked about the law and democratic rights? Taken a vote? As an experienced seaman, Holmes knew there was only one way to save the boat . . . a terrible way . . .

lighten it. And that is what he did. Considering the women and children first, he gave the order to cast over the male passengers . . . among them a man he loved and admired . . . a man in whom all his hopes for the future were placed—indeed, the very person he had come to save. Can you imagine the dreams which will torment him for the rest of his life? *(Quietly, but with rising strength)* Holmes acted out of duty, because it was his duty to save the boat, and out of love, because he believed human lives to be sacred . . . And so he saved most of the passengers. *(He turns suddenly to face the witnesses.)* Look at them. Would they be here today if it were not for Holmes? *(Turns swiftly to jury)* How can you declare him guilty?

(Fade out

Fade in slowly: HOLMES *is standing before* JUDGE.*)*

CLERK. Gentlemen of the Jury, have you agreed upon a verdict?

FOREMAN. We have.

CLERK. And how do you find, gentlemen?

FOREMAN. We find the defendant . . . guilty. *(We hear a gasp, a cry from spectators.)* But we recommend mercy.

(We hear murmuring in courtroom.)

JUDGE *(pounds gavel)*. Order. *(Murmuring dies out.)* David Holmes, you have broken the law upon which our civilization rests. You have taken into your hands a right which lies only in the people at large and in God himself. Although there are many circumstances which are of a sort to make you admired by this court and indeed by all humanity—the law demands punishment. In accordance with the jury's recommendation of mercy, I hereby sentence you, David Holmes, to six months in prison. Court dismissed!

(Noise in court. HOLMES *stands there swaying.*

ARMSTRONG *comes up to him, places his arm about his shoulder, leads him slowly down aisle toward doors in rear. As they reach doors,* PAT *approaches.)*

PAT *(choked, trembling)*. David . . . I understand . . . *(They look at each other.)* Don't go back to sea . . . . *(Pause)* Buy the farm . . . .

HOLMES *(speechless)*. Yes . . . .

(ARMSTRONG takes him off. PAT *continues to watch until the two men have disappeared down the corridor. Her eyes are wet.*

Slow fade)

Responding to the Play

1. Did your opinion of David Holmes change from the beginning to the end of the play? Explain.
2. The jury questions what became of the two men who were unaccounted for. How does Mrs. Reston's testimony about their deaths hurt or help Holmes's case?
3. How would *Survival* be different if it were produced for the stage rather than for television?
4. Make a plot diagram that indicates the conflict, rising action, turning point, and resolution for this play.
5. Create a logo for this play using only the title, *SURVIVAL.*

About Early Ocean Travel

The fictional merchant ship *William Brown,* like the actual luxury liner *Titanic,* left many dead when it sank. In 1841, the year in which *Survival* takes place, an ocean voyage was a risky undertaking. Travel from Ireland to the United States could take well over a month, and storms, winds, and icebergs were always a threat. In those days, lifeboats were considered frivolous, with only a fraction available for the many on board. So, when large ships sank, many lives were lost. In 1912, over 1,500 people died when the *Titanic* sank. After that tragedy, action was finally taken to assure that lifeboats would be available for all passengers.

Creating and Performing

1. You be the jury. With eight classmates, discuss the evidence presented in the trial of David Holmes and render your verdict to the class. Be prepared to defend your decision.
2. With a partner, create a series of letters written between David and Pat while David is in prison. Read your letters to the class.
3. Who would you cast in a new television production of *Survival*? Be prepared to defend your casting decisions.

The Play as Literature: Motivation

Actors in the movies often ask the director, "What's my motivation in this scene?" "Why am I saying these words?" they seem to ask. "What reason do I have for behaving the way I am asked to?"

Questions about motivation are very important in literature and drama. Motivation should account for all the character says, feels, does, and fails to do. It is the result of a combination of the character's situation in life as well as his or her personality.

In the play you are about to read, the playwright, Kikuchi Kan, has seen to it that each character has his or her own unique motivation.

The Play as Theatre: Voice

An actor's voice—the pitch, speed, rhythm, accents, and clarity of his or her speech—is crucial in bringing a character to life for an audience. It is important when trying to develop an idea for a character's voice that you ask questions about the character. "What clues do the character's words give to the way he or she might speak?" "What instructions does the playwright give about how the character speaks?" "Do other characters mention this character's voice or way of speaking?" Once you have gathered all the information you can about a character's voice, you can begin to investigate how voice captures a character's emotions. Then you can think about how your own voice might be made to suit a certain character.

As you read *Madman on the Roof*, imagine the voice of the Priestess as she assumes the persona of the god Kompira.

WARM UP!

Practice motivation by analyzing the personalities and situations of the characters below. Then write a short dialogue for them. The characters, Jo and Ralph, are stuck in an elevator together.

- Jo is a spoiled but pleasant sixteen-year-old who has just failed her driving exam for the third time.
- Ralph is a shy but honest forty-year-old professor of English who has just had his novel rejected by yet another publisher.

MADMAN ON THE ROOF

by Kikuchi Kan

Setting	Characters	Time
A small island in the Inland Sea	**KATSUSHIMA YOSHITARO,** The Madman, twenty-four years of age **KATSUSHIMA SUEJIRO,** His Brother, a seventeen-year-old high school student **KATSUSHIMA GISUKE,** Their Father **KATSUSHIMA OYOSHI,** Their Mother **TOSAKU,** A Neighbor **KICHIJI, A MANSERVANT,** twenty years of age **A PRIESTESS,** about fifty years of age	1900

*T*he stage setting represents the back yard of the KATSUSHIMAS, *who are the richest family on the island. A bamboo fence prevents one from seeing more of the house than the high roof, which stands out sharply against the rich, greenish sky of the southern island summer. At the left of the stage one can catch a glimpse of the sea shining in the sunlight.*

YOSHITARO, *the elder son of the family, is sitting astride the ridge of the roof and is looking out over the sea.*

GISUKE (*speaking from within the house*). Yoshi is sitting on the roof again. He'll get a sunstroke—the sun's so terribly hot. (*Coming out*) Kichiji!— Where is Kichiji?

KICHIJI (*appearing from the right*). Yes! What do you want?

GISUKE. Bring Yoshitaro down. He has nothing on, up there in the hot sun. He'll get a sun stroke. How did he get up there, anyway? From the barn? Didn't you put wire around the barn roof as I told you to the other day?

KICHIJI. Yes. I did exactly as you told me.

GISUKE (*coming through the gate to the center of the stage and looking up to the roof*). I don't see how he can stand it, sitting on that hot slate roof. (*He calls.*) Yoshitaro! You'd better come down. If you stay up there you'll get a sunstroke and maybe die.

KICHIJI. Young master! Come on down. You'll get sick if you stay there.

GISUKE. Yoshi! Come down quick! What are you doing up there, anyway? Come down, I say! (*He calls loudly.*) Yoshi!

YOSHITARO (*indifferently*). Wha-a-at?

GISUKE. No "whats"! Come down right away. If you don't come down, I'll get after you with a stick.

YOSHITARO (*protesting like a spoiled child*). No, I don't want to. There's something wonderful. The priest of the god Kompira is dancing in the clouds. Dancing with an angel in pink robes. They're calling to me to come. *(Crying out ecstatically)* Wait! I'm coming!

GISUKE. If you talk like that, you'll fall just as you did once before. You're already crippled and insane—what will you do next to worry your parents? Come down, you fool!

KICHIJI. Master, don't get so angry. The young master will not obey you. You should get some fried bean cake; when he sees it, he will come down, because he likes it.

GISUKE. No, you had better get the stick after him. Don't be afraid to give him a good shaking up.

KICHIJI. That's too cruel. The young master doesn't understand anything. He's under the influence of evil spirits.

GISUKE. We may have to put bamboo guards on the roof to keep him down from there.

KICHIJI. Whatever you do won't keep him down. Why, he climbed the roof of the Honzen Temple without even a ladder; a low roof like this one is the easiest thing in the world for him. I tell you, it's the evil spirits that make him climb. Nothing can stop him.

GISUKE. You may be right, but he worries me to death. If we could only keep him in the house, it wouldn't be so bad, even though he is crazy; but he's always climbing up to high places. Suejiro says that everybody as far as Takamatsu knows about Yoshitaro the Madman.

KICHIJI. People on the island all say he's under the influence of a fox spirit, but I don't believe that. I never heard of a fox climbing trees.

GISUKE. You're right. I think I know the real reason. About the time Yoshitaro was born, I bought a very expensive imported rifle, and I shot every monkey on the island. I believe a monkey spirit is now working in him.

KICHIJI. That's just what I think. Otherwise, how could he climb trees so well? He can climb anything without a ladder. Even Saku, who's a professional climber, admits that he's no match for Yoshitaro.

GISUKE *(with a bitter laugh)*. Don't joke about it! It's no laughing matter having a son who is always climbing on the roof. *(Calling again)* Yoshitaro, come down! Yoshitaro!—When he's up there on the roof, he doesn't hear me at all—he's so engrossed. I cut down all the trees around the house so he couldn't climb them, but there's nothing I can do about the roof.

KICHIJI. When I was a boy, I remember there was a gingko tree in front of the gate.

GISUKE. Yes, that was one of the biggest trees on the island. One day Yoshitaro climbed clear to the top. He sat out on a branch, at least ninety feet above the ground, dreaming away as usual. My wife and I never expected him to get down alive, but after a while, down he slid. We were all too astonished to speak.

KICHIJI. That was certainly a miracle.

GISUKE. That's why I say it's a monkey spirit that's working in him. *(He calls again.)* Yoshi! Come down! *(Dropping his voice)* Kichiji, you'd better go up and fetch him.

KICHIJI. But when anyone else climbs up there, the young master gets angry.

GISUKE. Never mind his getting angry. Pull him down.

KICHIJI. Yes, master.

(KICHIJI goes out after the ladder. TOSAKU, the neighbor, enters.)

TOSAKU. Good day, sir.

GISUKE. Good day. Fine weather. Catch anything with the nets you put out yesterday?

TOSAKU. No, not much. The season's over.

GISUKE. Maybe it is too late now.

TOSAKU *(looking up at YOSHITARO)*. Your son's on the roof again.

GISUKE. Yes, as usual. I don't like it, but when I keep him locked in a room, he's like a fish out of water. Then, when I take pity on him and let him out, back he goes up on the roof.

TOSAKU. But after all, he doesn't bother anybody.

GISUKE. He bothers us. We feel so ashamed when he climbs up there and shouts.

TOSAKU. But your younger son, Suejiro, has a fine record at school. That must be some consolation for you.

GISUKE. Yes, he's a good student, and that is a consolation to me. If both of them were crazy, I don't know how I could go on living.

TOSAKU. By the way, a Priestess has just come to the island. How would you like to have her pray for your son?— That's really what I came to see you about.

GISUKE. We've tried prayers before, but it's never done any good.

TOSAKU. This Priestess believes in the god Kompira. She works all kinds of miracles. People say the god inspires her, and that's why her prayers have more effect than those of ordinary priests. Why don't you try her once?

GISUKE. Well, we might. How much does she charge?

TOSAKU. She won't take any money unless the patient is cured. If he is cured, you pay her whatever you feel like.

GISUKE. Suejiro says he doesn't believe in prayers . . . But there's no harm in letting her try.

(KICHIJI enters carrying the ladder and disappears behind the fence.)

TOSAKU. I'll go and bring her here. In the meantime you get your son down off the roof.

GISUKE. Thanks for your trouble. *(After seeing that TOSAKU has gone, he calls again.)* Yoshi! Be a good boy and come down.

KICHIJI *(who is up on the roof by this time)*. Now then, young master, come down with me. If you stay up here any longer, you'll have a fever tonight.

YOSHITARO *(drawing away from KICHIJI as a Buddhist might from a heathen)*. Don't touch me! The angels are beckoning to me. You're not supposed to come here. What do you want?

KICHIJI. Don't talk nonsense! Please come down.

YOSHITARO. If you touch me, the demons will tear you apart. (KICHIJI *hurriedly catches* YOSHITARO *by the shoulder and pulls him to the ladder.* YOSHITARO *suddenly becomes submissive.*)

KICHIJI. Don't make any trouble now. If you do, you'll fall and hurt yourself.

GISUKE. Be careful!

(YOSHITARO *comes down to the center of the stage, followed by* KICHIJI. YOSHITARO *is lame in his right leg.*)

GISUKE. *(calling).* Oyoshi! Come out here a minute.

OYOSHI *(from within).* What is it?

GISUKE. I've sent for a Priestess.

OYOSHI *(coming out).* That may help. You never can tell what will.

GISUKE. Yoshitaro says he talks with the god Kompira. Well, this Priestess is a follower of Kompira, so she ought to be able to help him.

YOSHITARO *(looking uneasy).* Father! Why did you bring me down? There was a beautiful cloud of five colors rolling down to fetch me.

GISUKE. Idiot! Once before you said there was a five-colored cloud, and you jumped off the roof. That's the way you became a cripple. A Priestess of the god Kompira is coming here today to drive the evil spirit out of you, so don't you go back up on the roof.

(TOSAKU *enters, leading the* PRIESTESS. *She has a crafty face.*)

TOSAKU. This is the Priestess I spoke to you about.

GISUKE. Ah, good afternoon. I'm glad you've come—this boy is really a disgrace to the whole family.

PRIESTESS *(casually).* You needn't worry any more about him. I'll cure him at once with the god's help. *(Looking at* YOSHITARO*)* This is the one?

GISUKE. Yes. He's twenty-four years old, and the only thing he can do is climb up to high places.

PRIESTESS. How long has he been this way?

GISUKE. Ever since he was born. Even when he was a baby, he wanted to be climbing. When he was four or five years old, he climbed onto the low shrine, then onto the high shrine of Buddha, and finally onto a very high shelf. When he was seven, he began climbing trees. At fifteen he climbed to the tops of mountains and stayed there all day long. He says he talks with demons and with the gods. What do you think is the matter with him?

PRIESTESS. There's no doubt but that it's a spirit. I will pray for him. *(Looking at* YOSHITARO*)* Listen now! I am the messenger of the god Kompira. All that I say comes from the god.

YOSHITARO *(uneasily).* You say the god Kompira? Have you ever seen him?

PRIESTESS *(staring at him).* Don't say such sacrilegious[1] things! The god cannot be seen.

YOSHITARO *(exultantly).* I have seen him many times! He's an old man with

---

1. sacrilegious, showing disrespect for something held sacred

Madman on the Roof by Kikuchi Kan   **273**

white robes and a golden crown. He's my best friend.

PRIESTESS (*taken aback at this assertion, and speaking to* GISUKE). This is a fox spirit, all right, and a very extreme case. I will address the god.

(*She chants a prayer in a weird manner.* YOSHITARO, *held fast by* KICHIJI, *watches the* PRIESTESS *blankly. She works herself into a frenzy and falls to the ground in a faint. Presently she rises to her feet and looks about her strangely.*)

PRIESTESS (*in a changed voice*). I am the god Kompira!

(*All except* YOSHITARO *fall to their knees with exclamations of reverence.*)

PRIESTESS (*with affected*[2] *dignity*). The elder son of this family is under the influence of a fox spirit. Hang him up on the branch of a tree and purify him with the smoke of green pine needles. If you fail to do what I say, you will all be punished!

(*She faints again. There are more exclamations of astonishment.*)

PRIESTESS (*rising and looking about her as though unconscious of what has taken place*). What has happened? Did the god speak?

GISUKE. It was a miracle.

PRIESTESS. You must do at once whatever the god told you, or you'll be punished. I warn you for your own sake.

GISUKE (*hesitating somewhat*). Kichiji, go and get some green pine needles.

OYOSHI. No! It's too cruel, even if it is the god's command.

PRIESTESS. He will not suffer, only the fox spirit within him. The boy

himself will not suffer at all. Hurry! (*Looking fixedly at* YOSHITARO.) Did you hear the god's command? He told the spirit to leave your body before it hurt you.

YOSHITARO. That was not Kompira's voice. He wouldn't talk to a priestess like you.

PRIESTESS (*insulted*). I'll get even with you. Just wait! Don't talk back to the god like that, you horrid fox!

(KICHIJI *enters with an armful of green pine boughs.* OYOSHI *is frightened.*)

PRIESTESS. Respect the god or be punished!

(GISUKE *and* KICHIJI *reluctantly set fire to the pine needles, then bring* YOSHITARO *to the fire. He struggles against being held in the smoke.*)

YOSHITARO. Father! What are you doing to me? I don't like it! I don't like it!

PRIESTESS. That's not his own voice speaking. It's the fox within him. Only the fox is suffering.

OYOSHI. But it's cruel!

(GISUKE *and* KICHIJI *attempt to press* YOSHITARO's *face into the smoke. Suddenly* SUEJIRO's *voice is heard calling within the house, and presently he appears. He stands amazed at the scene before him.*)

SUEJIRO. What's happening here? What's the smoke for?

YOSHITARO (*coughing from the smoke and looking at his brother as at a savior*). Father and Kichiji are putting me in the smoke.

---

2. affected, pretending; acting in an artificial way to impress others

SUEJIRO (angrily). Father! What foolish thing are you doing now? Haven't I told you time and time again about this sort of business?

GISUKE. But the god inspired the miraculous Priestess . . .

SUEJIRO (interrupting). What nonsense is that? You do these insane things merely because he is so helpless.

(With a contemptuous[3] look at the PRIESTESS he stamps the fire out.)

PRIESTESS. Wait! That fire was made at the command of the god! (SUEJIRO sneeringly puts out the last spark.)

GISUKE (more courageously). Suejiro, I have no education, and you have, so I am always willing to listen to you. But this fire was made at the god's command, and you shouldn't have stamped on it.

SUEJIRO. Smoke won't cure him. People will laugh at you if they hear you've been trying to drive out a fox. All the gods in the country together couldn't even cure a cold. This Priestess is a fraud. All she wants is the money.

GISUKE. But the doctors can't cure him.

SUEJIRO. If the doctors can't, nobody can. I've told you before that he doesn't suffer. If he did, we'd have to do something for him. But as long as he can climb up on the roof, he is happy. Nobody in the whole country is as happy as he is— perhaps nobody in the world. Besides, if you cure him now, what can he do? He's twenty-four years old and he knows nothing, not even the alphabet. He's had no practical experience. If he were cured, he would be conscious of being crippled, and he'd be the most miserable man alive. Is that what you want to see? It's all because you want to make him normal. But wouldn't it be foolish to become normal merely to suffer? (Looking sidewise at the PRIESTESS) Tosaku, if you brought her here, you had better take her away.

PRIESTESS (angry and insulted). You disbelieve the oracle[4] of the god. You will be punished! (She starts her chant as before. She faints, rises, and speaks in a changed voice.) I am the great god Kompira! What the brother of the patient says springs from his own selfishness. He knows if his sick brother is cured, he'll get the family estate. Doubt not this oracle!

SUEJIRO (excitedly knocking the PRIESTESS down). That's a damned lie, you old fool.

(He kicks her.)

PRIESTESS (getting to her feet and resuming her ordinary voice). You've hurt me! You savage!

SUEJIRO. You fraud! You swindler!

TOSAKU (coming between them). Wait, young man! Don't get in such a frenzy.

SUEJIRO. (still excited). You liar! A woman like you can't understand brotherly love!

TOSAKU. We'll leave now. It was my mistake to have brought her.

---

3. contemptuous, showing scorn or dislike
4. oracle, someone said to be able to communicate with a god

GISUKE (giving TOSAKU some money). I hope you'll excuse him. He's young and has such a temper.

PRIESTESS. You kicked me when I was inspired by the god. You'll be lucky to survive until tonight.

SUEJIRO. Liar!

OYOSHI (soothing SUEJIRO). Be still now. (To the PRIESTESS) I'm sorry this has happened.

PRIESTESS (leaving with TOSAKU). The foot you kicked me with will rot off!

(The PRIESTESS and TOSAKU go out.)

GISUKE (to SUEJIRO). Aren't you afraid of being punished for what you've done?

SUEJIRO. A god never inspires a woman like that old swindler. She lies about everything.

OYOSHI. I suspected her from the very first. She wouldn't do such cruel things if a real god inspired her.

GISUKE (without any insistence). Maybe so. But, Suejiro, your brother will be a burden to you all your life.

SUEJIRO. It will be no burden at all. When I become successful, I'll build a tower for him on top of a mountain.

GISUKE (suddenly). But where's Yoshitaro gone?

KICHIJI (pointing at the roof). He's up there.

GISUKE (having to smile). As usual.

(During the preceding excitement, YOSHITARO has slipped away and climbed back up on the roof. The four persons below look at each other and smile.)

SUEJIRO. A normal person would be angry with you for having put him in the smoke, but you see, he's forgotten everything. (He calls.) Yoshitaro!

YOSHITARO (For all his madness, there is affection for his brother.) Suejiro! I asked Kompira, and he says he doesn't know her!

SUEJIRO (smiling). You're right. The god will inspire you, not a priestess like her.

(Through a rift in the clouds, the golden light of the sunset strikes the roof.)

SUEJIRO (exclaiming). What a beautiful sunset!

YOSHITARO (his face lighted by the sun's reflection). Suejiro, look! Can't you see a golden palace in that cloud over there? There! Can't you see? Just look! How beautiful!

SUEJIRO (as he feels the sorrow of sanity). Yes, I see. I see it, too. Wonderful.

YOSHITARO (filled with joy). There! I hear music coming from the palace. Flutes, what I love best of all. Isn't it beautiful?

(The parents have gone into the house. The mad brother on the roof and the sane brother on the ground remain looking at the golden sunset.)

MADMAN ON THE ROOF

Reader Response

1. How do you think you would describe this day if you were Yoshitaro? Share your description with the class.
2. Think of another title for this play. Explain why this title would be suitable.
3. List each character and describe the kind of voice you believe each would have.
4. To better understand Gisuke's motivation, write three questions concerning his actions throughout the play.
5. Draw your concept of the set for *Madman on the Roof.*

About Society and the Mentally Ill

The mentally ill have had a troubled place in society. In seventeenth century Japan, they were often left to their own devices—to wander off and starve or die of exposure. In eighteenth century England they were herded into dark, unclean asylums with little care and no attempt at cure. In the United States from the 1920's through the 1940's, shock therapy and operations on the brain were performed on mental patients—sometimes inappropriately and often to no avail. Today research is being done throughout the world to isolate a chemical and/or genetic predisposition for mental illness. Drug therapy is now the most common treatment.

CREATING AND PERFORMING

1. Each character in the play has his or her own unique perspective regarding Yoshitaro. Choose one character and write a monologue entitled, "Yoshitaro As I See Him."
2. Think about how Yoshitaro would move and speak. Practice a scene as Yoshitaro.
3. Pick two characters and say a few of their lines using different voices. Share your voices with the class.

Before Reading

Lost in Yonkers

The Play as Literature: Tone

In the same way an artist's brushstrokes give a painting depth and texture, an author's tone shapes and colors a piece of writing. The tone of a work reveals the author's attitudes about the subject as well as his or her feelings toward the audience.

Tone can take many forms—among them serious, playful, solemn, ironic, intimate, and touching. Neil Simon, author of *Lost in Yonkers,* is best known for humorous, lighthearted plays full of colorful, interesting characters. While he does not forsake creating heartwarming and amusing characters in this play, his tone here is often somber. (See p. 329 for more about Neil Simon.)

The Play as Theatre: Listening and Reacting

The dramatic interaction between actors in a play is what holds the presentation together. An actor's life on stage is one of action and reaction. Being a good speaker is, of course, a prerequisite when one is performing, but being a good listener is equally important. By listening consciously, alertly, and creatively, an actor can then react in the most appropriate way. And reaction is the key to a good performance.

When you act, be alert to any cues, verbal or physical, that another actor is giving. Your own vocal responses and movement should then offer an honest response to his or her words.

As you read *Lost in Yonkers* be aware of how each actor in the play would react physically and verbally to the other actors' comments.

Warm Up!

Look at the characters listed below. Assume a position, or pose, that reflects each character's personality. Share your poses with the class.

- an embarrassed teenager
- a woman killing a bug
- a child telling about a dream
- a man diapering a baby

Lost in Yonkers

by Neil Simon

Act One
Scene 1

We are in an apartment that sits just above "Kurnitz's Kandy Store." It consists of a living room, dining room, small kitchen, one bathroom, and two bedrooms. The entrance door leads from downstairs directly to the candy store.

It's about six-thirty in the evening on a hot, sultry day in August. It's still quite light outside. A fan blows in the living room.

Two young boys are in the living room. One, ARTHUR KURNITZ, about thirteen and a half, sits on an old armchair, looking apprehensive. He is wearing an old woolen suit, his only one, with knickered pants, a shirt, tie, long socks, and brown shoes.

The other boy is his brother, JAY KURNTIZ, not quite sixteen. He sits on the sofa, in a suit as well, but with long pants, shirt, tie, and shiny black shoes. He looks more sullen and angry than apprehensive.

ARTY keeps wiping his sweaty brow with his handkerchief.

JAY. I hate coming here, don't you?

ARTY (in front of fan). It's hot. I'm so hot.

JAY. I'd hate coming here if I was cool. Pop doesn't even like to come and it's his own mother . . . I was so afraid of her when I was a kid. She'd come out of that door with a limp and a cane and look like she was going to kill you. When I was five, I drew a picture of her and called it "Frankenstein's Grandma."

ARTY. Did she ever see it?

JAY. If she did, you'd be an only child today. Pop said she could swing her cane so fast, she could have been one of the greatest golfers in the world.

ARTY. All I remember was, I hated kissing her. It felt like putting your lips on a wrinkled ice cube.

JAY. Yeah, she's cold alright. She was the only one at Mom's funeral who didn't cry . . . I wonder what Pop's talking to her so long for.

ARTY. Because she's deaf in one ear, isn't she?

JAY. Yeah . . . Did you ever notice there's something wrong with *everyone* on Pop's side of the family? Mom used to tell me that.

ARTY. She didn't tell me. Like who?

JAY. Like all of them. Like Aunt

Bella . . . She's a little—*(Points to his head)*—you know—closed for repairs.

ARTY. I don't care. I like her. Nicer than "hot house" Grandma.

JAY. I didn't say she wasn't nice. But she's got marbles rolling around up there . . . Mom said she got that way because when she was a kid, Grandma kept hitting her in the head every time she did something stupid . . . which only made her stupider.

ARTY *(He lies down on the floor, in front of the sofa.)* She wasn't stupid at making great ice cream sodas.

JAY. Hooray! Wonderful! She's thirty-five years old and she can make ice cream sodas. They don't give you a high school diploma for getting the cherry on top of the whipped cream.

ARTY. She went to high school?

JAY. A little. She missed the first year because she couldn't find it.

(The bedroom door opens. Their father, EDDIE KURNITZ, *about forty-one, steps out into the room. He wears a suit and tie and seems hot and nervous. He wipes his brow with a hanky.)*

EDDIE. You kids alright?

JAY. Yeah, Pop. Fine.

EDDIE. I'll be through talking to Grandma in a few minutes. *(To* ARTY*)* What are you lying on the floor? Don't do that, Arty. You'll crease your pants. You want Grandma to see you with creased pants?

(He goes back in and closes the door.)

ARTY *(stands)*. What's he want me to do, carry an iron with me?

JAY. He's afraid of her the same as Aunt Bella. Like Aunt Bella couldn't count so good, so instead of two scoops of ice cream in a soda, she'd put in three or four. For the same price. And if Grandma saw it, Whacko! Another couple of IQ points gone. *(He picks up a photo from behind the sofa.)* Here, look at this. Aunt Gert when she was a kid! See how her head is down? Probably ducking. The old cane was coming at her . . . You don't think Aunt Gert's a little coconuts too?

ARTY. No. She's just sick. She's got bad lungs or something.

JAY. Bad lungs, my eye. She can't talk right. She says the first half of a sentence breathing out and the second half sucking in. You've seen it.

ARTY. Do it for me.

JAY. I don't want to.

ARTY. Come on, do it.

JAY. No, I don't want to.

ARTY. Do it!

JAY *(Imitating* AUNT GERT. *He breathes out.)* "Oh, hello, Jay, how are you? And how is your father? And—*(Then talks as he sucks in breath)*—how is your little brother, Arty?"

ARTY *(laughs)*. I love it! I love when you do that.

JAY. I once saw her try to blow out a candle and halfway there she sucked it back on.

ARTY. You didn't.

JAY. With these two eyes. Mom says she talks that way because she was so afraid of Grandma. She never allowed her kids to cry.

ARTY. Never?

JAY. Never. Well, if you're growing up here like Aunt Gert and you're not allowed to cry, you're going to end up sucking in the last half of your sentences.

(EDDIE *comes back in.*)

EDDIE. Grandma's worried about the doilies. Don't lean your head back on the doilies. It gets grease on them. She just had them laundered.

(*He goes back in.*)

ARTY (*to* JAY). You mean only people who just had a shampoo can sit here?

JAY. And what about Uncle Louie? You know what *he* is, don't you?

ARTY. Yeah. A gangster. You believe that?

JAY. You bet. They say he's some big mobster's henchman.

ARTY. You mean he's got a bad back?

JAY. Not a hunchback. A *henchman!* . . . And real tough. He's a bagman.

ARTY. What do you mean, a bagman? He puts people in bags?

JAY. Not people. Money. *Hot* money. He collects bags of it from one guy and delivers it to the mob . . . (ARTY *rises and crosses to the window.*) Listen, I'm not going to tell you any more because he could walk right in on us. They say he comes back here to sleep every once in a while.

ARTY (*Looking out the window*). Hey! There's Aunt Bella . . .

JAY. Is she coming up?

ARTY. No. She's walking past the house.

JAY. I'll bet she's lost again. (*He looks out the window, then calls down.*) Aunt Bella? . . . Hi! . . . It's Jay and Arty . . . Up here. (*He waves to her.*) That's right. Up here . . . Here she comes. (*They walk away from the window.*) She ought to wear a compass or something.

(*The bedroom door opens.* EDDIE *comes out again.*)

EDDIE. Will you keep your voices down. Grandma said, "What are they yelling for?"

JAY. We were calling down to Aunt Bella. She's on her way up.

ARTY. Can I take my jacket off?

EDDIE. After Grandma sees you. And no ice cream sodas from Aunt Bella. Even if she asks you. I don't want to get Grandma upset now. Fix the doilies.

JAY. Is she alright?

EDDIE. Her back is bothering her. When Aunt Bella comes in, tell her Momma wants a back rub . . . Comb your hair, Arty, and don't make a mess.

(EDDIE *goes back in. We hear a knock on the front door.*)

BELLA (*offstage*). Jay? Arty? It's me. Aunt Bella. Can I come in?

JAY. Guess who forgot how to open a door? . . .

JAY *opens the door.* BELLA KURNITZ, *in her mid-thirties, stands there. Although she's a mess at dressing—nothing matches at all— she is neat and sweet and pretty, if looking a little older than her age. She's as warm and congenial as she is emotionally arrested.*

BELLA *(smiles).* I forgot my key.

JAY. How'd you get in downstairs?

BELLA. I used my spare key. I'm glad you called me. I walked right by the house, didn't I? Sometimes I day-dream so much, I think I should carry an alarm clock . . . Oh, God, I'm so happy to see you. Arty! Jay! My two favorite cousins.

JAY. Aren't we your nephews?

BELLA. Of course you are. My cousins, my nephews, my boys. Come here, give your Aunt Bella a kiss. *(She puts down her purse, pulls* JAY *and* ARTY *into her arms, and kisses them both.)* Let me look at you. You both got so much bigger. You're growing up so fast, it almost makes me cry . . . Where's your father? I haven't seen your father in so long . . . *(She calls out.)* Eddie! It's Bella . . . Is he here?

ARTY. He's in there, talking to Grandma.

BELLA *(suddenly nervous).* Oh, I'd better not disturb them . . . Did she ask for me?

JAY. Pop said her back was hurting. She wanted you to give her a back rub when you came in?

BELLA. Oh. Did you tell her I was here?

JAY. No. You just came in.

BELLA. Did you tell her where I went?

JAY. We didn't know where you went.

BELLA. Well, let's not tell her I'm here yet. Then we won't be able to visit. *(She takes off her sweater.)* Oh, you're both getting so handsome.

JAY. Thank you.

ARTY. Thank you, Aunt Bella.

BELLA. I bet I look much older to you two. Do I? The truth. Tell me.

JAY. I don't think so.

ARTY. No.

BELLA. I was hoping you'd say that. I'm thirty-five. And I don't even look it, do I?

JAY. No.

ARTY. Not to me.

BELLA. And how old are you boys now? About twenty?

ARTY. I'm thirteen and a half.

JAY. I'm fifteen and a half.

BELLA. Well, that adds up to about thirty-five. So we could be brother and sisters. Isn't that wonderful?

JAY. Yeah.

BELLA. Yeah . . . I just got back from the movies. I had the most wonder-ful time. I wish I knew you were here, we all could have gone.

JAY. What did you see?

BELLA. I don't know. I couldn't find the theater I was looking for, so I went to the one I found. But it was better than the picture I wanted to see. It was with Bette Davis and George Brent . . . Maybe we could all go again next week, if I can find the wrong theater again.

ARTY. Sure. I'd love to.

JAY. Except we won't be here next week. We're going to the Yankee game with Pop.

BELLA. Oh, well, you do that. Boys like baseball much better than love sto-ries . . . Why don't you take your jackets off, you two? Look at you both perspiring.

ARTY. We're fine. We're cool in here with the fan.

Lost in Yonkers by Neil Simon   **283**

BELLA. That fan doesn't cool anything off. It just makes the hot air go faster . . . They had air-conditioning at the movie house. I was actually cold. I felt so happy for the actors to be in an air-conditioned theater.

JAY (*He looks at* ARTY, *then at* BELLA.) I don't think the actors feel it. They're just pictures on the screen.

BELLA. Well, I know that, silly. I meant they'd be happy to know that people who were watching their movies were nice and cool so we enjoyed the movie better.

JAY. Oh. Right. I bet they would.

BELLA. I bet I know what would make you two cool in a second. How about a big ice cream soda deluxe? With everything in it? Look at your faces lighting up. Come on. I'll make it for you downstairs.

JAY. I think we have to wait here. Pop'll be out in a second and he wants us to see Grandma.

BELLA. Well, I'll bring them up here. That's no trouble. What kind? Chocolate? Vanilla? Butter Pecan? What's your favorite, Arty?

ARTY. All of them.

BELLA. I can make that. With three different kinds of ice cream. I used to make one with four different kinds. They were selling like crazy, but we lost a fortune . . . How long ago did she ask for me?

JAY. Grandma? A couple of minutes ago.

BELLA. Did you tell her I was here?

JAY. No, we told Pop we saw you from the window. But maybe he didn't say

anything to her.

BELLA. It doesn't make any difference. She heard my footsteps coming up the stairs.

ARTY. How? Isn't she partly deaf?

BELLA. Oh, sure. But the other part hears perfectly . . . What about a small sundae? Chocolate ice cream with hot-fudge sauce and some whipped cream and chopped walnuts? Are you going to say no to that, Arthur? I bet you can't. Say no. Let me hear you.

ARTY (*He looks at* JAY.) It sounds like just a small one.

JAY (*to* BELLA). He can't. We're having dinner soon. It's just that Pop told us to wait.

BELLA. Oh, your father. He never takes anything from anybody. I couldn't even give your mother a cup of coffee . . . Did you know that? . . . Where is she, anyway?

(JAY *looks confused.*)

JAY. She's dead. Mom is dead.

BELLA (*She looks confused a moment.*) Yes. I know . . . I mean where is she buried?

JAY. At Mount Israel Cemetery in the Bronx. You were at the funeral. Remember?

BELLA. You mean the first time?

JAY. What do you mean, the first time?

BELLA. When I came in the car. Not the bus.

ARTY. The bus?

BELLA (*thinks*). No. No. I'm thinking of someone else. Sometimes my mind wanders. The kids in school used to say, "Hey, Bella. Lost and Found called and said, 'Come get your brains.' "... (She laughs.)... but I didn't think that was funny. (The boys nod.) I bet you miss Mom a lot, don't you? Don't you, Arty?

ARTY. Yeah. A lot.

BELLA. She was a lot like your father. Very independent. Stuck to her own family mostly. (She lowers her voice.) She didn't get along too well with your grandmother. Nobody does. My sister, Gert, was once engaged to a man. She brought him over to meet Grandma. The next day he moved to Boston.

JAY. That's too bad.

BELLA. Don't tell Grandma I said that.

ARTY. I won't.

BELLA. What?

ARTY. I won't.

BELLA. You're both so shy. I used to be shy. Grandma didn't like me to talk too much ... I had a lot of friends, but I didn't talk to them ... It's a shame your mother couldn't have had more children ... She didn't, did she?

JAY. No.

BELLA. No ... Because it would be easier for you now that she's gone. Big families are important when you have trouble in your life. We were a big family ... Me and your father and Louie and Gert ... That was before Rose and Aaron died ... Rose was just a baby but Aaron was almost twelve so I didn't know Rose as well as Aaron ... You never knew them, did you?

JAY. I don't think we were born yet.

BELLA. No. I don't think so ... My father died before I was born. But I wasn't sad about that.

JAY. That's good.

BELLA. Because I loved him so much. Did you know you could love somebody who died before you were born?

JAY. I guess so.

BELLA. Because I knew he would have taken care of me ... Like your father takes care of you. You know what I mean?

JAY. I think so.

BELLA. So what about that sundae? It's going to sit down there melting on the counter if I make it and you don't eat it ... Last time I'm asking, Arthur. Yes or no?

ARTY. I'd ... I'd like to ... (He looks at JAY who shakes his head "No.") ... Maybe later.

BELLA (snaps coldly, angrily). NO! NOT LATER!! IT'S TOO LATE NOW!!! ... I'm not asking you again. You hurt my feelings, the both of you. You tell your father to teach you better manners before I'm ever nice to you again ... I know you miss your mother but that doesn't mean you can be disrespectful to me ... I always liked your mother whether she took coffee from me or not. And you can tell that to your father, the both of you. You hear me? ... I'm sick of it.

(She goes into the bathroom and slams the door hard. JAY and ARTY just look at each other.)

JAY. You see why I don't like to come here too much?

(The bedroom door opens, and a bedraggled EDDIE *comes out and looks around.)*

EDDIE. Where's Aunt Bella? I thought I just heard her.

JAY. She's in the bathroom.

EDDIE. I heard the door slam. Did you say anything to upset her?

JAY. Yeah. Everything.

ARTY. Is it time to go yet, Pop?

EDDIE. We'll go when I tell you. You haven't even seen your grandmother. Stop rushing me. You just got here, didn't you?

ARTY. It's okay. Talk as long as you want, Pop.

EDDIE. And then the three of us have to talk. You, me, and Arty. *(He knocks on the bathroom door.)* Bella! It's Eddie. Momma wants to see you. It's her back again . . . Bella? *(No answer. To the boys.)* Is she alright?

JAY. How do you know when she's alright?

EDDIE. Hey! No remarks about Aunt Bella, you hear me? She loves you boys. Always has. She'd do anything for you two. So just sit there and be quiet. God, my head is splitting.

(He goes back into the bedroom and closes the door.

The bathroom door opens and BELLA *steps out, holding a towel and oil.)*

BELLA. Was that your father banging on the door just now?

JAY. Yes.

BELLA. Is he angry with me?

JAY. With you? No.

BELLA. I hope not. Do I look better?

ARTY. Better than when?

BELLA. Than before. When you said I wasn't looking well.

ARTY. I didn't say that.

BELLA. Then who said it? . . . Jay?

ARTY. Maybe. Did you say it, Jay?

JAY. Nobody said anything.

BELLA. Oh. I know. It was Grandma. She didn't like the way I looked today. She hates this dress . . . I made it myself.

ARTY. Really?

BELLA *(She nods.)* It took me almost a year.

JAY. . . . Grandma wants you, Aunt Bella.

BELLA. Oh, yeah . . . As soon as I finish Momma's rub, I'll start dinner . . . Are you boys hungry?

ARTY. I don't know. Jay knows. Tell her, Jay.

JAY. I'm not so sure we're staying for dinner.

BELLA. Of course you are. You think I'd let you go all the way home without dinner? . . . Are you going to say no to me again, Arty?

ARTY *(quickly).* I'm not. I'm eating. I'm hungry. No matter what Jay does. I'm eating.

BELLA. Well, we're all eating. It's Sunday. The family always eats together on Sunday. And you think about what you want for dessert, Arty, because whatever you want is what you're going to get . . . Start thinking now.

ARTY. I started! I started! I want a big ice cream soda with a sundae with whipped cream and hot-fudge sauce. Is that okay?

BELLA. Sounds perfect to me. And don't give any to Jay. He missed the deadline.

(She puts her nose up to JAY *and goes into* GRANDMA'*s room.)*

ARTY *(to* JAY*).* Don't be mad. I had to say it. I was afraid she was going to strangle me with the towel.

JAY. It's up to Pop. We'll see what Pop says.

*(*ARTY *lies on the sofa. The bedroom door opens.* EDDIE *comes out. He looks strained. He crosses to the open window and takes a deep breath of air.)*

EDDIE. Jay! Get me a glass of water, please.

JAY. Right, Pop.

(He rushes into the kitchen.)

EDDIE. It must be over a hundred in here. *(He looks at* ARTY.*)* Get your shoes off the sofa, what's wrong with you?

ARTY *(moves his shoes).* I'm feeling kind of faint.

EDDIE. What do you mean, faint? Kids your age don't faint.

ARTY. Maybe I'm getting older.

JAY *(He comes in with the glass.)* Here you go, Pop. Nice and cool.

EDDIE. Don't spill it on the rug. *(He takes the glass and drinks, then puts the glass down.)* Alright . . . Time to talk. Sit down, Jay. Next to Arty. *(*JAY *sits on the sofa next to* ARTY. EDDIE *sits on the stool. He is thinking about how to start.)*

I er . . . I wanted to tell you boys—

(And suddenly he breaks and tears come to his eyes. He quickly tries to stifle it. He wipes his eyes. He goes to the window for some air.)

ARTY. Is anything the matter, Po—

EDDIE. It's so damn hot in here, isn't it? . . . So, I just had a talk inside with your grandmother . . . Because I've had a problem . . . When your mother and I had a problem, we always tried to keep it from you boys because we didn't want to worry you . . . The first year she was sick, I never even told you about it . . . Well, you can't keep cancer a secret forever . . . You knew without me telling you, didn't you, Jay?

JAY. Yes, Pop.

EDDIE. I did everything I could. The best doctors, the best hospital I could get into . . . She had a nice room, didn't she? Semiprivate, no wards or anything . . . I paid the nurse extra to put her next to the window. She loved looking at that tree every day . . . It was worth whatever it cost.

JAY. It was a great tree, Pop.

EDDIE. Do you remember how long she was in that hospital? Remember, Arty?

ARTY. A long time.

EDDIE. Almost four months . . . She wanted to go home because of the money but I knew she wouldn't get the same care at home. Even with a private nurse, they don't always show up. And with this war, you're lucky to find one.

JAY. I know, Pop.

EDDIE. We're not rich people, boys. I know that doesn't come as a surprise to you . . . but I'm going to tell you something now I hoped I'd never have to tell you in my life . . . The doctors, the hospital, cost me everything I had . . . and everything I didn't have . . . And finally it cost me everything I was *going* to have . . . I was broke and I went into debt . . . into hock . . . Only I didn't have anything left to hock . . . So I went to a man . . . a Shylock, they call him . . . a loan shark . . . a moneylender . . . I couldn't go to a bank because they don't let you put up heartbreak and pain as collateral . . . You know what collateral is, Arty? . . . If you want to borrow ten dollars, you have to give them something to hold that's worth eleven dollars . . . That's for their interest . . . A Shylock doesn't need collateral . . . His collateral is your desperation . . . So he gives you his money . . . And he's got a clock. And when you get your money, the clock starts . . . And what it keeps time of is your promise . . . If you keep your promise, he turns off the clock . . . and if not, it keeps ticking . . . and after a while, your heart starts ticking louder than his clock . . . This man becomes a cloud that darkens your life wherever you go . . . Understand something. This man kept your mother alive . . . It kept that tree outside her window . . . It was his painkillers that made her last days bearable . . . And for that I'm grateful . . . Jay! Remember what I taught you about taking things from people?

JAY *(He nods.)* Never take because you'll always be obligated.

EDDIE. So you never take for yourself . . . But for someone you love, there comes a time when you have no choice . . . There's a man in New York I owe a lot of money to . . . nine thousand dollars . . . I don't have nine thousand dollars . . . I could work and save four more years and I won't have nine thousand dollars . . . He wants his money this year. To his credit, I'll say one thing. He sent flowers to the funeral. No extra charge on my bill . . .

JAY. Pop—

EDDIE. Let me finish . . . There is no way I can pay this man back . . . So what'll he do? Kill me? . . . Maybe . . . If he kills me, he not only loses his money, it'll probably cost him again for the flowers for my funeral . . . Don't look worried. I'm not going to die . . . I wouldn't tell you all this if there wasn't a happy ending . . . I needed a miracle . . . And the miracle happened . . . This country went to war . . . A war between us and the Japanese and the Germans . . . And if my mother didn't come to this country thirty-five years ago, I could have been fighting for the other side . . . Except I don't think they're putting guns in the hands of Jews over there . . . And if I didn't marry your mother and have two children to support, I'd be fighting for this side . . . I'm too old. So neither side needs me and neither side wants me . . . Except the man with the ticking clock . . . Let me tell you something. I love this country. Because they took in the Jews. They took in the Irish, the Italians, and everyone else . . . Remember this. There's a lot of Germans in this country fighting for America, but there are no Americans over there fighting for Germany . . . I hate this war, and God forgive me for saying this, but it's going to save my life . . . There are jobs I can get now that I could never get before . . . And I got a job . . . I'm working for a company that sells scrap iron . . . I thought you threw scrap iron away. Now they're building ships with it . . . Without even the slightest idea of what I'm doing, I can make that nine thousand dollars in less than a year . . .

JAY. That's great, Pop.

EDDIE. Don't say it till I finish . . . The factories that I would sell to are in the South . . . Georgia, Kentucky, Louisiana, Texas, even New Mexico. Places that I never thought I'd see in my lifetime . . . I'd be gone about ten months . . . Living in trains, buses, hotels, any place I can find a room . . . We'd be free and clear and back together again in less than a year . . . Okay? . . . So now comes the question, where do you two live while I'm gone?

(There is a deafening silence as JAY *and* ARTY *turn and look at each other.)*

ARTY *(wiping his brow).* . . . God, it's so hot in here.

JAY. Please, Pop, don't make us live here . . . That's what you're thinking, isn't it?

EDDIE. I have no choice, Jay. I don't know where else to turn.

JAY *(to* EDDIE*).* Why can't we stay where we are?

EDDIE. I gave the apartment up. I told the landlady yesterday.

ARTY *(astonished).* You gave it up?

EDDIE. She raised the rent. *Every*body's looking to make money out of this war. And the truth is, by the end of the year, it'll be eleven thousand. While I'm away, the clock doesn't stop ticking.

JAY. Grandma wouldn't be happy with us. We're slobs. We leave everything on the floor. Arty's always breaking things.

ARTY *(to* EDDIE*).* Remember when I broke the good water pitcher? And the ink stains on the sofa. All mine! . . . I'm dangerous, Pop.

EDDIE. Listen to me, both of you. It took me an hour and a half to convince her. It's not that she doesn't like you. But she's old. She's set in her ways. And she's worried about people being around Bella.

ARTY. Me too.

EDDIE. She hasn't even said positively yet. She's thinking about it. She'll come out. She'll talk to you. She'll see how it goes. It's up to us to convince her that you two won't be any trouble . . . That's why I want you both looking so neat. Don't you see how important this is?

JAY. And what if she *did* take us in? Then you'd be obligated, Pop. Don't you think you have enough obligations now?

EDDIE. I'm not asking for myself. I'm asking for my boys. For my boys, I'll be obligated . . . There's nothing to discuss anymore . . . It's up to Grandma now . . . And it's up to you. *(He crosses to* GRANDMA's *bedroom door.)* I'll see if she's ready. *(He turns back to them.)* If she says no, I can't take this job. I can't pay back the man I gave my promise to . . . You're good kids, both of you. Just show Grandma what a terrific present she's getting to have you boys live with her . . . Fix your tie, Jay. Straighten your collar, Arty . . . Stand straight, both of you . . . *(They stand straight. He nods.)* That's my boys.

(He goes into GRANDMA's *room. The boys look at each other.)*

JAY. Oh, my God. What if Grandma says "Yes"?

ARTY. She won't. Because I'm going to break something. What's her favorite thing in this room?

JAY. You're not breaking anything. Because we have to stay here and save Pop's life.

ARTY. And what about *our* lives? We could grow up like Aunt Bella. I could be in the seventh grade for the next twenty years.

JAY. Listen, if you act like this when Grandma comes out, that's like putting a gun to Pop's head and pulling the trigger.

ARTY. Oh. So we stay here and get whacked in the head every time we cry . . . or suck candles back on like Aunt Gert. *(He sucks his breath in and says)* "Hello, Arty. How are you?"

JAY. *(He grabs* ARTY *by his shirt collar.)* One more word from you and I'll whack you, I swear to God. *(*ARTY *pulls away but* JAY *holds on . . . and* ARTY's *collar gets torn halfway off and dangles there.)* Oh, my God. It tore!

ARTY. Well, that's it. The war is over for us . . . I hope Pop bought the grave next to Mom.

JAY. *(looking in a drawer).* Jesus! It's all your damn fault . . . Look for a pin, maybe we could stick it back together.

ARTY. Right. I'm going to be looking in drawers when Grandma walks in. I'm sure she wants to adopt a couple of crooks.

(He rushes to JAY, *but the drawer slams shut and* JAY *howls in pain.)*

JAY. *(starting to cry).* Dammit! I hate you so much. I hate Mom for dying. I hate Pop for putting us in this spot. I hate Grandma for being such a rotten old lady. I hate everybody in the whole damn world.

(And the bedroom door opens and EDDIE *comes out with a smile.)*

EDDIE. You ready, boys? *(And then he looks at them.)* . . . What the hell is going on here? . . . What are you crying about? What happened to your collar?

(He quickly closes the bedroom door.)

ARTY. Nothing.

EDDIE. Don't tell me nothing. Were you fighting? Of course you were fighting, just look at you. I can't believe it. If I can't trust you for two minutes, how can I trust you for a year? . . . And do you think I would do this to my mother? To my sister,

Bella? . . . I knew this was a stupid idea in the first place. I never would have tried it if I wasn't so desperate . . . I'm ashamed of you. I'm ashamed of you both . . . Wait outside for me. Out in the street. I don't want to look at you . . . Go on, get out.

ARTY. We weren't fighting. It was an accident. I was trying to straighten my tie and I straightened it too tight.

JAY. I was crying about Mom. She'd be so sad to see you in such trouble . . . We really want to stay here. We like Yonkers. We were just praying that Grandma would *let* us stay.

ARTY. Gee, I hope she does . . . It looks like such a nice place to live.

EDDIE. Are you serious? Or are you just trying to lie your way out of this?

JAY. Serious. Very serious.

ARTY. It's the most serious we've been in our lives.

EDDIE. I hope so. For all our sakes . . . Alright. Fix yourself up. Tuck in your collar. Wipe your eyes . . . I'll get Grandma. *(The door opens and* BELLA *comes out. She rushes to the sofa and throws herself on it, sobbing.)* Oh, Jesus! Bella? . . . What's wrong? . . . What is it, Bella? (*She buries her face in a pillow like a five-year-old child.* ARTY *and* JAY *look at each other . . .* EDDIE *sits next to* BELLA *and puts his arm around her shoulder. To* BELLA, *softly.)* . . . Did Momma say something? . . . Was she angry with you? (BELLA *whispers in* EDDIE*'s ear.)* No, no, Bella. She does too love your back rubs, she told me that . . . She's just got a lot on her mind today. *(He looks at the boys disapprovingly, then back to* BELLA.*)* You alright now, sweetheart? (BELLA *whispers again to him.)* Yes, I know you're lonely . . . I know it's hard to be alone with her all the time . . . But, Bella, I have good news for you . . . Maybe you won't be alone anymore . . . You know who's going to stay here, Bella? If Momma says yes . . . Arthur and Jay . . . Wouldn't that be nice? . . . To have Arthur and Jay here? . . . They'd live here and spend time with you and you'd have someone to talk to at nights. (ARTY *and* JAY *look at each other.)* Would you like that, honey?

BELLA *(beams).* Yes.

EDDIE *(to* BELLA*).* Alright. Then give me a smile and a hug.

(BELLA *throws her arms around* EDDIE*'s neck.)*

BELLA. Don't go away, Eddie . . . Stay and live with us . . . I miss you so much . . . She's so mean sometimes.

EDDIE. No, she's not. She's just getting old . . . I can't stay, honey. I have to go away for a while. But the boys will be with you. They're looking forward to it . . . Look how happy they look. (ARTY *and* JAY *force two big smiles at her.)* . . . Would you like to lie down in your room for a while, Bella? Momma has to talk to the boys now.

BELLA *(grabs his hand).* No. I want to stay here with you.

EDDIE. It would be easier, I think, if Momma and the boys talked alone.

BELLA *(sternly).* I want to stay here with you.

Lost in Yonkers by Neil Simon   **291**

EDDIE. Ohh, God . . . Alright. You sit right there. But you be very quiet now, alright? . . . Just don't interrupt because we don't want to get Momma upset . . . Okay. Here we go.

(He crosses to the bedroom door, knocks, and goes in.

JAY and ARTY look at BELLA. She looks up at the ceiling.)

JAY. Er . . . Arty and I are really hoping it works out, Aunt Bella.

BELLA *(She puts her finger to her lips.)* Shhh. Mustn't interrupt.

JAY. Oh, yeah. Right.

(EDDIE comes out of the bedroom and arranges the boys to greet GRANDMA.)

EDDIE. Her back is killing her but she doesn't want me to help her. *(He calls in.)* Okay, Momma.

(There is a beat, as Momma is going to make her entrance when she wants.)

GRANDMA KURNITZ *enters slowly from the bedroom. She is a big woman, or, hopefully, gives that appearance. Not fat, but buxom, with a strong, erect body, despite her seventy-odd years. She has white hair pulled back in European style with buns. She carries a cane and walks with a slight dragging of one foot. She wears rimless glasses and has a pasty-white complexion. She wears a large-print dress of the period with a cameo brooch pinned on. Authority and discipline seem to be her overriding characteristics and she would command attention in a crowd. She speaks with few but carefully chosen words, with a clear German accent.*

She walks to the armchair, not looking at anybody, least of all the boys. Then she sits and looks at EDDIE.

GRANDMA. So?

(EDDIE motions with his head to the boys.)

JAY *(on cue).* Hello, Grandma.

ARTY. Hello, Grandma.

(EDDIE looks at them again and gives them another head signal. JAY steps up and kisses her quickly on her cheek and steps back. ARTY does the same and steps back. GRANDMA KUR-NITZ hardly reacts.)

EDDIE. I know you haven't seen the boys in a long time, Mom. They wanted to come, but with their mother sick so long, they felt they should spend as much time as they could with her . . . I bet they've grown since you've seen them, haven't they?

GRANDMA *(She looks at them, then points her cane at ARTY.)* Dis iss the little one?

EDDIE. Yes. Arthur. He's two years younger, right, Arty?

ARTY. Yes. I'm two years younger . . . than him.

GRANDMA *(She looks at JAY, points her cane at him.).* Dis one I remember more . . . Dis one looks like his mother.

JAY. Yes. A lot of people tell me that.

GRANDMA. Vot's wrong with your eyes?

JAY. My eyes? Oh. They're a little red. I got something in them and I scratched them too hard.

GRANDMA. You vere crying maybe?

JAY. Me? No. I never cry.

GRANDMA. Big boys shouldn't cry.

JAY. I know. I haven't cried in years. A couple of times when I was a baby.

EDDIE. Oh, they're strong kids, Ma. Both of them.

GRANDMA (looks at JAY). Yakob, heh?

JAY. Yes, but they call me Jay.

GRANDMA. No. I don't like Jay . . . Yakob iss a name.

JAY. Sure. Yakob is fine.

GRANDMA. And Arthur.

ARTY. Arthur. But they call me Arty.

GRANDMA. I don't call you Arty.

ARTY. Sure. I love Arthur. Like King Arthur.

GRANDMA. You go to school?

ARTY. Yeah.

GRANDMA. Vat?

ARTY. Yes. I go to the same school as Yakob.

GRANDMA. Vitch one iss da smart one?

(JAY and ARTY look at each other.)

EDDIE. They both do very well in school.

GRANDMA (She points her cane at EDDIE.) They'll tell me. (She looks at them.) Vitch one iss da smart one?

ARTY (pointing to JAY). Yakob is. He gets A's in everything. I'm better at sports.

GRANDMA. Shports?

ARTY. Baseball. Basketball. Football.

GRANDMA. You play in the mud? In the dirt? You come home with filthy shoes and make marks all over the floor?

ARTY. No. Never. I clean them off at the field. I bring a brush and polish and shine them up on a bench.

(He looks at EDDIE to see if he got away with that.)

GRANDMA. If the smart one iss smart, he'll make sure you do.

EDDIE. No, the boys are very neat. Even their mother said so.

(GRANDMA taps her cane a few times on the floor, like an announcement.)

GRANDMA. So tell me . . . vy do you vant to live with Grandma?

(The boys look at each other.)

ARTY. . . . Why don't you tell Grandma, Yakob?

(JAY glares at him.)

JAY. . . . Well . . . because . . . Pop has to go away. And we had to give up our apartment . . . and when Pop said we had the opportunity to live here with you—our only living grandmother . . . and our only living Aunt Bella . . . I thought that families should sort of stick together now that our country is at war with Germ—Japan . . . so we can all be together during times like this . . . and I also think that—no. That's all.

GRANDMA (nods). Hmm . . . And this is the smart one?

EDDIE. I thought he said that very well, Momma.

GRANDMA (She points her cane at ARTY.) And what about this King Artur? . . . Vy do you vant to live with Grandma?

ARTY (after looking at GRANDMA). Because we have no place else to go.

EDDIE. Arty!! . . . I think what Arty is trying to say, Momma—

GRANDMA (pointing her cane at EDDIE). No! . . . he knows vot he vants to say . . . (She looks at ARTY.) I tink maybe diss is da smart one.

EDDIE. He's always been very honest. But he's just a boy, Momma—

GRANDMA. So! You haff no place else to go. Dot's vy you vant to live vith Grandma . . . Alright . . . Alright . . . So now Grandma vill tell you vy she doesn't tink you should live vit her . . . Dis house is no place for boys. I'm an old woman. I don't like to talk. I don't like noise. I don't like people in my house. I had six children once, I don't need more again . . . Bella and I take care of the store six days a veek and on Sunday ve rest. Today is Sunday and I'm not resting . . . Bella is not—she's not goot vit people too long. A little bit yes, then she gets too excited . . . You understand vot I'm saying? . . . Vot vould you do here? There's no games in dis house. There's no toys in dis house. I don't like the radio after six o'clock. The news yes, dot's all . . . Ve go to sleep nine o'clock, ve get up five o'clock. I don't have friends. Bella don't have friends. You vould not be happy here. And unhappy boys I don't need.

EDDIE. Momma, can I just say something—?

GRANDMA (*She holds up her cane.*) I'll just say something . . . I think about dis inside. Because anger hass been in me for a long time . . . Vy should I do dis? . . . Vot do I owe your father? . . . Ven did he ever come around here after he married your mother? I never saw him . . . Because she turned him against me. His own mother . . . She didn't like me, I didn't like her. I'm not afraid to tell da truth either . . . I don't vish anybody's death. Maybe she vas a goot mother to you, may she rest in peace, to me she vas nothing . . . And your father was afraid of her. Dot's vy he stopped coming here. You're big boys now, how many times haff I seen you since you were born? Four, five times? . . . Dose are not grandchildren. Dose are strangers . . . And now he comes to me for help? . . . He cried in my bedroom. Not like a man, like a child he cried. He vas always dot vay . . . I buried a husband and two children und I didn't cry. I didn't haff time. Bella vas born vit scarlet fever and she didn't talk until she vas five years old, und I didn't cry . . . Your father's sister, Gertrude, can't talk vitout choking und I didn't cry . . . Und maybe one day, they'll find Louie dead in da street und I von't cry . . . Dot's how I vas raised. To be strong. Ven dey beat us vit sticks in Germany ven ve vere children, I didn't cry . . . You don't survive in dis vorld vitout being like steel. Your father vants you to grow up, first let *him* grow up . . . Ven he learns to be a father, like I learned to be a mother, den he'll be a man. Den he von't need my help . . . You think I'm cruel? You tink I'm a terrible person? Dot a grandmother should say tings like dis? I can see it in your faces vot you tink . . . Goot, it'll make you hard. It'll make you strong. Den you'll be able to take care of yourselves vitout anybody's help . . . So dot's my decision. Maybe one day you'll tank me for it. (*She gets up.*) Give da boys an ice cream cone, Bella. Den come inside and finish my legs.

(She starts for the bedroom. They all stand, stunned. BELLA, *who has remained seated, seems impervious to this.)*

EDDIE *(without anger).* . . . You're right, Momma. I am the weak one. I am the crybaby . . . Always was. When you wouldn't pick me up and hug me as a child, I cried . . . When my brother and sister died, I cried . . . And I still haven't stopped crying since Evelyn died . . . But you're wrong about one thing. She never turned me against you. She turned me towards her . . . To loving, to caring, to holding someone when they needed holding . . . I'm sorry about not bringing the boys out here more. Maybe the reason I didn't was because I was afraid they'd learn something here that I tried to forget . . . Maybe they just learned it today . . . I'm sorry I bothered you on your Sunday. I'm sorry I imposed on your rest. I'm sorry about what they did to you as a child in Berlin. I'm sure it was terrible. But this is Yonkers, Momma. I'm not angry at you for turning me and the boys down. I'm angry at myself for not knowing better . . . Take care of yourself, Momma . . . Never mind the ice cream cones, Bella. I used up all my obligations for this year. *(He crosses to the door.)* Come on, boys. We're going. (JAY *and* ARTY *are too dumbstruck to move, to have been in the middle of all this.)* I said let's go.

(They start for the door.)

BELLA. Arty? *(She gets up with a warm, sweet smile on her face.)* We'll have dinner another night . . . Why don't you and Jay go home and pack your things and I'll get your bed ready and make room in the closet for when you move in.

(The boys stop, look at EDDIE.*)*

EDDIE. Thank you, Bella . . . but Momma and I just decided it's not a good idea.

BELLA *(Still smiling, she begins to make up the sofa bed.)* And, Jay, you make a list of all the things you boys like for breakfast, and I'll make sure we have it . . . And don't forget your toothbrushes because we don't carry them in the store . . . And each of you bring something from your house that you really love, even if it's big, and we'll find someplace to put it.

GRANDMA. Dot's enough, Bella. Diss is not your business.

BELLA *(to the boys).* How about a picture of your mother? And we can put it right here on the table. It'll be the last thing you see at night and the first thing you see in the morning . . . It's going to be such fun with you both here . . . Momma's right. I do get so excited around people, but it makes me so happy.

GRANDMA. Bella! Nicht sprecken! Enough!! . . . They're going. Dot's the end of it.

BELLA *(quite calmly).* No, Momma. They're not going. They're staying. Because if you make them go, I'll go too . . . I know I've said that a thousand times, but this time I mean it . . . I could go to the Home. The Home would take me . . . You're always telling me that . . . And if I go, you'll be all alone . . . And you're afraid to be alone, Momma . . . Nobody else knows that but me . . . But you don't have to be, Momma. Because we'll all be together now . . . You and me and Jay and Arty . . . Won't that be fun, Momma?

(*They stand there, all frozen, except* BELLA, *who is beaming . . .*

The stage goes to black.)

Scene 2

Over the sound of the train, in the black, we hear EDDIE's voice.

EDDIE (*voice-over*). "Dear Jay and Arty . . . I tried phoning you the other night, but I forgot the phone is in the candy store and you probably couldn't hear it . . . Well, I've been through Kentucky, Georgia, Tennessee, and West Virginia . . . Don't complain about Aunt Bella's cooking to me because I haven't eaten anything down here that wasn't fried, smoked, hashed, gritted, or poned . . . or wasn't caught in a swamp, a tree, or coming out of a hole in the ground . . . Right now I'd go into debt again just to eat an onion roll . . . ."

(*The lights come up and the letter continues to be read by* JAY. *They are both in bed, one lamp on. It is late at night.*)

JAY (*He reads.*) "Although business is good, I've had one minor setback. I've developed what the doctor calls an irregular heartbeat. He says it's not serious, but doesn't think I should be traveling so much. But I can't afford to stop now." (*He looks at* ARTY.) An irregular heartbeat doesn't sound too good . . . God, I wish there was some way we could make some money. Not "kid" money. I mean *real* money.

ARTY. What if one night we cut off Grandma's braids and sold it to the army for barbed wire?

JAY. I can't believe we're fighting a war to make this a better world for someone like you.

(*The front door opens and* BELLA *comes in, closing the door quietly. She looks at the boys and puts her finger to her lips to be quiet.*)

BELLA. Is Grandma sleeping? Don't tell me, you'll wake her up . . . Arty! Jay! The most wonderful and exciting thing happened to me tonight. But don't ask me. I can't tell you. You're my good luck charms, both of you.

GRANDMA (*Appearing suddenly out of her room. To* BELLA.) You tink I don't hear you coming up the stairs? You tink I don't know it's eleven o'clock? You tink I don't know where you've been?

BELLA. Just to the movies, Ma.

GRANDMA. Movies, movies, movies. You waste your money and your life in da movies. Und den you walk home by yourself. Do you know what kind of men are on the street at eleven o'clock?

BELLA. I didn't see a soul, Ma.

GRANDMA. Ya, ya, ya! Look for trouble, you'll find trouble.

BELLA. No one bothers me, Ma.

GRANDMA. Then you waste money on movie magazines? Fill your head with Hollywood and dreams that don't happen to people like us?

BELLA. Sometimes they do.

GRANDMA. Never. NEVER!! . . . *(Holding out her hand)* Give it to me. I don't want trash in this house.

BELLA. It's my magazine, Ma. I bought it with my own money.

GRANDMA. No! My money. I pay for everything here. You don't have anything unless I give you. Give—me—the—magazine!

BELLA. Please don't do this to me in front of the boys, Momma.

GRANDMA. You bring it home in front of the boys, you'll give me the magazine in front of the boys. *(Holds her hand out)* Give it to me now, Bella. *(BELLA looks at the boys, embarrassed, then gives her the magazine. GRANDMA looks at the magazine and nods in disgust.)* When I'm dead, you can buy your own magazine.

BELLA. No, I won't, Momma. Because you'll find a way to get them anyway.

(She rushes into her room. GRANDMA looks at the boys.)

GRANDMA. . . . You like to pay my electric bill? (JAY *quickly turns out the light. It is dark, except for the light from* GRANDMA'*s room.*) . . . And you try cutting my braids off, you'll get your fingers chopped off.

(She goes in and slams her door. The lights go to black and we hear the train again.)

Scene 3

In the dark, we hear the voice of EDDIE *again.*

EDDIE *(voice-over).* "Dear Boys . . . This'll just have to be a short one. I'm in Houston, Texas, and I just got plumb tuckered out. That's how they talk down here. I had to take a week off and rest. Nothing to worry about. I'll be on the road again real soon, and I promise I'll make up the time . . . . Love, Pop."

(The lights come up. It is Sunday afternoon, weeks later. ARTY *stands on* GRANDMA'*s chair, his hand upraised, and he is jubilant.)*

ARTY *(yelling).* Alone at last!! Grandma's out! Aunt Bella's out! We have the house to ourselves. We're free! Ya ya ya ya ya!!!

JAY. Will you shut up! She could walk back in any minute. You know what she'd do if she found you jumping on her chair?

ARTY *(with German accent).* Ya! She vould chop off my legs . . . And Aunt Bella vould cook dem for dinner.

(He jumps on the bed.)

JAY *(looks out the window).* Hey! Arty! There's that car again.

ARTY. What car?

JAY. The black Studebaker. It's the two guys who came looking for Uncle Louie. They look like killers to me . . . What do you think they want?

ARTY *(looks out the window).* I don't know. Let's give 'em Grandma. Ya ya ya ya ya!

JAY (*pulling him away*). Get out of there. (*He peeks again.*) They just keep circling and circling. Aren't you afraid of guys like that?

ARTY. No. I lived up here for a month. I can take anything.

(*The front door opens and* BELLA *comes in.*)

BELLA. Is Momma home?

JAY. No. She's still at Aunt Gert's.

BELLA. I don't want to cry. I don't want to cry. I don't want to cry.

JAY. Is there anything we can do? . . . You can talk to us, Aunt Bella.

BELLA. Do you think so? Do you think I can trust you? You're still so young.

JAY. You don't have to be old to be trusted.

BELLA. And you'd never tell Grandma what I tell you? Because if she ever found out, she'd put me in the Home . . . She would. For the rest of my life.

JAY. I don't think she would do that. She just says that to scare you sometimes.

BELLA. No. She would do it. Sometimes she'd take me on the trolley, and we'd go by the Home and she'd say, "That's where you'll live if you're not a good girl."

ARTY. You said she wouldn't do that because she's afraid to be alone.

BELLA. But she's not alone anymore. She's got you two here.

ARTY. Oh, no. If you left, we'd go with you to the Home.

JAY. Arty, knock it off . . . If you don't want to tell us, Aunt Bella, you don't have to. We're your friends.

BELLA. No. I have to tell somebody . . . I wish Eddie was here. Eddie would know what to do.

JAY. We're Eddie's sons. That's almost the same thing.

BELLA. Yes. That's true . . . Alright . . . Come here. Sit down, both of you. (*She crosses to the sofa bed and sits. They sit on either side of her.*) This is our secret now, alright? . . . A sacred secret. Say it, the both of you.

ARTY and JAY and BELLA. This is a sacred secret.

BELLA. Alright then . . . (*She smiles.*) I'm going to get married . . . I'm going to be a wife and I'm going to have lots and lots of children and live in a place of my own . . . Isn't that wonderful news? (*The boys look at each other.*) You're the only ones that know this . . . Jay! Arty! I'm going to get married.

(*They are, of course, dumbstruck.*)

JAY. Gee, that's swell, Aunt Bella.

ARTY. Have you met anybody yet?

BELLA. What do you mean, have I met anyone? . . . Of course I have . . . I met him ten days ago at the movies. At the Orpheum Theatre . . . I saw him there four times this week.

JAY. You both went to the same movie four times?

BELLA. I didn't mind. And he has to, because he works there. He's an usher . . . And he looks so wonderful in his uniform.

ARTY. He's an usher?

BELLA. And his name is Johnny. I always thought I would marry someone named Johnny.

ARTY. What a great guess.

BELLA. Anyway, we went out later for some coffee . . . And we went for walks in the park . . . and down near the river. And then today, just like in the movies, at exactly two o'clock . . . or two-fifteen . . . or two-thirty . . . he asked me to marry him . . . And I said I would have to think it over, but the answer was yes.

ARTY. That was pretty quick thinking it over.

BELLA. I know. I didn't want him to change his mind . . . Are you as happy about this as I am?

JAY. Oh, sure . . . sure . . . sure . . . How old is he?

BELLA. He's thirty . . . Maybe not. Maybe about forty . . . But he's so handsome. And so polite. And quiet. I had to do all of the talking. All he said was, "Would you marry me?"

JAY. Was he ever married before?

BELLA. Oh, no. I would never marry someone who was married before. I want it to be the first time for both of us.

JAY. If he has no children, how come he's not in the army?

BELLA. Oh, he wanted to go but they wouldn't take him because of his handicap.

JAY. What handicap?

BELLA. He has a reading handicap.

JAY. You mean he has bad eyes?

BELLA. No. He just has trouble learning things. The way I did. He went to a special school when he was a boy. The one near the Home. He was there once, in the Home, for about six months, and he said it was terrible . . . So his parents took him out . . . And now he's much happier.

ARTY. Oh, I get it . . . Do you get it, Jay?

JAY. I can tell why you're not anxious to tell Grandma . . . I mean, because it's so sudden like.

BELLA. And he doesn't want to be an usher forever . . . He wants to open up a restaurant. Because he said the one thing people always have to do is eat. Don't you agree? *(ARTY and JAY nod together.)* . . . I would be the cook and he would be the manager. I would love that more than anything in the whole world.

JAY. Could he do that? Manage a restaurant? If he couldn't read the menus?

BELLA. Well, I would do all that. I would help him . . . The only thing is, his parents are poor and he doesn't make much money and we'd need about five thousand dollars to open a restaurant . . . And I don't know if Momma would give it to me.

JAY. Your mother has five thousand dollars?

BELLA. Oh, more. Ten or fifteen thousand. I'm not supposed to tell anyone.

JAY. Where does she keep it? In the bank?

BELLA. No. It's here in the house somewhere. She changes the hiding place every year. No one knows she has it . . . Not Eddie or Gert or Louie. No one . . . So my problem is, I have to get her to say yes to marrying Johnny, and yes to opening the restaurant and moving away, and yes to giving me the five thousand dollars. But I don't think she's going to say yes, do you?

JAY. I don't think she's going to let you go to the movies much anymore.

BELLA. She won't know if you don't tell her. You won't tell her, will you, Jay?

JAY. I swear.

BELLA. Arty?

ARTY. She and I have very short conversations.

BELLA. I have to go inside now and think this out. I'm not good at thinking things out. I'm much better with my hands . . . But you're smart. Both of you. Maybe you'll think it out for me . . . Please do. I'd be grateful to you for the rest of my life. (*She starts to go, then stops.*) Oh. I thought of a name for the restaurant, too . . . "La Bella Johnnie."

JAY. That's nice.

BELLA. Yeah. I just hope he can read it. (*She goes into her bedroom.*)

ARTY. Wait'll he meets Grandma. He'll be back in the Home in a week.

JAY. Fifteen thousand!! Wow! You think she would have loaned some of it to Pop. (*Looking around*) Where would be the safest place to hide it? Where no one would think of looking?

ARTY. You're not really thinking of stealing it, are you?

JAY. No, but what if we just borrowed it? I would just love to send Pop an envelope with nine thousand dollars in it.

ARTY. And who would he think sent it to him? God???

JAY. He had an uncle in Poland who died. He left the money in his will for Pop.

ARTY. You think the Germans would let some Jew in Poland send nine thousand dollars to some Jew in Alabama?

Blackout

Scene 4

We *hear the train . . . then* EDDIE*'s voice . . .*

EDDIE (*voice-over*). " . . . Dear Boys . . . Traveling through the South has been a whole new education for me. Some people are very warm and polite and educated and very well spoken. And then there are some on the train who spit tobacco juice on the windows . . . A lot of people have trouble with my New York accent. I didn't even know I had one till I got here . . . I met a nice Jewish family in Atlanta, but I couldn't understand them either. This woman, Mrs. Schneider, said to me, 'You all come over to the synagogue this Shabuss and you'll meet some mighty fine folks.' I didn't want to hurt her feelings so I said, 'Sho nuff.' And she just looked at me and said, 'Who's Shonuff?' . . . I guess it takes a while to learn the dialect. Love, Pop."

(*The lights come up. It is one week later, about twelve o'clock at night. The room is dark except for the full moon that shines brightly in through the window.*)

The boys' bed is open. Neither of them is in it. ARTY, *in pajamas, is standing near the door that leads downstairs.)*

ARTY. Jay! Hurry up! What if Grandma wakes up? . . . This is crazy. Why would she hide money in the store? *(Suddenly, we see the flashlight coming from downstairs.* ARTY *rushes back into bed.* JAY *comes in with the flashlight.)*

JAY. I looked everywhere. There's no money down there. *(He shivers.)* God, I'm freezing. I was looking under the ice cream cartons. *(He gets into bed.)* I think I got frostbite.

ARTY. Why would she keep money under ice cream? We use those cartons up every week.

JAY. Not the boysenberry. Boysenberry sits there for months. Nobody's ever going to look under boysenberry.

ARTY. I can't believe we're stealing money from our own grandmother.

(They put out the flashlight and turn to go to sleep . . . A moment passes . . . Then the front door opens. We see a man in a hat enter, close the door, then slowly, quietly cross toward the window. He carries a small black bag.)

JAY. Who's that?

(Turning the flashlight on the man)

LOUIE. Get that light outa my face and go back to sleep, kid.

JAY. There's nothing here to steal, mister. I swear.

LOUIE. Is that you, Jay?

JAY. Yeah. Who are you?

LOUIE. It's Uncle Louie.

JAY. Uncle Louie? No kidding? . . . Arty! It's Uncle Louie.

ARTY. Uncle Louie? . . . Really? Hi, Uncle Louie.

LOUIE. Is that Arty?

ARTY. Yeah. It's Arty . . . Hi, Uncle Louie.

LOUIE. Wait a second. (LOUIE *turns on the lamp.* LOUIE KURNITZ *is about thirty-six years old. He wears a double-breasted suit with a hanky in the breast pocket, black pointy shoes, a dark blue shirt, and a loud tie. He also wears a fedora hat*[1] *and carries a small black satchel, not unlike a doctor's bag.)* Whaddya know? Look at you! Couple a big guys now, ain't you? . . . You don't come around for a while and you grow up on me. . . Come here. Come on. I want a hug. You heard me. Move it. *(The boys look at each other, not thinking* LOUIE *was the hugging type. They quickly climb out of bed and go to him. He puts his arms around both their shoulders and pulls them in to him. He looks at* JAY.*)* Picture of your mother. Pretty woman, your mother. . . *(To* ARTY*)* And you. You look like a little bull terrier. Is that what you are, a bull terrier? *(He musses* ARTY's *hair.)*

ARTY. Yeah, I guess so.

LOUIE *(fakes a punch at* JAY's *midsection).* Hey, watch it! What are you now, a middleweight or what? Who's been beefin' you up?

JAY. Aunt Bella. She's a good cook.

LOUIE *(taking off his hat).* And a couple a midnight trips down to the ice cream freezer, heh? Diggin' into the

---

1. fedora hat, a soft felt hat with a crease the length of the crown

boysenberry with your flashlight?
. . . That's breakin' and enterin', kid.
Two to five years.

JAY. You saw me?

LOUIE (*Crosses to* GRANDMA's *door and listens*). I been down there since Ma closed the store.

JAY. Sitting in the dark?

LOUIE. Yeah. Waitin' for her to go to sleep. I wasn't in no mood for long conversations.

JAY (*looks at* ARTY, *then at* LOUIE). I just took a fingerful, that's all. I love boysenberry.

LOUIE. Big mistake, kid. Mom reads fingerprints. She'll nail you in the morning.

JAY. Are you serious?

LOUIE. Get outa here. What are you? A couple of pushovers? Like your old man. . .What'd he bring up for you, Arty? A thumbful of pistachio?

ARTY. No. Nothing. I wasn't hungry.

LOUIE. You think your pop and I didn't do that when we were kids? That was the beauty part. Never took nothin' durin' the day. A ton a ice cream, a store full a candy, anything we wanted. Never took nothin' . . . But as soon as Ma let her braids down and turned out the lights, we were down there lappin' up the cream and meowin' like cats . . . Ain't that the way? It's only fun when there's a chance a gettin' caught. Nothin' sweeter than danger, boys, am I right?

JAY. I guess so.

LOUIE. Damn right.

ARTY. I didn't know Pop was like that.

LOUIE. Yeah, well, he was no good at it anyway. Ma knew what was goin' on. She could tell if there was salt missin' from a pretzel . . . But she wouldn't say nothin'. She'd come up from the store with the milk, siddown for breakfast, knowin' that two scoops of everything was missin', and she'd just stare at you . . . right into your eyeballs, pupil to pupil . . . never blinkin' . . . Her eyes looked like two district attorneys . . . and Eddie couldn't take the pressure. He'd always crack. Tears would start rollin' down his cheeks like a wet confession . . . and Whack, he'd get that big German hand right across the head . . . But not me. I'd stare her right back until her eyelids started to weigh ten pounds each . . . And she'd turn away from me, down for the count . . . And you know what? She loved it . . . because I knew how to take care of myself . . . Yeah, me and Ma loved to put on the gloves and go the distance.

(*He takes off his jacket and puts it on the back of the chair.*)

JAY. Nobody told us you were coming over tonight.

LOUIE. Nobody knew. It was even a surprise for me. I gotta stay here a couple days, maybe a week. They're paintin' my apartment.

ARTY. You didn't know they were going to paint your apartment?

LOUIE. They just found the right color paint tonight. Hard to find with the war on. (*He takes off his jacket, reveal-*

ing a holster with a pistol in it.) So, you kids been keepin' your nose outa trouble?

(The boys look at the gun, mesmerized.)

JAY. Huh?

LOUIE. How's Pop? Ma tells me he's in the junk business. Is that right, Arty?

ARTY *(looking at the gun).* Huh?

LOUIE. Sellin' scrap iron or somethin', ain't that it?

BOTH BOYS. Huh?

LOUIE. Whatsamatter? *(He looks at the gun.)* This? *(He smiles.)* Hey, don't worry about it. *(He takes it out of its holster.)* I'm holdin' it for a friend. This policeman I know went on vacation, he didn't want to lose it. They have to pay for it when they lose it . . . *(He puts it in his pants, under the belt, just over the fly.)* Also, the ladies like it. You dance with 'em close, gives 'em a thrill.

(He winks at them.)

JAY. Is it . . . is it loaded?

LOUIE. Gee, I hope not. If it went off, I'd have to become a ballerina. *(He winks at the boys. He hangs the gun and holster on a chair, comes back, and resumes getting undressed.)* Does your pop ever send you some loose change once in a while?

JAY. Oh, yeah. Whenever he can.

LOUIE. Like never, right? You think I don't know what's goin' on? The sharks are puttin' the bite on him, right? He shoulda come to me. There's lotsa ways of borrowin' money. Your pop don't understand that. Sometimes bein' on the up and up just gets you down and down,

know what I mean, Jay?

JAY. Yeah . . . I never knew a policeman could lend his gun to someone.

LOUIE *(looks at him, then at* ARTY*).* You got a smart brother there, Arty, you know that? You're right, Jay. It's my gun. I'm a bodyguard for a very prominent and distinguished political figure. It's sort of like an FBI man, only they call it something else.

ARTY. You mean a henchman?

LOUIE *(glaring at him).* Who's been telling you stories like that? Jay?

ARTY. No. I swear.

LOUIE. Don't ever repeat that word around to anyone again, you understand?

ARTY. I didn't mean to say it. I was thinking of hunchback.

lOUIE. A couple of jokers here, heh? Don't pull my leg, Arty, it might come off in your hands . . . So, we got a little business to discuss. You boys got any problem with makin' a little after-school money?

JAY. You mean a job? I've been looking, but Grandma wants us in the store after school. To help pay our expenses.

LOUIE. Tell you what. How'd you like to work for me? Five bucks a week, split between you, cash on the barrel. Only first you gotta guess what number I'm thinkin' of. Make a mistake and the deal's off . . . Take a guess, boys.

ARTY. Three

JAY. Seven.

LOUIE. Thirty-seven. That's right. Good guess. You're on Louie's payroll now.

(He takes a five-dollar bill out of his garter and hands it to JAY*)* . . . Now, Arty, can you drive a car?

ARTY. Me? I'm only thirteen and a half.

LOUIE. Too bad. I need someone who can drive a car.

ARTY. I'm a pretty good roller skater.

LOUIE *(He smiles.)* That's good, 'cause I'm spinnin' your wheels, kid. Now your leg's bein' pulled. Wake up and live. It's a fast world out there.

JAY. Uncle Louie . . . This five-dollar bill . . . It has your picture on it.

LOUIE *(to* ARTY*)*. He ain't no faster than you. Look in your pocket, Arty.

*(*ARTY *feels in his pajama pocket and takes out a five-dollar bill, unfolded.)*

ARTY. It's five dollars. A real one. How'd you do that?

LOUIE. These fingers were touched by genius. I could have been a concert violinist, but the handkerchief kept fallin' off my neck.

JAY. What do we have to do for the money?

LOUIE. Nothin'. Like if anyone comes around here lookin' for me, you don't know nothin', you ain't seen nothin', you ain't heard nothin'. You think you can handle that?

ARTY. There were two men here the other day looking for you.

LOUIE. Yeah? What'd they look like?

ARTY. One had a broken nose and the other one had—

LOUIE. —a Betty Grable tie.

ARTY. Right.

LOUIE. Hollywood Harry. Got all the stars hand-painted on silk. He's got a Gypsy Rose Lee tie you can see when you get a little older . . . So if they show up here again askin' questions, what do you say to 'em?

BOTH. Nothing.

LOUIE. Smart boys. Look in Jay's pocket, Arty.

*(*ARTY *looks in* JAY*'s pocket, takes out a bill.)*

ARTY. Another five dollars.

LOUIE. I could have played Carnegie Hall.

JAY. We wouldn't be doing anything wrong, would we?

LOUIE. You're my brother's kids, you think I'm gonna get you involved with somethin' stupid? Don't be stupid. There's a couple of guys who don't like me 'cause I've been seein' a lady I shouldn't a been seeing. A minor neighborhood problem . . . Okay. It's late. I'm gonna wash up. We'll bunk up together tonight, okay?

ARTY. Sure. There's plenty of room.

LOUIE. Oh. One last thing. *(Pointing to his black satchel)* Don't touch this. I got my valuables in there. My draft card. My driver's license . . . My good cuff links. I'll put it somewhere you won't have to worry about it. *(He starts for the bathroom with the bag, then stops.)* Oh, Arty. See if there's anything else in your pajama bottoms.

ARTY *(looks)*. No. There's nothing there.

LOUIE. Well, don't worry. You're young yet.

(He chuckles and goes into the bathroom.)

ARTY. He's incredible. It's like having a

James Cagney movie in your own house.

JAY. We're not taking that money. They're not painting his apartment at midnight. He's a bagman and he's got a bag and a gun and Pop wouldn't want us to get paid for saying "Nothin' " to Hollywood Harry in the Betty Grable tie. Forget it.

(BELLA's door opens and she comes out quietly.)

BELLA. Jay? Arty? Have you thought of anything yet? About how I should tell Grandma about you-know-who?

JAY. Gee. No. We've been very busy ourselves.

BELLA. Sure. I understand. But if you *do* think of something, I'm going to give you each a dollar. I know you could use it. I'll let you go back to sleep. I was having such a good dream. I'm gonna go back and finish it.

(She goes back in her room and closes the door.)

JAY. You know, we could make a great living just from this family.

(The bathroom door opens and LOUIE comes out carrying his black bag. He puts it where he can see it from the bed, then sits, takes off his garters and socks, and gets into bed.)

LOUIE. You guys have to go to the bathroom?

JAY. No. Why?

LOUIE. I don't like anybody getting up while I'm sleeping.

ARTY. Sure . . . How late do you sleep?

LOUIE. Until I see something I don't like.

JAY. You can see while you're sleeping?

LOUIE (smiles). Don't try me, kid. I wake up grouchy. (He looks around contentedly.) Yeah, it's good to be home. In my own bed.

ARTY. Is this where *you* slept?

LOUIE. Yeah. Me and Eddie. And Gert slept with Bella. And Ma slept with her cane . . . There's nothing like family, boys. The one place in the world you're safe, is with your family . . . Right?

JAY. Right.

ARTY. Right.

LOUIE. Right. So unless something unforeseen goes wrong, I'll see you in the morning, pals . . . (He turns out the lamp.) Sleep tight.

(He turns on his side, away from them. There is a silence . . . then:)

ARTY. Jay?

JAY. What?

ARTY. I have to go to the bathroom.

LOUIE (without moving). Save it.

(In the dark we hear:)

EDDIE (voice-over). "Dear Boys . . . The one thing that keeps me going is knowing you're with my family. Thank God you're in good hands. Love, Pop."

Curtain

Act Two
Scene 1

In the dark, we hear the "train" music and a letter from EDDIE.

As the lights come up, we see ARTY in bed, wrapped up in a bathrobe, a comic book on *his lap. He is reading a letter as* EDDIE *'s voice continues:*

EDDIE *(voice-over).* "Dear Boys . . . Sorry I haven't kept up my letter writing. The truth is, I was in the hospital a few days. Nothing serious. The doctor said it was just exhaustion. I remember when I was a boy, if I got sick, my mother used to give me the worst tasting German mustard soup. God, how I hated it. Luckily, they don't serve it in Mississippi. I'll write soon. Love, Pop."

(The front door opens and JAY *comes in carrying a bowl of soup.)*

JAY. You got it real rough. Reading comic books and missing school. I wish *I* had a fever. Here. Drink this.

ARTY *(looking at it suspiciously).* What is it?

JAY. Grandma made you soup.

ARTY. Forget it. I'm not drinking it.

JAY. Don't start in with her, Arty. She's in a rotten mood today.

ARTY. You mean all those other days she was in a *good* mood?

JAY. Just drink it . . . . Where's Uncle Louie?

ARTY. Taking a nap in Aunt Bella's room.

JAY. Well, tell him he got a phone call this morning. One of the guys from the Studebaker.

ARTY. But you said you don't know nothin', right?

JAY. Right. And he said, "You tell Louie that Friday night the dance is over."

ARTY. What dance?

JAY. The "Goodbye Louie" dance.

ARTY. You mean he's double-crossing the mob?

JAY. You got it.

ARTY. Wow! . . . You think they're going to kill him?

JAY. Maybe all three of us. We work for him, don't we?

(The front door opens. GRANDMA *walks in wearing her candy store apron, looking angry.)*

GRANDMA *(to* JAY*).* It takes twenty minutes to bring up soup? . . . I got one sweeper not sweeping downstairs, I don't need two.

JAY. I was just going.

GRANDMA. And don't let the kids sit on the stool all day. One buys a malted and the other two steal pretzels. If they steal, you pay for it.

JAY. Sure. That's only fair.

(He crosses to the front door.)

GRANDMA. Vot was dot?

JAY. I said, "Yes, I hear."

GRANDMA. He's fresh to me, dat one. *(She pulls the covers off of* ARTY*.)* Come on. Out of da bed. It's enough lying around already.

ARTY *(He pulls the sheet back up.)* I'm freezing. And I'm burning up with fever. You can feel my head.

GRANDMA. You lay in bed, you get fever. You get up and walk, da fever looks for somebody else. *(She hits the bed with her cane twice.)* Out! Out!

ARTY *(He gets out of bed, stands, and shivers.)* My mother always kept me in bed when I had a fever.

GRANDMA *(She straightens the sheets and starts to fold the bed back into a sofa.)*

You're not in your mother's house no more. *(Pointing to the chair at the living room table)* You sit in dat chair and you do your homevork. And no funny books. And you finish dat soup. All of it.

ARTY. I tried. I can't get it down.

GRANDMA. If you eat it qvick, you von't taste it.

ARTY. I would taste this if I didn't have a tongue.

GRANDMA. You listen to me. You're not fresh yet like da other one, but I see it coming. No, sir. Not in dis house . . . You live vith me, you don't stay in bed two days . . . You get better qvick und you get dressed und you come downstairs und you vash up the soda fountain und you sveep up the store. I didn't ask to take care of you, but if I take care of you, you'll do vot I tell you. *Don't turn away from me!* You'll look at me!! . . . You're not going to vin dis argument, I tell you dot right now. You understand me?

ARTY. . . . Yes.

GRANDMA. Den put da soup in your mouth right now or I do it for you.

(He looks at her. She obviously means business. He quickly puts the soup in his mouth. He keeps it there.)

ARTY. . . . I can't swallow it. (GRANDMA *crosses to him, pulls his head back, and the soup goes down.)* You could drown me like that . . . Why are you so mean to me? I'm your own grandson.

GRANDMA. Dot's right. And vot am I?

ARTY. What do you mean?

GRANDMA. *Vot am I??* . . . Am I a nobody?

ARTY. No. You're my grandmother.

GRANDMA. Den vere's da respect? Da respect I never got from you or your family since da day you vere born?

ARTY. You're just mad at my mother and you're taking it out on me. You don't care about your rotten soup or making me get better. You just want me to be miserable because somebody made you miserable in Germany. Even Pop said it . . . Well, that's not my fault. Take it out on Hitler, not on me.

GRANDMA. Und if you vere a boy growing up in Germany, you vould be dead by now.

ARTY. That's right. Maybe I would. And if I ate this soup, I would be just as dead. Would that make you happy then? You want to be happy, Grandma? Watch! *(And he quickly eats six or seven spoonfuls of the soup.)* Okay? Now you can stand there and watch me die.

GRANDMA. No. You von't die. You'll be better dis afternoon. It's not so important dat you hate me, Artur . . . It's only important dat you live. *(She crosses to the door and opens it.)* Dot's something dot I could never teach your father.

(She exits.

BELLA*'s bedroom door opens and* LOUIE *comes out with sleepy eyes and mussed hair. He wears an undershirt, pants, and socks, no shoes.)*

LOUIE. Ever hear of General Rommel?

ARTY. Who?

LOUIE. General Irwin Rommel. German tank commander. Right now he's rollin' right across Egypt, cuttin' through the whole British army. Tough as they come . . . But if Momma wanted him to eat the soup, he would eat the soup.

ARTY. Did you eat it when you were a kid?

LOUIE. Oh, yeah.

ARTY. I thought you weren't afraid of her.

LOUIE. I wasn't. That's how I proved it to her. I hated that soup worse than you. But I would drink three bowls of it and ask for more. She knew she couldn't win with me.

ARTY. I wish I was as tough as you.

LOUIE. Hey, you're gettin' there. You took her on, kid. That took guts. That took moxie.

ARTY. What's moxie?

(LOUIE *stands in a defiant position, in his body and in his face.*)

LOUIE. *That's* moxie! . . . Where's Jay-Jay?

ARTY. Downstairs guarding the pretzels . . . Uncle Louie . . . There was a telephone call for you.

LOUIE. For me?

ARTY. Jay took it. He told them he never heard of you.

LOUIE. But they left a message, right?

ARTY. Yeah. They said, "Tell Louie that Friday night the dance is over."

LOUIE (*smiles*). Yeah. Well, that don't mean nothin'. A couple a Bronx boys like to talk tough. It's just

horsin' around. You know what I mean? Huh? . . . Whatsa matter? Grandma got you down?

ARTY. I think she loves doing it.

LOUIE. Hey, let me tell you somethin'. Guess who hates livin' here more than you? (*He points to* GRANDMA's *door.*) The old lady with the cane. That's right. Grandma hates runnin' this store. She hates livin' in Yonkers. You know how many friends she's made here in thirty years? . . . Zippo.

ARTY. She doesn't exactly put herself out with people.

LOUIE. I never said she was a lot a laughs. I'll tell you the truth. I don't like her much myself. She knows it. Why should I? She used to lock me in a closet for breakin' a dish. A ten-cent dish, I'd get two, three hours in the closet. And if I cried, I'd get another hour . . . No light, no water, just enough air to breathe. That's when I learned not to cry. And after a few times in the closet, I toughened up. But I also never broke another dish . . . No, I didn't like her, but I respected her. Hell of a teacher, Ma was.

ARTY. Wouldn't it have been easier if she bought paper plates?

LOUIE. Then where's the lesson? There's no respect for paper plates. Hear me out . . . She was no harder on us than she was on herself. When she was twelve years old, her old man takes her to a political rally in Berlin. The cops broke it up. With sticks, on horsebacks. Someone throws a rock, a cop bashes in her old man's head, a horse goes down and crushes Ma's foot. Nobody ever fixed it. It hurts every day of her life, but I never once seen her take even an aspirin . . . She coulda had an operation, but she used the money she saved to get to this country with her husband and six kids. That's moxie, kid.

ARTY. Did she ever put my father in the closet?

LOUIE. Not a chance. She'd open the closet door and he'd tie himself to the radiator. Even if it was hot. No, he was too afraid to go up against her. He was careful. He never broke nothin' except maybe himself . . . .

ARTY. Didn't you ever want to run away?

LOUIE. I did. Twelve times. Still a record in Yonkers. The last time she wouldn't take me back. Told the policeman she didn't know me. I had no place to go, so I lived under the house with a couple of cats for two weeks. Dead of winter. Bella would come out and bring me sandwiches, a blanket, couple a candles. Mom caught her and put her in the closet overnight. But Bella don't understand anything, so she thought it was kinda fun. Or maybe she thought it was the safest place to be . . . Now, Gert—Gert was more scared than your old man. Gert used to talk in her sleep, and Mom heard her one night sayin' things she didn't like. So Gert didn't get supper that week. Until she learned to sleep holdin' her breath.

ARTY. I don't blame you for hating her.

LOUIE. I didn't say "hate." I didn't *like* her. That's different. How you feelin'?

ARTY. I think my fever's gone.

LOUIE. Lousy soup but it works . . . When Jay comes up, tell him to bring me some coffee and a doughnut. I'll be in the shower. I wanna clean up before I go.

ARTY. You're leaving? When?

LOUIE. Tonight. No point waitin' till the dance is over.

(*He winks, then starts for the bathroom.*)

ARTY. Uncle Louie . . . ? (LOUIE *stops.*) Are you in trouble?

LOUIE (*He smiles*). Arty! I was never *not* in trouble.

(*He goes into the bathroom and closes the door.*

The front door opens and JAY *storms in, looking furious. He slams the door closed.*)

JAY. I hate her! . . . I hate her guts. No wonder Mom never wanted us to come here.

ARTY. What did she do?

JAY. She charged me for three pretzels. Three pretzels that some kids stole while she was downstairs and I was upstairs with your soup . . . She says, "No, there were twelve pretzels in the glass when I went upstairs and nine pretzels when I came down." . . . Not even Sherlock Holmes would notice that . . . .

ARTY. Two cents a pretzel, it's only six cents.

JAY. Oh, is that all it is? Then *you* pay it . . . . Is Uncle Louie still sleeping?

ARTY. He's taking a shower. He's leaving tonight.

JAY. Leaving? I have to talk to him.

ARTY. About what?

JAY. It's private business.

ARTY. Jay, you don't *have* any business. All you got is a job that costs you six cents a day . . . Come on, tell me, Jay. I'll find out sooner or later.

JAY. . . . I'm going to ask Uncle Louie to take me with him.

ARTY. *WHAT* ???

JAY. Will you be quiet?

ARTY. Are you crazy? Go with Uncle Louie?

JAY. I have to make money. Get a good job somewhere. But I can't leave here with minus six cents in my pocket. Uncle Louie is my ticket out.

ARTY. Running away. That's all Pop has to hear.

JAY. Well, we just can't count on Pop anymore. Maybe I can take care of him better than he's taking care of us.

ARTY. Doing what?

JAY. Maybe Uncle Louie can teach me a few things.

ARTY. Oh, great. To become what? A junior bagman? "The Pocketbook Kid"?

JAY. If Uncle Louie says yes, you can't stop me.

ARTY. . . . Then take me with you.

JAY. Take *you*? You're only a kid. Besides, she doesn't treat you the way she treats me.

ARTY. I'm afraid of her, Jay. A horse fell on her when she was a kid and she hasn't taken an aspirin yet.

JAY. Look, if I can get set up somewhere with a good-paying job, I'll send for you.

ARTY. You promise?

JAY. I swear on Momma's grave.

ARTY. Artur and Yakob, the gangsters. I can't believe it.

(*The front door opens and* BELLA *comes in.*)

BELLA (*to* JAY). Oh, here you are. Momma sent me up to look for you. She didn't know where you were for twenty minutes.

JAY. I'm coming right down. I just have to ask Uncle Louie something. He's in the shower.

BELLA (*to* ARTY). Are you feeling better, Arty?

ARTY. Oh. Much.

BELLA. No more fever?

ARTY. No. It got scared away.

BELLA. I'm glad. Because we're having company tonight. My sister Gertrude. Do you remember her?

JAY. Sort of.

BELLA. She hasn't been well. She doesn't breathe right. I think it's because she used to sleep with her head inside the pillow.

ARTY. *Inside?*

(BELLA *nods, quickly closes the front door, then crosses closer to the boys.*)

BELLA (*whispering*). Tonight's the night.

JAY. Tonight's what night?

BELLA. The night that I talk to Momma. About you-know-what.

JAY. Just the two of you?

BELLA. No. With Aunt Gertrude and Uncle Louie here. And you and Arty. I wouldn't dare talk to Momma without the family here. To back me up . . . You *are* going to back me up, aren't you? You promised.

JAY. It's not going to go very late, is it?

BELLA. Not if everybody backs me up . . . You're not going anyplace, are you?

JAY. Me? No. Where would *I* be going?

BELLA. My heart hasn't stopped pounding all day. I'm so nervous, I can't stop eating. I ate three pretzels before and I *never* eat pretzels.

JAY. *You* ate the pretzels? . . . If you eat anything else, would you tell Grandma first?

BELLA. Oh, she knows I ate the pretzels. She even said to me, "Why are you eating so much? You nervous about something?" . . . I'd better get downstairs. (*She crosses to the door.*) You too, Jay. I don't want to do anything to upset Momma before tonight. (*She opens the door.*) Arty, if you want more soup, just let me know.

(*She goes and closes the door.*)

JAY (*furious*). She *knew* Aunt Bella ate the pretzels!! . . . Grandma's crazy, Arty. Where did that horse fall, on her *head*?

(LOUIE *comes out of the bathroom, his hair wet and combed straight back. He has a towel around his neck and he carries the little black satchel.*)

LOUIE. Perfect timing, Jay-Jay. (*He looks around.*) You got my coffee and doughnut?

ARTY. Oh. I forgot to tell him.

LOUIE. So tell him.

ARTY (*to* JAY). Uncle Louie wanted some coffee and a doughnut.

JAY. Coming right up . . . Would you tell Grandma it's for you? Because doughnuts are expensive.

LOUIE (*smiles*). What is she doing, charging you for missing doughnuts?

JAY. No. Missing pretzels. How did you know?

LOUIE. It's her favorite trick. I once owed her two dollars for a missing bag of pistachio nuts. One minute they were on the counter, the next minute they were gone. She blamed me. Until I found them in her drawer. She said, "You're responsible if somebody steals from this store. Even me." . . . Hey, Arty. Get my shirt, will ya? It's on the bed.

(ARTY *crosses into* BELLA*'s room.*)

JAY. Did you pay her the two dollars?

LOUIE. No. I stole the nuts back that night. But I got the lesson.

JAY. You've learned a lot in your life, haven't you, Uncle Louie?

LOUIE. No one takes me for pistachios no more.

(ARTY *comes out with* LOUIE*'s shirt.*)

JAY. I can see . . . A guy could learn a lot from you, I bet.

LOUIE (*He takes the shirt and puts it on.*) I could write a book.

JAY. You wouldn't have to write. I mean, if someone just hung around you watching, they would pick up a lot, don't you think?

LOUIE *(He sits on the sofa and begins to shine his shoes.)* A lotta what?

JAY. A lot of anything.

LOUIE. I don't think so. 'Cause I don't like nobody hangin' around watchin' me.

JAY *(He looks at* ARTY, *then at* LOUIE.*)* Uncle Louie . . . I have an important question to ask you.

LOUIE. Don't ask questions, kid. That's probably the best thing I could teach you. Never ask questions.

JAY. I'm sorry . . . I'll just tell you then . . . I want to leave here . . . Tonight . . . I made up my mind. I'm definitely going . . .

LOUIE. Where you goin'?

JAY. As far away as I can get.

LOUIE. How far away is that? Five-dollars far? Ten-dollars far? A dozen pretzels far?

JAY. No. Just a-pair-of-shoes far. Until they wear out.

LOUIE. And then what? You better have better transportation than a pair of shoes.

JAY. I never did this before. That's why I'm asking your advice.

LOUIE. You're gonna make your grandma very unhappy, Jay-Jay.

JAY. No, I won't. Besides, that never stopped you.

*(*LOUIE *stops brushing and looks at* JAY.*)*

ARTY. Would you like me to brush your shoes, Uncle Louie?

LOUIE *(to* ARTY*).* Hey! One guy work on me at a time, okay? *(He brushes again; to* JAY.*)* So why you wanna go? It's cold out there. It's lonely out there . . . and it's dangerous out there.

JAY. I know that . . . but there's money out there.

LOUIE. Oh, I see . . . You lookin' to get rich fast?

JAY. Not for me. For Pop.

LOUIE. Ain't that nice? Like Robin Hood, heh?

JAY. I don't want to rob people.

LOUIE. No? . . . Who *do* you want to rob?

JAY. No one.

LOUIE. That sorta rules out gettin' rich fast.

JAY. *Some* people do it.

LOUIE. Yeah? How?

JAY. You'll think this is a question.

LOUIE *(angrily).* Then don't ask it. I can't help you, kid. I got nothin' to teach you and nothin' I wanna teach you . . . Is that what you think I do? Rob banks? Rob liquor stores? Grocery stores? Little old ladies in the park? Is that what you think I am?

JAY. No . . . I don't think so.

LOUIE. You don't think so? What is that, a compliment? . . . You wanna know what I do? I'm a businessman. I'm a free-lance money manager. A twenty-four-hour-a-day investment adviser. You been dyin' to ask me that all day so now I told you. School's out. You graduated. Now find a girl and go to your prom, okay?

JAY. Thank you . . . I just have one minor question to ask.

LOUIE *(smiles).* You got balls, kid . . . Did you know you got balls?

JAY. I'm aware of them, yes.

LOUIE *(to ARTY).* I love your brother . . . Reminds me of me. *(To JAY)* What's your minor question?

JAY. Are there any openings in your business?

LOUIE *(staring at him).* . . . You got balls but I think they're in your head.

JAY. I'll do anything and I won't ask any questions.

LOUIE. There are no openings. The reason there are no openings is because there's no business no more. I'm relocating. I have urgent opportunities in a more desirable and advantageous territory. It's a one-man operation outa town . . . That's the end of this conversation. As far as I'm concerned, this conversation is deceased. Okay?

JAY. . . . Take me with you . . . I'll get off wherever you want me to, but please, take me with you tonight.

LOUIE. Are you deaf or somethin'? *(To ARTY)* Is he deaf? Doesn't he hear what I just said? Did *you* hear what I just said?

ARTY. I caught most of it, yeah.

LOUIE *(to JAY).* Take you with me for what? For company? Your company's starting to pester me already. What do I need you for? What can you do for me? Heh?

(He exits into the bathroom.)

JAY. . . . I could carry your little black satchel.

(LOUIE comes out, wearing his shoulder holster. He has fire in his eyes. LOUIE moves toward JAY.)

LOUIE . . . You interested in my little black satchel?

JAY. No . . . I just thought—

LOUIE. No? But you want to carry it . . . Why? Does it look heavy to you? . . . You think I got a broken arm, I can't carry a little bag like that?

JAY. No.

LOUIE. So maybe you have some other interest in it . . . You been foolin' around with this bag?

JAY. I swear. No.

LOUIE. So what are you curious about? How much it weighs or something? . . . You want to pick it up, go ahead, pick it up.

JAY. I don't want to pick it up.

LOUIE. Pick it up, Jay. It ain't gonna bite you . . . You won't be happy till you pick it up. Go ahead, kid. Pick it up.

JAY. I really don't want to.

ARTY. Come on, Jay. Please pick it up.

JAY. Stay out of this.

LOUIE. No, no . . . Arty, come here.

ARTY. Me?

LOUIE. That's right. You're Arty. *(ARTY comes to him. LOUIE puts his arm around ARTY's shoulder.)* I want you to go over to that stool and pick up the black bag.

ARTY. Jay is closer.

LOUIE. Jay is not interested. I want you to do it. *(ARTY goes over and stands next to the stool where the black bag sits.)* Okay, Arty. Pick it up.

ARTY (*His face screws up.*) I don't know why, but I think I'm going to cry.

LOUIE. Just pick it up, Arty. (ARTY *picks it up.*) Is it heavy?

ARTY. No.

LOUIE. Is it light?

ARTY. No.

LOUIE. So what is it?

ARTY. . . . Medium.

LOUIE. Okay, so it's medium . . . So what do you think is in the bag? . . . Money? . . . Fives and tens and twenties and hundreds all stuck together with rubber bands? . . . WHAT?? . . . I said *WHAT!!!*

ARTY. I don't know.

LOUIE. You don't know . . . Well, then, maybe you'd better look in the bag and see . . . Why don't you do that, Arty? . . . Open the bag . . . Okay?

ARTY. Please, Uncle Louie—

LOUIE (*He takes a step closer.*) I'm only gonna ask you one more time, Arty . . . because I'm runnin' out of patience . . . Open—the bag!

(ARTY *looks at him, helpless, terrified . . . and then suddenly*)

JAY. Don't do it, Arty . . . Leave him alone, Uncle Louie. You want the bag open, do it yourself. (*He takes the bag from* ARTY *and tosses it at* LOUIE'*s feet.*) Maybe you don't rob banks or grocery stores or little old women. You're worse than that. You're a bully. You pick on a couple of kids. Your own nephews. You make fun of my father because he cried and was afraid of Grandma. Well, everyone in *Yonkers* is afraid of Grandma . . . And let me tell you something about my father. At least he's doing something in this war. He's sick and he's tired but he's out there selling iron to make ships and tanks and cannons. And I'm proud of him. What are you doing? Hiding in your mother's apartment and scaring little kids and acting like Humphrey Bogart. Well, you're no Humphrey Bogart . . . And I'll tell you something else—No. That's all.

(LOUIE *has hardly blinked an eye. He shifts his body and takes one small step towards* JAY.)

LOUIE (*smiles*). That was thrilling. That was beautiful. I had tears in my eyes, I swear to God . . . You got more guts than I thought, Jay. You know what you got, Jay? You got moxie.

JAY. What's moxie?

LOUIE. Tell him, Arty.

(ARTY *makes* LOUIE'*s gesture of what moxie is.*)

ARTY (*to* JAY). That's moxie.

LOUIE. Yeah . . . Your father's a lucky guy, let me tell you . . . That's why I don't think you should go with me, Jay. You take care of Arty here. And Momma and Bella. And maybe one day you'll be proud of your old Uncle Louie, too. (*He picks up the bag and puts it on the table.*) And don't worry what was in the bag. It's just laundry. Dirty laundry, boys. That's all.

(*He crosses to the mirror to finish getting dressed as* GRANDMA *walks in.*)

GRANDMA (*sternly, to* JAY). Are you a banker? Is dis your lunch hour? Well, dis is not a bank. Go down and help Bella close up da store . . . Artur, get your clothes on. Ve haff company tonight.

(ARTY *runs into the bathroom.*)

LOUIE. I don't think I can stay, Ma.

GRANDMA. I didn't ask you to. Bella asked you. You'll stay. (*To* JAY) You haff something to say to me? No? Den get downstairs . . . Und you und I haff someting else to talk about later.

JAY. About what?

GRANDMA. About a jar of pistachio nuts dat are missing, dot's about vot.

(JAY *looks at* LOUIE, *then goes.* LOUIE *puts on his suit coat and hat.* GRANDMA *looks at him. It's more of a scowl. She takes a few bills out of her pocket.*)

GRANDMA. You're getting careless, Louie. You dropped money on my dresser this morning.

LOUIE. Louie's never careless, Ma. It's for you. I had a good week.

GRANDMA. A good week for you is a bad week for someone else . . . I don't want your profits, Louie.

LOUIE. It's just a hundred bucks. Happy Birthday, Ma. It's tomorrow, right?

GRANDMA (*She puts the money on the table.*) Don't pay me for being born. I've been paid enough.

LOUIE (*He picks up the money.*) Then take it for putting me up. You know how I hate hotels.

(*He offers it to her.*)

GRANDMA (*angrily*). I don't take from you!!! . . . Not what you haff to

give . . . You were always the strongest one. The survivor . . . *Live*—at any cost I taught you, yes. But not when someone else has to pay the price . . . Keep your filthy money, Louie. (*She starts to go.*)

LOUIE (*smiles*). You're terrific, Ma. One hundred percent steel. Finest grade made. Eddie's out there lookin' for scrap iron and the chump doesn't know he's got a whole battleship right here . . . Nah. You can't get me down, Ma. I'm too tough. You taught me good. And whatever I've accomplished in this life, just remember—you're my partner. (*He blows her a ferocious kiss.*)

Blackout

Scene 2

In the dark, we hear the voice of EDDIE *again.*

EDDIE (*voice-over*). "Dear Momma . . . The boys tell me you're getting along fine with them. I told you they wouldn't be any trouble. Enclosed, I'm sending you twenty-five dollars to cover their food and Arty's medicine . . . Yakob tells me some kids have been stealing pretzels and pistachio nuts. It's amazing that hasn't stopped in almost thirty years . . . Love, Eddie."

(*Later that night.*)

BELLA *and* JAY *are clearing the dining table of its remaining dishes and straightening out the chairs.*

GRANDMA *sits in her usual chair, wearing a sweater and crocheting or doing needlepoint.* LOUIE, *wearing his suit jacket, paces, looking like he's anxious to go.* AUNT GERT, *in her mid-to-late thirties, sits on the sofa. She holds a purse and her handkerchief, which she uses now and then to wipe her mouth.* ARTY *is in the kitchen, unseen, helping clean off the dishes.)*

BELLA. Would anyone like more coffee? Momma? Gert?

*(*GRANDMA *doesn't answer.)*

GERT *(nods).* Mmm.

BELLA. Strudel with it?

GERT *(hoarsely).* No.

BELLA. Jay, go in and get Aunt Gert some more coffee, but no strudel.

*(*JAY *goes in.)* Louie? Wouldn't you like another piece?

LOUIE *(distracted).* I had enough, Bella.

BELLA. You always have two pieces.

LOUIE. One strudel is enough tonight, okay, Bella?

(He looks at his watch . . . BELLA *starts to put the chairs from the dining table into the circle of seats in the living room.)*

BELLA. Don't help me with the chairs, anyone. I know just how I want it to be.

*(*LOUIE *looks at his watch as* BELLA *puts a chair in the right spot.)*

LOUIE. Listen, Momma. I'm gonna run along, now. I'll call you next week. Gert, it was good seein' you, sweetheart. You're lookin' terrific.

BELLA. Louie, you're going to sit right here.

LOUIE. Bella, I'm sorry. I really gotta go. It was a topnotch dinner, no kiddin'. *(He kisses her cheek. He calls off into the kitchen.)* Jay! It'll work out. Trust me. Where's Arty? I'm leavin'.

BELLA. No!! You can't go yet, Louie . . . You promised.

LOUIE. I promised I'd stay for dinner. I stayed for dinner. How many dinners you want me to stay for?

BELLA. But the family hasn't had a talk yet.

LOUIE. We did. We talked all through dinner. I never had a chance to swallow nothin'. I'm all talked out, Bella.

BELLA. There's still something that hasn't been talked about. It wasn't something that could be talked about at dinner . . . You sit here. This is your place.

LOUIE (*exasperated*). I told you I had to go right after the coffee. I had my coffee. I had my strudel. I had my dinner. I have to go, Bella.

BELLA (*nervously*). Momma! Gert! Tell him to stay . . . Louie, you can't go. You have to be here. The whole family has to be here. Momma, tell him.

GRANDMA (*sternly*). You're getting excited, Bella.

BELLA. I won't get excited. I promise. I'm fine, Momma . . . Just ask Louie to stay. Let me get the boys in.

GERT. He'll stay, Bella.

BELLA (*calls out*). Jay? Arty! Forget the dishes. We'll do them later . . . Everybody inside.

(JAY *comes in with* GERT's *coffee.* ARTY *follows, eating the last bite of a piece of strudel. He is dressed now.*)

JAY. Here's your coffee, Aunt Gert.

GERT. Thank you.

BELLA. Jay! Arty! Sit on the sofa with Aunt Gert. Momma, you stay there. I'll sit here and, Louie, sit on the chair.

LOUIE. I've been sittin' all night, Bella. I can stand up, okay?

BELLA. But it would be so much better if you were sitting, Louie. I pictured everybody sitting.

LOUIE. *I don't wanna sit!!* Change the picture. Picture everybody sittin' and me standin', alright?

(*This is the first time we hear* AUNT GERT *say her first full sentence, where her affliction becomes apparent. She speaks normally for the first half of the sentence and then somewhere past the middle, she sucks in her breath, so the words go to a higher pitch, and it sounds very difficult for her.*)

GERT. Louie, can't you just sit for a few minutes until Bella tells us what it is—(*She sucks in now.*)—she wants to talk to us about.

(ARTY *and* JAY *look at each other.*)

LOUIE. Okay. Okay. (*He sits on the window seat.*) Here? Alright? Is this the way you pictured it, Bella?

BELLA. No. I pictured you sitting on the chair I picked out.

LOUIE (*He crosses to "his" chair, but doesn't sit.*) Bella! It's very important that I leave here soon. Very important. I don't want to upset you, sweetheart, but I can't spend the rest of the night getting the seating arrangements right . . . I'm gonna stand up, I'm gonna listen, and then I'm gonna go.

BELLA (*She puts her head down and sulks, childlike.*) I pictured everybody sitting.

LOUIE. Jesus!

GERT. Louie, stop arguing with her and sit down, for God sakes, before—(*She sucks in.*)—she gets into one of her moods again.

GRANDMA. Louie, sit! Gertrude, stop it.

LOUIE. Louie sit! Louie stand! Louie eat! . . . You don't scare me anymore, Ma. Maybe everyone else here, but not me. You understand?

GRANDMA (*still crocheting*). Sit down, Louie!

(LOUIE *sits.*)

BELLA. Alright. *(She sits.)* Are we all seated now?

LOUIE. Yes, Bella. We're all seated. You wanna take a picture of what you pictured?

GERT. Stop it, Louie.

BELLA *(She looks around, then smiles, content with the seating.)* Now . . . who wants to start?

LOUIE *(rises).* Who wants to *start*? . . . Start *what*? . . . Momma, I haven't got time for this. Maybe when I was twelve years old, but not tonight. It's one of her games. Her crazy games, for crise sakes.

GERT. Is this a game, Bella? Are you just playing—*(Sucks in)*—a game with us, darling?

BELLA. It's not a game. It's very impor-tant . . . But I don't know how to start to say it. So somebody else has to help me and start first.

LOUIE *(to BELLA).* You have something important to tell us and you want *us* to start? *(He starts toward the front door.)* Listen, Gert. You understand her better than I do. When you fig-ure out what it is, let me know.

JAY *(to BELLA).* Aunt Bella, have you . . . *(LOUIE and everyone else stop and look at JAY.)* . . . have you been going to the movies lately, Aunt Bella?

BELLA *(She smiles.)* Thank you, Jay . . . Yes. I have been going to the movies a lot lately . . . *(LOUIE looks at her in disbelief.)* . . . Three times last week.

JAY. Really? . . . Did you see anything good?

BELLA. Oh, yes. I saw a picture with William Holden and Jean Arthur . . .

I really liked it . . . That's why I saw it three times.

LOUIE. This is what I stayed to dinner for? This is what I had to sit in the right seat to listen to? Jean Arthur and William Holden? Are they in the picture you pictured here?

GERT. Is that what this is about, Bella? Is this all about what movies—*(sucks in)*—you went to last week?

BELLA. No, but I'm getting to it. Ask me more questions, Jay. You're good at this.

JAY. Uh, let's see . . . Did you—go alone?

BELLA. Oh, yes. I always go alone. But it's interesting you asked me that . . . Because I met a friend there . . . You can ask me questions too, Gert.

GERT. I don't know what kind of ques-tions—*(Sucks in)*—to ask you.

ARTY. Ask her who the friend was.

GERT. Who was the friend?

BELLA. Well, his name is Johnny. I always see him there because he's the head usher. He's very nice.

JAY. So you just saw him in the theater?

BELLA. Well, once or twice we went out for coffee and once we took a walk in the park.

LOUIE. . . . You went to the park with this guy?

BELLA. Just to talk . . . You have to sit down if you're going to ask me ques-tions, Louie. *(LOUIE comes back and sits down.)* Now whose turn is it?

GRANDMA. Dis is ven you came home at eleven o'clock?

BELLA. Maybe. I think so. Was that it?

GERT. What did you do until eleven—*(Sucks in)*—o'clock?

BELLA. We walked and we talked . . . And we got to know each other . . . He doesn't want to be an usher forever. One day he wants to open up his own restaurant.

LOUIE. His own restaurant? And he's an usher? What is he, fifteen, sixteen?

BELLA. No. He's forty . . . And he wants to open up the restaurant with me.

(There is silence. She has finally gotten their attention.)

LOUIE. Why with you?

BELLA *(starting to get nervous)*. Because I can do all the cooking . . . and write out the menus . . . and keep the books.

GERT. And what would he do?

BELLA. He would be the manager.

(She sees this isn't going too well.)

LOUIE. If he's the manager, why doesn't *he* write out the menus and keep the books?

BELLA. Well, he has a—*(She looks at* ARTY *and* JAY.*)*—a reading handicap.

LOUIE. A what?

BELLA. A reading handicap.

LOUIE. Okay, hold it. Wait a minute. *(He rises.)* What do you mean? He can't read?

BELLA. You're not supposed to get out of your chair. That's not how I pictured it.

LOUIE. Yeah, well, now I'm getting my *own* picture . . . This guy is what? Illiterate?

BELLA. He can read . . . a little.

LOUIE. What's a little? His *name?* . . . This guy is either pulling your leg or he's after something, Bella . . . Is he after something?

BELLA. Maybe this isn't a good time to talk about it.

LOUIE. No, it's the *perfect* time to talk about it . . . What is this guy after, Bella? Has he touched you? . . . Has he fooled around with you?

BELLA. NO!!! He's not that kind of person.

LOUIE. Well, what kinda person *is* he? . . . He's forty years old, he takes you to the park at night. He wants to open up a restaurant with you and he can't read or write . . . How are you going to open up a restaurant? Who's going to put up the money?

BELLA. It'll only cost five thousand dollars.

LOUIE *(laughs)*. Five thousand dollars? Why not five million? And who's got the five grand? Him?

BELLA. I don't think so . . . He doesn't have any money.

LOUIE. Oh. Too bad . . . Well, then who does that leave?

BELLA. Don't yell at me, Louie.

LOUIE. I'm not yelling at you, Bella. I'm just asking you a question. Who does that leave to put up the five thousand dollars?

GERT. This is too terrible. Momma, please tell them—*(Sucks in)*—to stop this awful thing.

LOUIE. Who does that leave, Bella?

BELLA. I'll get the money somewhere.

LOUIE. Where is somewhere, Bella? . . .

There is no somewhere. You want Momma to sell the store? Is that what this guy asked you to do?

BELLA. He didn't ask me anything.

LOUIE. And he's either very smart or very dangerous. Well, he doesn't sound too smart to me. So that just leaves dangerous.

BELLA. He's *not* dangerous.

LOUIE. How do you know that?

BELLA. Because they don't take you at the Home if you're dangerous.

LOUIE. . . . The *Home???*

GRANDMA. Oh, my Gott!!

GERT. I don't understand this. Can somebody please—(*She sucks in.*)—explain all this to me.

LOUIE (*to* BELLA). Bella, honey. This man sounds very troubled . . . Is he living at the Home now?

BELLA. No. With his parents. He didn't like the Home. They weren't very nice to him there. (*She looks at* GRANDMA, *pointedly.*) . . . It's *not a nice place,* Momma!

LOUIE. Bella, sweetheart. Don't go to that movie anymore. Don't see that fella again. He may be very nice, but he sounds like he's got a lot of whacky ideas, you know what I mean, sweetheart?

BELLA. You promised you would support me . . . Jay! Arty! You said you would back me up. You promised.

LOUIE. Back you up with what, Bella? . . . The restaurant? The money? Is that what this guy is after?

BELLA. He wants *more* than that.

LOUIE. What could possibly be more than that, Bella?

BELLA. Me! He wants *me!* He wants to marry me! (*She starts to cry.*) I want to marry *him* . . . I want to have his children . . . I want my own babies.

LOUIE. (*sits back*). Jesus Christ!

GRANDMA (*shocked at this*). Dot's enough! . . . I don't vant to hear dis anymore!

BELLA. You think I can't have healthy babies, Momma? Well, I can . . . I'm as strong as an ox. I've worked in that store and taken care of you by myself since I'm twelve years old, that's how strong I am . . . Like *steel*, Momma. Isn't that how we're supposed to be? . . . But my babies won't die, because I'll love them and take care of them . . . And they won't get sick like me or Gert or be weak like Eddie and Louie . . . My babies will be happier than we were, because I'll teach them to be happy . . . Not to grow up and run away or never visit when they're older or not be able to breathe because they're so frightened . . . and never, *ever* to make them spend their lives rubbing my back and my legs because you never had anyone around who loved you enough to want to touch you, because you made it so clear you never wanted to be touched with love . . . Do you know what it's like to touch steel, Momma? It's hard and it's cold, and I want to be warm and soft with my children . . . Let me have my babies, Momma. Because I have to love somebody. I have to love someone who'll love me back before I die . . . Give me that, Momma, and I promise you, you'll never worry about being alone . . . Because you'll have us . . . Me and my husband and my babies . . . Louie, tell her how wonderful that would be . . . Gert, wouldn't that make her happy? . . . Momma? . . . Please say yes . . . I need you to say yes . . . Please?

(It is deathly silent. No one has moved. Finally, GRANDMA *gets up slowly, walks to her room, goes in, and quietly closes the door.)*

BELLA. *(looks at the others).* Hold me . . . Somebody please hold me.

*(*GERT *gets up and puts her arms around* BELLA *and rocks her gently.)*

We go to black.

Scene 3

ARTY *(voice-over).* "Dear Pop . . . Things are really bad here. Really, *really* bad. I wish you were home. Even just for a weekend. Last night I cried for you . . . and for Mom . . . but Jay was afraid Grandma would hear, so he stuck a sock in my mouth. I miss you and love you. Your son, Arty . . . Not Artur."

(Sunday, the following week. About midday. ARTY *is seated at the table, writing in his notebook.* JAY *stands looking out the window.)*

JAY. Where do you think Aunt Bella could be? Missing for two nights, somewhere out there in the city. I'm worried.

ARTY. Maybe Uncle Louie took her with him.

JAY. If he didn't take me, you think he's going to take Aunt Bella and her forty-year-old usher from the Home? . . .

(The door to GRANDMA's *room opens and* AUNT GERT *comes out.)*

GERT. I'm going now. I think Momma feels better since—*(A breath)*—Aunt Bella called me.

JAY. No idea where she is?

GERT. Yes. *(She moves away from* GRANDMA's *door.)* . . . She's at my house.

JAY. *Your* house?

GERT. Shhh. She doesn't want Momma to know.

ARTY. You mean she's been there all the time?

*(*GERT *nods "yes.")*

JAY. Is she ever coming back?

GERT. She's meeting with that man today . . . We'll know soon.

ARTY. Do you think they'll get married?

GERT. Who knows? . . . She been crying for—*(A breath)*—two days now. I'm sorry. It's hard for me to talk.

JAY. Isn't there anything the doctors can do about that, Aunt Gert?

GERT. I don't have it that much. It's mostly—*(Sucks in)*—when I come here.

JAY. Oh.

GERT. You boys take care of Grandma now. If Bella doesn't come back you're all she has.

JAY. I know.

GERT. If you run into trouble, do you have my number?

JAY. I don't think so.

GERT. It's Westchester seven—*(Sucks in)*—four-six-six-nine.

ARTY. What?

GERT. Westchester seven—*(Sucks in)*— four-six—

JAY. I have it! I have it!

GERT. Good-bye, darlings. Take care. I love you. *(She goes, closing the front door.)*

ARTY. It could be worse. Suppose we were left with her instead?

JAY. That's not funny.

ARTY. Yes, it is.

JAY. Alright. It's funny. But I feel sorry for her. I feel sorry for this whole family . . . Even Grandma . . . Don't you? (ARTY *looks at* JAY, *says nothing.*) Well, I do. And you should, too. (GRANDMA's *door opens. She comes out, looking tired.*) Hi, Grandma. How you feeling?

ARTY. Is there anything we can get you?

GRANDMA *(She sits.)* Vot are you doing in the house on Sunday? Vy don't you go for a valk or something?

JAY. We thought we'd keep you company.

GRANDMA. I don't need to be kept company.

ARTY. You want the radio on, Grandma? They have Sunday news on today.

GRANDMA. I had enough news already this week.

JAY. Things are getting better in North Africa. They captured twenty thousand Germans this month.

GRANDMA. Twenty thousand Germans . . . Goot. Dot's goot news.

ARTY. The football game is on now. Sometimes they interrupt the game for news reports.

GRANDMA. Don't trick me into listening to football. *(She turns her head.)* Vas dot the phone? Did you hear the phone downstairs?

JAY. No.

GRANDMA. No. It don't ring on Sundays . . . How is your father?

JAY. He's feeling better. He thinks he could be home for good in about eight months.

GRANDMA. Eight months . . . You'll be glad to go home, ya?

ARTY. Ya . . . Yes . . . Sort of.

JAY. But we'll still come out and visit you, Grandma.

GRANDMA. Maybe I von't be here . . . Maybe I'll sell da store.

JAY. Sell the store? What would you do without the store?

GRANDMA. Don't vorry so much about your grandma. Your grandma knows how to take care of herself, believe me . . . Go on outside, both of you. You talk too much.

JAY. You sure you don't mind being alone?

GRANDMA *(She sits back and closes her eyes.)* . . . Maybe dis is da first Sunday I'll get some rest.

(The front door opens and BELLA *comes in. She is wearing a hat and coat and carries her purse and a small suitcase. She also has a cake box.)*

JAY. Aunt Bella!

ARTY. Are you okay?

GRANDMA *(She doesn't react to this. She remains sitting back with her eyes still closed.)* Go already. How many times do I haff to tell you?

(The boys look at her, then turn and leave, closing the door. BELLA *stands there looking at her mother, who has still refused to open her eyes.)*

BELLA. Hello, Momma . . . *(GRANDMA doesn't respond.)* . . . Would you like some tea? It's chilly in here . . . I bought a coffee cake at Grossman's. It's still warm . . . It's alright if you don't want to talk to me, Momma. I know you must be very angry with me.

GRANDMA *(She looks away from* BELLA*).* You're home for goot or dis is a visit?

BELLA. I don't know . . . I thought I'd come back and talk to you about it.

GRANDMA. Like you talked to me da night you left? . . . Vidout a vord?

BELLA. You're the one who didn't talk, Momma. You never gave me a chance to say anything.

GRANDMA. I heard vot you had to say. I didn't haff to hear no more.

BELLA *(nods).* Look, Momma, I'm not crying . . . I know you're very angry with me, but I'm not crying. And it's not because I'm afraid to cry. It's because I have no tears left in me. I feel sort of empty inside. Like *you* feel all the time.

GRANDMA. How vould you know how I feel?

BELLA. You don't think I know anything, do you? You think I'm stupid, don't you, Momma?

GRANDMA. No. You're not stupid.

BELLA. Then what? Am I crazy? Do you think I'm crazy, Momma?

GRANDMA. Don't use dot word to me.

BELLA. Why not? Are you afraid of it? If that's what I am, Momma, then don't be afraid to say it. Because if I'm crazy, I should be in the Home, shouldn't I? But then you'd be alone and you wouldn't like that. Is that why you don't use that word, Momma?

GRANDMA. . . . You vant to know vot you are, Bella? . . . You're a child. Dot's vot da doctors told me. Not crazy. Not stupid . . . A child! . . . And dot's how I treat you. Because dot's all you understand . . . You don't need doctors. You're not sick. You don't need to live in da Home. *Dis* is vere you live. Vere you can be vatched and taken care of . . . You'll always be a child, Bella. And in dis vorld, vere dere is so much hate and sickness and death, vere nobody can live in peace, den maybe you're better off . . . Stay a child, Bella, and be glad dot's vot Gott made you.

BELLA. Then why did he make me look like a woman? . . . And feel like a woman inside of me? And want all the things a woman should have? Is that what I should thank him for? Why did he do that, Momma, when I can do everything but *think* like a woman? . . . I know I get confused sometimes . . . and frightened. But if I'm a child, why can't I be happy like a child? Why can't I be satisfied with dolls instead of babies?

GRANDMA. I'm not so smart I can answer such things.

BELLA. But I *am* smart, Momma. Maybe only as smart as a child, but some children are smarter than grown-ups.

Some grown-ups I've seen are very stupid. And very mean.

GRANDMA. You don't haff responsibilities, Bella. And responsibilities is vot makes meanness.

BELLA. I don't want to be your responsibility. Then maybe you won't be so mean to me.

GRANDMA. Den who will be responsible for you? Yourself? Dot man you ran away with? Who vants money from you? Who vants other things from you? God only knows vot else. Things you vould never know about. Stay the vay you are, Bella, because you don't know vot such feelings vould do to you.

BELLA. Yes, I do, Momma. I know what other things you're talking about . . . Because they've happened to me, Momma . . . Oh, yes . . . They've happened because I wanted them to happen . . . You angry at me?

GRANDMA (*She turns away, dismissing this.*) You don't know vot you're saying, Bella.

BELLA. You mean am I telling you the truth? Yes. I know what the truth is . . . Only I've been afraid to tell it to you for all these years. Gertrude knows. She's the only one . . . Do you hate me, Momma? Tell me, because I don't know if I did wrong or not.

GRANDMA. You're angry so you tell me lies. I don't vant to hear your childish lies.

(*She waves* BELLA *away.*)

BELLA. No! You *have* to listen, Momma . . . When I was in school, I let boys touch me . . . And boys that I met in the park . . . And in the movies . . . Even boys that I met here in the store . . . Nights when you were asleep, I went down and let them in . . . And not just boys, Momma . . . men too.

GRANDMA. Stop dis, Bella. You don't know vot you're saying . . . You dream these things in your head.

BELLA. I needed somebody to touch me, Momma. Somebody to hold me. To tell me I was pretty . . . *You* never told me that. Some even told me they loved me, but I never believed them because I knew what they wanted from me . . . Except John. He *did* love me. Because he understood me. Because he was like me. He was the only one I ever felt safe with. And I thought maybe for the first time I *could* be happy . . . That's why I ran away. I even brought the five thousand dollars to give to him for the restaurant. Then maybe he'd find the courage to leave home too.

GRANDMA (*She looks at her disdainfully.*) Is dis someting else you dreamed up? Vere vould you get five thousand dollars?

(BELLA *opens her purse and takes out a stack of bills tied in rubber bands. She puts it on the table.*)

BELLA. Does this look like a dream, Momma?

GRANDMA (*She picks up the bills and looks at them.*) Vere did you get dis? (*She turns quickly and looks toward her room.*) Did you steal from me? You know vere I keep my money. Nobody else knows but you. (*She throws her cup of tea in* BELLA's *face.*) You thief!!

You steal from your own mother?
Thief!!

BELLA (*screams at her*). Go on, hit me, Momma! Crack my head open, make me stupid and crazy, because that's what you really think anyway, isn't it?

GRANDMA. Get out of my house. Go live vith your thief friend. You vant da rest of the money, go, take it . . . It von't last you long . . . You'll both haff to steal again to keep alive, believe me.

BELLA. I don't want the rest of your money . . . You can have this too . . . Louie gave it to me. I stayed in Gertrude's house the last two nights . . . Louie came to say good-bye and he gave me this out of his little black satchel and God knows how much more he had . . . I didn't ask him. Maybe he's a thief too, Momma, but he's my brother and he loved me enough to want to help me . . . Thieves and sick little girls, that's what you have, Momma . . . Only God didn't make them that way. *You* did. We're alive, Momma, but that's all we are . . . Aaron and Rose are the lucky ones.

GRANDMA (*crushed*). NOOO!! . . . Don't say dat! . . . Please Gott, don't say dat to me, Bella.

BELLA. I'm sorry, Momma . . . I didn't mean to hurt you.

GRANDMA. Yes. You do . . . It's my punishment for being alive . . . for surviving my own children . . . Not dying before them is my sin . . . Go, Bella. Take Louie's money . . . You tink I don't know vot he is . . . He stole since he vas five years old . . . The year Aaron died . . . And I closed off from him and everybody . . . From you and Louie . . . From Gert and Eddie . . . I lost Rose, then Aaron, and I stopped feeling because I couldn't stand losing anymore . . .

BELLA. Momma!

GRANDMA. Go open your restaurant, live your own life, haff your own babies. If it's a mistake, let it be your mistake . . . If I've done wrong by you, then it's for me to deal with . . . That's how I've lived my life and no one, not even you, can change that for me now.

BELLA. . . . There is no restaurant, Momma . . . He's afraid to be a businessman or a manager . . . He likes being an usher . . . He likes to be in the dark all day, watching movies whenever he wants . . . Then he can live in a world he can feel safe in . . . He doesn't want babies . . . He doesn't want to get married . . . He wants to live with his parents because he knows that they love him . . . And that's enough for him.

GRANDMA. Then maybe he's more lucky than you.

BELLA. Maybe he is . . . But I'll never stop wanting what I don't have . . . It's too late to go back for me . . . Maybe I'm still a child, but now there's just enough woman in me to make me miserable. We have to learn how to deal with that somehow, you and me . . . And it can never be the same anymore . . . (*She gets up.*) I'll put my things away . . . I think we've both said enough for today . . . don't you?

BELLA *picks up her things, crosses into her room, and closes the door.*

GRANDMA *sits, stoically . . . and then her hand goes to her mouth, stifling whatever feelings are beginning to overcome her.*

We go to black.

BELLA *(voice-over).* "Dear Eddie . . . This postcard is from Bella. I just want to tell you that Arty and Jay are alright and I have good news for you except I don't have no more room. Love, Bella."

(Nine months later. We hear the church bells chime.

ARTY *and* JAY *are dressed in the same outfits they wore on that first day. They each have a suitcase sitting in the middle of the room.)*

ARTY. . . . How long you think Pop's going to be in there?

JAY. I don't know, but we made it, Arty. Ten months here and we're still alive. We got through Grandma and we're alright.

ARTY. You know who I miss? Uncle Louie . . . I'm glad those two guys never caught him.

JAY. No, but maybe the Japs will. You think he's safer fighting in the South Pacific?

ARTY. No. But he's probably the richest guy on Guadalcanal.

(The front door opens and BELLA *comes in carrying two shopping bags.)*

BELLA. Oh, thank God. I thought you'd be gone before I got back. I ran all over Yonkers looking for these . . . *(She puts the bags down.)* Okay. Close your eyes. *(They do. She takes out a basketball and a football. She gives the bas-*

ketball to JAY.) The football is for you, Jay. *(She gives the football to* ARTY.) And the basketball is for you, Arty. Do you like 'em?

ARTY. Ho-lee mackerel!

JAY. This is incredible.

BELLA. I hope it's the right size. I just took a guess.

JAY. This is one of the best gifts I ever got, Aunt Bella.

BELLA. Well, you two were the best gifts I ever got too. I hate to give you up.

JAY. You don't have to. We're coming out all the time.

ARTY. I really love this, Aunt Bella. Thank you.

BELLA. Well, it's not just from me. It's from Grandma too. I just have to tell her later.

(The bedroom door opens and EDDIE *comes out.)*

EDDIE. Well, Grandma and I are through talking, boys. You ready to go?

JAY. Hey, Pop. Look! It's from Aunt Bella. And Grandma.

ARTY. Aunt Bella, go out for a pass.

*(*GRANDMA *comes out of the bedroom, just as* ARTY *throws the football to* JAY.)*

GRANDMA. Vot's dis? Vot did I tell you about games in da house?

EDDIE. They're not playing games, Momma. They know better than that.

GRANDMA. If dey break someting, dey'll pay plenty, believe me.

JAY. Thank you for the ball, Grandma. I love it.

ARTY. I never owned a football in my life, Grandma.

EDDIE. Alright. Grandma's tired, boys. Let's say good-bye and go.

GRANDMA. Ve said good-bye dis morning. Two good-byes is too much.

EDDIE (*with some sincerity*). Well, Momma . . . I just wanted to say thank you. You did a lot for me and the boys. I don't know how to repay you for that.

GRANDMA. I'll tell you how. Don't do it again.

EDDIE. I pray to God I won't have to.

GRANDMA. And if you have to, I'll say no again. And this time I'll mean it . . . When Louie left for the army, I thought about sending you the money. Even Bella asked me to. But then I said no . . . Eddie has to do things for himself. And you did it. That's good.

EDDIE. Yes, Momma. I'm glad you finally approve of me.

GRANDMA. I didn't say that. All I said was "Good."

EDDIE. I'll accept that, Momma.

GRANDMA. So, I suppose you'll get married again, and I von't see you boys for another ten years.

EDDIE. I'm not ready for marriage yet, Momma, but from now on the boys won't be strangers anymore. They'll be grandchildren . . . And I'm going to kiss you good-bye whether you like it or not. (*He leans over and kisses her.*) Thank you for not putting up a fight. (*He nods, then turns to* BELLA.) Good-bye, Bella.

What can I say?

BELLA. I know, Eddie. I know.

EDDIE. I love you so much. (*He hugs her.*) I'll meet you downstairs, boys. Thank Grandma, go on.

(*And he goes before the tears come.*)

JAY. I er . . . I just want to say thank you for taking us in, Grandma. I know it wasn't easy for you.

GRANDMA. Dot's right. It vasn't.

JAY. It wasn't easy for us either. But I think I learned a lot since I'm here. Some good and some bad. Do you know what I mean, Grandma?

GRANDMA (*She looks up at him.*) You're not afraid to say the truth. Dot's good . . . You vant to hear vot my truth is? . . . Everything hurts. Vot it is you get good in life, you also lose someting.

JAY. I guess I'm too young to under-stand that.

GRANDMA. And I'm too old to forget it . . . Go on. Go home. Take care of your father. He's a good boy, but he always needs a little help.

(JAY *nods and crosses to the door, waiting for* ARTY.)

ARTY. Well, you sure gave me and Yakob a lot of help, Grandma. Danker Schein . . . That means, "Thank you."

GRANDMA. He's sneaky, dis one. Tries to get around me . . . Don't try to change me. Sometimes old people aren't altogether wrong.

ARTY. You're absolutely right . . . Can King Artur give you a kiss good-bye?

(*He kisses her and crosses to the door.*)

GRANDMA. . . . What were you two looking for that night under the boysenberry? My money maybe?

ARTY. No! I swear!

GRANDMA. You should have looked behind the malted machine.

(The boys hit themselves for their stupidity and leave. BELLA *looks at her mother.)*

BELLA. Well, I'll get dinner started . . . Do you mind eating early, because I'm going out tonight. With a friend. *(*GRANDMA *looks at her.)* It's a girl, Momma. I have a new girlfriend. She likes me and I like her . . . And she also has a brother I like . . . He works in the library . . . He can read everything . . . I'd like to have them both over for dinner one night . . . Can we do that, Momma? *(*GRANDMA *looks away, not knowing how to deal with this.)* It's alright . . . It's no rush. You don't have to make up your mind right now. *(She turns on the radio.)* . . . I thought Thursday would be a good night. *(The music, "Be Careful, It's My Heart" sung by Bing Crosby, comes up.* BELLA *hums along happily.)* It's called music, Momma.

(And she disappears into the kitchen.

GRANDMA *watches* BELLA, *then nods her head as if to say, "So it's come to this . . .")*

Curtain

Responding to the Play

1. Which character in this play would you most like to portray? Why?
2. What does the title *Lost in Yonkers* signify?
3. The tone of this play is somber and somewhat dark, yet there are many elements of humor. Think of a play with similar characteristics and compare it to *Lost in Yonkers.*
4. Think about how you might portray Louie or Bella. Choose either character, then analyze how he or she reacts to the following people: Bella (if you choose Louie), Louie (if you choose Bella), Grandma, and Jay.
5. Imagine that Bella is looking for a new job. Write a resume for her.

More About Neil Simon

In the early days of television, Neil Simon wrote for Sid Caesar's *Your Show of Shows* and for *The Phil Silvers Show.* His first play, *Come Blow Your Horn,* was made into a film and a musical called *Little Me.* Since the 1960's, Simon has had a play running in New York just about every year. Most of his plays, including *Barefoot in the Park, Plaza Suite, The Sunshine Boys, Brighton Beach Memoirs, Biloxi Blues,* and *Jake's Women* have been adapted for the screen. His play *The Odd Couple* was developed into a television series that ran for many years.

Creating and Performing

1. Pick a scene in the play in which you believe Grandma reveals her true character. Read it for the class.
2. Read a scene from the play that includes the character you would most like to portray. Work on the voice and movement of your character.
3. Much of Eddie's presence in the play is accomplished by letters in the form of voice-overs. Look at each letter he writes and create a graphic organizer that will show 1) his mood 2) how he feels about himself 3) his goals and 4) any changes in his personality.

The Play as Literature: Protagonist/Antagonist

The *protagonist* of a literary work is the main character, often the person whose viewpoint is most clearly represented. The person who opposes the protagonist is the *antagonist.* In many works of modern literature the delineation between these characters is not clear-cut. There may be more than one protagonist or none at all. There may be many antagonists. Sometimes the antagonist is not a person but an event, an idea, or the protagonist's own inner conflict.

As you read *My Children! My Africa!* try to decide which of the three characters you think is the protagonist.

The Play as Theatre: Dramatic Monologue

A *monologue* is any fairly lengthy speech that a single character in a play addresses to the audience. Unlike a *soliloquy,* which represents what a character is thinking inwardly, the monologue is presented directly to the listeners.

The *dramatic monologue* is said to reveal "a soul in action" through the speech of the character. In the play you are about to read, each of the characters has a very telling dramatic monologue.

WARM UP!

Imagine that you are to play the role of someone who must choose between friendship and integrity. Your character knows that a friend is going to break the law. Your character cannot convince the friend not to break this law. Think about what your character would feel and what he or she would do in this situation. Write a short monologue in which your character discusses the problem.

MY CHILDREN!
MY AFRICA!

by Athol Fugard

ACT ONE

SCENE 1

Classroom of the Zolile High School

T RISE: MR. M *is at a table with* THAMI *and* ISABEL *on either side of him. A lively inter-school debate is in progress. Everybody is speaking at the same time.*

MR. M. Order, please!

ISABEL. I never said anything of the kind.

THAMI. Yes, you did. You said that women were more . . .

MR. M. I call you both to order!

ISABEL. What I said was that women . . .

THAMI. . . . were more emotional than men . . .

ISABEL. Correction! That women were more intuitive than men . . .

MR. M. Miss Dyson and Mr. Mbikwana! Will you both please . . .

ISABEL. You are twisting my words and misquoting me.

THAMI. I am not. I am simply asking you . . .

MR. M. Come to order! (*Grabs the school bell and rings it violently. It works. Silence.*) I think it is necessary for me to remind all of you exactly what a debate is supposed to be. (*Opens and reads from a little black dictionary that is at hand on the table*) My dictionary defines it as follows: "the orderly and regulated discussion of an issue with opposing viewpoints receiving equal time and consideration." Shouting down the opposition so that they cannot be heard does not comply with that definition. Enthusiasm for your cause is most commendable but without personal discipline it is as useless as having a good donkey and a good cart but no harness. We are now running out of time. I am therefore closing the open section of our debate. No more interruptions from the floor, please. We'll bring our proceedings to a close with a brief, I repeat *brief,* three minutes at the most, summing up of our arguments. Starting with the proposers of the motion: Mr. Thami Mbikwana of the Zolile High School, will you please make your concluding statement?

(THAMI *stands up. Wild round of applause from the audience. He is secure and at ease . . . he is speaking to an audience of schoolmates. His "concluding statement" is outrageous and he knows it and enjoys it.*)

THAMI. I don't stand here now and speak to you as your friend and schoolmate. That would lessen the seriousness of my final words to you. No! Close your eyes, forget that you know my face and voice, forget that you know anything about Thami Mbikwana. Think of me rather as an oracle, of my words as those of the great ancestors of our traditional African culture, which we turn our back on and desert to our great peril!

The opposition has spoken about sexual exploitation and the need for women's liberation. Brothers and sisters, these are foreign ideas. Do not listen to them. They come from a culture, the so-called Western Civilization, that has meant only misery to Africa and its people. It is the same culture that shipped away thousands of our ancestors as slaves, the same culture that has exploited Africa with the greed of a vulture during the period of Colonialism and the same culture which continues to exploit us in the twentieth century under the disguise of concern for our future.

The opposition has not been able to refute my claim that women cannot do the same jobs as men because they are not the equals of us physically and that a woman's role in the family, in society, is totally different to that of a man's. These facts taken together reinforce what our fathers and our grandfathers and our great grandfathers knew; namely that happiness and prosperity for the tribe and the nation is achieved when education of the little ladies takes these facts into consideration. Would it be right for a woman to go to war while man sits at the sewing machine? I do not have milk in my breasts to feed the baby while my wife is out digging up roads for the Divisional Council. (*Wild laughter*)

Brothers and sisters, it is obvious that you feel the same as I do about this most serious matter. I hope that at the end of this debate, your vote will reflect your agreement with me. (*Wild applause and whistles*)

MR. M. Thank you, Mr. Mbikwana.

(THAMI *sits.*)

MR. M. And now finally, a last statement from the captain of the visiting team, Miss Isabel Dyson of Camdeboo Girls High.

ISABEL (*Polite applause. Stands. She takes on the audience with direct unflinching eye contact. She is determined not to be intimidated.*) You have had to listen to a lot of talk this afternoon about traditional values, traditional society, your great ancestors, your glorious past. In spite of what has been implied, I want to start off by telling you that I have as much respect and admiration for your history and tradition as anybody else. I believe most strongly that there are values and principles in traditional African society which could be studied with great profit by the Western Civilization so scornfully rejected by the previous speaker. But at the same time, I know, and you know, that Africa no longer lives in that past. For better or for worse it is part now of the twentieth century and all the nations on this continent are struggling very hard to come to terms with that reality. Arguments about sacred traditional values, the traditional way of life, et cetera and et cetera, are used by those who would like to hold back Africa's progress and keep it locked up in the past.

Maybe there was a time in the past when a woman's life consisted of bearing children and hoeing the fields while men sharpened their spears and sat around waiting for another war to start. But it is a silly argument that relies on that old image of primitive Africa for its strength. It is an argument that insults your intelligence. Times have changed. Sheer brute strength is not the determining factor anymore. You do not need the muscles of a prize fighter when you sit down to operate the computers that control today's world. The American space program now has women astronauts on board the space shuttle doing the same jobs as men. As for the difference in the emotional and intellectual qualities of men and women, remember that it is a question of difference and not inferiority, and that with those differences go strengths which compensate for weaknesses in the opposite sex.

And lastly, a word of warning. The argument against equality for women, in education or any other field, based on alleged "differences" between the two sexes, is an argument that can very easily be used against any other "different" group. It is an argument based on prejudice, not fact. I ask you not to give it your support. Thank you. *(She sits. Polite applause.)*

MR. M. Thank you, Miss Dyson. We come now to the vote. But before we do that, a word of caution. We have had a wonderful experience this afternoon. Don't let it end on a frivolous and irresponsible note. Serious issues have been debated. Vote accordingly. To borrow a phrase from Mr. Mbikwana, forget the faces, remember the words. If you believe that we have the right to vote out there in the big world, then show here in the classroom that you know how to use it. We'll take it on a count of hands, and for the benefit of any over-enthusiastic supporters, only one hand per person, please. Let me read the proposal once again: "That in view of the essential physical and psychological differences between men and women, there should be correspondingly different educational syllabuses for the two sexes." All those in favor raise a hand.

(MR. M, THAMI, *and* ISABEL *count hands.*)

MR. M. Seventeen?

(THAMI *and* ISABEL *nod agreement.*)

MR. M. All those against.

(They all count again.)

MR. M. Twenty-four?

(Reactions from THAMI and ISABEL)

MR. M. The proposal is defeated by twenty-four votes to seventeen. Before we break, just a reminder about the special choir practice this afternoon. Members of the choir must please join Mrs. Magada in Number Two Classroom after school. *(To* ISABEL *and* THAMI*)* Allow me to offer you my congratulations, Miss Dyson, on a most well deserved victory. What do you say, Mbikwana?

THAMI *(to* ISABEL*).* Your concluding statement was a knockout.

MR. M. You didn't do too badly yourself.

ISABEL. You made me so angry!

THAMI *(all innocence).* I did?

ISABEL. Ja, you did.

(THAMI *laughs.*)

ISABEL. I was beginning to think you actually believed what you were saying.

THAMI. But I do!

ISABEL. Oh, come on . . .!

MR. M *(rubbing his hands with pleasure).* All I can say is . . . Splendid! Splendid! Splendid! The intellect in action. Challenge and response. That is what a good debate is all about. And whatever you do, young lady, don't underestimate your achievement in winning the popular vote. It wasn't easy for that audience to vote against Mbikwana. He's one of them, and a very popular "one of them," I might add. *(Waving a finger at* THAMI*)* You were quite shameless in the way you tried to exploit that loyalty.

THAMI *(another laugh).* Was that wrong?

MR. M. No. As the saying goes, all is fair in love, war, and debating. But the fact that you didn't succeed is what makes me really happy. I am very proud of our audience. In my humble opinion they are the real winners this afternoon. You two just had to talk and argue. Anybody can do that. They had to listen . . . intelligently!

ISABEL. They certainly gave me a good time.

MR. M. That was very apparent, if I may say so, Miss Dyson. I can't thank you enough for coming to us today. I sincerely hope there'll be another occasion.

ISABEL. Same here.

MR. M. Good! *(Consults his watch)* Now you must excuse me. There is a staff meeting waiting for me. Will you look after Miss Dyson please, Mbikwana?

THAMI. Yes, teacher.

(MR. M *leaves.* ISABEL *and* THAMI *pack away into their schoolcases the papers and books they used in the debate. Without the mediating presence of* MR. M *they are both a little self-conscious. First moves in the ensuing conversation are awkward.*)

ISABEL. I wish we had a teacher like . . . Mr. . . . *(Pronouncing the name carefully)* . . . M ya lat ya. Did I say it right?

THAMI. Yes, you did, but nobody calls him that. He's just plain Mr. M to everybody.

ISABEL. Mr. M.

THAMI. That's right.

ISABEL. Well, I think he's wonderful.

THAMI. He's okay.

ISABEL. I had a geography teacher in Standard Seven who was a little bit like him. Full of fun and lots of energy.

THAMI. Ja, that's Mr. M all right. *(Pause)*

ISABEL. I meant what I said to him. I really did have a good time.

THAMI. Same here.

ISABEL. You did? Because to be honest with you, I wasn't expecting it.

THAMI. Me neither.

ISABEL. No?

THAMI. Nope.

ISABEL. Why not?

THAMI *(embarrassed).* Well . . . you know . . .

ISABEL. Let me guess. You've never debated with girls before.

(He nods, smiling sheepishly.)

ISABEL. And white girls at that! I don't believe it. You boys are all the same.

THAMI. But you were good!

ISABEL. Because I happen to feel very strongly about what we were debating. But it was also the whole atmosphere, you know. It was so . . . so free and easy. The debates at my school are such stuffy affairs. And so

boring most of the time. Everything is done according to the rules with everybody being polite and nobody getting excited . . . lots of discipline but very little enthusiasm. This one was a riot!

THAMI *(finger to lips).* Be careful.

ISABEL. Of what?

THAMI. That word.

ISABEL. Which one?

THAMI. Riot! Don't say it in a black township. Police start shooting as soon as they hear it.

ISABEL. Oh. I'm sorry.

THAMI *(having a good laugh).* It's a joke, Isabel.

ISABEL. Oh . . . you caught me off guard. I didn't think you would joke about those things.

THAMI. Riots and police? Oh yes, we joke about them. We joke about everything.

ISABEL. Okay, then I'll say it again; this afternoon was a riot.

THAMI. Good! Try that one on your folks when you get home tonight. Say the newspapers have got it all wrong. You had a wonderful time taking part in a little township riot.

(This time ISABEL does get the joke. A good laugh.)

ISABEL. Oh ja, I can just see my mom and dad cracking up at that one.

THAMI. They wouldn't think it was funny? *(The subject of white reaction to location humor amuses him enormously.)*

ISABEL. Are you kidding? They even take the Marx Brothers seriously. I can just hear my mom: "Isabel, I think it is very wrong to joke about those things."

THAMI. Dyson! That's an English name.

ISABEL. Sober, sensible, English-speaking South African. I'm the third generation.

THAMI. What does your dad do?

ISABEL. He's a chemist. The chemist shop in town. Karoo Pharmacy. That's ours. My mother and sister work in it as well; and on Saturdays, provided there isn't a hockey match, so do I.

THAMI. Any brothers?

ISABEL. No. Just the four of us.

THAMI. A happy family.

ISABEL. Ja, I suppose you could call us that. Mind you, Lucille would say it would be a lot happier if her little sister would be, as she puts it, "more accommodating of others."

THAMI. What does she mean?

ISABEL. She means she doesn't like the fact that I've got opinions of my own. I'm the rebel in the family.

THAMI. That sounds most interesting.

ISABEL. I can't help it. Whenever it's time for a family *indaba* . . . you know, when we sit down in the lounge to discuss family business and things . . . I just always seem to end up disagreeing with everybody and wanting to do things differently. But other than that, ja, an average sort of family. What else do you want to know? Go ahead, anything . . . provided I also get a turn to ask questions.

(THAMI *studies her.*)

ISABEL. Eighteen years old. I think I want to be a writer. My favorite subject is English and my favorite sport, as you might have guessed, is hockey. Anything else?

THAMI. Yes. What did you have for breakfast this morning?

ISABEL. Auntie, our maid, put down in front of me a plate of steaming, delicious jungle oats over which I sprinkled a crust of golden, brown sugar, and while that was melting on top I added a little moat of chilled milk all around the side. That was followed by brown-bread toast, quince jam, and lots and lots of tea.

THAMI. Yes, you're a writer.

ISABEL. You think so?

THAMI. You made me hungry.

ISABEL. My turn now?

THAMI. Yep.

ISABEL. Let's start with your family.

THAMI. Mbikwana!! (*He clears his throat.*) Mbikwana is an old Bantu name and my mother and my father are good, reliable, ordinary, hardworking, Bantu-speaking, black South African natives. I am the one hundred thousandth generation.

ISABEL. You really like teasing, don't you?

THAMI. Amos and Lilian Mbikwana. They're in Cape Town. My mother is a domestic and my father works for the railways. I stay here with my grandmother and married sister. I was sent to school in the peaceful platteland because it is so much safer, you see, than the big city with all its temptations and troubles.

(THAMI *laughs.*) Another Bantu joke.

ISABEL. You're impossible!

(They are now beginning to relax with each other. ISABEL *finds the class register on the desk.)*

ISABEL. "Zolile High School. Standard Ten." *(She opens it and reads.)* Awu.

THAMI *(pointing to the appropriate desk in the classroom).* There. Johnny. Center-forward in our soccer team.

ISABEL. Bandla.

THAMI. There.

ISABEL. Cwati.

THAMI. Cwati. There.

ISABEL. Who was the chap sitting there who laughed at all your jokes and applauded everything you said?

THAMI. Stephen Gaika. He's mad!

ISABEL. And your best friend?

THAMI. They are all my friends.

ISABEL. And where does . . . *(She finds his name in the register.)* . . . Thami Mbikwana sit?

(THAMI points. ISABEL *goes to the desk and sits.)*

THAMI. Yes, that's the one. For nearly two years I've sat there . . . being educated!

ISABEL *(reading names carved into the wood of the desk).* John, Bobby, Zola, Bo . . . Boni . . .

THAMI. Bonisile.

ISABEL. Where's your name?

THAMI. You won't find it there. I don't want to leave any part of me in this classroom.

ISABEL. That sounds very heavy.

THAMI. It's been heavy. You've got no problems with it, hey?

ISABEL. With school? No, not really. Couple of teachers have tried their best to spoil it for me, but they haven't succeeded. I've had a pretty good time, in fact. I think I might even end up with the old cliché . . . you know, school years, best years, happiest years . . . Whatever it is they say.

THAMI. No. I won't be saying that.

ISABEL. That surprises me.

THAMI. Why?

ISABEL. Ja, come on, wouldn't you be if I said it? You're obviously clever. I'll bet you sail through your exams.

THAMI. It's not as simple as just passing exams, Isabel. School doesn't mean the same to us that it does to you.

ISABEL. Go on.

THAMI. I used to like it. Junior school? You should have seen me. I wanted to have school on Saturdays and Sundays as well. Yes, I did. Other boys wanted to kill me. I hated the holidays.

ISABEL. So what happened?

THAMI. I changed.

ISABEL. Ja, I'm listening.

THAMI *(a shrug).* That's all. I changed. Things changed. Everything changed.

ISABEL *(realizing she is not going to get any more out of him).* Only five months to go.

THAMI. I'm counting.

ISABEL. What then?

THAMI. After school? *(Another shrug)* I don't know yet. Do you?

ISABEL. Ja, Rhodes University. I want to study journalism.

THAMI. Newspaper reporter.

ISABEL. And radio, TV. It's a very wide field now. You can specialize in all sorts of things. *(Perplexed)* Don't you want to study further, Thami?

THAMI. I told you. I'm not sure about anything yet.

ISABEL. What does Mr. M say?

THAMI. It's got nothing to do with him.

ISABEL. But you're his favorite, aren't you?

(Non-committal shrug from THAMI*)*

ISABEL. I bet you are. And I also bet you anything you like that he's got a career planned out for you.

THAMI *(sharply)*. What I do with my life has got nothing to do with him.

ISABEL. Sorry.

THAMI. I don't listen to what he says and I don't do what he says.

ISABEL. I said I'm sorry, I didn't mean to interfere.

THAMI. That's all right. It's just that he makes me so mad sometimes. He always thinks he knows what is best for me. He never asks me how I feel about things. I know he means well, but I'm not a child anymore. I've got ideas of my own now.

ISABEL *(placating)*. Ja, I know what you mean. I've had them in my life as well. They always know what is best for you, don't they? So anyway, listen . . . I'm going to write up the debate for our school newspaper. I'll send you a copy if you like.

THAMI. You got a school newspaper!

How about that!

ISABEL. It's a bit unethical reporting on a contest in which I took part, and won, but I promise to be objective. I made notes of most of your main points.

THAMI. You can have my speech if you want it.

ISABEL. Well, thanks. That will make it much easier . . . and guarantee there won't be any misquotes!

*(*THAMI *hands over the speech. It is obvious that they both want to prolong the conversation, but this is prevented by the sound of* MR. M*'s bell being rung vigorously in the distance. They check wristwatches.)*

ISABEL. Oh, look at the time!

(They grab their schoolcases and run.)

SCENE 2

ISABEL *(Alone. She speaks directly to the audience.)* It's on the edge of town, on the right hand side when you drive out to join the National Road going north to Middleberg. Unfortunately, as most of Camdeboo would say, you can't miss it. I discovered the other day that it has actually got a name . . . Brakwater . . . from the old farm that used to be there. Now everybody just calls it "the location." There's been a lot of talk lately about moving it to where it can't be seen. Our mayor, Mr. Pienaar, was in our shop the other day and I heard him say to my dad that it was "very much to be regretted" that the first thing that greeted any visitor to the town was the "terrible mess of the location." To be fair to old Pienaar, he has got a point, you know. Our town is very pretty. We've got a lot of nicely restored National Monument houses and buildings. 'Specially in the Main Street. Our shop is one of them. The location is quite an eyesore by comparison. Most of the houses—if you can call them that!—are made of bits of old corrugated iron or anything else they could find to make four walls and a roof. There are no gardens or anything like that. You've got to drive in first gear all the time because of the potholes and stones, and when the wind is blowing and all the dust and rubbish flying around . . . ! I think you'd be inclined to agree with our mayor.

I've actually been into it quite a few times. With my mom to visit Auntie, our maid, when she was sick. And with my dad when he had to take emergency medicines to the clinic. I can remember one visit, just sitting in the car and staring out of the window trying to imagine what it would be like to live my whole life in one of those little *pondoks*. No electricity, no running water. No privacy! Auntie's little house has only got two small rooms and nine of them sleep there. I ended up being damn glad I was born with a white skin.

But don't get the wrong idea. I'm not saying I've spent a lot of time thinking about it seriously or anything like that.

It's just been there, you know, on the edge of my life, the way it is out there on the edge of town. So when

Miss Brockway, our principal, called me in and told me that the black school had started a debating society and had invited us over for a debate, I didn't have any objections. She said it was a chance for a "pioneering intellectual exchange" between the two schools.

She also said she had checked with the police and they had said it would be all right, provided we were driven straight to the school and then straight out afterwards. There's been a bit of trouble in the location again and people are starting to get nervous about it. So off we went . . . myself, Renee Vermaas, and Cathy Bullard, the C.G.H. Debating Team . . . feeling very virtuous about our "pioneering" mission into the location. As Renee tactfully put it: "Shame! We must remember that English isn't their home language. So don't use too many big words and speak slowly and carefully."

They were waiting for us in what they called Number One Classroom. *(Shaking her head)* Honestly, I would rate it as the most bleak, depressing, dingy classroom I have ever been in. Everything about it was grey—the cement floor, the walls, the ceiling.

When I first saw it I thought to myself, how in heaven's name does anybody study or learn anything in here? But there they were, about forty of them, my age, mostly boys, not one welcoming smile among the lot of them. And they *were* studying something and very intently . . . three privileged and uncomfortable white girls, in smart uniforms, from a posh school, who had come to give them a lesson in debating. I know I'm a good debater and one of the reasons for that is that I always talk very directly to the audience and the opposition. I am not shy about making eye contact. Well, when I did it this time, when it was my turn to speak and I stood up and looked at those forty unsmiling faces, I suddenly realized that I hadn't prepared myself for one simple but all important fact: they had no intention of being grateful to me. They were sitting there waiting to judge me, what I said and how I said it, on the basis of total equality. Maybe it doesn't sound like such a big thing to you, but you must understand I had never really confronted that before, and I don't just mean in debates. I mean in my life!

I'm not saying I've had no contact across the color line. Good heavens no! I get as much of that as any average young white South African. I have a great time every morning with Auntie in the kitchen when she's cooking breakfast and we gossip about everything and everybody in town. And then there's Samuel with his crash helmet and scooter . . . he delivers medicines for my dad . . . I have wonderful long conversations with him about religion and the meaning of life generally. He's a very staunch Zionist. Church every Sunday. But it's always "Miss Isabel," the baas' daughter, that he's talking to. When

I stood up in front of those black matric pupils in Number One Classroom it was a very different story. I wasn't at home or in my dad's shop or in my school or any of the other safe places in my life.

I was in Brakwater! It was *their* school. It was *their* world. I was the outsider and I was being asked to prove myself. Standing there in front of them like that I felt . . . exposed! . . . in a way that has never happened to me before. Cathy told me afterwards that she's never heard me start a debate so badly and finish it so strongly.

It was good! I don't know when exactly it happened, but about halfway through my opening address, I realized that everything about that moment . . . the miserable little classroom, myself, my voice, what I was saying and them hearing and understanding me, because I knew they understood me . . . they were staring and listening so hard I could feel it on my skin! . . . all of it had become one of the most real experiences I have ever had. I have never before had so . . . so exciting . . . a sense of myself! Because that *is* what we all want, isn't it? For things to be real—our lives, our thoughts, what we say and do? That's what I want, now. I didn't really know it before that debate, but I do now. You see, I finally worked out what happened to me in the classroom. I discovered a new world! I've always thought about the location as just a sort of embarrassing backyard to our neat and proper little white world, where our maids and our gardeners and our delivery boys went at the end of the day. But it's not. It's a whole world of its own with its own life that has nothing to do with us. If you put together all the Brakwaters in the country, then it's a pretty big one . . . and if you'll excuse my language . . . there's a hell of a lot of people living in it! That's quite a discovery you know. But it's also a little . . . what's the word? . . . disconcerting! You see, it means that what I thought was out there for me . . . No, it's worse than that! It's what I was made to believe was out there for me . . . the ideas, the chances, the people . . . 'specially the people! . . . all of that is only a small fraction of what it could be. (*Shaking her head*) No. Or as Auntie says in the kitchen, when she's not happy about something . . . *Aikona!* Not good enough. I'm greedy. I want more. I want as much as I can get.

SCENE 3

AT RISE: ISABEL *alone.*

MR. M *enters, hat in hand, mopping his brow with a handkerchief.*

MR. M. Miss Dyson! There you are.

ISABEL (*surprised*). Hello!

MR. M. My apologies for descending on you out of the blue like this, but I've been looking for you high and low. One of your schoolmates said I would find you here.

ISABEL. Don't apologize. It's a pleasure to see you again, Mr. M.

MR. M (*delighted*). Mr. M! How wonderful to hear you call me that.

ISABEL. You must blame Thami for my familiarity.

MR. M. Blame him? On the contrary, I will thank him most gratefully. Hearing you call me Mr. M like all the others at the school gives me a happy feeling that you are also a member of my very extended family.

ISABEL. I'd like to be.

MR. M. Then welcome to my family, Miss—

ISABEL (*before he can say it*). "Isabel" if you please, Mr. M, just plain Isabel.

MR. M (*bowing*). Then doubly welcome, young Isabel.

ISABEL (*curtsy*). I thank you, kind sir.

MR. M. You have great charm, young lady. I can understand now how you managed to leave so many friends behind you after only one visit to the school. Hardly a day passes without someone stopping me and asking: When is Isabel Dyson and her team coming back?

ISABEL. Well? When are we?

MR. M. You would still welcome a return visit?

ISABEL. But of course.

MR. M. Why so emphatically "of course?"

ISABEL. Because I enjoyed the first one so emphatically very much.

MR. M. The unruly behavior of my young family wasn't too much for you?

ISABEL. Didn't I also get a little unruly once or twice, Mr. M?

MR. M. Yes, now that you mention it. You certainly gave as good as you got.

ISABEL *(with relish).* And that is precisely why I enjoyed myself . . .

MR. M. You like a good fight.

ISABEL. Ja. 'Specially the ones I win!

MR. M. Splendid! Splendid! Splendid! Because that is precisely what I have come to offer you.

ISABEL. Your Thami wants a return bout, does he?

MR. M. He will certainly welcome the opportunity to salvage his pride when it comes along . . . his friends are teasing him mercilessly . . . but what I have come to talk to you about is a prospect even more exciting than that. I have just seen Miss Brockway and she has given it her official blessing. It was her suggestion that I approach you directly. So here I am. Can you spare a few minutes?

ISABEL. As many as you like.

MR. M. It came to me as I sat there in Number One trying to be an impartial referee, while you and Thami went for each other hammer and tongs, no holds barred and no quarter given or asked. I don't blame our audience for being so unruly. Once or twice I felt like doing some shouting myself. What a contest! But at the same time, what a waste, I thought! Yes, you heard me correctly. A waste! They shouldn't be fighting each other. They should be fighting together! If the sight of them as opponents is so exciting, imagine what it would be like if they were allies. If those two stood side by side and joined forces, they could take on anybody . . . and win! For the next few days that is all I could think of. It tormented me. When I wrote my report about the debate in the school diary, that was the last sentence. "But, oh what a waste!"

The truth is, I've seen too much of it, Isabel. Wasted people! Wasted chances! It's become a phobia with me now. It's not easy, you know, to be a teacher, to put your heart and soul into educating an eager young mind which you know will never get a chance to develop further and realize its full potential. The thought that you and Thami would be another two victims of this country's lunacy, was almost too much for me.

The time for lamentations is passed. *(Taking envelope from his pocket)* Two days ago I received this in the mail. It's the program for this year's Grahamstown Schools Festival. It has given me what I was looking for . . . an opportunity to fight the lunacy. The Standard Bank is sponsoring a new event: An inter-school English literature quiz. Each team to consist of two members. I'll come straight to the point. I have suggested to Miss Brockway that Zolile High and Camdeboo High join forces and enter a combined team. As I have already told you, she has agreed and so has the Festival director who I spoke to on the telephone this morning. There you have it, Isabel Dyson. I anxiously await your response.

ISABEL. I'm on the team?

MR. M. Yes.

ISABEL. And . . .? *(Her eyes brighten with anticipation.)*

MR. M. That's right.

ISABEL. Thami!

MR. M. Correct!

ISABEL. Mr. M, you're a genius!

MR. M *(Holding up a hand to stop what was obviously going to be a very enthusiastic response).* Wait! Wait! Before you get carried away and say yes, let me warn you about a few things. It's going to mean a lot of very hard work. I am appointing myself team coach and as Thami will tell you, I can be a very hard taskmaster. You'll have to give up a lot of free time, young lady.

ISABEL. Anything else?

MR. M. Not for the moment.

ISABEL. Then I'll say it again. Mr. M, you're a genius! *(Her joy is enormous and she shows it.)* How's that for unruly behavior?

MR. M. The very worst! They couldn't do it better on the location streets. What a heartwarming response, Isabel!

ISABEL. What were you expecting? That I would say no?

MR. M. I didn't know what to expect. I knew that you would give me a sympathetic hearing, but that I would be swept off my feet, literally and figuratively . . . No. I was most certainly not prepared for that. Does my silly little idea really mean that much to you?

ISABEL. None of that, Mr. M! It's not silly and it's not little and you know it.

MR. M. All right. But does it really mean that much to you?

ISABEL. Yes, it does.

MR. M *(persistent).* But why?

ISABEL. That visit to Zolile was one of the best things that has happened to me. I don't want it to just end there. One visit and that's it.

(MR. M listens quietly, attentively, an invitation to ISABEL to say more.)

ISABEL. It feels like it could be the beginning of something. I've met you and Thami and all the others and I would like to get to know you all better. But how do I do that? I can't just go after you chaps like . . . well, you know what I mean. Roll up and knock on your doors like you were neighbors or just living down the street. It's not as easy as that with us, is it? You're in the location, I'm in the town . . . and all the rest of it. So there I was feeling more and more frustrated about it all when along you come with your "silly little" idea. It's perfect! Do I make sense?

MR. M. Most definitely. Make some more.

ISABEL. I've been thinking about it, you see. When I told my mom and dad about the debate and what a good time I'd had, I could see that they didn't really understand what I was talking about. 'Specially my mom. I ended up getting very impatient with her, which wasn't very smart of me because the harder I tried to make her understand the more nervous she got. Anyway, I've cooled off now and I realize why she was like that. Being with black people on an equal footing, you know . . . as equals, because that is how I ended up feeling with Thami and his friends . . . that was something that had never happened to her. She didn't know what I was talking about. And because she knows nothing about it, she's frightened of it.

MR. M. You are not.

ISABEL. No. Not anymore.

MR. M. So you were.

ISABEL. Well, not so much frightened as sort of uncertain. You see I thought I knew what to expect, but after a few minutes in Number One Classroom I realized I was wrong by a mile.

MR. M. What had you expected, Isabel?

ISABEL. You know, that everybody would be nice and polite and very, very grateful.

MR. M. And we weren't?

ISABEL. You were, but not them. Thami and his friends. *(She laughs at the memory.)* Ja, to be honest Mr. M, that family of yours was a bit scary at first. But not anymore! I feel I've made friends with Thami . . . and the others, so now it's different.

MR. M. Simple as that.

ISABEL. Simple as that.

MR. M. Knowledge has banished fear.

ISABEL. That's right.

MR. M. Bravo. Bravo. And yet again Bravo! If you knew what it meant to me to hear you speak like that. I wasn't wrong. From the moment I first shook hands with you I knew you were a kindred spirit.

ISABEL. Tell me more about the competition.

MR. M. First prize is five thousand Rand which the Bank has stipulated must be spent on books for the school library. We will obviously divide it equally between Camdeboo and Zolile when you and Thami win.

ISABEL. Yes; what about my teammate. What does he say? Have you asked him yet?

MR. M. No, I haven't *asked* him Isabel, and I won't. I will *tell* him, and when I do I trust he will express as much enthusiasm for the idea as you have. I am an old-fashioned traditionalist in most things, young lady, and my classroom is certainly no exception. I teach, Thami learns. He understands and accepts that that is the way it should be. You don't like the sound of that do you?

ISABEL. Does sound a bit dictatorial, you know.

MR. M. It might sound that way, but I assure you it isn't. We do not blur the difference between the generations in the way that you white people do. Respect for authority, right authority, is deeply ingrained in the African soul. It's all I've got when I stand in there in Number One. Respect for my authority is my only teaching aid. If I ever lost it, those young people will abandon their desks and take to the streets. I expect Thami to trust my judgment of what is best for him, and he does. That trust is the most sacred responsibility in my life.

ISABEL. He's your favorite, isn't he?

MR. M. Good heavens! A good teacher doesn't have favorites! Are you suggesting that I might be a bad one? Because if you are. . . . *(Looking around)* you would be right, young lady. Measured by that yardstick I am a very bad teacher indeed. He is my favorite. Thami Mbikwana! Yes, I have waited a long time for him. To tell you the truth I had given up all hope of him ever coming along. Any teacher who takes his calling seriously, dreams about that one special pupil, that one eager and gifted young head into which he can pour all that he knows and loves and who will justify all the years of frustration in the classroom. There have been pupils that I'm proud of, but I've always had to bully them into doing their school work. Not with Thami. *He* wants to learn the way other boys want to run out of the classroom and make mischief. If he looks after himself he'll go far and do big things. He's a born leader, Isabel, and that is what your generation needs. Powerful forces are fighting for the souls of you young people. You need *real* leaders. Not rabble-rousers. I know Thami is meant to be one. I know it with such certainty it makes me frightened. Because it is a responsibility. Mine and mine alone.

I've got a small confession to make. In addition to everything I've already said, there's another reason for this idea of mine. When you and Thami

shine at the Festival, as I know you will, and win first prize and we've pocketed a nice little check for five thousand Rand, I am going to point to Thami and say: And now, ladies and gentlemen, a full university scholarship, if you please.

ISABEL. And you'll get it. We'll shine, we'll win, we'll pocket that check and Thami will get a scholarship.

MR. M *(His turn for an enthusiastic response. Embarrassment and laughter.)* Your unruly behavior is very infectious!

ISABEL. My unruly behavior? I like that! I caught that disease in the location, I'll have you know.

MR. M. The future is ours, Isabel. We'll show this stupid country how it is done.

ISABEL. When do we start?

MR. M. Next week. We need to plan our campaign very carefully.

ISABEL. I'll be ready.

SCENE 4

MR. M *(Alone. He talks directly to the audience.)* "I am a man who in the eager pursuit of knowledge forgets his food and in the joy of its attainment forgets his sorrow, and who does not perceive that old age is coming on." *(He shakes his head.)* No. As I'm sure you have already guessed, that is not me. My pursuit of knowledge is eager, but I do perceive, and only too clearly, that old age is coming on, and at the best of times I do a bad job of forgetting my sorrows. Those wonderful words come from the finest teacher I have ever had, that most wise of all the ancient philosophers . . . Confucius! Yes. I am a Confucian. A black Confucian! There are not many of us. In fact I think there's a good chance that the only one in the country is talking to you at this moment.

I claim him as my teacher because I have read very carefully, and many times, and I will read it many times more, a little book I have about him, his life, his thoughts and utterances. Truly, they *are* wonderful words, my friends, wonderful, wonderful words! My classroom motto comes from its pages: "Learning undigested by thought is labor lost, Thought unassisted by learning is perilous!" But the words that challenge me most these days, is something he said towards the end of his life. At the age of seventy he turned to his pupils one day and said that he could do whatever his heart prompted, without transgressing what was right.

What do you say to that?

Think about it. *Anything* his heart prompted, *anything* that rose up as a spontaneous urge in his soul, *without* transgressing what was right!

What a heart, my friends! Aren't you envious of old Confucius? Wouldn't it be marvelous to have a heart you could trust like that? Imagine being able to wake up in the morning in your little room, yawn and stretch, scratch a few flea bites and then jump out of your bed and eat your bowl of mealie-pap and sour milk with a happy heart because you know that when you walk out into the world you will be free to obey and act out, with a clear conscience, all the promptings of your heart. No matter what you see out there on the battle grounds of location streets, and believe me, there are days now when my eyesight feels more like a curse than a blessing, no matter what stories of hardship and suffering you hear, or how bad the news you read in the newspaper, knowing that the whole truth, which can't be printed, is even worse . . . in spite of all that, you need have no fear of your spontaneous urges, because in obeying them you will not transgress what is right.

(Another shake of his head, another rueful smile) No, yet again. Not in this life, and most certainly not in this world where I find myself, will those wonderful words of Confucius be mine. Not even if I live to be one hundred and seventy, will I end up with a calm, gentle Chinese heart like his. I wish I could. Believe me, I really wish I could. Because I am frightened of the one I've got. I don't get gentle promptings from it, my friends. I get heart attacks. When I walk out into those streets, and I see what is happening to my people, it jumps out and savages me like a wild beast. *(Thumping his chest with a clenched fist)* I've got a whole zoo in here, a mad zoo of hungry animals . . . and the keeper is frightened! All of them. Mad and savage!

Look at me! I'm sweating today. I've been sweating for a week. Why? Because one of those animals, the one called Hope, has broken loose and is looking for food. Don't be fooled by its gentle name. It is as dangerous as Hate and Despair would be if they ever managed to break out. You think I'm exaggerating? Pushing my metaphor a little too far? Then I'd like to put you inside a black skin and ask you to keep Hope alive, find food for it on these streets where our children, our loved and precious children go hungry and die of malnutrition. No, believe me, it is a dangerous animal for a black man to have prowling around in his heart. So how do I manage to keep mine alive, you ask? Friends, I am going to let you in on a terrible secret. That is why I am a teacher.

It is all part of a secret plan to keep alive this savage Hope of mine. The truth is that I am worse than Nero feeding Christians to the lions. I feed young people to my Hope. Every young body behind a school desk keeps it alive.

So you've been warned! If you see a hungry gleam in my eyes when I look at your children . . . you know what it means. That is the monster that stands here before you. Full name: Anela Myalatya. Age: fifty-seven. Marital status: bachelor. Occupation: teacher. Address: The back room of the Reverend Mbopa's house next to the Anglican Church of St. Mark. It's a little on the small side. You know those big kitchen size boxes of matches they sell these days . . . well if you imagine one of those as Number One Classroom at Zolile High, then the little match box you put in your pocket is my room at the Reverend Mbopa's. But I'm not complaining. It has got all I need . . . a table and chair where I correct homework and prepare lessons, and a comfortable bed for a good night's insomnia and a reserved space for my chair in front of the television set in the Reverend Mbopa's lounge.

So there you have it. What I call my life rattles around in these two matchboxes . . . the classroom and the back room. If you see me hurrying along the streets you can be reasonably certain that one of those two is my urgent destination. The people tease me. "Faster, Mr. M" they shout to me from their front door. "You'll be late." They think it's a funny joke. They don't know how close they are to a terrible truth . . .

Yes! the clocks are ticking, my friends. History has got a strict timetable. If we're not careful we might be remembered as the country where everybody arrived too late.

SCENE 5

MR. M *waiting.* ISABEL *hurries on, carrying hockey stick, togs, and her schoolcase. She is hot and exhausted.*

ISABEL. Sorry, Mr. M, sorry. The game started late.

MR. M. I haven't been waiting long.

(ISABEL *unburdens herself and collapses with a groan.*)

MR. M. Did you win?

ISABEL. No. We played a team of friendly Afrikaans-speaking young Amazons from Jansenville and they licked us hollow. Four–one! It was brutal! They were incredibly fit. And fast. They ran circles around us on that hockey field. I felt so stupid. I kept saying to myself "It's only a game, Isabel. Relax! Enjoy it! Have a good time!" But no, there I was swearing under my breath at poor little Hilary Castle for being slow and not getting into position for my passes. (*Laughing at herself*) You want to know something really terrible? A couple of times I actually wanted to go over and hit her with my hockey stick. Isn't that awful? It's no good, Mr. M, I've got to face it: I'm a bad loser. Got any advice for me?.

MR. M. On how to be a good one?

ISABEL. Ja. How to lose graciously. With dignity. I mean it, I really wish I could.

MR. M. If I did have advice for you Isabel, I think I would be well advised to try it out on myself first . . .

ISABEL. Why? You one as well?

(MR. M *nods.*)

ISABEL. I don't believe it.

MR. M. It's true, Isabel. I'm ashamed to say it but when I lose I also want to grab my hockey stick and hit somebody.

(*A good laugh from* ISABEL)

MR. M. Believe me, I can get very petty and mean if I'm not on the winning side. I suppose most bachelors end up like that. We get so used to having everything our own way that when something goes wrong . . . So there's my advice to you. Get married! If what I've heard is true, holy matrimony is the best school of all for learning how to lose.

ISABEL. I don't think it's something you can learn. You've either got it or you haven't. Like Thami. Without even thinking about it I know *he's* a good loser.

MR. M. Maybe.

ISABEL. No. No maybes about it. He'd never grab his hockey stick and take it out on somebody else if he didn't win.

MR. M. You're right. I can't see him doing that. You've become good friends, haven't you?

ISABEL. The best. These past few weeks have been quite an education. I owe you a lot, you know. I think Thami would say the same . . . if you would only give him the chance to do so.

MR. M. What do you mean by that remark, young lady?

ISABEL. You know what I mean by that remark, *Mr. Teacher!* It's called Freedom of Speech.

MR. M. I've given him plenty of freedom, within reasonable limits, but he never uses it.

ISABEL. Because you're *always* the teacher and he's *always* the pupil. Stop teaching him all the time, Mr. M. Try just talking to him for a change . . . you know, like a friend.

I bet you in some ways I already know more about Thami than you.

MR. M. I don't deny that. In which case tell me, is he happy?

ISABEL. What do you mean? Happy with what? Us? The competition?

MR. M. Yes, and also his school work and . . . everything else.

ISABEL. Why don't you ask him?

MR. M. Because all I'll get is another polite "Yes, teacher." I thought maybe he had said something to you about the way he really felt.

ISABEL (*shaking her head*). The two of you! It's crazy! But ja, he's happy. At least I think he is. He's not a blabber-mouth like me, Mr. M. He doesn't give much away . . . even when we talk about ourselves. I don't know what it was like in your time, but being eighteen years old today is a pretty complicated business as far as we're concerned. If you asked me if I was happy, I'd say yes, but that doesn't mean I haven't got any problems. I've got plenty and I'm sure it's the same with Thami.

MR. M. Thami has told you he's got problems?

ISABEL. Come on, Mr. M! We've all got problems. I've got problems, you've got problems, Thami's got problems.

MR. M. But did he say what they were?

ISABEL. You're fishing for something, Mr. M. What is it?

MR. M. Trouble, Isabel. I'm sorry to say it, but I'm fishing for trouble and I'm trying to catch it before it gets too big.

ISABEL. Thami is in trouble?

MR. M. Not yet, but he will be if he's not careful. And all his friends as well. It's swimming around everywhere trying to stir up things. In the classroom, out on the streets.

ISABEL. Oh, you mean that sort of trouble. Is it really as bad as people are saying?

MR. M. There's a dangerous, reckless mood in the location. 'Specially among the young people. Very silly things are being said, Isabel, and I've got a suspicion that even sillier things are being whispered among themselves. I know Thami trusts you. I was wondering if he had told you what they were whispering about.

ISABEL (*shocked by what* MR. M *was asking of her*). Wow! that's a hard one you're asking for, Mr. M. Just suppose he had, do you think it would be right for me to tell you? *We* call that splitting, you know, and you're not very popular if you're caught doing it.

MR. M. It would be for his own good, Isabel.

ISABEL. Well, he hasn't . . . thank heavens! So I don't have to deal with that one. (*Pause*) If I ever did that to him, and he found out, that would be the end of our friendship, you know. I wish you hadn't asked me.

MR. M (*realizing his mistake*). Forgive me, Isabel. I'm just over-anxious on his behalf. One silly mistake now could ruin everything. Forget that I asked you and . . . please . . . don't mention anything about our little chat to Thami. I'll find time to have a word with him myself.

THAMI (*Appears. Also direct from the sports field.*) Hi, folks. Sorry I'm late.

ISABEL. I've just got here myself. Mr. M is the one who's been waiting.

THAMI. Sorry, teacher. The game went into extra time.

ISABEL. Did you win?

THAMI. No. We lost one–nil.

ISABEL. Good.

THAMI. But it was a good game. We're trying out some new combinations and they nearly worked. The chaps are really starting to come together as a team. A little more practice, that's all we need.

ISABEL. Hear that, Mr. M? What did I tell you? And look at him. Smiling! Happy! Even in defeat, a generous word for his teammates.

THAMI. What's going on?

ISABEL. Don't try to look innocent, Mbikwana. Your secret is out. Your true identity has been revealed. You arc a good loser, and don't try to deny it.

THAMI. Me? You're wrong. I don't like losing.

ISABEL. It's not a question of liking or not liking, but of being able to do so without a crooked smile on your face, a knot in your stomach, and murder in your heart.

THAMI. You lost your game this afternoon.

ISABEL. Whatever made you guess! We were trounced. So be careful. I'm looking for revenge.

MR. M. Good! Then let's see if you can get it in the arena of English literature. What do we deal with today?

THAMI. Nineteenth-century poetry.

MR. M (*with relish*). Beautiful! Beautiful! Beautiful! (*Making himself comfortable*) Whose service?

(THAMI *picks up a stone, hands behind his back, then clenches fists for* ISABEL *to guess. She does. She wins. Their relationship is now obviously very relaxed and easy.*)

ISABEL. Gird your loins, Mbikwana. I want blood.

THAMI. I wish you the very best of luck.

ISABEL. God, I hate you.

MR. M. First service, please.

ISABEL. Right. I'll give you an easy one to start with. The Lake Poets. Name them.

THAMI. Wordsworth . . .

ISABEL. Yes, he was one. Who else?

THAMI. Wordsworth and . . .

ISABEL. There was only one Wordsworth.

THAMI. I pass.

ISABEL. Wordsworth, Southey and Coleridge.

THAMI. I should have guessed Coleridge!

MR. M. One–love.

ISABEL. First line of a poem by each of them please.

THAMI. Query, Mr. Umpire . . . how many questions is that?

MR. M. One at a time please, Isabel.

ISABEL. Coleridge.

THAMI. "In Xanadu did Kubla Khan a stately pleasure dome decree . . . "

And if you don't like that one what about:

"Tis the middle of the night by the castle clock

And the owls have awakened the crowing cock

Tu-whit Tu-whoo."

And if you're still not satisfied . . .

ISABEL. Stop showing off, young man.

MR. M. One–all.

ISABEL. Wordsworth.

THAMI. Earth has not anything to show more fair;

Dull would be he of soul who could pass by

A sight so touching in its majesty and not be moved."

MR. M. One–two.

ISABEL. Southey.

THAMI. Pass.

ISABEL. "From his brimstone bed at break of day

A-walking the devil is gone

His coat was red and his breeches were blue

And there was a hole where his tail came through."

THAMI. Hey, I like that one!

ISABEL. A poet laureate to boot.

MR. M. Two–all.

ISABEL. One of them was expelled from school. Who was it and why?

THAMI. Wordsworth. For smoking in the lavatory.

ISABEL (*after a good laugh*). You're terrible, Thami. He should be penalized, Mr. Umpire . . . for irreverence! It was Southey and the reason he was expelled—you're going to like this—was for writing a "precocious" essay against flogging.

THAMI. How about that!

MR. M. Three–two. Change service.

THAMI. I am not going to show you any mercy. What poet was born with deformed feet, accused of incest and died of fever while helping the Greeks fight for freedom? "A love of liberty characterizes his poems and the desire to see the fettered nations of Europe set free."

ISABEL. Byron.

THAMI. Lord Byron, if you please.

MR. M. Two–four.

ISABEL. One of your favorites.

THAMI. You bet. "Yet, freedom, Yet thy banner torn but flying,

Streams like a thunderstorm against the wind."

Do you know the Christian names of Lord Byron?

ISABEL. Oh dammit! . . . it's on the tip of my tongue. Henry?

(THAMI *shakes his head.*)

ISABEL. Herbert?

THAMI. How many guesses does she get, Mr. Umpire?

ISABEL. All right, give him the point. I pass.

THAMI. George Gordon.

MR. M. Three–four.

THAMI. To whom was he unhappily married for one long year?

ISABEL. Pass.

THAMI. Anne Isabella Milbanke.

MR. M. Four–all.

THAMI. Father's occupation?

ISABEL. Pass.

THAMI. John Byron was a captain in the army.

MR. M. Five–four.

THAMI. What other great poet was so overcome with grief when he heard news of Lord Byron's death, that he went out and carved into a rock: "Byron is dead."

ISABEL. Matthew Arnold?

THAMI. No. Another aristocrat . . . Alfred Lord Tennyson.

MR. M. Six–four. Change service.

ISABEL. Right. Whose body did your Lord Byron burn on a beach in Italy?

THAMI. Shelley.

MR. M. Four–seven.

ISABEL. And what happened to Mr. Shelley's ashes?

THAMI. In a grave beside John Keats in Rome.

MR. M. Four–eight.

ISABEL. Shelley's wife. What is she famous for?

THAMI. Which one? There were two. Harriet Westbrook, sixteen years old, who he abandoned after three years and who drowned herself? Or number two wife—who I think is the one you're interested in—Mary Wollstonecraft, the author of *Frankenstein*.

MR. M. Four–nine.

ISABEL. How much?

MR. M. Four–nine.

ISABEL. I don't believe this! *(She grabs her hockey stick.)*

THAMI *(enjoying himself immensely)*. I crammed in two poets last night, Isabel. Guess who they were?

ISABEL. Byron and Shelley. In that case we will deal with Mr. John Keats. What profession did he abandon in order to devote himself to poetry?

THAMI. Law.

ISABEL. You're guessing and you're wrong. He qualified as a surgeon.

MR. M. Five–nine.

ISABEL. What epitaph, composed by himself, is engraved on his tombstone in Rome?

THAMI. Pass.

ISABEL. "Here lies one whose name was writ on water."

MR. M. Six–nine. Let's leave the Births, Marriages and Deaths column please. I want to hear some more poetry.

THAMI. Whose service?

MR. M. Yours.

THAMI. "I must go down to the seas again, to the lonely sea and the sky
And all I ask is a tall ship and a star to steer her by . . . "

ISABEL. "And the wheel's kick and the wind's song and the white sails shaking

And a grey mist on the sea's face and a grey dawn breaking.

I must go down to the seas again, to the vagrant gypsy life

To the gull's way and the whale's way where the wind's like a whetted knife . . . "

THAMI. "And all that I ask is a merry
    yarn from a laughing fellow rover

And a quiet sleep and sweet dream
    when the long trek's over."

MR. M. Bravo! Bravo! Bravo! But who
gets the point?

ISABEL. Give it to John Masefield,
Mr. Umpire. (To THAMI) Nineteenth
century?

THAMI. He was born in 1878. To tell
you the truth I couldn't resist it. You
choose one.

ISABEL. "I met a traveler from an
    antique land

Who said: two vast and trunkless legs
    of stone

Stand in the desert . . . near them,
    on the sand, half sunk, a shat-
    tered visage lies, whose frown

And wrinkled lip, and sneer of cold
    command

Tell that its sculptor well those
    passions read

Which yet survive, stamped on these
    lifeless things

The hand that mocked them, and
    the heart that fed:

And on the pedestal these words
    appear:"

THAMI. "My name is Ozymandias, King
    of Kings.

Look on my works, oh ye mighty,
    and despair!"

ISABEL. "Nothing beside remains.

'Round the decay of that colossal
    wreck, boundless and bare,

The lone and level sands stretch far
    away."

THAMI. And that point goes to Mr.
Shelley.

ISABEL (notebook from her schoolcase).
You'll be interested to know, gentlemen, that Ozymandias is not a fiction of Mr. Shelley's very fertile
imagination. He was a real, live
Egyptian king. Rameses the Second!
According to Everyman's
Encyclopedia . . . "One of the most
famous of the Egyptian kings . . .
erected many monuments . . . but his
oppressive rule left Egypt impover-
ished and suffering from an
incurable decline."

THAMI. What happened to the statue?

ISABEL. You mean how was it toppled?

THAMI. Yes.

ISABEL. Didn't say. Weather I suppose.
And time. Two thousand four
hundred B.C. . . . that's over four
thousand years ago. Why? What were
you thinking?

THAMI. I had a book of Bible stories
when I was small, and there was a
picture in it showing the building of
the pyramids by the slaves.
Thousands of them, like ants, pulling
the big blocks of stone with ropes,
being guarded by soldiers with whips
and spears. According to that picture
the slaves must have easily outnum-
bered the soldiers one hundred to
one. I actually tried to count them
all one day but the drawing wasn't
good enough for that.

ISABEL. What are you up to, Mbikwana?
Trying to stir up a little social unrest
in the time of the Pharoahs, are you?

THAMI. Don't joke about it, Miss Dyson,
there are quite a few Ozymandiases

in this country waiting to be toppled. And you'll see it happen. We won't leave it to time to bring them down.

MR. M *(Has been listening to the exchange between* THAMI *and* ISABEL *very attentively. Trying to put a smile on it.)* Who is the *we* you speak of with such authority, Thami?

THAMI. The People.

MR. M *(recognition).* Yes, yes, yes, of course . . . I should have known. "The People" . . . with a capital P. Does that include me? Am I one of "The People?"

THAMI. If you choose to be.

MR. M. I've got to choose, have I? My black skin doesn't confer automatic membership. So how do I go about choosing?

THAMI. By identifying with the fight for our freedom.

MR. M. As simple as that? Then I am most definitely one of "The People." I want our freedom as much as any of you. In fact, I was fighting for it in my own small way long before you were born! But I've got a small problem. Does that noble fight of ours really have to stoop to pulling down a few silly statues? Where do you get the idea that we, The People, want you to do that for us?

THAMI *(trying).* They are not our heroes, teacher.

MR. M. They are not our statues, Thami! Wouldn't it be better for us to rather put our energies into erecting a few of our own? We've also got heroes, you know.

THAMI. Like who, Mr. M? Nelson Mandela? *(Shaking his head with disbelief)* Hey! *They* would pull *that* statue down so fast . . .

MR. M *(cutting him).* In which case they would be just as guilty of gross vandalism . . . because that is what it will be, regardless of who does it to whom. Destroying somebody else's property is inexcusable behavior! No, Thami. As one of The People you claim to be acting for, I raise my hand in protest. Please don't pull down any statues on my behalf. Don't use me as an excuse for an act of lawlessness. If you want to do something "revolutionary" for me let us sit down and discuss it, because I have a few constructive alternatives I would like to suggest. Do I make myself clear?

THAMI. Yes, teacher.

MR. M. Good. I'm glad we understand each other.

ISABEL *(intervening).* So, what's next? Mr. M? How about singling out a few specific authors who we know will definitely come up. Like Dickens. I bet you anything you like there'll be questions about him and his work.

MR. M. Good idea. We'll concentrate on novelists. A short list of hot favorites.

ISABEL. Thomas Hardy . . . Jane Austen . . . who else, Thami?

MR. M. Put your heads together and make a list. I want twenty names. Divide it between the two of you and get to work. I must be on my way.

ISABEL. Just before you go, Mr. M, I've got an invitation for you and Thami from my mom and dad. Would the two of you like to come to tea one afternoon?

MR. M. What a lovely idea!

ISABEL. They've had enough of me going on and on about the all-knowing Mr. M and his brilliant protégé Thami. They want to meet you for themselves. Thami? All right with you?

MR. M. Of course we accept, Isabel. It will be a pleasure and a privilege for us to meet Mr. and Mrs. Dyson. Tell them we accept most gratefully.

ISABEL. Next Sunday.

MR. M. Perfect.

ISABEL. Thami?

MR. M. Don't worry about him, Isabel. I'll put it in my diary and remind him at school. *(Leaves)*

ISABEL *(sensitive to a change in mood in* THAMI*).* I think you'll like my folks. My mom's a bit on the reserved side but that's just because she's basically very shy. But you and my dad should get on well. Start talking sport with him and he won't let you go. He played cricket for E.P., you know. *(Pause)* You will come, won't you?

THAMI *(edge to his voice).* Did you hear Mr. M? "A delight and a privilege! We accept most gratefully." *(Writing in his notebook)* Charles Dickens . . . Thomas Hardy . . . Jane Austen . . .

ISABEL. Was he speaking for you as well?

THAMI. He speaks for me on nothing!

ISABEL. Relax . . . I know that. That's why I tried to ask you separately and why I'll ask you again. Would you like to come to tea next Sunday to meet my family? It's not a polite invitation. They really want to meet you.

THAMI. Me? Why? Are they starting to get nervous?

ISABEL. Oh come off it, Thami. Don't be like that. They're always nervous when it comes to me. But this time it happens to be genuine interest. I've told you. I talk about you at home. They know I have a good time with you . . . that we're a team . . . which they are now very proud of, incidentally . . . and that we're cramming like lunatics so that we can put up a good show at the Festival. Is it so strange that they want to meet you after all that? Honestly, sometimes dealing with the two of you is like walking on a tight rope. I'm always scared I'm going to put a foot wrong and . . . well, I just *hate* being scared like that. *(A few seconds of truculent silence between the two of them.)* What's going on, Thami? Between you two? There's something very wrong, isn't there?

THAMI. No more than usual.

ISABEL. No, you don't! A hell of a lot more than usual and don't deny it because it's getting to be pretty obvious. I mean I know he gets on your nerves. I knew that the first day we met. But it's more than that now. These past couple of meetings I've caught you looking at him, watching him in a . . . I don't know . . . in a sort of hard way. Very critical. Not just once. Many times. Do you know you're doing it?

(Shrug of shoulders from THAMI*)*

ISABEL. Well, if you know it or not, you are. And now he's started as well.

THAMI. What do you mean?

ISABEL. He's watching you.

THAMI. So? He can watch me as much as he likes. I've got nothing to hide. Even if I had he'd be the last person to find out. He sees nothing, Isabel.

ISABEL. I think you are very wrong.

THAMI. No, I'm not. That's his trouble. He's got eyes and ears but he sees nothing and hears nothing.

ISABEL. Go on. Please. (*Pause*) I mean it, Thami. I want to know what's going on.

THAMI. He is out of touch with what is really happening to us blacks and the way we feel about things. He thinks the world is still the way it was when he was young. It's not! It's different now, but he's too blind to see it. He doesn't open his eyes and ears and see what is happening around him or listen to what people are saying.

ISABEL. What are they saying?

THAMI. They've got no patience left, Isabel. They want change. They want it now!

ISABEL. But he agrees with that. He never stops saying it himself.

THAMI. No. His ideas about change are the old-fashioned ones. And what have they achieved? Nothing. We are worse off now than we ever were. The people don't want to listen to his kind of talk anymore.

ISABEL. I'm still lost, Thami. What kind of talk is that?

THAMI. You've just heard it, Isabel. It calls our struggle vandalism and lawless behavior. It's the sort of talk that expects us to do nothing and wait quietly for White South Africa to wake up. If we listen to it our grandchildren still won't know what it means to be free.

ISABEL. And those old-fashioned ideas of his . . . are we one of them?

THAMI. What do you mean?

ISABEL. You and me. The competition.

THAMI. Let's change the subject, Isabel. (*His notebook*) Charles Dickens . . . Thomas Hardy . . . Jane Austen . . .

ISABEL. No! You can't do that! I'm involved. I've got a right to know. Are we an old-fashioned idea?

THAMI. Not our friendship. That is our decision, our choice.

ISABEL. And the competition.

THAMI (*uncertain of himself*). Maybe . . . I'm not sure. I need time to think about it.

ISABEL (*foreboding*). Oh boy. This doesn't sound so good. You've got to talk to him, Thami.

THAMI. He won't listen.

ISABEL. Make him listen!

THAMI. It doesn't work that way with us, Isabel. You can't just stand up and tell your teacher he's got the wrong ideas.

ISABEL. Well, that's just your bad luck because you are going to have to do it. Even if it means breaking sacred rules and traditions, you have got to stand up and have it out with him. I don't think you realize what all of this means to him. It's a hell of a lot more than just an "old-fashioned idea" as far as he's concerned. This competition, you and me, but especially you, Thami Mbikwana, has become a sort of crowning achievement to his life as a teacher. It's become a sort of symbol for him, and if it were to all suddenly collapse . . .! No. I don't want to think about it.

THAMI (*flash of anger and impatience*). Then don't! Please leave it alone now and just let's get on with whatever it is we've got to do.

ISABEL. Right, if that's the way you want it . . . (*Her notebook*) . . . Charles Dickens, Thomas Hardy, Jane Austen . . . who else?

THAMI. I'm sorry. I know you're only trying to help, but you've got to understand that it's not just a personal issue between him and me. That would be easy. I don't think I would care then. Just wait for the end of the year and then get out of that classroom and that school as fast as I can. But there is more to it than that. I've told you before: sitting in a classroom doesn't mean the same thing to me that it does to you. That classroom is a political reality in my life . . . it's a part of the whole political system we're up against and Mr. M has chosen to identify with it.

ISABEL (*trying a new tack*). All right. I believe you. I accept everything you said . . . about him, your relationship, the situation. No arguments. Okay? But doesn't all of that only make it still more important that the two of you start talking to each other? I know he wants to, but *he*

doesn't know how to start. It's *so* sad . . . because I can see him trying to reach out to you. Show him how it's done. Make the first move. Oh Thami, don't let it go wrong between the two of you. That's just about the worst thing I could imagine. We all need each other.

THAMI. I don't need him.

ISABEL. I think you do, just as much as he . . .

THAMI. Don't tell me what I need, Isabel! And stop telling me what to do! You don't know what my life is about, so keep your advice to yourself.

ISABEL. I'm sorry. I don't mean to interfere. I thought we were a team and that what involved you two concerned me as well. I'll mind my own business in future. (*She is deeply hurt. She collects her things.*) Let's leave it at that then. See you next week . . . I hope! (*Starts to leave, stops, returns and confronts him*) You used the word friendship a few minutes ago. It's a beautiful word and I'll do anything to make it true for us. But don't let's cheat, Thami. If we can't be open and honest with each other and say what is in our hearts, we've got no right to use it. (*She leaves.*)

SCENE 6

THAMI (*alone singing*).

Masiye masiye skolweni
Masiye masiye skolweni
Eskolweni sasakhaya
Eskolweni sasakhaya (Repeat.)

Gongo gongo
Iyakhala intsimbi
Gongo gongo
Iyakhala intsimbi

(*Translating*)

Come, come, let's go to school
Let's go to our very own school
Gongo gongo
The bell is ringing
Gongo gongo
The bell is calling!

Singing that at the top of his voice and holding his slate under his arm, seven-year-old THAMI MBIKWANA marched proudly with the other children every morning into his classroom.

Gongo gongo. The school bell is ringing!

And what a wonderful sound that was for me. Starting with the little farm school, I remember my school bells like beautiful voices calling to me all through my childhood . . . and I came running when they did. You should have seen me, man. In junior school I was the first one at the gates every morning. I was waiting there when the caretaker came to unlock them. Oh yes! Young Thami was a very eager scholar. And what made it even better, he was also one of the clever ones. "A most particularly promising pupil" is how one of my school reports described me. My first real scholastic achievement was a composition I wrote about myself in Standard Two. Not only did it get me top marks in the class, the teacher was so proud of me, she made me read it out to the whole school at assembly.

(*His composition*) "The story of my life so far. By Thami Mbikwana. The story of my life so far is not yet finished because I am only ten years old and I am going to live a long, long time.

"I come from King Williamstown. My father is Amos Mbikwana and he works very hard for the baas on the railway. I am also going to work very hard and get good marks in all my classes and make my teacher very happy. The story of my life so far has also got a very happy ending because when I am big I am going to be a doctor so that I can help people. I will drive to the hospital every day in a big white ambulance full of nurses. I will make black people better free of charge. The white people must pay me for my medicine because they have got lots of money. That way I will also get lots of money. My mother and my father will stop working and come and live with me in a big house. That is the story of my life up to where I am in Standard Two."

I must bring my story up to date because there have been some changes and developments since little Thami wrote those hopeful words eight years ago. To start with, I don't think I want to be a doctor any-more. That praiseworthy ambition has unfortunately died in me. It still upsets me very much when I think about the pain and suffering of my people, but I realize now that what causes most of it is not an illness that can be cured by the pills and bottles of medicine they hand out at the clinic. I don't need to go to university to learn what my people really need is a strong double-dose of that traditional old Xhosa remedy called *Inkululeko*. Freedom. So right now I'm not sure what I want to be anymore. It's hard, you see, for us "bright young blacks" to dream about wonderful careers as doctors, or lawyers when we keep waking up in a world which doesn't allow the majority of our people any dreams at all. But to get back to my composition, I did try my best to keep that promise I made in it. For a long time . . . Standard Three, Standard Four, Standard Five . . . I did work very hard and I did get good marks in all my subjects. This "most particularly promising pupil" made a lot of teachers very happy.

I'm sorry to say but I can't do it anymore. I have tried very hard, believe me, but it is not as simple and easy as it used to be to sit behind that desk and listen to the teacher. That little world of the classroom where I used to be happy, where they used to pat me on the head and say: Little Thami, You'll go far! . . . That little room of wonderful promises, where I used to feel so safe, has become a place I don't trust anymore. Now I sit at my desk like an animal that has smelt danger, heard something moving in the bushes and knows it must be very, very careful.

At the beginning of this year the Inspector of Bantu Schools in the Cape Midlands Region, Mr. Dawid Grobbelaar—he makes us call him Oom Dawie— came to give us Standard Tens his usual pep talk. He does it every year. We know Oom Dawie well. He's been coming to Zolile for a long time. When he walked into our classroom we all jumped up as usual but he didn't want any of that. "Sit, sit. I'm not a bloody sergeant major." Oom Dawie believes he knows how to talk to us. He loosened his tie, took off his jacket and rolled up his sleeves. It was a very hot day.

"Dis better. *Nou kan ons lekker gesels.* Boys and girls or maybe I should say 'young men' and 'young women' now, because you are coming to the end of your time behind those desks . . . you are special! You are the elite! We have educated you because we want you to be major shareholders in the future of this wonderful Republic of ours. In fact, we want *all* the peoples of South Africa to share in that future . . . black, white, brown, yellow, and if there are some green ones out there, then them as well." Ho! Ho! Ho!

I don't remember much about what he said after that because my head was trying to deal with that one word: the Future! He kept using it . . . "our future," "the country's future," "A wonderful future of peace and prosperity." What does he really mean, I kept asking myself? why does my heart go hard and tight as a stone when he says it? I look around me in the location at the men and women who went out into that "wonderful future" before me. What do I see? Happy and contented shareholders in this exciting enterprise called the Republic of South Africa? No. I see a generation of tired, defeated men and women crawling back to their miserable little *pondocks* at the end of a day's work for the white baas or madam. And those are the lucky ones. They've at least got work. Most of them are just sitting around wasting away their lives while they wait helplessly for a miracle to feed their families, a miracle that never comes.

Those men and women are our fathers and mothers. We have grown up watching their humiliation. We have to live every day with the sight of them begging for food in this land of their birth, and their parents' birth . . . all the way back to the first proud ancestors of our people. Black people lived on this land for centuries before any white settler had landed! Does Oom Dawie think we are blind? That when we walk through the streets of the white town we do not see the big houses and the beautiful gardens with their swimming pools full of laughing people, and compare it with what we've got, what we have to call home? Or does Oom Dawie just think we are very stupid? That in spite of the wonderful education he has given us, we can't use the simple arithmetic of add and subtract, multiply and divide to work out the rightful share of twenty-five million

black people?

Do you understand me, good people? Do you understand now why it is not as easy as it used to be to sit behind that desk and learn only what Oom Dawie has decided I must know? My head is rebellious. It refuses now to remember when the Dutch landed, and the Huguenots landed, and the British landed. It has already forgotten when the Old Union became the proud young Republic. But it does know what happened in Kliptown in 1955, in Sharpville on 21st March, 1960, and in Soweto on the 16th of June, 1976. Do you? Better find out, because those are dates your children will have to learn one day. We don't need Zolile classrooms anymore. We know now what they really are . . . traps which have been carefully set to catch our minds, our souls. No, good people. We have woken up at last. We have found another school . . . the streets, the little rooms, the funeral parlors of the location . . . anywhere the people meet and whisper names we have been told to forget, the dates of events they try to tell us never happened, and the speeches they try to say were never made.

Those are the lessons we are eager and proud to learn, because they are lessons about our history, about our heroes. But the time for whispering them is past. Tomorrow we start shouting.

AMANDLA!

ACT TWO

SCENE 1

ISABEL *and* THAMI. *She has books and papers. Behind a relaxed and easy manner, she watches* THAMI *carefully.*

ISABEL. What I've done is write out a sort of condensed biography of all of them . . . you know, the usual stuff . . . date of birth, where they were born, where they died, who they married . . . et cetera, et cetera. My dad made copies for you and Mr. M. Sit. *(Hands over a set of papers to* THAMI*)* You okay?

THAMI. Ja, ja.

ISABEL. For example . . . *(Reading)* . . . Bronte sisters . . . I lumped them all together . . . Charlotte 1816–1855; Emily 1818–1848; Anne 1820–1849 . . . Can you believe that: Not one of them reached the age of forty. Anne died when she was twenty-nine, Emily when she was thirty, and Charlotte reached the ripe old age of thirty-nine! Family home: Haworth, Yorkshire. First publication a joint volume of verse . . . "Poems by Currer, Ellis, and Acton Bell." All novels published under these *nommes de plume.*[1] Charlotte the most prolific . . . *(Abandoning the notes)* Why am I doing this? You're not listening to me.

THAMI. Sorry.

ISABEL *(She waits for more, but that is all she gets.)* So? Should I carry on wasting my breath or do you want to say something?

THAMI. No, I must talk.

ISABEL. Good. I'm ready to listen.

THAMI. I don't know where to begin.

ISABEL. The deep end. Take my advice, go to the deep end and just jump right in. That's how I learnt to swim.

THAMI. No. I want to speak carefully because I don't want you to get the wrong ideas about what's happening and what I'm going to say. It's not like it's your fault, that it's because of anything you said or did . . . you know what I mean?

ISABEL. You don't want me to take personally whatever it is you are finding so hard to tell me.

THAMI. That's right. It's not about you and me personally. I've had a good time with you, Isabel.

ISABEL. And I've had an important one with you.

THAMI. If it was just you and me, there wouldn't be a problem.

ISABEL. We've got a problem have we?

THAMI. I have.

ISABEL *(losing patience).* Oh for heaven's sake, Thami. Stop trying to spare my feelings and just say it. If you are trying to tell me that I've been wasting my breath for a lot longer than just this afternoon . . . just go ahead and say it! I'm not a child. I can take it. Because that is what you are trying to tell me, isn't it? That it's all off.

THAMI. Yes.

---

1. *nommes de plume,* pen names

ISABEL. The great literary quiz team is no more. You are pulling out of the competition.

THAMI. Yes.

ISABEL. You shouldn't have made it so hard for yourself, Thami. It doesn't come as all that big a surprise. I've had a feeling that something was going to go wrong somewhere. Been a strange time these past few weeks, hasn't it? At home, at school, in the shop . . . everywhere! Things I've been seeing and doing my whole life, just don't feel right anymore. Like my Saturday chats with Samuel—I told you about him, remember, he delivers for my dad—well you should have heard the last one. It was excruciating. It felt so false, and forced, and when I listened to what I was saying and how I was saying it . . . . It sounded as if I thought I was talking to a ten-year-old. Halfway through our misery my dad barged in and told me not to waste Samuel's time because he had work to do, which, of course, led to a flaming row between me and my dad . . . Am I changing, Thami? My dad says I am.

THAMI. In what way?

ISABEL. Forget it. The only thing I do know at this moment is that I don't very much like the way anything feels right now, starting with myself. So have you told Mr. M yet?

THAMI. No.

ISABEL. Good luck. I don't envy you that little conversation. If I'm finding the news a bit hard to digest, I don't know what he is going to do with it. I've just got to accept it. I doubt very much if he will.

THAMI. He's got no choice, Isabel. I've decided and that's the end of it.

ISABEL. So do you think we can at least talk about it? Help me to understand? Because to be absolutely honest with you, Thami, I don't think I do. You're not the only one with a problem. What Mr. M had to say about the team and the whole idea made a hell of a lot of sense to me. You owe it to me, Thami. A lot more than just my spare time is involved.

THAMI. Talk about what? Don't you know what is going on?

ISABEL. Don't be stupid, Thami! Of course I do! You'd have to be pretty dumb not to know that the dreaded "unrest" has finally reached us as well.

THAMI. We don't call it that. Our word for it is "Isiqalo" . . . The Beginning.

ISABEL. All right then, "the Beginning." I don't care what it's called. All I'm asking you to do is explain to me how the two of us learning some poetry, cramming in potted bios . . . interferes with all of that.

THAMI. Please just calm down and listen to me! I know you're angry and I don't blame you. I would be as well. But you must understand that pulling out of this competition is just a small side issue. There was a meeting in the location last night. It was decided to call for a general stay-at-home. We start boycotting classes tomorrow as part of that campaign.

ISABEL. Does Mr. M know about all of this?

THAMI. I think he does now.

ISABEL. Wasn't he at that meeting?

THAMI. The meeting was organized by the comrades. He wasn't welcome.

ISABEL. Because his ideas are old-fashioned.

THAMI. Yes.

ISABEL. School boycott! Comrades! So our safe, contented little Camdeboo is really going to find out what it's all about. How long do you think it will last?

THAMI. I don't know. It's hard to say.

ISABEL. A week?

THAMI. No. It will be longer.

ISABEL. A month? Two months?

THAMI. We'll go back to school when the authorities scrap Bantu Education and recognize and negotiate with Student Committees. That was the resolution last night.

ISABEL. But when the boycott and . . . you know . . . everything is all over, could we carry on then, if there was still time?

THAMI. I hadn't thought about that.

ISABEL. So think about it. Please.

THAMI (nervous about a commitment). It's hard to say, Isabel . . . but, ja, maybe we could . . . I'm not sure.

ISABEL. Not much enthusiasm there, Mr. Mbikwana! You're right. Why worry about a stupid competition? It will most probably be too late anyway. So that's it then. Let's just say we gave ourselves a crash course in English literature. Could have done a lot worse with our spare time, couldn't we? I enjoyed myself. I read a lot of beautiful poetry I might never have got around to. (Uncertain of herself) It doesn't mean the end of everything though, does it? I mean, we can go on meeting, just as friends?

THAMI (warily). When?

ISABEL. Oh . . . I mean, you know, like any time. Next week! (Pause) I'm not talking about the competition, Thami. I accept that it's dead. I think it's a pity . . . but so what? I'm talking now about you and me just as friends. (She waits. She realizes. She collects herself.) So our friendship is an old-fashioned idea after all. Well don't waste your time here. You better get going and look after . . . whatever it is that's beginning. And good luck!

(THAMI starts to go.)

ISABEL. No! Thami, come back here!! (Struggling ineffectually to control her anger and pain) There is something very stupid somewhere and it's most probably me but I can't help it . . . It just doesn't make sense! I know it does to you and I'm sure it's just my white selfishness and ignorance that is stopping me from understanding, but it still doesn't make sense! Why can't we go on seeing each other and meeting as friends? Tell me what is wrong with our friendship?

THAMI. You're putting words in my mouth, Isabel. I didn't say there was anything wrong with it. But others will not see it the way we do.

ISABEL. Who? Your comrades?

THAMI. Yes.

ISABEL. And they are going to decide whether we can or can't be friends!

THAMI. I was right. You don't understand what's going on.

ISABEL. And you're certainly not helping me to.

THAMI (*trying*). . . . Visiting you like this is dangerous. People talk. Your maid, Usipumla . . . has seen me. She could mention, just innocently but to the wrong person, that Thami Mbikwana is visiting and having tea with the white people she works for.

ISABEL. And of course that is such a big crime!

THAMI. In the eyes of the location . . . Yes! My world is also changing, Isabel. I'm breaking the boycott by being here. The comrades don't want any mixing with the whites. They have ordered that contact must be kept at a minimum.

ISABEL. And you go along with that.

THAMI. Yes.

ISABEL. Happily!

THAMI (*goaded by her lack of understanding*). Yes! I go along happily with that!!

ISABEL. Hell, Thami, this great Beginning of yours sounds like . . . (*Shakes her head*) . . . I don't know. Other people deciding who can and who can't be your friends, what you must do and what you can't do. Is this the freedom you've been talking to me about? That you were going to fight for?

MR. M (*Enters quietly. His stillness is a disturbing contrast to the bustle and energy we have come to associate with him.*) Don't let me interrupt you. Please carry on. (*To* THAMI) I'm most interested in your reply to that question. (*Pause*) I think he's forgotten what it was, Isabel. Ask him again.

ISABEL (*backing out of the confrontation*). No. Forget it.

MR. M (*persisting*). Isabel was asking you how you managed to reconcile your desire for freedom with what the comrades are doing.

ISABEL. I said forget it, Mr. M. I'm not interested anymore.

MR. M (*insistent*). But I am.

THAMI. The comrades are imposing a discipline which our struggle needs at this point. There is no comparison between that and the total denial of our freedom by the white government. They have been forcing on us an inferior education in order to keep us permanently suppressed. When our struggle is successful there will be no more need for the discipline the comrades are demanding.

MR. M (*grudging admiration*). Oh, Thami . . . you learn your lessons so well! The "revolution" has only just begun and you are already word perfect. So then tell me, do you think I agree with this inferior "Bantu Education" that is being forced on you?

THAMI. You teach it.

MR. M. But unhappily so! Most unhappily, unhappily so! Don't you know that? Did you have your fingers in your ears the thousand times I've said so in the classroom? Where were you when I stood there and said I regarded it as my duty, my deepest obligation to you young men and women to sabotage it, and that my conscience would not let me rest until I had succeeded. And I have! Yes, I have succeeded! I have got irrefutable proof of my success. You! Yes. You can stand here and accuse me, unjustly, because I have also had a struggle and I have won mine! I have liberated your mind in spite of what the Bantu education was trying to do to it. Your mouthful of big words and long sentences which the not-so-clever comrades are asking you to speak and write for them, your wonderful eloquence at last night's meeting which got them all so excited—yes, I heard about it!—you must thank me for all of that, Thami.

THAMI. No, I don't. You never taught me those lessons.

MR. M. Oh, I see. You have got other teachers have you?

THAMI. Yes. Yours were lessons in whispering. There are men now who are teaching us to shout. Those little tricks and jokes of yours in the classroom liberated nothing. The struggle doesn't need the big English words you taught me how to spell.

MR. M. Be careful, Thami. Be careful! Be careful! Don't scorn words. They are sacred! Magical! Yes, they are. Do you know that without words a man can't think? Yes, it's true. Take that thought back with you as a present from the despised Mr. M and share it with the comrades. Tell them the difference between a man and an animal is that man thinks, and he thinks with words. Consider the mighty ox. Four powerful legs, massive shoulders, and a beautiful thick hide that gave our warriors shields to protect them when they went into battle. Think of his beautiful head, Thami, the long horns, the terrible bellow from his lungs when he charges a rival! *But it has got no words and therefore it is stupid!* And along comes that funny little, hairless animal that has got only two thin legs, no horns, and a skin worth nothing, and he tells that ox what to do. He is its master and he is that because he can speak! If the struggle needs weapons give it words, Thami. Stones and petrol bombs can't get inside those armored cars. Words can. They can do something even more devastating than that . . . they can get inside the heads of those inside the armored cars. I speak to you like this because if I have faith in anything, it is faith in the power of the word. Like my master, the great Confucius, I believe that, using only words, a man can right a wrong and judge and execute the wrongdoer. You are meant to use words like that. Talk to others. Bring them back into the classroom. They will listen to you. They look up to you as a leader.

THAMI. No I won't. You talk about them as if they were a lot of sheep waiting to be led. They know what they are doing. They'd call me a traitor if I tried to persuade them otherwise.

MR. M. Then listen carefully, Thami. I have received instructions from the department to make a list of all those who take part in the boycott. Do you know what they will do with that list when all this is over? . . . because don't fool yourself, Thami, it will be. When your boycott comes to an inglorious end like all the others . . . they will make all of you apply for re-admission and if your name is on that list . . . *(He leaves the rest unspoken.)*

THAMI. Will you do it? Will you make that list for them?

MR. M. That is none of your business.

THAMI. Then don't ask me questions about mine.

MR. M *(His control finally snaps. He explodes with anger and bitterness.)* Yes, I will! I will ask you all the questions I like. And you know why? Because I am a man and you are a boy. And if you are not in that classroom tomorrow you will be a very, very silly boy.

THAMI. Then don't call me names, Mr. M.

MR. M. No? Then what must I call you? Comrade Thami? Never! You are a silly boy now, and without an education you will grow up to be a stupid man!

(For a moment it looks as if THAMI *is going to leave without saying anything more, but he changes his mind and confronts* MR. M *for the last time.)*

THAMI. The others called *you* names at the meeting last night. Did your spies tell you that? Government

stooge, sell-out, collaborator. Did your spies tell you that I tried to stop them saying those things? Don't wait until tomorrow to make your list, Mr. M. You can start now. Write down the first name: Thami Mbikwana. *(He leaves.)*

(A few seconds of silence after THAMI*'s departure.* ISABEL *makes a move towards* MR. M *but he raises his hand sharply, stopping her, keeping her at a distance.)*

ISABEL. This hateful country! *(She leaves.)*

SCENE 2

MR. M *alone. To start with, the mood is one of quiet, vacant disbelief.*

MR. M. It was like being in a nightmare. I was trying to get to the school, I knew that if I didn't hurry I was going to be late so *I had to get to the school* . . . but every road I took was blocked by policemen and soldiers with their guns ready, or comrades building barricades. First I tried Jubulani Street, then I turned into Kwaza Rd. and then Lamini St. . . . and then I gave up and just wandered around aimlessly, helplessly, watching my world go mad and set itself on fire. Everywhere I went . . . overturned buses, looted bread vans, the government offices . . . everything burning and the children dancing around rattling boxes of matches and shouting Tshisa Qhumisa! Tshisa Qhumisa! Qhumisa! . . . and then running for their lives when the police armored cars appeared. They were everywhere, crawling around in the smoke like giant dung-beetles.

I ended up on the corner where Mrs. Makatini always sits selling *vetkoek* and prickly pears to people waiting for the bus. The only person there was little Sipho Fondini from Standard Six, writing on the wall: "Liberation First, then Education." He saw me and he called out: "Is the spelling right, Mr. M?" And he meant it! The young eyes in that smoke-stained little face were terribly serious.

Somewhere else a police van raced past me crowded with children who should have also been in their desks in school. Their hands waved desperately through the bar, their voices called out: "Teacher! Teacher! Help us! Tell our mothers. Tell our fathers." "No Anela," I said. "This is too much now. Just stand here and close your eyes and wait until you wake up and find your world the way it was." But that didn't happen. A police car came around the corner and suddenly there were children everywhere throwing stones, and tear gas bombs falling all around, and I knew that I wasn't dreaming, that I was coughing and choking and hanging on to a lamp-post in the real world. No! No!

Do something, Anela. Do something. Stop the madness! Stop the madness!

SCENE 3

MR. M *alone in Number One Classroom. He is ringing his school bell wildly.*

MR. M. Come to school! Come to school! Before they kill you all, come to school! (*Silence.* MR. M *looks around the empty classroom. He goes to his table, and after composing himself, opens the class register and reads out the names as he did every morning at the start of a new school day.*)

Johnny Awu, living or dead? Christopher Bandla, living or dead? Zandile Cwati, living or dead? Semphiwe Dambuza . . . Ronald Gxasheka . . . Noloyiso Mfundeweni . . . Steven Gaika . . . Zachariah Jabavu . . . Thami . . . Thami Mbikwana . . . (*Pause*) Living or dead?

How many young souls do I have present this morning? There are a lot of well-aimed stray bullets flying around on the streets out there. Is that why this silence is so . . . heavy? But what can I teach you? (*Picks up his little black dictionary on the table*) My lessons were meant to help you in this world. I wanted you to know how to read and write and talk in *this* world of living, stupid, cruel men. (*Helpless gesture*) Now? Oh, my children! I have no lessons that will be of any use to you now. Mr. M and all of his wonderful words are . . . useless, useless, useless!

(*The sound of breaking glass. Stones land in the classroom.* MR. M *picks up one.*) No! One of you is still alive. Ghosts don't throw stones with hot, sweating young hands. (*Grabs the bell and rings it wildly again*) Come to school! Come to school!

THAMI (*Appears. Quietly.*) Stop ringing that bell, Mr. M.

MR. M. Why? It's only the school bell, Thami. I thought you liked the sound of it. You once told me it was almost as good as music . . . don't you remember?

THAMI. You are provoking the comrades with it.

MR. M. No, Thami. I am summoning the comrades with it.

THAMI. They say you are ringing the bell to taunt them. You are openly defying the boycott by being here in the school.

MR. M. I ring this bell because according to my watch it is school time and I am a teacher and those desks are empty! I will go on ringing it as I have been doing these past two weeks, at the end of every lesson. And you can tell the comrades that I will be back here ringing it tomorrow and the day after tomorrow and for as many days after that as it takes for this world to come to its senses. Is that the only reason you've come? To tell me to stop ringing the school bell?

THAMI. No.

MR. M. You haven't come for a lesson, have you?

THAMI. No, I haven't.

MR. M. Of course not. What's the matter with me. Slogans don't need much in the way of grammar, do they? As for these . . . *(The stone in his hand)* No, you don't need me for lessons in stone throwing either. You've already got teachers in those very revolutionary subjects, haven't you? *(Picks up his dictionary, the stone in one hand, the book in the other)* You know something interesting,

Thami . . . if you put these two on a scale I think you would find that they weighed just about the same. But in this hand I am holding the whole English language. This . . . *(The stone)* . . . is just *one* word in that language. It's true! All that wonderful poetry that you and Isabel tried to cram into your beautiful heads . . . in here! Twenty-six letters, sixty thousand words. The greatest souls the world has ever known were able to open the floodgates of their ecstasy, their despair, their joy! . . . with words in this little book. Aren't you tempted? I was. *(Opens the book at the fly-leaf and reads)* "Anela Myalatya. Cookhouse. 1947" One of the first books I ever bought. *(Impulsively)* I want you to have it.

THAMI *(ignoring the offered book)*. I've come here to warn you.

MR. M. You've already done that and I've already told you that you are wasting your breath. Now take your stones and go. There are a lot of unbroken windows left.

THAMI. I'm not talking about the bell now. It's more serious than that.

MR. M. In my life nothing is more serious than ringing the school bell.

THAMI. There was a meeting last night. Somebody stood up and denounced you as an informer.

(Pause. THAMI waits. MR. M says nothing.)

THAMI. He said you gave names to the police.

(MR. M says nothing.)

THAMI. Everybody is talking about it this morning. You are in big danger.

MR. M. Why are you telling me all this?

THAMI. So that you can save yourself. There is a plan to march to the school and burn it down. If they find you here . . . *(Pause)*

MR. M. Go on. *(Violently)* If they find me here *what*?

THAMI. They will kill you.

MR. M *(He writes on the blackboard.)* "They will kill me." That's better. Remember what I taught you . . . if you've got a problem, put it into words so that you can look at it, handle it, and ultimately solve it. They will kill me! You are right. That is very serious. So then . . . what must I do? Must I run away and hide somewhere?

THAMI. No, they will find you. You must join the boycott.

MR. M *(He writes on the blackboard.)* "Solution: Join the Boycott." I'm listening.

THAMI. Let me go back and tell them that we have had a long talk and that you have realized you were wrong and have decided to join us. Let me say that you will sign the declaration and that you won't have anything to do with the school until all demands have been met.

MR. M. And they will agree to that? Accept me as one of them even though it is believed that I am an informer?

THAMI. I will tell them you are innocent. That I confronted you with the charge and that you denied it and that I believe you.

MR. M. I see. *(Studying* THAMI *intently)* You don't believe that I am an

informer.

THAMI. No.

MR. M. Won't you be taking a chance in defending me like that? Mightn't they end up suspecting you?

THAMI. They'll believe me. I'll make them believe me.

MR. M. You can't be sure. Mobs don't listen to reason, Thami. Hasn't your revolution already taught you that? Why take a chance like that to save a collaborator? Why do you want to do all this for me?

THAMI *(Avoiding* MR. M *'s eyes)*. I'm not doing it for you. I'm doing it for the Struggle. Our Cause will suffer if we falsely accuse and hurt innocent people.

MR. M. I see. My "execution" would be an embarrassment to the Cause. I apologize, Thami. For a moment I allowed myself to think that you were doing it because we were . . . who we are . . . the "all-knowing Mr. M and his brilliant protégé Thami!" I was so proud of us when Isabel called us that.

Well, young comrade, you have got nothing to worry about. Let them come and do whatever it is they want to. Your Cause won't be embarrassed because, you see, they won't be "hurting" an innocent man.

(He makes his confession simply and truthfully.) That's right, Thami. I am guilty. I did go to the police. I sat down in Captain Lategan's office and told him I felt it was my duty to report the presence in our community of strangers from the north. I

told him that I had reason to believe that they were behind the present unrest. I gave the Captain names and addresses. He thanked me and offered me money for the information, which I refused.

(Pause) Why do you look at me like that? Isn't that what you expected from me? . . . A government stooge, a sell-out? Isn't that what you were all secretly hoping I would do . . . so that you could be proved right? (Appalled) Is that why I did it? Out of spite? Can a man destroy himself, his life for a reason as petty as that?

I sat here before going to the police station saying to myself that it was my duty, to my conscience, to you, to the whole community to do whatever I could to put an end to this madness of boycotts and arson, mob violence and lawlessness . . . and maybe that is true . . . but only maybe . . . because, Thami, the truth is that I was so lonely! You had deserted me. I was so jealous of those who had taken you away. Now, I've really lost you, haven't I? Yes. I can see it in your eyes. You'll never forgive me for doing that, will you?

You know, Thami, I'd sell my soul to have you all back behind your desks for one last lesson. Yes. If the devil thought it was worth having and offered me that in exchange . . . one lesson! He could have my soul. So then it's all over! Because this . . . (The classroom) . . . is all there was for me. This was my home, my life, my one and only ambition . . . to be a good teacher! (His dictionary) Anela

Myalatya, twenty years old, from Cookhouse, wanted to be that the way your friends wanted to be big soccer stars playing for Kaizer Chiefs! That ambition goes back to when he was just a skinny little ten-year-old at the top of the Wapadsberg Pass.

We were on our way to a rugby match at Somerset East. The lorry stopped at the top of the mountain so that we could stretch our legs and relieve ourselves. It was a hard ride on the back of that lorry. The road hadn't been tarred yet. So there I was, ten years old and sighing with relief as I aimed for the little bush. It was a hot day. The sun right over our heads . . . not a cloud in the vast blue sky. I looked out . . . it's very high up there at the top of the pass . . . and there it was, stretching away from the foot of the mountain, the great pan of the Karoo . . . stretching away forever, it seemed, into the purple haze and heat of the horizon. Something grabbed my heart at that moment, my soul, and squeezed it until there were tears in my eyes. I had never seen anything so big, so beautiful in all my life. I went to the teacher who was with us and asked him: "Teacher, where will I come to if I start walking that way?" . . . and I pointed. He laughed. "Little man," he said, "that way is north. If you start walking that way and just keep on walking, and your legs don't give in, you will see all of Africa! Yes, Africa, little man! You will see the great rivers of the continent: the Vaal, the Zambesi, the

Limpopo, the Congo, and then the mighty Nile. You will see the mountains: the Drakensberg, Kilimanjaro, Kenya, and the Ruwenzori. And you will meet all our brothers: the little Pygmies of the forests, the proud Masai, the Watusi . . . tallest of the tall, and the Kikuyu standing on one leg like herons in a pond waiting for a frog." "Has teacher seen all that?" I asked. "No," he said. "Then how does teacher know it's there?" "Because it is all in the books, and I have read the books, and if you work hard in school, little man, you can do the same without worrying about your legs giving in."

He was right, Thami. I have seen it. It is all there in the books just as he said it was, and I have made it mine. I can stand on the banks of all those great rivers, look up at the majesty of all those mountains, whenever I want to. It is a journey I have made many times. Whenever my spirit was low and I sat alone in my room, I said to myself: Walk, Anela! Walk! . . . and I imagined myself at the foot of the Wapadsberg setting off for that horizon that called me that day forty years ago. It always worked! When I left that little room, I walked back into the world a proud man, because I was an African and all the splendor was my birthright.

(Pause) I don't want to make that journey again, Thami. There is someone waiting for me now at the end of it who has made a mockery of all my visions of splendor. He has in his arms my real birthright.

I saw him on the television in the Reverend Mbop's lounge. An Ethiopian tribesman, and he was carrying the body of a little child that had died of hunger in the famine . . . a small bundle carelessly wrapped in a few rags. I couldn't tell how old the man was. The lines of despair and starvation on his face made him look as old as Africa itself.

He held that little bundle very lightly as he shuffled along to a mass grave, and when he reached it, he didn't have the strength to kneel and lay it down gently . . . He just opened his arms and let it fall. I was very upset when the program ended. Nobody had thought to tell us his name and whether he was the child's father, or grandfather, or uncle. And the same for the baby? Didn't it have a name? How dare you show me one of our children being thrown away and not tell me its name! I demand to know who is in that bundle!

(Pause) Not knowing their names doesn't matter anymore. They are more than just themselves. The tribesmen and dead child do duty for all of us, Thami. Every African soul is either carrying that bundle or in it.

What is wrong with this world that it wants to waste you all like that . . . my children . . . my Africa! (Holding out a hand as if he wanted to touch THAMI's face) My beautiful and proud young Africa!

(More breaking glass and stones and the sound of a crowd outside the school. MR. M *starts to move.* THAMI *stops him.*)

THAMI. No! Don't go out there. Let me speak to them first. Listen to me! I will tell them I have confronted you with the charges and that you have denied them and that I believe you. I will tell them you are innocent.

MR. M. You will lie for me, Thami?

THAMI. Yes.

MR. M *(desperate to hear the truth).* Why?

(THAMI *can't speak.*)

MR. M. Why will you lie for me, Thami?

THAMI. I've told you before.

MR. M. The "Cause?"

THAMI. Yes.

MR. M. Then I do not need to hide behind your lies.

THAMI. They will kill you.

MR. M. Do you think I'm frightened of them? Do you think I'm frightened of dying? (MR. M *breaks away from* THAMI. *Ringing his bell furiously he goes outside and confronts the mob. They kill him.*)

SCENE 4

THAMI *waiting.* ISABEL *arrives.*

THAMI. Isabel.

ISABEL *(It takes her a few seconds to respond.)* Hello, Thami.

THAMI. Thank you for coming.

ISABEL *(She is tense. Talking to him is not easy.)* I wasn't going to. Let me tell you straight out that there is nothing in this world . . . nothing! . . . that I want to see less at this moment than anything or anybody from the location. But you said in your note that it was urgent, so here I am. If

you've got something to say, I'll listen.

THAMI. Are you in a hurry?

ISABEL. I haven't got to be somewhere else, if that's what you mean. But if you're asking because it looks as if I would like to run away from here, from you! . . . very fast, then the answer is yes. But don't worry, I'll be able to control that urge for as long as you need to say what you want to.

THAMI *(awkward in the face of* ISABEL *'s severe and unyielding attitude).* I just wanted to say goodbye.

ISABEL. Again?

THAMI. What do you mean?

ISABEL. You've already done that, Thami. Maybe you didn't use that word, but you turned your back on me and walked out of my life that last afternoon the three of us . . . *(She can't finish.)* How long ago was that?

THAMI. Three weeks I think.

ISABEL. So why do you want to do it again? Aren't you happy with the last time? It was so dramatic, Thami.

THAMI *(patiently).* I wanted to see you because I'm leaving the town, I'm going away for good.

ISABEL. Oh, I see. This is meant to be a "sad" goodbye is it? *(She is on the edge.)* I'm sorry if I'm hurting your feelings but I thought you wanted to see me because you had something to say about recent events in our little community . . . *(Out of a pocket a crumpled little piece of newspaper which she opens with unsteady hands)* . . . a certain unrest related . . . I think that is the phrase they use . . . yes . . . here it is . . . (*Reading*) " . . . unrest related incident in which according to witnesses the defenseless teacher was attacked by a group of blacks who struck him over the head with an iron rod before setting him on fire."

THAMI. Stop it, Isabel.

ISABEL (*fighting hard for self-control*). Oh, Thami, I wish I could! I've tried everything, but nothing helps. It just keeps going around and around inside my head. I've tried crying. I've tried praying! I've even tried confrontation. Ja, the day after it happened I tried to get into the location. I wanted to find the witnesses who reported it so accurately and ask them: . . . why didn't you stop it! There was a police roadblock at the entrance and they wouldn't let me in. They thought I was crazy or something and "escorted" me back into the safekeeping of two now very frightened parents.

There is nothing wrong with me! All I need is someone to tell me why he was killed. What madness drove those people to kill a man who had devoted his whole life to helping them. He was such a good man, Thami! He was one of the most beautiful human beings I have ever known and his death is the ugliest thing I have ever known.

THAMI (*Gives her a few seconds to calm down. Gently.*) He was an informer, Isabel. Somehow or the other somebody discovered that Mr. M was an informer.

ISABEL. You mean that list of pupils taking part in the boycott? You call that informing?

THAMI. No. It was worse than that. He went to the police and gave them the names and addresses of our political action committee. All of them were arrested after his visit. They are now in detention.

ISABEL. Mr. M did that?

THAMI. Yes.

ISABEL. I don't believe it.

THAMI. It's true, Isabel.

ISABEL. No! What proof do you have?

THAMI. His own words. He told me so himself. I didn't believe it either when he was first accused, but the last time I saw him, he said it was true, that he had been to the police.

ISABEL (*stunned disbelief*). Mr. M? A police spy? For how long?

THAMI. No. It wasn't like that. He wasn't paid or anything. He went to the police just that one time. He said he felt it was his duty.

ISABEL. What do you mean?

THAMI. Operation Qhumisa . . . the boycotts and strikes, the arson . . . you know he didn't agree with any of that. But he was also very confused about it all. I think he wished he had never done it.

ISABEL. So he went to the police just once.

THAMI. Yes.

ISABEL. As a matter of conscience.

THAMI. Yes.

ISABEL. That doesn't make him an "informer," Thami!

THAMI. Then what do you call some-body who gives information to the police?

ISABEL. No! You know what that word really means, the sort of person it suggests. Was Mr. M one of those? He was acting out of concern for his people . . . you said so yourself. He thought he was doing the right thing! You don't murder a man for that!

THAMI (near the end of his patience). Be careful, Isabel.

ISABEL. Of what?

THAMI. The words you use.

ISABEL. Oh? Which one don't you like? Murder? What do you want me to call it . . . "an unrest related inci-dent?" If you are going to call him an informer, then I am going to call his death murder!

THAMI. It was an act of self-defense.

ISABEL. By who?

THAMI. The People.

ISABEL (almost speechless with outrage). What? A mad mob attacks one unarmed defenseless man and you want me to call it . . .

THAMI (Abandoning all attempts at patience. He speaks with the full authori-ty of the anger inside him.) Stop it, Isabel! You just keep quiet now and listen to me. You're always saying you want to understand us and what it means to be black . . . well if you do, listen to me carefully now. I don't call it murder, and I don't call the people who did it a mad mob and yes, I do expect you to see it as an act of self-defense . . . listen to me! . . .

blind and stupid but still self-defense.

He betrayed us and our fight for freedom. Five men are in detention because of Mr. M's visit to the police station. There have been other arrests and there will be more. Why do you think I'm running away? How were those people to know he wasn't a paid informer who had been doing it for a long time and would do it again? They were defending themselves against what they thought was a terrible danger to themselves. What Anela Myalatya did to them and their cause is what your laws define as treason when it is done to you and threatens the safety and security of your comfortable white world. Anybody accused of it is put on trial in your courts and if found guilty they get hanged. Many of my people have been found guilty and have been hanged. Those hangings we call murder!

Try to understand, Isabel. Try to imagine what it is like to be a black person, choking inside with rage and frustration, bitterness, and then to discover that one of your own kind is a traitor, has betrayed you to those responsible for the suffering and misery of your family, of your people. What would you do? Remember there is no magistrate or court you can drag him to and demand that he be tried for that crime. There is no justice for black people in this country other than what we make for ourselves. When you judge us for what happened in front of the school four days ago just remember that you carry a share of the responsibility for it. It is your laws that have made simple, decent black people so desperate that they turn into "mad mobs."

(ISABEL *has been listening and watching intently. It looks as if she is going to say something but she stops herself.*)

THAMI. Say it, Isabel.

ISABEL. No.

THAMI. This is your last chance. You once challenged me to be honest with you. I'm challenging you now.

ISABEL *(She faces him.)* Where were you when it happened, Thami? *(Pause)* And if you were there, did you try to stop them?

THAMI. Isn't there a third question, Isabel? Was I one of the mob that killed him?

ISABEL. Yes. Forgive me, Thami . . . please forgive me! . . . But there is that question as well. Only once! Believe me, only once . . . late at night when I couldn't sleep. I couldn't believe it was there in my head, but I heard the words . . . "Was Thami one of the ones who did it?"

THAMI. If the police catch me, that's the question they will ask.

ISABEL. I'm asking you because . . . *(An open, helpless gesture)* . . . I'm lost! I don't know what to think or feel anymore. Help me. Please. You're the only one who can. Nobody else seems to understand that I loved him. *(This final confrontation is steady and unflinching on both sides.)*

THAMI. Yes, I was there. Yes, I did try to stop it. *(THAMI *gives* ISABEL *the time to deal with his answer.*)* I knew how angry the people were. I went to warn him. If he had listened to me he would still be alive, but he wouldn't. It was almost as if he wanted it to happen. I think he hated himself very much for what he had done, Isabel. He kept saying to me that it was all over. He was right. There was nothing left for him. That visit to the police station had finished everything. Nobody would have ever spoken to him again or let him teach their children.

ISABEL. Oh, Thami, it is all so wrong! So stupid! That's what I can't take . . . the terrible stupidity of it. We needed him. All of us.

THAMI. I know.

ISABEL. Then why is he dead?

THAMI. You must stop asking these questions, Isabel. You know the answers.

ISABEL. They don't make any sense, Thami.

THAMI. I know what you are feeling. *(Pause)* I also loved him. Doesn't help much to say it now, I know, but I did. Because he made me angry and impatient with his "old-fashioned" ideas, I didn't want to admit it. Even if I had, it wouldn't have stopped me from doing what I did, the boycott and everything, but I should have tried harder to make him understand why I was doing it. You were right to ask about that. Now . . .? *(A helpless gesture)* You know the most terrible words in your language, Isabel? Too late.

ISABEL. Ja.

THAMI. I'll never forgive myself for not trying harder with him and letting him know . . . my true feelings for him. Right until the end I tried to deny it . . . to him, to myself.

ISABEL. I'm sorry. I . . .

THAMI. That's all right.

ISABEL. Are the police really looking for you?

THAMI. Yes. Some of my friends have already been detained. They're pulling in anybody they can get their hands on.

ISABEL. Where are you going? Cape Town?

THAMI. No. That's the first place they'll look. I've written to my parents telling them about everything. I'm heading north.

ISABEL. To where?

THAMI. Far, Isabel. I'm leaving the country.

ISABEL. Does that mean what I think it does?

THAMI (nods). I'm going to join the movement. I want to be a fighter. I've been thinking about it for a long time. Now I know it's the right thing to do. I don't want to end up being one of the mob that killed Mr. M—but that will happen to me if I stay here.

ISABEL. Oh, Thami.

THAMI. I know I'm doing the right thing. Believe me.

ISABEL. I'll try.

THAMI. And you?

ISABEL. I don't know what to do with myself, Thami. All I know is that I'm frightened of losing him. He's only been dead four days and I think I'm already starting to forget what he looked like. But the worst thing is that there's nowhere for me to go and . . . you know . . . just be near him. That's so awful. I got my father to phone the police but they said there wasn't enough left of him to justify a grave. What there was had been disposed of in a "Christian manner." So where do I go? The burnt-out ruins of the school? I couldn't face that.

THAMI. Get your father or somebody to drive you to the top of the Wapadsberg Pass. It's on the road to Craddock.

ISABEL. I know it.

THAMI. It was a very special place to him. He told me that it was there where it all started, where he knew what he wanted to do with his life . . . being a teacher, being the Mr. M we knew. You'll be near him up there. I must go now.

ISABEL. Do you need any money?

THAMI. No. *Sala Kakuhle*, Isabel. That's the Xhosa goodbye.

ISABEL. I know it. Asipumla taught me how to say it. *Hamba Kakhule*, Thami.

(THAMI *leaves.*)

SCENE 5

ISABEL (*Alone. She stands quietly, examining the silence. After a few seconds she nods her head slowly.*) Yes! Thami was right, Mr. M. He said I'd feel near you up here.

He's out there somewhere, Mr. M . . . travelling north. He didn't say where exactly he was going, but I think we can guess, can't we?

I'm here for a very "old-fashioned" reason, so I know you'll approve. I've come to pay my last respects to Anela Myalatya. I know the old-fashioned way of doing that is to bring flowers, lay them on the grave, say a quiet prayer, and then go back to your life. But that seemed sort of silly this time. You'll have enough flowers around here when the spring comes . . . which it will. So instead I've brought you something which I know will mean more to you than flowers or prayers ever could. A promise. I am going to make Anela Myalatya a promise.

You gave me a little lecture once about wasted lives . . . how much of it you'd seen, how much you hated it, how much you didn't want that to happen to Thami and me. I sort of understood what you meant at the time. Now, I most certainly do. Your death has seen to that.

My promise to you is that I am going to try as hard as I can, in every way that I can, to see that it doesn't happen to me. I am going to try my best to make my life useful in the way yours was. I want you to be proud of me. After all, I am one of your children, you know. You did welcome me to your family. *(A pause)* The future is still ours, Mr. M.

(The actress leaves the stage.)

THE END

MY CHILDREN! MY AFRICA!

Reader Response

1. Mr. M says "Hope. . . is as dangerous as Hate and Despair. . . ." Is it Hope, Hate, or Despair that kills Mr. M.? Explain your answer.
2. Thami equates what Mr. M. did in turning people in to the police with treason. Is he justified in his belief? Why or why not?
3. Choose one of the monologues in the play and list the range of emotions the speaker goes through as he or she speaks.
4. Who is the protagonist of this play and who is the antagonist?
5. Write a review of *My Children! My Africa!* Be sure to include what you see as its strengths and weaknesses.

About Apartheid in South Africa

White Europeans arrived in Africa in the 1600's, and by 1795 they occupied most of the good southern farmland. When diamonds and gold were discovered during the nineteenth century, more whites began arriving. Over the following decades, blacks were systematically denied any voice in the government. In 1948 a rigid policy of racial separation, *apartheid* (*separateness* in Afrikaans), was established. Housing, schooling, employment, parks, and transportation were all segregated. For decades the ANC (African National Congress) fought for black rights, holding boycotts and strikes in the 1950's. PAC (the Pan-African Congress) staged rallies, and in 1960 in Sharpeville, the police killed 69 black protestors. In 1976 blacks in Soweto rioted, and 600 people were killed. By 1986 the government had declared a state of emergency—jailing people without formally charging them. Finally, in 1991, the government abolished apartheid, and in 1994 the country held its first open elections. The ANC won by a landslide and Nelson Mandela became president.

CREATING AND PERFORMING

1. With two others, find a scene featuring Isabel, Thami, and Mr. M. Read the scene. Try to capture their feelings for one another.
2. Write a letter from Isabel to Thami ten years after they've parted.
3. Write a eulogy for Mr. M and present it for the class.

Phaeton and the Sun Chariot

The Play as Literature: Myth

Myths reflect a people's perception of life's deepest truths. Whether Greek, Roman, or Norse—the most familiar myths to English readers—myths share common themes and aspirations. Often following the adventures of heroes and gods, myths attempt to explain the world—how it began and why it works the way it does. (For more about Greek deities, see p. 403.)

The play you are about to read retells the Greek myth of the young lad Phaeton in contemporary terms. Like most teenage boys of today, Phaeton longs to take a spin in his dad's fancy set of wheels. As you read, think about the similarities Phaeton exhibits to teenagers you know.

The Play as Theatre: Roles

There is a saying in the theatre that there are no small parts, only small actors. Theatre people believe that every part is important because every character is there for a reason—to help create a well-balanced play.

The *leading roles* in a play are headed by the protagonist, or hero, and the antagonist, or villain. *Supporting roles* are slightly smaller, but just as important. They add depth and interest to the story. Next come the *minor roles,* characters of lesser importance to the story who nevertheless help move the play along or give it atmosphere. Actors with *bit parts* only have a few lines to say in the play, but still help shape the play as a whole. The *walk-ons* are much like scenery—they help set the scene just as extras do in a movie.

Warm Up!

Think of a familiar myth or fairy tale. Create a graphic organizer listing which characters would play the leading roles, supporting roles, minor roles, bit roles, and walk-ons.

Phaeton
and the Sun Chariot

by Wim Coleman

Mythical
Greece, India,
and the sky

URANIA (yu̇ rā′ nē ə)
CLYMENE (klī mē′nē)
PHAETON (fā′ə thon)
TIME
HELIOS (hē′lē ōs)
WINTER
SPRING
SUMMER
FALL
NEWSCASTER
FOUR REPORTERS
LEO
TAURUS
CANCER
SCORPIO
MOTHER EARTH
ZEUS (züs)
HERA (hir′ə)
CHARON (ker′ən)

No time in
particular

URANIA *enters onto a bare stage. She looks around briefly, then goes offstage. She comes back with two small stools and sets them center stage.*

URANIA. Can I have the lights down, please? Just a little bit?

(The lights dim slightly.)

URANIA. That's it. Nice "dusk" effect. Think "dusk" a minute. Not quite dark. No, not quite night yet. Maybe just a star or two. Soon, very soon, the sky will be filled with monsters.

(Stopping to survey the audience) Oh, I see you're going to be one of *those* audiences. Not going to swallow this "monsters-in-the-sky" bit. No, you're too smart for that. You know too much. You know that stars are made of flaming gas, all about light years, supernovas, quasars, galaxies, black holes, that kind of thing. You're a regular bunch of astronomers. Well, I'm Urania, the Muse of the Sky, and you'll have to forgive me if I insult your ultra-educated minds for just a little while. In the days of my story,

the sky was filled with monsters. People traveling the heavens met a great bull, stomping and snorting and threatening to charge. And also a hungry lion, ready to devour any living thing that came along. They braved the deadly claws of a giant crab, the poisonous tail of a great scorpion. I know it sounds silly, but that's how it was.

(PHAETON *and* CLYMENE *come onto the stage.* PHAETON *sits on a stool.* CLYMENE *stands nearby. They freeze into these positions.*)

URANIA. But it's dusk, remember. The monsters are just starting to show themselves. I take you to a modest little house in Greece. A young man sits on the front porch, watching as the sky begins to fill with stars.

(URANIA *steps aside to watch.* PHAETON *and* CLYMENE *come to life.*)

CLYMENE (*looking up from a list she's been making*). Phaeton, why are you sitting out here? It's getting chilly.

PHAETON. I'm just thinking.

CLYMENE. Do you want me to get your jacket?

PHAETON. No.

CLYMENE (*sitting next to him*). Could you pick up some things on the way home from school tomorrow? We need more milk. And cheese. And lamb, don't forget lamb.

(But PHAETON *isn't listening to her.*)

PHAETON (*looking at the sky*). The sky's so clear. You'll be able to see every star tonight. There. They're starting to come out. (*Pointing*) There's

Venus. And do you see that dim strip of light? That's the Milky Way. That's his road. That's where the Sun rides across the sky.

CLYMENE. What did I just ask you to do?

PHAETON. I'm sorry. I wasn't listening.

CLYMENE. What makes you think of your father?

PHAETON. I think about him all the time.

CLYMENE. You never ask about him.

PHAETON. You never seem to want to talk about him.

CLYMENE. We can if you want to. What do you want me to tell you?

PHAETON. Why did you leave him?

CLYMENE. I've told you that.

PHAETON. No you haven't. Not really.

CLYMENE (*a bit evasively*). Well, it wasn't my kind of life, being married to a god. The Sun Palace was rather gaudy for my taste. Everything was very bright. It hurt my eyes. And I never took to gods that well. Oh, the talk was so serious. All about history and destiny and fate all the time. I was bored. And to tell the truth, I bored the gods. I was too simple for them. They were happy to see me go.

PHAETON. I've heard all this before. Those aren't the real reasons.

CLYMENE. What makes you say that?

PHAETON. I just know. (*Pause*) Didn't you love him?

CLYMENE. Oh, Phaeton, really.

PHAETON. Well, didn't you?

CLYMENE. I—I loved him early on, and he loved me, but . . . your father and I, we—(*Touching her forefingers together)*—we just didn't meet here and here. I don't know how else to say it. Why now, Phaeton? Why do you want to talk about him all of a sudden?

PHAETON. Don't you think it's about time? I'm not a kid anymore. All my life, I've tried to tell people who I am, who my father was. Nobody's ever believed me, not once. When I was little, all the other kids teased me. "Phaeton doesn't have a daddy," they'd say.

CLYMENE. You never said anything about it.

PHAETON. But you knew.

CLYMENE. Yes, of course I did. Well, you showed everybody you were a winner, no matter what they thought.

PHAETON. But nobody believes the truth. Doesn't that bother you? Don't you care what people say about—?

(PHAETON stops himself in mid-sentence.)

CLYMENE *(finishing his thought).* About me? That I'm some crazy woman who claims she was once married to the Sun? No, it doesn't bother me. I don't know why, but it doesn't. Your sisters are his children, too, and it doesn't seem to bother them.

PHAETON. I'm not like them.

CLYMENE. Phaeton, I swear to you it's true. The Sun really is your father. If I'm lying, let Zeus kill me here and now. I'm sure he's got a bolt of lightning handy.

PHAETON. I believe you. I've always believed you. I just want to know why you left him, really. Was he cruel?

Did he mistreat you? Was he such a terrible father?

CLYMENE. No. He was—is very good.

PHAETON. Then why?

CLYMENE *(reluctantly).* Because I wanted you and your sisters to live human lives. I thought it would be hard for you, growing up among immortals. Too much pressure, too many expectations. Your father was against our leaving. So were all the gods. They fought me tooth and nail. I was just a mortal girl, and I couldn't do anything, not even bring up my own children. But I did what I thought I had to do. I left the Sun Palace and brought you here. He sent me money, but I sent it back. I worked in the vineyards and olive groves and made as much time as I could for my children. But . . .

PHAETON. But what?

CLYMENE. I've always wondered if I did the right thing.

PHAETON. You did. We couldn't ask for a better home—or a better family.

CLYMENE. So, what do you want?

PHAETON. I want to know—what does it mean to be part god? Do I have powers I don't know about? Or duties? Will I die someday—or will I live forever?

CLYMENE. I don't know.

PHAETON. Then how do I find out?

(Pause)

CLYMENE. Go to see him. Ask him yourself—in person. That's what you want to do, isn't it?

PHAETON. Will you come with me?

CLYMENE. No. *(Pause)* Come on. We'd better get you packed.

(CLYMENE and PHAETON freeze. URANIA steps forward.)

URANIA. I think we can skip the journey. You've seen lots of "journeys-to-the-East" in movies. This one won't be any different.

(PHAETON and CLYMENE exit.)

URANIA. As our hero makes his way, though, I'd better clear up one or two things. You're all used to living on a round little world that hurtles around the sun, a veritable moving target for asteroids and meteors and comets and the like. And the sun itself wobbles chaotically from the weight of nine planets tugging at it from different directions. All this doesn't even seem to worry you. Time was, though, when the Earth was much more stable, just a great platform resting squarely on the shoulders of a Titan. And the Sun was a god who rode a fiery chariot. You might be too young to remember. Ask your parents about it.

(TIME enters, wearing sunglasses and carrying a tall stool. She sets the stool in front of one of the small ones, as if it were a desk. She sits behind it and freezes.)

URANIA. The god Helios lives in the Sun Palace—a classy place, all gold and ivory decorated with precious jewels, located in a very cosmopolitan, very posh district of India.

(TIME comes to life. She pantomimes answering a phone.)

TIME. Sun Enterprises, Far East Office, this is Time speaking. Could you hold, please? Thank you. *(Pantomiming again)* Sun Enterprises, Far East Office, this is Time speaking. Could you hold, please? Thank you. *(Again)* Sun Enterprises, Far East Office, this is Time speaking. Could you hold, please? Thank you. *(Throwing up her hands in exasperation)* It'll never stop! *(She freezes again.)*

URANIA. Now the poet Ovid doesn't mention Helios having a secretary/receptionist. In his version of our story, the Sun god is waited on by servants named Hour, Day, Year, and Century. But if you ask me, a celebrity who travels day in and day out can't get by without a receptionist. I hope no one minds my writing one in.

(URANIA steps aside to watch. PHAETON enters cautiously. TIME doesn't see him at first.)

TIME *(picking up the phone again).* Sun Enterprises, Time speaking, thank you for holding, can I help you? No, he's not giving interviews this week. I'm sorry, but that's positively the last word. Good-by.

PHAETON. Excuse me—

TIME. What are you doing here?

PHAETON. I want to talk to Helios.

TIME. Have you got an appointment?

PHAETON. Well, no, but I—

TIME. How did you get past Security?

PHAETON. I just walked in.

TIME. Those guys are never on the job.

PHAETON. You're Time?

TIME. That's right. I'm in charge of years, months, days, hours, minutes, and seconds. If you want an appointment with Helios, I'm the one to talk to. But I can tell you right now, you'll never get to see him.

PHAETON. But you don't understand—

TIME. No, *you* don't. He's got a flight leaving in five minutes. He's not seeing anyone right now, with or without an appointment. Now if you don't mind, I've got a lot of calls. *(Picking up the phone again)* Sun Enterprises, Time speaking, thank you for holding, can I help you? No, there's no truth to that rumor, and if you print it you'll hear from our lawyers. Look, buddy, if you've got a problem, call Public Relations.

PHAETON. If you'll just let me explain—

TIME. Do you want me to call a guard? *(To the phone)* Sun Enterprises, Time speaking, thank you for holding, can I help you? Oh, Zeus, thank you for returning his call.

PHAETON *(excitedly).* Zeus? You're talking to Zeus?

TIME *(to PHAETON).* Do you mind? This is long distance. *(To the phone)* Yes, Zeus, I'm sorry. The office is a little crazy this morning. Helios just wondered if you could give him a little cloud cover. Nothing overcast, just a few scattered—what did he call them?—cirrus clouds. At about 20,000 feet. You know, just for variety. Weather's been awfully clear lately. Public gets tired of it. Oh, thank you very much. He'll really appreciate it. *(To PHAETON)* Still here, huh?

PHAETON. My name is Phaeton.

TIME. So?

PHAETON. I'm his son.

TIME. Oh, brother.

PHAETON. It's true.

TIME. Do you know how often I hear that one? *(To the phone)* Sun Enterprises, Time speaking, thank you for holding, can I help you? If I've told you once, I've told you a thousand times, he will not endorse your chariots. He doesn't even ride one of yours. No, he doesn't want one for free, he's happy with the one he's got, thank you very much.

PHAETON. I won't leave till I talk to him.

TIME. I'm not a baby-sitter.

PHAETON. Then you'd better let me see him.

TIME. You don't know his temper.

PHAETON. I'll take my chances.

TIME *(to the phone).* Mr. Helios? There's a kid here to see you, making a real pain of himself. What do you want me to do with him?

PHAETON. Tell him who I am.

TIME. He says he's your son.

PHAETON. Phaeton.

TIME. Yes, I know, the third one this week.

PHAETON. Clymene's son.

TIME. He says he's Phaeton, the son of—*(To PHAETON)* Who was that again?

PHAETON. Clymene.

TIME. Clymene's son. *(A bit surprised by what she hears on the phone.)* Oh. All right. I'll tell him. *(To PHAETON)* He'll be right out.

PHAETON. Thanks. I'll be sure to tell him how pleasant you've been.

TIME. Don't get cute. Have you got sunglasses?

PHAETON. What?

TIME *(handing him a pair of sunglasses).* You can't look at him without sunglasses. Do you want to go blind?

PHAETON *(putting on the sunglasses).* Oh. I almost forgot.

(HELIOS enters, wearing his bright solar headdress.)

HELIOS *(delightedly).* Phaeton!

PHAETON. Hello, Father.

(HELIOS shakes PHAETON's hand warmly.)

HELIOS. Is it really you, boy?

PHAETON. I could ask you the same.

HELIOS. Time, this is my son Phaeton. Phaeton, this is—

TIME. We've met.

HELIOS. Spitting image of his mother. Gorgeous woman. My, how you've grown. When was the last time I saw you?

PHAETON. I wouldn't remember.

HELIOS *(uncomfortably).* Yes, well, it has been quite some time, hasn't it? Have a seat, son. Make yourself comfortable. Would you like anything at all? Cigar, perhaps? A cup of coffee? Some of our delightful Oriental spiced tea?

TIME. Mr. Helios, you're due for your chariot in a minute and twenty-seven seconds.

HELIOS. I'll be going up late this morning.

TIME. Oh, no, please.

HELIOS. An hour or two, maybe.

TIME. The stars will disappear at their usual time, whether you're in the sky or not. And you know how mortals get when they're plunged into total darkness unexpectedly. Or have you forgotten the hysteria caused by the last solar eclipse?

HELIOS *(firmly).* I said I'll be late.

TIME. Am I taking the flack for this?

HELIOS. Of course not. Pass the buck. Go down the hall and tell Public Relations to take care of it. Oh, and while you're at it, send in my advisors, would you? I want them to meet my son.

TIME. I don't like this.

HELIOS. Relax. I'll give you a hefty raise next week.

TIME. If you're not going up yet, you might want to take off your headgear.

HELIOS *(absently).* Eh?

TIME. That way, the boy can skip the shades.

HELIOS. Oh, yes. Excellent suggestion.

(TIME exits. HELIOS sets his headdress aside, and PHAETON removes the sunglasses.)

HELIOS. Dedicated employee, Time. Been with the firm for an eternity. But she can be over-zealous. She greet you well? Make you feel at home?

PHAETON. She's very nice.

HELIOS. My boy, you're about to witness a crisis of international proportions. For the first time in hundreds of years—why, no, in millennia!—the sun is rising late. The world will go completely crazy. In just a little while, every emperor, king, president, prime minister, and dictator-for-life on the planet will call, asking what in the name of heaven has gone wrong. This phone will ring right off the hook. Oh, it will be fun! Don't know why I've stuck to such a tight schedule all this time. Responsibility gets to be a habit, I guess. So. Tell me everything. How are your sisters?

PHAETON. Fine.

HELIOS. And your mother. Does she speak well of me? No, let me rephrase that. Does she speak of me at all?

PHAETON. Not really.

HELIOS. Hardly any wonder. Our parting wasn't exactly a happy one.

PHAETON. So I'm told.

HELIOS. At least she's come to her senses and sent you here. Yes, I knew she'd finally see the light. That boring little peninsula—which is it, Greece?—is no home for a young demigod. India is the place for you.

PHAETON. But Father—

HELIOS (*ignoring him*). You're an ambitious boy. I can see it in your eyes. Mortal life hasn't quelled your godlike spirit. You want to move up in the world. Well, Sun Enterprises is just the place to do it. I'll get you your own office this afternoon, start you on an executive's salary.

PHAETON. Wait a minute. I don't even know if I want to stay here.

HELIOS (*startled*). Don't be absurd. Of course you'll stay. This is where you belong.

PHAETON. But I just came here to meet you, to get to know you. I just want us to talk.

HELIOS. And so we shall! I'll tell you what, I'll take the whole day off. The world can cope with an extra night this once. And before you know it, you'll forget all this nonsense about going back to Greece. Just wait and see.

PHAETON. But I don't even know you.

HELIOS. How can you say that? I'm your father.

PHAETON. Most boys my age have seen more of their fathers.

HELIOS. You're hitting a little low, son.

PHAETON. I'm sorry.

HELIOS. You've got a right, I suppose. I could blame it all on your mother, tell you she simply didn't want me to come around, but that wouldn't be fair. It was an awkward situation, one of those marriages no one quite approved of, mortals or gods. It seemed best for me to keep my distance. Someday you'll learn that no one's to blame in these matters.

PHAETON. That's supposed to explain everything?

HELIOS. Oh, come now. You surely didn't come all the way to India to whine about your life. If you did, I've got other business to attend to. You're testing my patience, and it's just not done. (*Pause*) I'm sorry. It's easy to forget you're my son.

PHAETON. That's just my point.

(SPRING, SUMMER, FALL, *and* WINTER *enter.* SPRING *is garrulous and outgoing, a cockeyed optimist.* WINTER *is fretful, anxious, and officious. The personalities of* SUMMER *and* FALL *are somewhere between these two extremes.*)

SPRING. Good morning, sir.

SUMMER. You called for us, sir?

FALL. Is there anything we can do, sir?

WINTER. Aren't you running just a little late this morning, sir?

HELIOS (*resuming his usual vigorous manner*). Come in, come in! I'm not going up today. No, don't argue, you'll soon see it's for a good reason. Phaeton, these are my trusted advisors, Spring, Summer, Fall, and Winter. Seasons, this is my son, Phaeton.

SPRING. The son of the Sun! What an unexpected pleasure!

SUMMER. Unexpected is right.

FALL. I didn't know you had a son.

WINTER. How do you know he *is* your son?

SPRING. Oh, Winter, you're such a killjoy.

WINTER. I think it's a good question, considering how many kids come around claiming to be his children.

FALL. He *is* the third one this week.

SUMMER. Surely the boss knows his own son when he sees him.

HELIOS (*a bit huffily*). Not that it's necessarily any of your business, Winter, but I once was married to a lovely mortal woman named Clymene.

SPRING. A mortal!

SUMMER. I never knew!

FALL. Don't you think, as your advisors, we might have been, well . . .

WINTER. Advised?

HELIOS. The marriage didn't work out, I'm sorry to say. But before it ended, we produced four splendid children.

PHAETON. Five.

HELIOS. Five splendid children. Well, this strapping lad says he's one of them, and I believe him. If I'm not flattering myself unduly, I believe I see something of myself in him. A bit of my drive, my ambition, my gusto, my get-up-and-go. Am I right, son?

PHAETON. Well—

HELIOS. Come now, don't be modest. Tell us some of your accomplishments.

PHAETON. I'm just a kid from Greece.

HELIOS. I'll hear none of that. There'll be time for false humility when you've made your mark in the world.

PHAETON. Well, I'm captain of the football team—

HELIOS. An athlete! Excellent!

PHAETON. —student body president—

HELIOS. A natural-born leader!

PHAETON. —top of my class academically—

HELIOS. A mental giant!

PHAETON. —a black belt in tae kwon do, a chess grand master, a theoretical physicist, a contender for the next Olympic decathlon, and the inventor of an all-purpose vaccine against every known disease. There's been talk of my winning the Nobel Prize, but the committee can't decide which of my accomplishments to nominate me for.

HELIOS. Don't stop there. Continue.

PHAETON. That's pretty much it.

HELIOS (*trying to hide his disappointment*). Well, you're still young. Stick with us, and we'll add untold glories to your name.

Phaeton and the Sun Chariot by Wim Coleman   **389**

WINTER. I still don't like it.

SPRING. You never like anything.

FALL. I'm not sure I do, either.

WINTER. How do we know whether this boy is telling us the truth?

PHAETON. Winter's got a point, Father. I haven't given you any proof. I brought along my birth certificate, but how do you know I didn't forge it? I need to *do* something to prove I'm really your son.

HELIOS. You've got nothing to prove. I've taken you at your word, and my decision is final. I won't be contradicted. Is that understood by everybody?

(The SEASONS all murmur their agreement.)

SUMMER. I guess that leaves us with the question of how to go public with this news.

FALL. *Should* we go public?

SPRING. Of course we should!

WINTER. Of course we shouldn't!

HELIOS. Yes! Absolutely! We'll issue a press release immediately. Announce to the world that Helios and his son have been reunited after fourteen years—

PHAETON. Fifteen.

HELIOS. —fifteen years, and that Phaeton is joining Sun Enterprises as executive vice president.

PHAETON. Father, I haven't even decided—

HELIOS. Don't interrupt, son, we're making big plans here.

SUMMER. If I may make a suggestion, sir, I think we need a publicity angle. It's not enough to just say the two of you are reunited, Phaeton's working for the firm, and blah-blah-blah. It lacks a certain drama, a certain— oomph. It'll leave the public cold.

FALL. Summer's right. We need something to humanize what's happening here. The whole world needs to feel this wonderful new bond between you two.

SUMMER. A gimmick!

FALL. A stunt!

HELIOS. Now you're talking! What have you got in mind?

SPRING. I've got it! Listen! You promise to grant Phaeton any wish he makes! You swear it by the River Styx!

WINTER. But that's the most binding oath there is. No god can go back on it.

SPRING. Exactly! That's what makes it so dramatic!

WINTER. It's a recipe for disaster! Don't you remember what happened when Zeus made the same oath to that mortal girl, what's-her-name?

SPRING. Semele.

WINTER. That's right, Semele. She asked to look Zeus in the face. Zeus knew that the sight of his celestial radiance would kill the poor thing outright. But he couldn't refuse his oath. So Semele looked at him and died.

HELIOS. Semele was a little mortal fool. My son's different. He takes after me. I like this idea!

SUMMER. It's got risk!

FALL. It's got emotion!

WINTER. It's insane!

HELIOS. We'll do it!

(HELIOS *turns toward* PHAETON *with solemnity.*)

HELIOS. Phaeton, my boy, I'm a deity with unimaginable power and influence. I can give you anything your heart desires. So make a wish. Anything. I swear by the River Styx to grant whatever you ask.

PHAETON. I want to drive your chariot across the sky today.

(*A tense silence*)

SUMMER. Oh, no.

FALL. What do we do now?

SPRING. Perhaps this wasn't such a good idea.

WINTER. Didn't I tell you?

PHAETON. What's everybody so upset about?

HELIOS. Son, you don't know what you're asking.

PHAETON. Sure, I do. This is the perfect way to prove to the world who I really am.

HELIOS. No one can drive that chariot except me.

PHAETON. And your son.

HELIOS. No. Even Zeus can't drive it.

PHAETON. If I'm your son, I can do things Zeus can't do. What's the matter with all of you? You wanted drama, you wanted "oomph." Well, here it is! Imagine the headlines! "Sun God Passes the Reins to His Son for a Day." It's perfect. It's sensational. You can't buy publicity like this.

HELIOS. Phaeton, I can't back out of my oath. But you can change your request.

PHAETON. Why would I want to do that?

HELIOS. Because you can't do this. It's much too dangerous.

PHAETON. It's not like I've never driven a chariot before. Did I happen to mention all the races I've won?

HELIOS. Listen to me. The ascent into the sky is so steep, my horses can barely climb it. And the height! It's frightening! Even I don't dare look down. And what do you think you'll find up there? Cities of gold? Beautiful forests? Angels, maybe? You'll find monsters waiting to kill you, and it sometimes takes more than a crack of a whip to scare them off. Then there's the descent—

PHAETON. You can't change my mind.

HELIOS. Phaeton, I beg you—

PHAETON. Don't beg. The father I've always dreamed of would never beg.

(*Pause*)

HELIOS (*resignedly*). Very well, then. Let's get on with it.

*T*he characters onstage freeze. URANIA *steps forward.*

URANIA. Well, there you have it. A solemn oath and a rash request. I don't suppose I'm giving away too much of my story to say that disaster is about to strike.

(PHAETON, HELIOS, *and the* SEASONS *exit.*)

URANIA. Human relationships are messy and confusing—especially between parents and children. Imagine that every little problem in your family affected the whole cosmos and every living thing in it. Well, that's how things used to be. The forces of the universe were all-too-human. What's human can go very wrong.

(A NEWSCASTER *comes onto the stage and freezes.*)

URANIA. And when things go wrong, you can always count on the media to swing into action.

(*The* NEWSCASTER *comes to life.*)

NEWSCASTER. As the whole world knows, there's been no sunrise today. The stars have disappeared, plunging the planet into darkness. Worldwide panic is setting in. The doors to the Sun Palace are shut tight, even to reporters. Unconfirmed rumors are rampant. What is the truth? What's gone wrong? Will the sun ever rise? I'm here in India to find out.

(TIME *enters, holding a sheet of paper. She is surrounded by four* REPORTERS.)

NEWSCASTER. Here's somebody from the palace. Perhaps she can tell us what's going on.

(*The* REPORTERS *all speak more or less at once.*)

FIRST REPORTER. Could you tell us, please—?

SECOND REPORTER. Do you have anything to say about—?

THIRD REPORTER. What is the meaning of—?

FOURTH REPORTER. Can you confirm reports of—?

TIME (*interrupting and silencing them*). I'm going to issue a brief statement.

We'll keep this short and sweet. I will take no questions afterwards. (*Clearing her throat*) "Today's sunrise, scheduled for six forty-five A.M., did not take place."

(*The* REPORTERS *speak more or less at once again.*)

FIRST REPORTER. But we already know—

SECOND REPORTER. What possible reason—?

THIRD REPORTER. When can we expect—?

FOURTH REPORTER. Will the Sun ever—?

TIME (*to the reporters, sternly*). Quiet, please. (*Reading again*) "Sunrise has been rescheduled for seven thirty-four A.M., give or take a few seconds. At the present moment, Sun Enterprises will not divulge the reason for this delay. We will make a full statement at sunset, at which time the entire planet will be satisfied with our explanation. But be assured that the situation is well in hand. The world is in no danger from permanent darkness or any other threat." (*Folding up her paper*) That concludes my statement.

FIRST REPORTER. Would you like to quell theories that Helios is too ill to fly?

TIME. No comment.

SECOND REPORTER. Is Helios actually on strike for Olympian status among the gods?

TIME. No comment.

THIRD REPORTER. Is is true that the gods intend to freeze the human race to death?

TIME. No comment.

FOURTH REPORTER. What about rumors that Helios' son is going to fly the chariot today? *(Pause.* TIME *is taken aback.)*

TIME. Totally unsubstantiated.

(The reporters speak at once again.)

FIRST REPORTER. But surely you can explain—

SECOND REPORTER. What is the meaning of—?

THIRD REPORTER. Why do you refuse—?

FOURTH REPORTER. What can we expect—?

TIME *(silencing them again).* I said there would be no questions. That's all for now. Thank you for your attention.

*(*TIME *folds up the sheet of paper and exits, followed by the four grumbling* REPORTERS. *The* NEWSCASTER *remains onstage.)*

NEWSCASTER. And there you have it—a statement marked by evasion and half-truth. It all smacks of a cosmic cover-up. Why this delay? Will the sun really go up at seven thirty-four A.M., or will there be no daylight ever again? If the sun does rise, should we reset our clocks? If it doesn't, is all life on the planet threatened with extinction? We will get back to you with every new development in this breaking story. *(With a flashy, professional smile)* And now, back to our regularly scheduled program.

(The NEWSCASTER *exits.* URANIA *steps forward.)*

URANIA. The ancient Greeks had a word for excessive pride. They called it "hubris." When good, moral, well-meaning people are flawed by hubris, it often leads to tragedy.

HAETON *and* HELIOS *enter. They place a small stool near the center of the stage, then freeze.*

URANIA. Now, I'm sure we all agree that Phaeton is a fine young man— capable, considerate, and honest. I'm sure we also agree that he's way too full of himself for his own good—that he suffers from a bad case of hubris. Which side of his family do you suppose he got it from?

*(*PHAETON *and* HELIOS *come to life, both standing to the right of the stool, which they pretend is* HELIOS' *chariot.* PHAETON *is upbeat and eager, examining the chariot closely.* HELIOS, *carrying his headgear at his side, is gloomy and depressed.)*

PHAETON. This chariot's a beauty. I've never seen anything like it. What are these jewels along the railing? Real diamonds?

HELIOS. Diamonds and chrysolites.

PHAETON. I had no idea. You can't see this stuff from the ground. And all this gold and silver leaf on the wheels and undercarriage—

HELIOS. It's not leaf. The rims, spokes, and axles are solid gold and silver. They're tempered by the god of the forge to make them as hard as any steel.

PHAETON. Incredible! *(He walks toward the front of the stool.)* And these horses! Magnificent—and huge! Their coats even match the gold on the chariot. What are they, some kind of palominos? *(To one of the horses)* Hey, big fellow, don't be shy.

HELIOS. Stay away from them.

PHAETON. Why? Shouldn't I give them a carrot or some sugar? I'd better make friends with them.

HELIOS. Those creatures are no friends of humankind—or of gods, either. Take a look at their nostrils.

PHAETON. They're breathing smoke!

HELIOS. Yes, and they breathe fire when they break into a gallop. They've got furnaces inside their bellies and lungs.

PHAETON. Like dragons!

HELIOS. Indeed, more like dragons than horses—strong, fast, and bad-tempered. Hold the reins tightly, or they'll turn against you. And whatever you do, don't use the whip on them. Save that for the other monsters in the sky.

PHAETON. How do I control them?

HELIOS. Their names. Say them often, and perhaps they won't run mad on you. *(Pointing to each of the horses)* Eous, Aethon, Pyrois, and Phlegon.

PHAETON. Got it.

HELIOS. Repeat them.

PHAETON. I said I've got it.

HELIOS *(insistently)*. Repeat them.

PHAETON. Eous, Aethon, Pyrois, and Phlegon, all right? When I say I've got something, I've really got it. Have a little confidence in your son.

HELIOS. There's a path of wheel tracks left by the chariot. Stay close to them. Don't swerve to the right or left. Don't go too near the sky, or too near the ground. Otherwise, you'll set heaven and earth on fire.

PHAETON. We've been over this already.

HELIOS. Take it slow, don't rush.

PHAETON. Father, I know what to do.

HELIOS *(rubbing his son's face with his hand)*. You'd better use some of this ointment.

PHAETON. Why?

HELIOS. To keep your flesh from burning to a crisp when you wear my helmet.

(**HELIOS** *reluctantly hands* **PHAETON** *his headgear.* **PHAETON** *puts it on. The two of them gaze at each other in silence for a moment.*)

HELIOS. Son, I can give you any treasure on the planet, any precious thing you can think of, all the wealth you can imagine—

PHAETON. This is what I want.

HELIOS. Remember one thing. It isn't just your own life you're risking. You're taking the safety of the universe in your hands. How does it feel to do that?

PHAETON. It feels right.

HELIOS. You're not frightened?

PHAETON. No.

HELIOS. Then you're not a god. You're a fool.

ELIOS *and* PHAETON *freeze.* URANIA *steps forward.*

URANIA. It's time for Dawn to set the scene for sunrise. She goes out into the world and chases away the last shadows of night. Then her paint-drenched fingers splash lovely brindle patterns[1] across the eastern sky. You know the colors—yellow, orange, and flaming rose, all pretty and pastel. A worried world begins to breathe more easily.

(HELIOS *exits.* PHAETON *places one foot on the stool. He holds imaginary reins in one hand, an imaginary whip in the other, posing as if driving a chariot. Then he freezes again.*)

URANIA. Then the sea goddess Tethys opens the doors to the Sun Palace, and our hero takes to the sky-road. The climb is steep and sheer, and Phaeton is impatient. Right away, he disobeys his father's orders. He uses his whip.

(PHAETON *comes to life, cracking his imaginary whip.*)

PHAETON (*to the horses*). Faster, you lead-footed mules! What do you think this is, some small-town parade? No staid old god is driving you today. I'm young, and for the first time in my life, I'm free! You've got bridles on, not me! I want the whole world to know who I am. So let's make the axle-sparks fly!

(PHAETON *freezes.*)

URANIA. Not wise. For you see, the first thing the horses notice is the lightness of their load. Phaeton is thin and gangling and lacks his father's heft. The steep climb into the sky, normally so difficult for the horses, is much too easy. Even without the whip, they'd be likely to run away with Phaeton. With the

whip . . . well, now they're positively furious.

(PHAETON *lurches about, tugging desperately at the reins.*)

PHAETON. Whoa, not *that* fast! Hey, the four of you stay together! Eous, don't rush out ahead! Aethon, stick to the track! Pyrois, don't veer to the right! Phlegon, keep up with the others!

(PHAETON *freezes again.*)

URANIA. Oh, he remembers the horse's names. Alas, he no longer knows which one is which! He's lost all control. And the world below is starting to take notice.

(*The* NEWSCASTER *comes onto the stage.*)

NEWSCASTER. We interrupt this program to bring you an urgent announcement. Our astronomical bureau reports that the morning sun is seriously off course. While there is no immediate danger to the earth or heavens, the Sun Chariot has strayed into dangerous territory. It is likely to be attacked by sky monsters.

(*The* NEWSCASTER *exits.* LEO *and* TAURUS *enter and freeze at opposite sides of the stage.*)

URANIA. Look up into the daytime sky and you won't see a single star, at least not from the ground. But that doesn't mean they're not there. Up where our hero is, he can see the starry monsters that live in the sky only too well. But he can't stop his horses from charging right toward Leo, the lion, and Taurus, the bull.

---

1. brindle patterns, patterns that are light with darker streaks or spots; speckled

Phaeton and the Sun Chariot by Wim Coleman　　**395**

(PHAETON *pantomimes pulling at the reins.* LEO *and* TAURUS *move toward him threateningly.*)

PHAETON (*to his horses*). You crazy beasts! Do you want to get us all killed? Can't you see those monsters coming toward us?

LEO (*crouched, with a rumbling growl*). Aha! The Sun Chariot has a new driver! And this one doesn't look as cunning with his whip or his steeds as the other one! He'll make a tasty hot lunch for me!

TAURUS (*stomping and snorting*). Not so fast, sky-cat. This one's mine.

LEO. Yours, you bovine bundle of fireflies? What do you want with him?

TAURUS. Why, to impale him upon my horns, of course.

LEO. But you're no flesh-eater.

TAURUS. It's a matter of sport, that's all. Now kindly stand aside.

LEO. Wait a minute. Perhaps we can both get something out of this. Some sport for you, some meat for me.

TAURUS. I kill him, you eat him?

LEO. Exactly!

TAURUS. Splendid idea! Allow me to turn him into a nice, fresh corpse!

(TAURUS, LEO, *and* PHAETON *all freeze.* URANIA *steps forward.*)

URANIA. But Taurus and Leo have dallied too long, and the horses have carried the chariot far beyond their reach. This doesn't mean that Phaeton is free and clear, however. Oh, far, far from it.

(TAURUS *and* LEO *exit.*)

URANIA. Our hero now sees a dire

threat, indeed—not just to himself, but to all earthly life.

(PHAETON *unfreezes, pantomiming the reins again.*)

PHAETON (*desperately, to the horses*). No! Not down! Not toward the earth! We'll set the world on fire! Up! Up, please, I beg you! Back to the sky-path!

(CANCER *enters at one side of the stage, waving imaginary claws.*)

URANIA. Now another sky monster appears. In his current straits, Phaeton finds even a monster a welcome sight.

PHAETON (*calling out to* CANCER). Cancer! The crab! You can help me!

CANCER. I?

PHAETON. Cut the horses' traces with your claws! Set them loose from the chariot! It's my only hope!

CANCER. But you're not the god who usually drives this chariot. Who are you to ask for such a favor?

PHAETON. I'm Phaeton—the son of Helios, the Sun god.

CANCER. But not the Sun himself?

PHAETON. It doesn't matter who I am!

CANCER (*haughtily*). I'm not accustomed to taking orders from the gods themselves, much less from an underling. Besides, if I cut loose your horses, they might come after me. And with their flaming breath, they could cook me alive! I'm afraid you're on your own.

(CANCER *turns away and exits.*)

PHAETON. Wait! Don't go! Can't you

see what will happen if I strike the earth? Have pity!

URANIA. Monsters seldom do what we want them to. Sometimes they even have a way of not being monstrous enough.

(SCORPIO *enters on the opposite side of the stage, also waving imaginary claws.*)

URANIA. This next beast, for example— a massive scorpion with a deadly, poisonous tail.

PHAETON (*calling out again*). You! Scorpio! You've got claws, too! Cut my horses' traces.

SCORPIO (*with vanity*). What, and risk breaking a claw? Oh, I hardly think so.

PHAETON. Then use your tail to kill my horses!

SCORPIO. But what have these poor beasts done to offend me?

PHAETON. Don't act like you've got a heart. You don't, and the whole world knows it. You yearn to kill every creature you meet.

SCORPIO (*with a cruel chuckle*). Yes, you're absolutely right. But consider this. I'll kill many, many more creatures than I ever dreamed of, just by letting your horses live and run amok. In fact, I'll preside over the end of all life everywhere! That's a spectacle I don't want to miss.

PHAETON. Then kill me.

SCORPIO (*surprised*). What?

PHAETON. You heard what I said. I don't want to live and see what happens next. Sting me with your tail. End it for me.

SCORPIO. It's tempting . . . but no. I believe I'll let you die in torment. It'll be much more fun.

(SCORPIO *turns away and exits.*)

PHAETON. Somebody, please listen! Please help! Where are you, Father? I was a fool, I know that now. I should never have asked to drive this chariot. You can punish me however you see fit. But won't you show the world some mercy?

(PHAETON *turns away, standing with his back to the audience.*)

URANIA. Do the gods hear Phaeton's call for help? If so, they show no sign of it—not yet, anyway. And just as Phaeton feared, his chariot plummets earthward, destroying everything in sight.

(*The* NEWSCASTER *enters.*)

NEWSCASTER (*with emotion*). It's every journalist's nightmare—to report the end of the world. How many people still live to hear my words? I have no idea. Everywhere I look, I see fire. The Sun Chariot has skidded across the mountain tops, causing them to explode like volcanoes, raining ash and lava everywhere. Now the chariot ravages the valleys, turning all farmland to glowing coals. Rivers all over the world are boiled dry. The lakes, seas, and oceans vanish in titanic clouds of steam, leaving cooked fish lying everywhere. Herds upon herds of wild animals flee burning forests. And the towns—oh, the humanity! One by one, the greatest cities in all civilization are instantly vaporized. Hundreds of millions of people perish by the very second.

And now . . . the inevitable has come! I see the blazing chariot hurtling toward me, drawn by its insane steeds! The light is blinding, the heat unendurable! In just another second . . .

(*The* NEWSCASTER *freezes.*)

URANIA. No mortal voice can be heard now. They're all drowned out by the roaring flames. The creatures who remain alive huddle helplessly in nooks, caves, and ditches—any refuge they can find from the deadly fire, smoke, and heat.

(*The* NEWSCASTER *exits.* MOTHER EARTH *enters and freezes.*)

URANIA. But another voice rises up to the heavens. No mortal can hear it, but the gods on Olympus can. It is the voice of Mother Earth herself.

URANIA *steps to one side.* MOTHER EARTH *unfreezes and speaks with pain and fury, facing straight ahead.*

MOTHER EARTH. Zeus, ruler of all the universe, what is the meaning of this madness? What have I done to deserve this punishment by fire? Have I insulted you? If so, I demand to know how! Long have I endured the presence of these two-legged creatures you have loosed upon me, long have I suffered their endless wounds and insults. They've cut my flesh with plows, disemboweled my mountains, poisoned the air and water that surround me. And yet, as you commanded, I give them life and nurture them. And this is your thanks—to turn one of these miserable animals loose in the Sun Chariot. My hair, my skin, my sinews, and my very bones are burning to a cinder. Do you wish my death? Kill me, then! Do it yourself, don't parcel out the job to some incompetent fool. And do it quickly! Do it now!

(MOTHER EARTH *freezes.* URANIA *comes forward.*)

URANIA. Now this is a voice the gods cannot ignore. And as you can well imagine, Olympus is already in great turmoil because of what's happening below.

(MOTHER EARTH *exits.* ZEUS, HERA, *and* HELIOS *enter and freeze.*)

URANIA. Helios has been called onto the carpet by Zeus and Hera, the king and queen of the gods.

(ZEUS, HERA, *and* HELIOS *come to life. For a few moments,* HERA *stands to one side and observes the other two gods disdainfully.*)

ZEUS. What do you have to say for yourself, Sun god?

HELIOS. Nothing . . . except that I'm sorry.

ZEUS. You're sorry? You've passed the most destructive power in the universe into half-mortal hands, and you say you're sorry?

HELIOS. I swore an oath by the River Styx. You made the same mistake with Semele.

ZEUS. Semele! How dare you throw Semele in my face at a time like this! The two situations have nothing in common. That poor girl asked only to look me in the face, not to wreak[2] universal destruction!

---

2. wreak (rēk), to inflict or carry out

HELIOS. That's not what my son intended.

ZEUS. It's certainly what he's doing.

HERA. You men! Always arguing when decisions must be made and action must be taken. The Sun Chariot is rising back up into the sky, setting the heavens on fire. We'll all be broiled alive while the two of you bicker away like children.

ZEUS. If you're so much wiser, dear, perhaps you can suggest a plan of action.

HERA. Indeed, I can. Kill the boy, and be quick about it.

HELIOS. What!

HERA. You heard what I said. It will be no great loss. His very existence was a mistake to begin with.

HELIOS. You're inhuman.

HERA. Exactly. And so are you. And so is my husband. We're gods, remember? And if you ask me, we spend entirely too much time concerning ourselves with human business. Particularly you men, who find mortal women so awfully attractive. Well, this is what it leads to. I hope you've both learned a lesson.

ZEUS. No lectures, Hera, please.

HELIOS. And no more talk of killing my son.

HERA. Oh, I'm so sorry. I had no idea that the little fool's life was of such value. By all means, let him live, and let the rest of the human race perish! Let poor Mother Earth die—and us gods, as well! Let Phaeton be the sole survivor of his own folly! It's only just.

ZEUS (*to* HELIOS). What choice do I have? I can spare your son, or spare the universe. Which do you seriously expect me to do?

HELIOS (*to* ZEUS). You have half-mortal children, too. Think of Dionysus. Think of Hercules. Could you bring yourself to kill either of them, for any reason?

ZEUS. I'd never have given them my thunderbolt, as you've given Phaeton your chariot. I always let my boys make it on their own.

HELIOS. There must be some other way.

ZEUS. Then kindly tell me what it is.

(PHAETON *turns around, pantomiming the reins again.*)

PHAETON (*desperately*). Father, where are you? Can't you hear me?

HERA (*turning toward* PHAETON). Listen. He's calling out again.

(ZEUS *and* HELIOS *turn toward* PHAETON *and listen, too.*)

PHAETON (*in agony*). The chariot's a raging furnace! Sparks are flying everywhere, blistering and burning me all over! My hair is on fire! Do something! Save me!

ZEUS (*to* HELIOS). He's calling to his father for help. What do you intend to do for him?

HELIOS (*to* ZEUS). Have pity! Spare him!

HERA. So that's how it is. Zeus could kill him in a painless instant, but you'd rather he'd die slowly from the smoke and flames. And you call it pity! A fine father you are.

HELIOS (*bitterly*). A fine father, indeed.

PHAETON. My eyes are full of soot and ashes. I can't see! The air scorches my lungs. And the smoke . . . *(Coughing)* I can't breathe! Zeus, father of the gods—

HERA. That's you, darling.

PHAETON. —end it for me. Slay me with your thunderbolt.

ZEUS *(to HELIOS).* Should I deny him his wish?

HELIOS *(quietly).* No. Do as he says.

(ZEUS raises up his arm, as if aiming a javelin at PHAETON.)

PHAETON. Father, if you can hear me, please forgive me!

HELIOS. Forgive *me,* son.

*Z*EUS *hurls his imaginary javelin.* ZEUS, HERA, *and* HELIOS *freeze.* PHAETON *slowly crumples to the ground as* URANIA *speaks.*

URANIA. Phaeton tumbles from the chariot, and the horses break loose from their traces. They dash madly in all directions until they finally plunge into the sea. Its axle broken, the Sun Chariot lurches and careens about, then smashes into fiery pieces.

(ZEUS, HERA, and HELIOS exit.)

URANIA. Phaeton hurtles downward for hours, blazing through the sky like a meteor. While he descends, the fires across the world begin to die away. A light rain falls. Mother Earth groans and tends to her injuries. All living things creep out from hiding, frightened that the fire might start again.

(PHAETON lies in a motionless huddle. HELIOS *and* CLYMENE *enter.)*

URANIA. At last, Phaeton tumbles into the River Eridanus—one of the few watery places left in the world. The river gently washes him, then places him on its banks where his father and mother can find him.

(HELIOS and CLYMENE come to life.)

CLYMENE. Here he is. Here's our boy. *(Touching PHAETON)* Oh, poor Phaeton. So badly burned! Come home with me. Let me bandage your wounds, soothe them with a healing balm. I'll take care of you. Soon, you'll be well again.

HELIOS. He's not coming home, Clymene.

CLYMENE. You're a god. You can make him live.

HELIOS. I can't.

CLYMENE. Why not? You told him how powerful you were. You promised him whatever his heart desired. And now you say you can't give him life again!

HELIOS. What the Fates decide even the gods cannot change.

CLYMENE. Is that another *rule* you gods live by? Like not breaking an oath by the River Styx?

HELIOS. I had to keep that oath.

CLYMENE. Was it better to kill your son? Couldn't you stop being a god for just a moment and be a father?

HELIOS. I couldn't. No.

CLYMENE. You're powerless, then. You can fill the daytime sky with radiant light, nourish the earth with comforting warmth, perform miracles past reckoning. But even so, you're powerless. I wouldn't be a god—not for anything in the world. We mortals have more choices.

HELIOS. Clymene, come home with me. Let's try again. We still have daughters. We can be a family together.

CLYMENE. Oh, Helios, Helios, haven't you heard? When our daughters learned that their brother was dead, they wept and wept and wept. They would have wept until the end of time, but some magical being showed them mercy, hushed them by turning them into poplar trees.

HELIOS. Perhaps I can bring *them* back.

CLYMENE. Why? So they can weep again? They're no longer in pain. Their tears have hardened into amber. I wish I were so blessed. Come. I'll show you where they're standing. They're not far from here.

(CLYMENE *takes* HELIOS *by the hand. They freeze.*)

URANIA. The next day doesn't come. Helios refuses to drive across the sky—swears never to fly again. All creation grows cold and dark. Helios' horses return to their stable, and the god of the forge makes a new Sun Chariot, but no other deity can drive it. One by one, the gods of Olympus beg Helios to end the perpetual night. At last, Helios relents and brings back the day. It's not easy for a god to change his nature.

(CLYMENE *and* HELIOS *exit.* CHARON *enters and freezes.*)

URANIA. But my story isn't quite over. You see, there is a world apart from our own world—a world which was unscathed by Phaeton's chariot, which scarcely noticed the blazing destruction. Phaeton is about to receive a visitor from this world.

(CHARON *comes to life—a spooky and funereal character. He speaks to* PHAETON.)

CHARON. Phaeton. Wake up. It's time to go.

PHAETON (*looking up at* CHARON). Who are you?

CHARON. A friend—and a guide. I've come to take you on your final journey.

PHAETON. Where?

CHARON. Across the River Styx.

PHAETON. To the world of the dead.

(CHARON *nods.*)

PHAETON. You're Charon, the ferryman, aren't you?

CHARON (*nodding again*). And the ferry is waiting. We mustn't waste eternity.

PHAETON. Can't I go tell my mother where I'm going?

CHARON. Oh, I believe she knows already. Besides, she'll be along herself before she knows it. Life is much shorter than anybody realizes. Come along.

PHAETON. Wait a minute. What's death like?

CHARON. It depends. It's different to everyone who dies. What do you *want* it to be like?

PHAETON (*with a smile*). An adventure.

CHARON. Then it will be an adventure.

PHAETON. Do you promise?

CHARON (*smiling*). I promise—by the River Styx.

(PHAETON *and* CHARON *begin to laugh, then freeze.*)

URANIA. Phaeton's spirit follows after Charon, but his bones and ashes remain beside the River Eridanus, where they rest to this very day. And there my story ends.

(PHAETON *and* CHARON *exit.*)

URANIA. But I can tell by your faces that you don't believe what I've told you—not much of it, anyway. Well, don't take my word for it. Go to the River Eridanus yourself and find the stone that marks Phaeton's grave. It bears an inscription which reads . . . (*Stopping and smiling*) No. I believe I'll let you read it for yourself. And when you're there, say hello to Phaeton's sisters—four small, slender trees growing near the grave. They stopped weeping ages ago, but they still get lonely for visitors. Tell them I sent you. Good-by . . . and travel safely.

(URANIA *exits.*)

End of play

Phaeton and the Sun Chariot

Responding to the Play

1. Who do you think had greater pride, Helios or Phaeton? Why?
2. Why do you think the dramatist, Wim Coleman, used Urania, Muse of the Sky, to narrate the play?
3. What can the Phaeton myth tell us about our world today?
4. Pick one of the supporting or bit parts and describe how you would create the role and give it depth.
5. Create an outline for a radio ad for *Phaeton and the Sun Chariot.*

More About Greek Gods and Goddesses

While the hierarchy of the Greek gods was not absolute, the diagram below lists some of the most important deities and their domains.

Zeus King of Olympus		**Hera** Queen of Olympus	
Hades God of the Underworld	**Poseidon** God of the Sea	**Demeter** Goddess of the Harvest	**Hestia** Goddess of the Hearth
Hermes Herald of the Gods	**Artemis** Goddess of the Hunt	**Dionysus** God of Wine	**Apollo** God of Light/ Music/Reason
Ares God of War	**Helios** God of the Sun	**Hephaestus** God of Fire/Forging	**Athena** Goddess of Wisdom/Victory

Creating and Performing

1. Cast and direct the radio ad you wrote for *Phaeton and the Sun Chariot* (number 5 above).
2. In groups of five, work on the scene in which the seasons convince Helios to grant Phaeton's wish. Share it with the class.
3. Show the class how you would portray Phaeton as he loses control of the horses and begs for help from the constellations.

Phaeton and the Sun Chariot by Wim Coleman　　**403**

SURE THING

The Play as Literature: Satire

Satire is a literary form that combines criticism with humor to point out an absurdity. Some satirists use the form to provoke social reform. Others, like David Ives, simply help us laugh at our social or cultural habits.

As you read *Sure Thing*, ask yourself what David Ives is satirizing in this comedy about dating.

The Play as Theatre: Improvisation

The format of this play is based on a convention of contemporary improvisation whereby actors begin with a premise or goal and then make up their actions and lines as they go along. When an improvised scene gets bogged down or reaches an impasse, the actors or their director will stop the scene and begin again. The actors will try new approaches until they find something that works. Often, they will "set," or keep, their most effective lines and actions, even as they improvise new material. (Read more about improvisation on p. 413.)

Notice how this play maintains an improvisational tone by having the characters make mistakes and start over.

WARM UP!

Improvise a meeting between two strangers who hope to get to know each other better. Ask your classmates to call "Stop!" when the scene begins to lag. Then step down and allow two different performers to continue the scene on a new note.

What could these two strangers be talking about?

Sure Thing

by David Ives

SETTING

A café table, with
a couple of chairs

CHARACTERS

BILL and BETTY,
both in their late twenties

TIME

The present

BETTY *is reading at a café table. An empty chair is opposite her.* BILL *enters.*

BILL. Excuse me. Is this chair taken?

BETTY. Excuse me?

BILL. Is this taken?

BETTY. Yes, it is.

BILL. Oh. Sorry.

BETTY. Sure thing.

(A bell rings softly.)

BILL. Excuse me. Is this chair taken?

BETTY. Excuse me?

BILL. Is this taken?

BETTY. No, but I'm expecting somebody in a minute.

BILL. Oh. Thanks anyway.

BETTY. Sure thing.

(A bell rings softly.)

BILL. Excuse me. Is this chair taken?

BETTY. No, but I'm expecting somebody very shortly.

BILL. Would you mind if I sit here till he or she or it comes?

BETTY *(glances at her watch).* They do seem to be pretty late . . . .

BILL. You never know who you might be turning down.

BETTY. Sorry. Nice try, though.

BILL. Sure thing.

(Bell)

Is this seat taken?

BETTY. No, it's not.

BILL. Would you mind if I sit here?

BETTY. Yes, I would.

BILL. Oh. *(Bell)* Is this chair taken?

BETTY. No, it's not.

BILL. Would you mind if I sit here?

BETTY. No. Go ahead.

BILL. Thanks. *(He sits. She continues reading.)* Everyplace else seems to be taken.

BETTY. Mm-hm.

BILL. Great place.

BETTY. Mm-hm.

BILL. What's the book?

BETTY. I just wanted to read in quiet, if you don't mind.

BILL. No. Sure thing.

(Bell)

BILL. Everyplace else seems to be taken.

BETTY. Mm-hm.

BILL. Great place for reading.

BETTY. Yes, I like it.

BILL. What's the book?

BETTY. *The Sound and the Fury.*

BILL. Oh. Hemingway.

(Bell)

What's the book?

BETTY. *The Sound and the Fury.*

BILL. Oh. Faulkner.

BETTY. Have you read it?

BILL. Not . . . actually. I've sure read *about* it, though. It's supposed to be great.

BETTY. It is great.

BILL. I hear it's great. *(Small pause)* Waiter?

(Bell)

What's the book?

BETTY. *The Sound and the Fury.*

BILL. Oh. Faulkner.

BETTY. Have you read it?

BILL. I'm a Mets fan, myself.

(Bell)

BETTY. Have you read it?

BILL. Yeah, I read it in college.

BETTY. Where was college?

BILL. I went to Oral Roberts University.

(Bell)

BETTY. Where was college?

BILL. I was lying. I never really went to college. I just like to party.

(Bell)

BETTY. Where was college?

BILL. Harvard.

BETTY. Do you like Faulkner?

BILL. I love Faulkner. I spent a whole winter reading him once.

BETTY. I've just started.

BILL. I was so excited after ten pages that I went out and bought every-

thing else he wrote. One of the greatest reading experiences of my life. I mean, all that incredible psychological understanding. Page after page of gorgeous prose. His profound grasp of the mystery of time and human existence. The smells of the earth . . . What do you think?

BETTY. I think it's pretty boring.

(Bell)

BILL. What's the book?

BETTY. *The Sound and the Fury.*

BILL. Oh! Faulkner!

BETTY. Do you like Faulkner?

BILL. I love Faulkner.

BETTY. He's incredible.

BILL. I spent a whole winter reading him once.

BETTY. I was so excited after ten pages that I went out and bought everything else he wrote.

BILL. All that incredible psychological understanding.

BETTY. And the prose is so gorgeous.

BILL. And the way he's grasped the mystery of time—

BETTY. —and human existence. I can't believe I've waited this long to read him.

BILL. You never know. You might not have liked him before.

BETTY. That's true.

BILL. You might not have been ready for him. You have to hit these things at the right moment or it's no good.

BETTY. That's happened to me.

BILL. It's all in the timing. *(Small pause)* My name's Bill, by the way.

BETTY. I'm Betty.

BILL. Hi.

BETTY. Hi. *(Small pause)*

BILL. Yes, I thought reading Faulkner was . . . a great experience.

BETTY. Yes. *(Small pause)*

BILL. *The Sound and the Fury* . . . *(Another small pause)*

BETTY. Well. Onwards and upwards. *(She goes back to her book.)*

BILL. Waiter—?

(Bell)

You have to hit these things at the right moment or it's no good.

BETTY. That's happened to me.

BILL. It's all in the timing. My name's Bill, by the way.

BETTY. I'm Betty.

BILL. Hi.

BETTY. Hi.

BILL. Do you come in here a lot?

BETTY. Actually I'm just in town for two days from Pakistan.

BILL. Oh. Pakistan.

(Bell)

My name's Bill, by the way.

BETTY. I'm Betty.

BILL. Hi.

BETTY. Hi.

BILL. Do you come in here a lot?

BETTY. Every once in a while. Do you?

BILL. Not much anymore. Not as much as I used to. Before my nervous breakdown.

(Bell)

Do you come in here a lot?

BETTY. Why are you asking?

BILL. Just interested.

BETTY. Are you really interested, or do you just want to pick me up?

BILL. No, I'm really interested.

BETTY. Why would you be interested in whether I come in here a lot?

BILL. I'm just . . . getting acquainted.

BETTY. Maybe you're only interested for the sake of making small talk long enough to ask me back to your place to listen to some music, or because you've just rented some great tape for your VCR, or because you've got some terrific unknown Django Reinhardt record, only all you really want to do is make out—which you won't do very well—after which you'll go into the bathroom and pee very loudly, then pad into the kitchen and get yourself a beer from the refrigerator without asking me whether I'd like anything, and then you'll confess that you've got a girlfriend named Stephanie who's away at medical school in Belgium for a year, and that you've been involved with her—*off and on*—in what you'll call a very "intricate" relationship, for about *seven YEARS*. None of which *interests* me, mister!

BILL. Okay.

(Bell)

Do you come in here a lot?

BETTY. Every other day, I think.

BILL. I come in here quite a lot, and I don't remember seeing you.

BETTY. I guess we must be on different schedules.

BILL. Missed connections.

BETTY. Yes. Different time zones.

BILL. Amazing how you can live right next door to somebody in this town and never even know it.

BETTY. I know.

BILL. City life.

BETTY. It's crazy.

BILL. We probably see each other in the street every day. Right in front of this place, probably.

BETTY. Yep.

BILL *(looks around).* Well, the waiters here sure seem to be in some different time zone. I can't seem to locate one anywhere . . . Waiter! *(He looks back.)* So what do you—*(He sees that she's gone back to her book.)*

BETTY. I beg pardon?

BILL. Nothing. Sorry.

(Bell)

BETTY. I guess we must be on different schedules.

BILL. Missed connections.

BETTY. Yes. Different time zones.

BILL. Amazing how you can live right next door to somebody in this town and never even know it.

BETTY. I know.

BILL. City life.

BETTY. It's crazy.

BILL. You weren't waiting for somebody when I came in, were you?

BETTY. Actually I was.

BILL. Oh. Boyfriend?

BETTY. Sort of.

BILL. What's a sort-of boyfriend?

BETTY. My husband.

BILL. Ah-ha.

(Bell)

You weren't waiting for somebody when I came in, were you?

BETTY. Actually I was.

BILL. Oh. Boyfriend?

BETTY. Sort of.

BILL. What's a sort-of boyfriend?

BETTY. We were meeting here to break up.

BILL. Mm-hm . . .

(Bell)

What's a sort-of boyfriend?

BETTY. My lover. Here she comes right now!

(Bell)

BILL. You weren't waiting for somebody when I came in, were you?

BETTY. No, just reading.

BILL. Sort of a sad occupation for a Friday night, isn't it? Reading here, all by yourself?

BETTY. Do you think so?

BILL. Well sure. I mean, what's a good-looking woman like you doing out alone on a Friday night?

BETTY. Trying to keep away from lines like that.

BILL. No, listen—

(Bell)

You weren't waiting for somebody when I came in, were you?

BETTY. No, just reading.

BILL. Sort of a sad occupation for a Friday night, isn't it? Reading here all by yourself?

BETTY. I guess it is, in a way.

BILL. What's a good-looking woman like you doing out alone on a Friday night anyway? No offense, but . . .

BETTY. I'm out alone on a Friday night for the first time in a very long time.

BILL. Oh.

BETTY. You see, I just recently ended a relationship.

BILL. Oh.

BETTY. Of rather long standing.

BILL. I'm sorry. *(Small pause)* Well listen, since reading by yourself is such a sad occupation for a Friday night, would you like to go elsewhere?

BETTY. No . . .

BILL. Do something else?

BETTY. No thanks.

BILL. I was headed out to the movies in a while anyway.

BETTY. I don't think so.

BILL. Big chance to let Faulkner catch his breath. All those long sentences get him pretty tired.

BETTY. Thanks anyway.

BILL. Okay.

BETTY. I appreciate the invitation.

BILL. Sure thing.

(Bell)

You weren't waiting for somebody when I came in, were you?

BETTY. No, just reading.

BILL. Sort of a sad occupation for a Friday night, isn't it? Reading here all by yourself?

BETTY. I guess I was trying to think of it as existentially romantic. You know—cappuccino, great literature, rainy night . . .

BILL. That only works in Paris. We *could* hop the late plane to Paris. Get on a Concorde. Find a café . . .

BETTY. I'm a little short on plane fare tonight.

BILL. Darn it, so am I.

BETTY. To tell you the truth, I was headed to the movies after I finished this section. Would you like to come along? Since you can't locate a waiter?

BILL. That's a very nice offer, but . . .

BETTY. Uh-huh. Girlfriend?

BILL. Two, actually.

(Bell)

BETTY. Girlfriend?

BILL. No, I don't have a girlfriend. Not if you mean the controlling witch I dumped last night.

(Bell)

BETTY. Girlfriend?

BILL. Sort of. Sort of.

BETTY. What's a sort-of girlfriend?

BILL. My mother.

(Bell)

I just ended a relationship, actually.

BETTY. Oh.

BILL. Of rather long standing.

BETTY. I'm sorry to hear it.

BILL. This is my first night out alone in a long time. I feel a little bit at sea, to tell you the truth.

BETTY. So you didn't stop to talk because you're a Moonie, or you have some weird political affiliation—?

BILL. Nope. Straight-down-the-ticket Republican.

(Bell)

Straight-down-the-ticket Democrat.

(Bell)

Can I tell you something about politics?

(Bell)

I like to think of myself as a citizen of the universe.

(Bell)

I'm unaffiliated.

BETTY. That's a relief. So am I.

BILL. I vote my beliefs.

BETTY. Labels are not important.

BILL. Labels are not important, exactly. Like me, for example. I mean, what does it matter if I had a two-point at—

(Bell)

—three-point at—

(Bell)

—four-point at college, or if I did come from Pittsburgh—

(Bell)

—Cleveland—

(Bell)

Westchester County?

BETTY. Sure.

BILL. I believe that a man is what he is.

(Bell)

A person is what he is.

(Bell)

A person is . . . what they are.

BETTY. I think so too.

BILL. So what if I admire Trotsky?

(Bell)

So what if I once had a total-body liposuction?

(Bell)

So what if I once spent a year in the Peace Corps? I was acting on my convictions.

BETTY. Sure.

BILL. You can't just hang a sign on a person.

BETTY. Absolutely. I'll bet you're a Scorpio.

(Many bells ring.)

Listen, I was headed to the movies after I finished this section. Would you like to come along?

BILL. That sounds like fun. What's playing?

BETTY. A couple of the really early Woody Allen movies.

BILL. Oh.

BETTY. Don't you like Woody Allen?

BILL. Sure. I like Woody Allen.

BETTY. But you're not crazy about Woody Allen.

BILL. Those early ones kind of get on my nerves.

BETTY. Uh-huh.

(Bell)

BILL. Y'know I was headed to the—

BETTY. *(simultaneously)* I was thinking about—

BILL. I'm sorry.

BETTY. No, go ahead.

BILL. I was going to say that I was headed to the movies in a little while, and . . .

BETTY. So was I.

BILL. The Woody Allen festival?

BETTY. Just up the street.

BILL. Do you like the early ones?

BETTY. I think anybody who doesn't out to be run off the planet.

BILL. How many times have you seen *Bananas*?

BETTY. Eight times.

BILL. Twelve. So are you still interested? *(Long pause)*

BETTY. Do you like Entenmann's crumb cake . . . ?

BILL. Last night I went out at two in the morning to get one. Did you have an Etch-a-Sketch as a child?

BETTY. Yes! And do you like Brussels sprouts? *(Pause)*

BILL. No, I think they're disgusting.

BETTY. They *are* disgusting!

BILL. Do you still believe in marriage in spite of current sentiments against it?

BETTY . Yes.

BILL. And children?

BETTY. Three of them.

BILL. Two girls and a boy.

BETTY. Harvard, Vassar, and Brown.

BILL. And will you love me?

BETTY. Yes.

BILL. And cherish me forever?

BETTY. Yes.

BILL. Do you still want to go to the movies?

BETTY. Sure thing.

BILL and BETTY *(together).* *Waiter!*

BLACKOUT

Responding to the Play

1. What do Betty and Bill have in common with you and your friends?
2. What does the bell signify?
3. What kind of relationship do you think Betty and Bill will have? Why?
4. How would you costume Betty? What would Bill wear?
5. How would you design the set to satirize today's cafés?

More About Improvisation

Although this play is based on a contemporary form of improvisation, the art form itself has roots in *commedia del'arte,* the comic theatre of sixteenth-century Italy. *Commedia* playwrights devised simple scenarios using stock characters—and then let the actors make up their own lines. Improvisation was also popular with early silent film stars such as Charlie Chaplin, who improvised comic moments in the midst of performing for the camera.

As theatre became a more organized endeavor, improvisation faded. But it regained its popularity in the late 1950's and early 1960's, when adventurous new companies began experimenting with new ways to create theatre. It has grown and flourished alongside conventional theatre ever since.

CREATING AND PERFORMING

1. Write a high school version of *Sure Thing* in which Bill asks Betty for a date. You may set your version in the cafeteria, in study hall, or at the lockers.
2. With one or two partners, write a draft of a satire on a stressful situation such as a sports tryout, a job interview, or a request to use the family car.
3. With a partner, improvise a scene between two students who have heard untrue rumors about each other. Ask classmates to redirect you when your improvisation gets bogged down.

The Play as Literature: Foreshadowing

While reading a story or watching a movie, have you ever said, "I knew that was going to happen"? If you have, the author or director probably helped you by using *foreshadowing*. Foreshadowing presents hints or clues about what may happen in the future.

Early in a story or script, foreshadowing usually suggests a wide range of possibilities. But as the drama moves forward, the range of possibilities narrows. In using foreshadowing, the author wants the audience to be both surprised by the climax and to find it perfectly logical. This is called the "Ah, hah!" effect.

As you read *Back There*, pay attention to the clues about future events, such as the discussion of time travel that begins on page 416. Look for that "Ah, hah!" effect.

The Play as Theatre: The Teleplay

The play you are about to read was produced as a teleplay. Teleplays, especially of the 1950's and 1960's, were a hybrid of stage plays and film scripts produced for television.

Like a stage production, a teleplay was limited in its choice of scenery. Teleplays were usually shot indoors on sound stages, which are like proscenium stages. As a result, the number of characters in a scene was limited. Like a film, scenes in a teleplay were re-shot until the director was satisfied (within budget). And like film, special effects were easy to insert into a teleplay.

Most of the teleplays for *The Twilight Zone*, the series for which *Back There* was created, had to be written to fit a twenty-five minute time slot, allowing five minutes or so for credits and commercials. Sponsors—those who bought advertising time—often censored scripts depending on the audience they were trying to reach.

Warm Up!

Commercials during a teleplay are like a curtain coming down on an act or like a fade-out in a film. Choose a story that would make a good teleplay. List the places where you might insert a commercial in the story. What kind of commercial would it be?

Back There

by Rod Serling

Setting

Washington, D.C.

Characters

PETER CORRIGAN, a young man
JACKSON, member of the Washington Club
MILLARD, member of the Washington Club
WHITAKER, member of the Washington Club
WILLIAM, attendant at the Washington Club
ATTENDANT ONE, at the Washington Club
ATTENDANT TWO, at the Washington Club
MRS. LANDERS, landlady of a rooming house
LIEUTENANT
LIEUTENANT'S WIFE
POLICE CAPTAIN
POLICEMAN
TURNKEY
POLICE OFFICER
JONATHAN WELLINGTON
LANDLADY
NARRATOR

Time

1965

Act One
Scene One

NARRATOR'S VOICE. Witness a theoretical argument, Washington D.C., the present. Four intelligent men talking about an improbable thing like going back in time. A friendly debate revolving around a simple issue: could a human being change what has happened before? Interesting and theoretical because who ever heard of a man going back in time? Before tonight, that is. Because this is *The Twilight Zone.*

Exterior of club at night. Near a large front entrance of double doors is a name plaque in brass which reads "The Washington Club, Founded 1858." In the main hall of the building is a large paneled foyer with rooms leading off on either side. An attendant, WILLIAM, carrying a tray of drinks, crosses the hall and enters one of the rooms. There are four men sitting around in the aftermath of a card game. PETER CORRIGAN is the youngest, then two middle-aged men named WHITAKER and MILLARD, and JACKSON, the oldest, a white-haired man in his sixties, who motions the tray from the attendant over to the table.

JACKSON. Just put it over here, William, would you?

WILLIAM. Yes, sir. *(He lays the tray down and walks away from the table.)*

CORRIGAN. Now what's your point? That if it were possible for a person to go back in time there'd be nothing in the world to prevent him from altering the course of history—is that it?

MILLARD. Let's say, Corrigan, that you go back in time. It's October, 1929. The day before the stock market crashed.[1] You know on the following morning that the securities are going to tumble into an abyss. Now using that prior knowledge, there's a hundred things you can do to protect yourself.

CORRIGAN. But I'm an anachronism[2] back there. I don't really belong back there.

MILLARD. You could sell out the day before the crash.

CORRIGAN. But what if I did and that started the crash earlier? Now history tells us that on October 24th, 1929, the bottom dropped out of the stock market. That's a fixed date. October 24th, 1929. It exists as an event in the history of our times. It *can't* be altered.

MILLARD. And I say it can. What's to prevent it? What's to prevent me, say, from going to a broker[3] on the morning of October 23rd?

CORRIGAN. Gentlemen, I'm afraid I'll have to leave this time travel to H.G. Wells.[4] I'm much too tired to get into any more metaphysics[5] this evening. And since nobody has ever gone back in time, the whole blamed thing is much too theoretical. I'll probably see you over the weekend.

WHITAKER. Don't get lost back in time now, Corrigan.

CORRIGAN. I certainly shall not. Good night, everybody.

VOICES. Good night, Pete. Good night, Mr. Corrigan. See you tomorrow.

(CORRIGAN *walks out into the hall and heads toward the front door.*)

WILLIAM (*going by*). Good night, Mr. Corrigan.

CORRIGAN. Good night, William. (*Then he looks at the elderly man a little more closely.*) Everything all right with you, William? Looks like you've lost some weight.

WILLIAM (*with a deference built of a forty-year habit pattern*). Just the usual worries, sir. The stars and my salary are fixed. It's the cost of living that goes up. (CORRIGAN *smiles, reaches in his pocket, starts to hand him a bill.*)

WILLIAM. Oh no, sir, I couldn't.

CORRIGAN (*forcing it into his hand*). Yes, you can, William. Bless you and say hello to your wife for me.

WILLIAM. Thank you so much, sir. (*A pause*) Did you have a coat with you?

CORRIGAN. No. I'm rushing the season a little tonight, William. I felt spring in the air. Came out like this.

---

1. stock market crashed, In October, 1929, stocks became greatly undervalued, leading to financial disaster and ruin for many people.
2. anachronism, anything out of keeping with the times
3. broker, a person who buys and sells stocks and bonds for clients; stockbroker
4. H. G. Wells, 1866–1946, English writer known for writing science fiction. One of his best-known novels, *The Time Machine*, is about time travel.
5. metaphysics, the philosophical study of the nature of reality, including such concepts as time and space

WILLIAM (*opening the door*). Well, April *is* spring, sir.

CORRIGAN. It's getting there. What is the date, William?

WILLIAM. April 14th, sir.

CORRIGAN. April 14th. (*Then he turns and grins at the attendant.*) 1965—right?

WILLIAM. I beg your pardon, sir? Oh, yes, sir. 1965.

CORRIGAN (*going out*). Good night, William. Take care of yourself. (*He goes out into the night.*)

Scene Two

Exterior of the club. The door closes behind CORRIGAN. *He stands there near the front entrance. The light from the street light illuminates the steps. There's the sound of chimes from the distant steeple clock.* CORRIGAN *looks at his wristwatch, holding it out toward the light so it can be seen more clearly. Suddenly his face takes on a strange look. He shuts his eyes and rubs his temple. Then he looks down at his wrist again. This time the light has changed. It's a wavery, moving light, different from what it had been.* CORRIGAN *looks across toward the light again. It's a gaslight[6] now. He reacts in amazement. The chimes begin to chime again, this time eight times. He once again looks at the watch, but instead of a wristwatch there is just a fringe of lace protruding from a coat. There is no wristwatch at all. He grabs his wrist, pulling at the lace and coat. He's dressed now in a nineteenth-century costume. He looks down at himself, looks again toward the gaslight that flickers, and then slowly backs down from the steps staring at the building from which he's just come. The plaque reads "Washington*

Club." He jumps the steps two at a time, slams against the front door, pounding on it. After a long moment the door opens. An attendant, half undressed, stands there peering out into the darkness.

ATTENDANT ONE. Who is it? What do you want?

CORRIGAN. I left something in there.

(*He starts to push his way in and the attendant partially closes the door on him.*)

ATTENDANT ONE. Now here you! The Club is closed this evening.

CORRIGAN. The devil it is. I just left here a minute ago.

ATTENDANT ONE (*peers at him*). You did what? You drunk, young man? That it? You're drunk, huh?

CORRIGAN. I am not drunk. I want to see Mr. Jackson or Mr. Whitaker, or William. Let me talk to William. Where is he now?

ATTENDANT ONE. Who?

CORRIGAN. William. What's the matter with you? Where did you come from? (*Then he looks down at his clothes.*) What's the idea of this? (*He looks up. The door has been shut. He pounds on it again, shouting.*) Hey! Open up!

VOICE (*from inside*). You best get away from here or I'll call the police. Go on. Get out of here.

(CORRIGAN *backs away from the door, goes down to the sidewalk, stands there, looks up at the gaslight, then up and down the street, starts at the sound of noises. It's the clip-clop of horses' hooves and the rolling, squeaky*

---

6. gaslight, street light fueled by gas, common during the nineteenth century

sound of carriage wheels. He takes a few halting, running steps out into the street. He bites his lip, looks around.)

CORRIGAN (*under his breath*). I'll go home. That's it. Go home. I'll go home. (*He turns and starts to walk and then run down the street, disappearing into the night.*)

Scene Three

Hallway of rooming house. There is the sound of a doorbell ringing. MRS. LANDERS, *the landlady, comes out from the dining room and goes toward the door.*

MRS. LANDERS. All right. All right. Have a bit of patience. I'm coming. (*Opening door*) Yes?

CORRIGAN. Is this 19 West 12th Street?

MRS. LANDERS. That's right. Whom did you wish to see?

CORRIGAN. I'm just wondering if . . . (*He stands there trying to look over her shoulder.* MRS. LANDERS *turns to look behind her and then suspiciously back toward* CORRIGAN.)

MRS. LANDERS. Whom did you wish to see, young man?

CORRIGAN. I . . . I used to live here. It's the oldest building in this section of town.

MRS. LANDERS (*stares at him*). How's that?

CORRIGAN (*wets his lips*). What I mean is . . . as I remember it . . . it was the oldest—

MRS. LANDERS. Well now really, young man. I can't spend the whole evening standing here talking about silly things like which is the oldest

building in the section. Now if there's nothing else—

CORRIGAN (*blurting it out*). Do you have a room?

MRS. LANDERS (*opens the door just a little bit wider so that she can get a better look at him; looks him up and down and appears satisfied*). I have a room for acceptable boarders. Do you come from around here?

CORRIGAN. Yes. Yes, I do.

MRS. LANDERS. Army veteran?

CORRIGAN. Yes. Yes, as a matter of fact I am.

MRS. LANDERS (*looks at him again up and down*). Well, come in. I'll show you what I have. (*She opens the door wider and* CORRIGAN *enters. She closes it behind him. She looks expectantly up toward his hat and* CORRIGAN *rather hurriedly and abruptly removes it. He grins, embarrassed.*)

CORRIGAN. I'm not used to it.

MRS. LANDERS. Used to what?

CORRIGAN (*points to the hat in his hand*). The hat. I don't wear a hat very often.

MRS. LANDERS (*again gives him her inventory look, very unsure of him now*). May I inquire as to what your business is?

CORRIGAN. I'm an engineer.

MRS. LANDERS. Really. A professional man. Hmmm. Well, come upstairs and I'll show you.

(*She points to the stairs that lead off the hall and* CORRIGAN *starts up as an* ARMY OFFICER *and his* WIFE *come down them.*)

MRS. LANDERS (*smiling*). Off to the play?

LIEUTENANT. That's right, Mrs. Landers.

Dinner at The Willard and then off to the play.

MRS. LANDERS. Well, enjoy yourself. And applaud the President for me!

LIEUTENANT. We'll certainly do that.

LIEUTENANT'S WIFE. Good night, Mrs. Landers.

MRS. LANDERS. Good night, my dear. Have a good time. This way, Mr. Corrigan.

(The LIEUTENANT *and* CORRIGAN *exchange a nod as they pass on the stairs. As they go up the steps,* CORRIGAN *suddenly stops and* MRS. LANDERS *almost bangs into him.)*

MRS. LANDERS. Now what's the trouble?

CORRIGAN *(whirling around).* What did you say?

MRS. LANDERS. What did I say to whom? When?

CORRIGAN. To the lieutenant. To the officer. What did you just say to him?

(The LIEUTENANT *has turned. His* WIFE *tries to lead him out, but he holds out his hand to stop her so that he can listen to the conversation from the steps.)*

CORRIGAN. You just said something to him about the President.

LIEUTENANT *(walking toward the foot of the steps).* She told me to applaud him. Where might your sympathies lie?

MRS. LANDERS *(suspiciously).* Yes, young man. Which army *were* you in?

CORRIGAN *(wets his lips nervously).* The Army of the Republic,[7] of course.

LIEUTENANT *(nods, satisfied).* Then why make such a thing of applauding President Lincoln? That's his due, we figure.

MRS. LANDERS. That and everything else, may the good Lord bless him.

CORRIGAN *(takes a step down the stairs, staring at the* LIEUTENANT*).* You're going to a play tonight? *(The* LIEUTENANT *nods.)*

LIEUTENANT'S WIFE *(at the door).* We may or we may not, depending on when my husband makes up his mind to get a carriage in time to have dinner and get to the theater.

CORRIGAN. What theater? *What* play?

LIEUTENANT. Ford's Theater, or course.

CORRIGAN *(looking off, his voice intense).* Ford's Theater. Ford's Theater.

LIEUTENANT. Are you all right? I mean do you feel all right?

CORRIGAN *(whirls around to stare at him).* What's the name of the play?

LIEUTENANT *(exchanges a look with his wife).* I beg your pardon?

CORRIGAN. The play. The one you're going to tonight at Ford's Theater. What's the name of it?

LIEUTENANT'S WIFE. It's called "Our American Cousin."

CORRIGAN *(again looks off thoughtfully).* "Our American Cousin" and Lincoln's going to be there. *(He looks from one to the other, first toward the landlady on the steps, then down toward the soldier and his wife.)* And it's April 14th, 1865, isn't it? Isn't it April 14th, 1865? *(He starts down the steps without waiting for an answer. The* LIEUTENANT *stands in front of him.)*

---

7. Army of the Republic, the northern army in the United States Civil War.

LIEUTENANT. Really, sir, I'd call your actions most strange.

(CORRIGAN *stares at him briefly as he goes by, then goes out the door, looking purposeful and intent.*

Scene Four

Alley at night. On one side is the stage door with sign over it reading "Ford's Theater." CORRIGAN *turns the corridor into the alley at a dead run. He stops directly under the light, looks left and right, then vaults over the railing and pounds on the stage door.*

CORRIGAN (*shouting*). Hey! Hey, let me in! President Lincoln is going to be shot tonight!

(*He continues to pound on the door and shout.*)

Act Two
Scene One

Police station at night. It's a bare receiving room with a POLICE CAPTAIN *at a desk. A long bench on one side of the room is occupied by sad miscreants* [8] *awaiting disposition. There is a line of three or four men standing in front of the desk with several policemen in evidence. One holds onto* CORRIGAN *who has a bruise over his eye and his coat is quite disheveled. The* POLICE CAPTAIN *looks up to him from a list.*

CAPTAIN. Now what's this one done? (*He peers up over his glasses and eyes* CORRIGAN *up and down.*) Fancy Dan with too much money in his pockets, huh?

CORRIGAN. While you idiots are sitting here, you're going to lose a President!

(*The* CAPTAIN *looks inquiringly toward the* POLICEMAN.*)

POLICEMAN. That's what he's been yellin' all the way over to the station. And that's what the doorman at Ford's Theater popped him on the head for. (*He nods toward* CORRIGAN.*) Tried to pound his way right through the stage door. Yelling some kind of crazy things about President Lincoln goin' to get shot.

CORRIGAN. President Lincoln *will* be shot! Tonight. In the theater. A man named Booth.

CAPTAIN. And how would you be knowin' this? I suppose you're clairvoyant [9] or something. Some kind of seer or wizard or something.

CORRIGAN. I only know what I know. If I told you *how* I knew, you wouldn't believe me. Look, keep me here if you like. Lock me up.

CAPTAIN (*motions toward a* TURNKEY, [10] *points to cell block door*). Let him sleep it off.

(*The* TURNKEY *grabs* CORRIGAN's *arm and starts to lead him out of the room.*)

CORRIGAN (*shouting as he's led away*). Well, you better hear me out. Somebody better get to the President's box at Ford's Theater. Either keep him out of there or put a cordon of men around him. A man named John Wilkes Booth

---

8. miscreant, one who behaves like a criminal
9. clairvoyant, seeming to have the ability to see or know things that are out of sight
10. turnkey, jailer

is going to assassinate him tonight!

(*He's pushed through the door leading to the cell block. A tall man in cape and black moustache stands near the open door at the other side. He closes it behind him, takes a step into the room, then with a kind of very precise authority, he walks directly over to the* CAPTAIN's *table, shoving a couple of people aside as he does so with a firm gentleness. When he reaches the* CAPTAIN's *table he removes a card from his inside pocket, puts it on the table in front of the* CAPTAIN.)

WELLINGTON. Wellington, Captain. Jonathan Wellington.

(*The* CAPTAIN *looks at the card, peers at it over his glasses, then looks up toward the tall man in front of him. Obviously the man's manner and dress impresses him. His tone is respectful and quiet.*)

CAPTAIN. What can I do for you, Mr. Wellington?

WELLINGTON. That man you just had incarcerated.[11] Mr. Corrigan I believe he said his name was.

CAPTAIN. Drunk, sir. That's probably what he is.

WELLINGTON. Drunk or . . . (*He taps his head meaningfully.*) Or perhaps, ill. I wonder if he could be remanded in my custody. He might well be a war veteran, and I'd hate to see him placed in jail.

CAPTAIN. Well, that's real decent of you, Mr. Wellington. You say you want him remanded in *your* custody?

WELLINGTON. Precisely. I'll be fully responsible for him. I think perhaps I might be able to help him.

CAPTAIN. All right, sir. If that's what you'd like. But I'd be careful of this one if I was you! There's a mighty bunch of crackpots running the streets these days and many of them his like, and many of them dangerous too, sir. (*He turns toward* TURNKEY.) Have Corrigan brought back out here. This gentleman's going to look after him. (*Then he turns to* WELLINGTON.) It's real decent of you, sir. Real decent indeed.

WELLINGTON. I'll be outside. Have him brought out to me if you would.

CAPTAIN. I will indeed, sir.

(WELLINGTON *turns. He passes the various people who look at him and make room for him. His walk, his manner, his positiveness suggest a commanding figure and everyone reacts accordingly. The* CAPTAIN *once again busies himself with his list and is about to check in the next prisoner, when a young* POLICE OFFICER *alongside says:*)

POLICE OFFICER. Begging your pardon, Captain.

CAPTAIN. What is it?

POLICE OFFICER. About that Corrigan, sir.

CAPTAIN. What about him?

POLICE OFFICER. Wouldn't it be wise, sir, if—

CAPTAIN (*impatiently*). If what?

POLICE OFFICER. He seemed so positive, sir. So sure. About the President, I mean.

CAPTAIN (*slams on the desk with vast impatience*). What would you have

---

11. incarcerate, put in jail

us do? Send all available police to Ford's Theater? And on what authority? On the word of some demented fool who probably left his mind someplace in Gettysburg.[12] If I was you, mister, I'd be considerably more thoughtful at sizing up situations or you'll not advance one-half grade the next twenty years. Now be good enough to stand aside and let me get on with my work.

POLICE OFFICER (*very much deterred by all this, but pushed on by a gnawing sense of disquiet*). Captain, it wouldn't hurt.

CAPTAIN (*interrupting with a roar*). It wouldn't hurt if what?

POLICE OFFICER. I was going to suggest, sir, that if perhaps we place extra guards in the box with the President—

CAPTAIN. The President has all the guards he needs. He's got the whole Federal Army at his disposal and if they're satisfied with his security arrangements, then I am too and so should you. Next case!

(*The young* POLICE OFFICER *bites his lip and looks away, then stares across the room thoughtfully. The door opens and the* TURNKEY *leads* CORRIGAN *across the room and over to the door. He opens it and points out.* CORRIGAN *nods and walks outside. The door closes behind him. The young* POLICE OFFICER *looks briefly at the* CAPTAIN, *then puts his cap on and starts out toward the door.*)

---

12. Gettysburg, a town in Pennsylvania, the site of a major battle of the Civil War in July, 1863

Scene Two

Lodging-house, WELLINGTON'*s room.* WELLINGTON *is pouring wine into two glasses.* CORRIGAN *sits in a chair, his face in his hands. He looks up at the proffered drink and takes it.*

WELLINGTON. Take this. It'll make you feel better. (CORRIGAN *nods his thanks, takes a healthy swig of the wine, puts it*

down, then looks up at the other man.)
Better?

CORRIGAN (*studying the man*). Who are you, anyway?

WELLINGTON (*with a thin smile*). At the moment I'm your benefactor and apparently your only friend. I'm in the Government service, but as a young man in college I dabbled in medicine of a sort.

CORRIGAN. Medicine?

WELLINGTON. Medicine of the mind.

CORRIGAN (*smiles grimly*). Psychiatrist.

WELLINGTON (*turning to him*). I don't know the term.

CORRIGAN. What about the symptoms?

WELLINGTON. They *do* interest me. This story you were telling about the President being assassinated.

CORRIGAN (*quickly*). What time is it?

WELLINGTON. There's time. (*Checks a pocket watch*) A quarter to eight. The play won't start for another half hour. What gave you the idea that the President would be assassinated?

CORRIGAN. I happen to know, that's all.

WELLINGTON (*again the thin smile*). You have a premonition?

CORRIGAN. I've got a devil of a lot more than a premonition. Lincoln *will* be assassinated. (*Then quickly*) Unless somebody tries to prevent it.

WELLINGTON. *I* shall try to prevent it. If you can convince me that you're neither drunk nor insane.

CORRIGAN (*on his feet*). If I told you what I was, you'd be convinced I *was*

insane. So all I'm *going* to tell you is that I happen to know for a fact that a man named John Wilkes Booth will assassinate President Lincoln in his box at Ford's Theater. I don't know what time it's going to happen . . . that's something I forgot—but—

WELLINGTON (*softly*). Something you forgot?

CORRIGAN (*takes a step toward him*). Listen, please—(*He stops suddenly, and begins to waver. He reaches up to touch the bruise on his head.*)

WELLINGTON (*takes out a handkerchief and hands it to* CORRIGAN). Here. That hasn't been treated properly. You'd best cover it.

CORRIGAN (*very, very shaky, almost faint, takes the handkerchief, puts it to his head and sits back down weakly*). That's . . . that's odd. (*He looks up, still holding the handkerchief.*)

WELLINGTON. What is?

CORRIGAN. I'm so . . . I'm so faint all of a sudden. So weak. It's almost as if I were—

WELLINGTON. As if you were what?

CORRIGAN (*with a weak smile*). As if I'd suddenly gotten drunk or some—(*He looks up, desperately trying to focus now as his vision starts to become clouded.*) I've never . . . I've never felt like this before. I've never—(*His eyes turn to the wine glass on the table. As his eyes open wide, he struggles to his feet.*) You . . . you devil! You drugged me, didn't you? (*He reaches out to grab* WELLINGTON, *half struggling in the process.*) You drugged me, didn't you?

WELLINGTON. I was forced to, my young friend. You're a very sick man and a sick man doesn't belong in jail. He belongs in a comfortable accommodation where he can sleep and rest and regain his . . . *(He smiles a little apologetically.)* his composure, his rationale. Rest, Mr. Corrigan. I'll be back soon. *(He turns and starts toward the door.* CORRIGAN *starts to follow him, stumbles to his knees, supports himself on one hand, looks up as* WELLINGTON *opens the door.)*

CORRIGAN. Please . . . please, you've got to believe me. Lincoln's going to be shot tonight.

WELLINGTON *(smiling again).* And *that's* odd! Because . . . perhaps I'm *beginning* to believe you! Good night, Mr. Corrigan. Rest well. *(He turns and goes out of the room, closing the door behind him, We hear the sound of the key being inserted, the door locked.)*
(CORRIGAN tries desperately to rise and then weakly falls over on his side. He crawls toward the door. He scrabbles at it with a weak hand.)

CORRIGAN *(almost in a whisper).* Please . . . please . . . somebody . . . let me out. I wasn't kidding . . . I know . . . the President's going to be assassinated! *(His arm, supporting him, gives out and he falls to his face, then in a last effort, he turns himself over so that he's lying on his back.)*
(There is a sound of a heavy knocking on the door. Then a LANDLADY's *voice from outside.)*

LANDLADY. There's no need to break it open, Officer. I've got an extra key. Now if you don't mind, stand aside.

(There's the sound of the key inserted in the lock and the door opens. The young POLICE OFFICER *from earlier is standing there with an angry-faced* LANDLADY *behind him. The* POLICE OFFICER *gets down on his knees, props up* CORRIGAN's *head.)*

POLICE OFFICER. Are you all right? What happened?

CORRIGAN. What time is it? *(He grabs the* OFFICER, *almost pulling him over.)* You've got to tell me what time it is.

POLICE OFFICER. It's ten-thirty-five. Come on, Corrigan. You've got to tell me what you know about this. You may be a madman or a drunk or I don't know what—but you've got me convinced and I've been everywhere from the Mayor's office to the Police Commissioner's home trying to get a special guard for the President.

CORRIGAN. Then go yourself. Find out where he's sitting and get right up alongside of him. He'll be shot from behind. That's the way it happened. Shot from behind. And the assassin jumps from the box to the stage and he runs out of the wings.

POLICE OFFICER *(incredulous).* You're telling me this as if, as if it has already happened.

CORRIGAN. It *has* happened. It happened a hundred years ago and I've come back to see that it *doesn't* happen. *(Looking beyond the* POLICE OFFICER*)* Where's the man who brought me in here? Where's Wellington?

LANDLADY (*peering into the room*). Wellington? There's no one here by that name.

CORRIGAN (*waves a clenched fist at her, still holding the handkerchief*). Don't tell me there's no one here by that name. He brought me in here. He lives in this room.

LANDLADY. There's no one here by that name.

CORRIGAN (*holds the handkerchief close to his face, again waving his fist*). I tell you the man who brought me here was named—(*He stops abruptly, suddenly caught by something he sees on the handkerchief. His eyes slowly turn to stare at it in his hand. On the border are the initials J.W.B.*)

CORRIGAN. J.W.B.?

LANDLADY. Of course! Mr. John Wilkes Booth who lives in the room, and that's who brought you here.

CORRIGAN. He said his name was Wellington! And *that's* why he drugged me. (*He grabs the* POLICE OFFICER *again.*) He gave me wine and he drugged me. He didn't want me to stop him. He's the one who's going to do it. Listen, you've got to get to that theater. You've got to stop him. John Wilkes Booth! He's going to kill Lincoln. Look, get out of here now! Will you stop him? Will you—

(*He stops abruptly, his eyes look up. All three people turn to look toward the window. There's the sound of crowd noises building, suggestive of excitement, and then almost a collective wail, a mournful, universal chant that comes from the streets, and as the sound builds we suddenly hear intelligible words that are part of the mob noise.*)

VOICES. The President's been shot. President Lincoln's been assassinated. Lincoln is dying.

(*The* LANDLADY *suddenly bursts into tears. The* POLICE OFFICER *rises to his feet, his face white.*)

POLICE OFFICER. Oh my dear God! You were right. You *did* know. Oh . . . my . . . dear . . . God!

(*He turns almost trance-like and walks out of the room. The* LANDLADY *follows him.* CORRIGAN *rises weakly and goes to the window, staring out at the night and listening to the sounds of a nation beginning its mourning. He closes his eyes and puts his head against the windowpane and with fruitless, weakened smashes, hits the side of the window frame as he talks.*)

CORRIGAN. I tried to tell you. I tried to warn you. Why didn't anybody listen? Why? Why didn't anyone listen to me?

(*His fist beats a steady staccato on the window frame.*)

Scene Three

The Washington Club at night. CORRIGAN *is pounding on the front door of the Washington Club.* CORRIGAN *is standing there in modern dress once again. The door opens. An* ATTENDANT *we've not seen before appears.*

ATTENDANT TWO. Good evening. Mr. Corrigan. Did you forget something, sir?

(CORRIGAN *walks past the* ATTENDANT, *through the big double doors that lead to the card room as in Act One. His three friends are in the middle of a discussion. The fourth man at the table, sitting in his seat, has his back to the camera.)*

MILLARD *(looking up).* Hello, Pete. Come on over and join tonight's bull session. It has to do with the best ways of amassing a fortune. What are your tried-and-true methods?

CORRIGAN *(his voice intense and shaky).* We were talking about time travel, about going back in time.

JACKSON *(dismissing it).* Oh that's old stuff. We're on a new tack now. Money and the best ways to acquire it.

CORRIGAN. Listen . . . listen, I want to tell you something. This is true. If you go back into the past you can't change anything. *(He takes another step toward the table.)* Understand? You can't change anything. *(The men look at one another, disarmed by the intensity of* CORRIGAN's *tone.)*

JACKSON *(rises, softly)* All right, old man, if you say so. *(Studying him intensely)* Are you all right?

CORRIGAN *(closing his eyes for a moment).* Yes . . . yes, I'm all right.

JACKSON. Then come on over and listen to a lot of palaver from self-made swindlers. William here has the best method.

CORRIGAN. William?

(He sees the attendant from Act One, but now meticulously dressed, a middle-aged millionaire obviously, with a totally different manner, who puts a cigarette in a holder with manicured hands in the manner of a man totally accustomed to wealth. WILLIAM *looks up and smiles.)*

WILLIAM. Oh yes. My method for achieving security is by far the best. You simply inherit it. It comes to you in a beribboned box. I was telling the boys here, Corrigan. My great-grandfather was on the police force here in Washington on the night of Lincoln's assassination. He went all over town trying to warn people that something might happen. *(He holds up his hands in a gesture.)* How he figured it out, nobody seems to know. It's certainly not recorded any place. But because there was so much publicity, people never forgot him. He became a police chief, then a councilman, did some wheeling and dealing in land and became a millionaire. What do you say we get back to our bridge, gentlemen?

*(*JACKSON *takes the cards and starts to shuffle.* WILLIAM *turns in his seat once again.)*

WILLIAM. How about it, Corrigan? Take a hand?

CORRIGAN. Thank you, William, no. I think I'll . . . I think I'll just go home.

(He turns very slowly and starts toward the exit. Over his walk we hear the whispered, hushed murmuring of the men at the table.)

VOICES. Looks peaked,[13] doesn't he? Acting so strangely. I wonder what's the matter with him.

*(*CORRIGAN *walks into the hall and toward the front door.)*

---

13. peaked, (pē′kəd) pale, lacking healthy color

NARRATOR'S VOICE. Mr. Peter Corrigan, lately returned from the place "Back There"—a journey into time with highly questionable results. Proving, on one hand, that the threads of history are woven tightly and the skein of events cannot be undone; but, on the other hand, there are small fragments of tapestry that *can* be altered. Tonight's thesis[14] to be taken as you will, in *The Twilight Zone!*

---

14. thesis, statement to be proven or maintained against objections

Back There

Responding to the Play

1. *Back There* was created for commercial television. Point out places in the play where you would insert a commercial.
2. Find three instances of foreshadowing in the first four pages of *Back There.* Discuss how the first clues suggest a range of possibilities that narrow as the drama moves forward.
3. There are two threads of foreshadowing in *Back There.* One thread gives you clues that Corrigan is trying to prevent President Lincoln's assassination, which is confirmed by the end of Act I. What is the other thread you are given clues about? Describe these clues.
4. How do you think *Back There* would work as a stage play and as a script for a motion picture? Explain your thinking.
5. Think about the narrator's introduction and conclusion. How do they help or hinder understanding the teleplay?

About Rod Serling

By the time *The Twilight Zone* appeared on television, Rod Serling had already won three Emmys and several Peabody Awards for writing. His teleplays *Patterns, Requiem for a Heavyweight,* and *The Comedian* were viewed by critics and viewers alike as outstanding.

Serling, however, became frustrated with network censorship. Sponsors objected to material with the slightest controversy. He turned then to imaginative fiction, and on October 2, 1959, *The Twilight Zone* was first seen on CBS. Serling was often able to do an end run around the censors. "Things which couldn't be said by a Republican or a Democrat, could be said by a Martian," he quipped.

The last *Twilight Zone* episode was aired June 19, 1964. Serling died in 1975. He was 50 years old.

Creating and Performing

1. At the beginning of *Back There,* William is a servant. At the end, he's a millionaire. Perform both roles.
2. Act out the scene in which Corrigan is drugged and collapses.
3. Write an outline for a script in which a character goes forward in time to correct a threatening situation happening now.

Glossary of Key Literary and Theatrical Terms

accent
the sound of speech in a particular region.

act
1. a major division in a play: *Let's read the second scene in the first act.*
2. to play the role of a character in a play: *My friend loves to act.*

actor
person who analyzes characters in relationship to a play, memorizes lines, learns blocking, and performs a role in a play.

allusion
a reference in a literary work to an historical or literary figure, happening, or event.

antagonist
the character who gets in the way of the protagonist, or main character; secondary character.

archetype
a stock character who represents a certain kind of person.

arena stage
a stage that is surrounded by the audience; theatre-in-the-round. The stage may actually be a round shape, but it can also be a square.

aside
a side remark a character makes to the audience or another character.

audio
things that are heard, especially recordings.

audition
1. to try out for a part in a play.
2. the actual trying out itself.

backdrop
a large canvas or muslin curtain on which a scene is painted.

backstage
the areas behind the stage that are not visible to the audience.

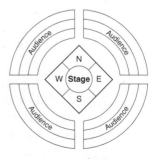

arena stage

beat
a special moment; actors and directors often divide scenes into beats.

biographical fiction
fiction based on research about a person. It reveals not only what the person did but what he or she might have done.

block
to arrange the movement of people, sets, and props on the stage.

book
a script, especially for a musical.

box office
the place where ticket sales take place.

business manager
person who creates the production budget, coordinates publicity and ticket sales, and prepares programs.

call
the time when actors should be on hand before a performance.

callback
an invitation to a second audition.

cast
to choose people for particular roles in a play.

center stage
the middle of a performance area.

characterization
the way in which an author reveals the characters to the reader.

choreograph
to design dancing, fighting, or other specialized movements for the stage.

chorus
a group of actors reciting, singing, or dancing in unison, often to comment on the action of a play.

climax
the turning point of a play.

cold reading
the reading of a script for the first time.

comedy
a light or humorous play that usually has a happy ending.

comedy of manners
a play that pokes fun at the actions and habits of the upper and upper middle class.

comic timing
pacing comic moments in a scene to create the most humorous effects.

commedia dell'arte
a form of theatrical improvisation developed in Italy in the 1500's, which includes stock characters and farcical situations.

Harlequin, a character in ***commedia dell'arte***

UR Upstage Right	UC Upstage Center	UL Upstage Left
R Right	C Center	L Left
DR Downstage Right	DC Downstage Center	DL Downstage Left

AUDIENCE

center stage

These actors are interpreting the **conflict** in a scene.

conflict
the struggle between opposing forces that is essential to a good dramatic work.

costume
the clothing an actor wears on-stage for a performance.

costume designer
the person who designs and makes or obtains costuming for the actors in a play.

costume plan
breakdown of the costumes characters wear in a play and the scenes in which they wear them.

credits
the list of people who contributed to a production.

cross
to move from one place to another.

cue
a signal, often the last lines spoken by another actor.

curtain
the end (because the draperies open at the beginning of a play and close at the end).

cyclorama
a curved wall or drop at the back of a stage, used to create an illusion of wide space or for lighting effects.

dialogue
the conversation between people in a literary work.

diction
the words an author chooses to use, dictated by the subject, audience, and effect intended in the literary work. Diction can be formal, informal, precise, complicated, old-fashioned, or contemporary.

direct
to give suggestions to actors and crew members as to how to fulfill their roles in the production.

director
a person who interprets a play, casts actors, develops blocking, and blends performances into a unified production.

down stage
the stage area closest to the audience.

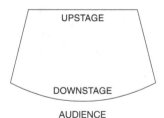

downstage

drama
a play that covers serious topics and may or may not have an unhappy ending.

432

dramatic monologue
a speech made by a single character that reveals something about the speaker or fills in important circumstances in the story.

dress rehearsal
a final practice of a play before the actual performance.

ensemble acting
a theatrical presentation that focuses on the coming together of all the roles rather than on a star's performance.

enter
to appear on the stage.

exit
to leave the stage area.

fable
a story intended to impart a useful truth; often one in which animals speak.

falling action
the part of a play following the turning point and approaching the resolution of the conflict.

falling action

farce
a comedy with exaggerated characters, physical humor, and a silly plot.

flashback
the interrupting of chronological order in a literary work by relating an event that happened earlier.

fly
a space above the stage, often used for storage.

footage
a portion of a film.

foreshadowing
clues or hints given by the author as to what is to come in the literary work.

fourth wall
an imaginary wall between the stage and the audience.

gesture
a movement that expresses a thought or emotion.

house
the audience, or the place where the audience sits.

house manager
the person who oversees the preparations for performance, supervises ushers, and has contact with the audience.

improvisation
to make things up as one goes along; to act without a script.

irony
the contrast between what one expects or what appears to be and what actually is.

lighting
the illumination of the actors and the set during a performance.

lighting designer
the person who creates and carries out a lighting plan.

lobby
the area where the audience waits before a performance and during intermissions.

makeup
the cosmetics, hair styling, masks, wigs, etc. used by performers.

Makeup can even include feathers and masks.

makeup designer
the person who designs and applies makeup for all the actors.

mime
1. to communicate through movement and gesture rather than words.

2. a person who communicates in this way.

monologue
a story or speech performed by an actor speaking alone.

mood
the atmosphere or overall feeling presented in a literary work.

motivation
a character's reasons for doing or saying something.

multimedia
using several forms of communication, such as acting, dancing, painting, audio, video, and computers.

musical
a play in which song and dance play an important part.

musical theatre
a play incorporating songs and dances throughout.

myth
a story that seeks to relate historical events in order to explain the world and its events to a people.

the **myth** of Phaeton

434

objective
a character's goals in a scene or play.

off book
having no need of the script.

pacing
the rate at which a play progresses.

pantomime
mime; to act out without using words or sounds.

papier-mâché
a technique for making props and masks out of torn strips of newspaper and glue made from flour and water.

physical comedy
comedy that uses such physical stunts as pratfalls and slapstick to elicit laughter.

pitch
the high or low sound of a voice.

play
a story created for performance.

plot
story line, generally including rising action, climax, and resolution.

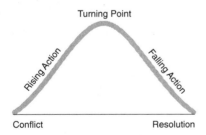

Turning Point

Rising Action

Falling Action

Conflict   Resolution

typical **plot** structure

point of view
the relationship of the teller of the story to the characters in the story.

posture
the way in which one holds one's body.

producer
a person who chooses the play, obtains the space, and sometimes casts actors.

production
the performance of a play for an audience.

project
to make one's voice loud and full enough to be heard in a big room.

prop
property; moveable objects used by actors on stage.

prop designer
a person who obtains or makes props.

properties
props; moveable objects used by actors on stage.

prop table
a place offstage where all props are kept when not in use.

protagonist
the character who moves the action of a play forward, usually the "good guy" or the character with whom the audience identifies.

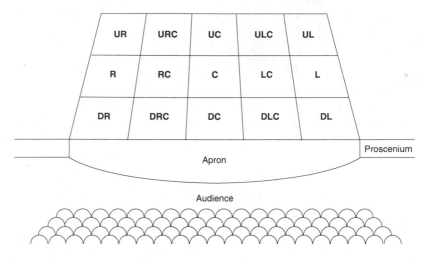

proscenium stage

proscenium stage
a "picture frame" stage; a stage that allows audience seating on the front side only.

rake
to incline a portion of the stage from the perpendicular.

reader's theatre
a dramatic reading of a story or play script.

realism
a style of writing or acting that attempts to be as lifelike as possible.

rising action
the middle part of a plot, including complications leading toward a climax.

role
a part in a play.

run
a period of time over which a play will be presented, typically four to six weeks.

satire
a literary form that ridicules human foibles and vices.

scenario
a plan or outline for a plot.

scene
part of an act; segment of a play that does not require a change of scenery.

scenery
large background pieces that create a sense of place on-stage.

screenplay
a film, video, or television script.

script
the text of a play.

set
the combination of scenery, furniture, and props.

set designer
a person who designs and creates sets, and obtains or makes set pieces such as furniture.

set pieces
large pieces of furniture for the stage.

setting
the location in which a play takes place.

shoot
film something.

sound
all sound-producing elements of a production, including live voices, music, and sound effects.

sound designer
a person who creates and carries out a sound effects plan.

stage
performance area. See **arena**, **proscenium**, and **thrust** for various types of stages.

UR Upstage Right	UC Upstage Center	UL Upstage Left
R Right	C Center	L Left
DR Downstage Right	DC Downstage Center	DL Downstage Left

The performance area of a **stage** may be divided into 9 distinct parts.

stage crew
the people handling sets, lighting, sound, costumes, or makeup.

stage left
the stage area to an actor's left when he or she faces the audience.

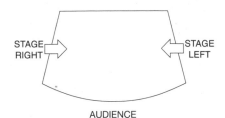

stage left/stage right

stage manager
a person who holds auditions, schedules acting and technical rehearsals, and keeps track of administration for a production.

stage right
the stage area to an actor's right when he or she faces the audience.

Stanislavski method
a method of acting, named after its founder, in which actors respond according to their motivations and emotional reactions in a scene.

stereotype
an oversimplified representation of characteristics of members of a certain group.

storyboard
a series of sketches showing possible scenes in a play.

style
an author's way of writing; the way an author writes about a subject.

subtext
the layer of meaning beneath the actual words in a play or novel.

suspense
the way an author maintains the reader's interest, creating a mood of anxiety and uncertainty.

symbolism
words and images that represent something more than their ordinary meaning.

teleplay
a television script.

theme
the underlying meaning of any literary work.

thrust stage
stage surrounded on three sides by the house, or audience.

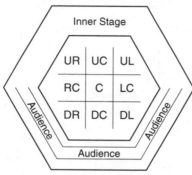

thrust stage

timing
the pacing of particular moments in a scene.

tone
the author's attitude toward his or her subject and toward the reader.

tragedy
a form of drama in which the main character comes to an unhappy end.

turning point
the decisive moment in a literary work in which the central problem of the plot must be resolved.

understudy
an actor who learns a role in order to substitute for an actor who is absent.

upstage
the stage area toward the back of the stage.

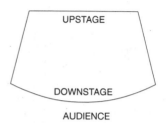

upstage

ushers
the crew members who seat the audience, hand out programs, and clean up the house after each performance.

video
things that are seen, especially recordings that can be seen on television.

voice-over
a recording of a voice that plays while action or other sounds are taking place, often indicated as VO in stage directions.

wings
the offstage areas to the right and left of the stage, where actors often wait before their entrances and after their exits.

Acknowledgments

(continued from page iv)

The Love Doctor by Marvin Kaye. Copyright © 1993 by Marvin Kaye. Reprinted by arrangement with the Author's agent, Donald Maas Literary Agency. CAUTION: All performance inquiries should be directed to Donald Maas Literary Agency, 157 West 57th Street, Suite 703, New York, NY 10019.

Haiku by Katherine Snodgrass. Copyright © 1988, 1989. Reprinted by permission of Samuel French Inc. CAUTION: Professionals and amateurs are hereby warned that *HAIKU*, being fully protected under the copyright laws of the United States of America, the British Commonwealth countries, including Canada, and the other countries of the Copyright Union, is subject to a royalty. All rights, including professional, amateur, motion picture, recitation, public reading, radio, television and cable broadcasting, and the rights of translation into foreign languages, are strictly reserved. Any inquiry regarding the availability of performance rights, or purchase of individual copies of the authorized acting edition, must be directed to Samuel French Inc., 45 West 25 Street, New York, NY 10010 with other locations in Hollywood and Toronto, Canada.

Sorry, Right Number by Stephen King from *Nightmares and Dreamscapes*. Copyright ©1993 by Stephen King. Reprinted by permission of Viking Penguin, a division of Penguin Putnam Inc. CAUTION: All performance inquiries should be directed to Penguin Putnam Inc., 375 Hudson Street, New York, NY 10014.

Death Knocks by Woody Allen from *Getting Even*. Copyright © 1968 by Woody Allen. Reprinted by permission of Random House, Inc. CAUTION: All performance inquiries should be directed to Random House, Inc., 201 east 50th Street, New York, NY 10022.

The Actor's Nightmare by Christopher Durang from *Christopher Durang Explains It All For You*. Copyright © 1982 by Christopher Durang. Reprinted by permission of Grove/Atlantic, Inc. CAUTION: All performance inquiries should be directed to Grove/Atlantic, Inc. 841 Broadway, New York, NY 10003.

The Post Office by Rabindranath Tagore from *The Post Office*. Copyright © 1996 by Krishna Dutta and Andrew Robinson. Reprinted by permission of St. Martin's Press, LLC. CAUTION: All performance inquiries should be directed to St. Martin's Press, 175 Fifth Avenue, New York, NY 10010-7848.

The Migrant Farmworker's Son by Silvia Gonzalez S. Copyright © 1996 by Silvia Gonzalez S. Printed in the United States of America. All rights reserved. Reprinted by permission of Dramatic Publishing Inc. CAUTION: The play printed in this anthology is not to be used as an acting script. All inquiries regarding performance rights should be addressed to Dramatic Publishing, 311 Washington Street, Woodstock, IL 60098. Phone (815) 338-7170. Fax (815) 338-8981.

The Janitor by August Wilson. Copyright © 1985 by August Wilson. Reprinted by permission of the author. CAUTION: All performance inquiries should be addressed to the author's office via facsimile at (206) 625-1734.

The Lottery by Shirley Jackson, dramatized by Brainerd Duffield. Copyright © 1953 by The Dramatic Publishing Company, renewed 1981 by Susan Shepard. Based upon the story "The Lottery" by Shirley Jackson © 1958 by THE NEW YORKER MAGAZINE, INC. Printed in the United States of America. All rights reserved. CAUTION: The play printed in this anthology is not to be used as an acting script. All inquiries regarding performance rights should be addressed to Dramatic Publishing, 311 Washington Street, Woodstock, IL 60098. Phone (815) 338-7170. Fax (815) 338-8981.

Survival by Alfred Brenner. Copyright © Alfred Brenner. Reprinted by permission of the author. CAUTION: All performance inquiries should be addressed to the author.

Madman on the Roof by Kikuchi Kan, translated by Yozan T. Iwaski and Glenn Hughes from *Modern Japanese Literature*. Copyright © 1956 by Grove Press, Inc. Reprinted by permission of Grove/Atlantic, Inc. CAUTION: All performance inquiries should be directed to Grove/Atlantic, Inc. 841 Broadway, New York, NY 10003.

Lost in Yonkers by Neil Simon. Copyright © 1991 by Neil Simon. Reprinted by permission of the author. CAUTION: Professionals and amateurs are hereby warned that LOST IN YONKERS is fully protected under the Berne Convention and the Universal Copyright Convention and is subject to royalty. All rights, including without limitation to professional, amateur, motion picture, television, radio, recitation, lecturing, public reading and foreign translation rights, computer media rights and the right of reproduction, and electronic storage or retrieval, in whole or in part and in any form, are strictly reserved and none of these rights can be exercised or used without written permission from the copyright owner. Inquiries for stock and amateur performances should be addressed to Samuel French, Inc., 45 West 25th Street, New York, NY 10010. All other inquiries should be addressed to Gary N. DaSilva, 111 N. Sepulveda Blvd., Suite 250, Manhattan Beach, CA 90266-6850.

My Children! My Africa! by Athol Fugard. Copyright

Photo and Art Credits